SELLING YOUR COINS & BANKNOTES?

Warwick and Warwick have an expanding requirement for
British and worldwide and for coins and notes of individual
increasing dramatically and we need an ever larger supply o
to keep pace with demand. The market has never been stron
are considering the sale of your collection, now is the time t

FREE VALUATIONS
We will provide a free, professional and without obligation
valuation of your collection. Either we will make you a fair,
binding private treaty offer, or we will recommend inclusion
of your property in our next specialist public auction.

FREE TRANSPORTATION
We can arrange insured transportation of your collection
to our Warwick offices completely free of charge. If you
decline our offer, we ask you to cover the return
carriage costs only.

FREE VISITS
Visits by our valuers are possible anywhere in the country
or abroad, usually within 48 hours, in order to value
larger collections. Please telephone for details.

VALUATION DAYS
We are staging a series of valuation days and will be visiting
all areas of England, Scotland, Wales and Ireland during
the coming months. Please visit our website or
telephone for further details.

EXCELLENT PRICES
Because of the strength of our customer base
we are in a position to offer prices that we
feel sure will exceed your expectations.

ACT NOW
Telephone or email Richard Beale today
with details of your property.

C000141501

MORTON & EDEN

Nash House   St George Street   London   W1S 2FQ

**Regular London auctions
of Coins, Medals
and Banknotes**

**William and Mary
five-guineas, 1693
elephant and castle**

**Price Realised
£192,000**

Roderick Richardson
Numismatist

THIS IS A FREE RANGE EGG
Ex Mrs McCluck
F.D.E (Fleur De Egg)

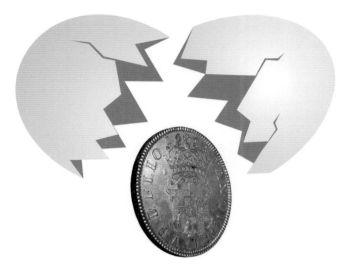

THIS IS A FREE RANGE COIN
UNENCUMBERED BY PLASTIC

Graded by a dealer with
more than 50 years experience

Roderick Richardson for Free Range Coins

The Old Granary Antiques Centre, King's Staithe Lane, King's Lynn, Norfolk
Tel: 01553 670833 | E-mail: roderickrichardson@yahoo.co.uk
Web site: www.roderickrichardson.com

THE

COIN
Yearbook

2020

Edited by
John W. Mussell, FRGS
and the Editorial Team of COIN NEWS

ISBN 978-1-908828-50-7

Published by
TOKEN PUBLISHING LIMITED
40 Southernhay East, Exeter, Devon EX1 1PE
Telephone: 01404 46972
email: info@tokenpublishing.com. Website: www.tokenpublishing.com

---

Printed in Great Britain by Latimer Trend & Company Ltd., Plymouth

Contents

Foreword

WELCOME to this the 2020 edition of the acclaimed COIN YEARBOOK—the bestselling guide to English Scottish, Irish and Island coins!

This is the 27th COIN YEARBOOK we at Token Publishing Ltd have produced and every year there is something else to talk about in the world of numismatics! Recently the news has been all about one of three things—either the continued interest in the new issue Beatrix Potter/Paddington/Gruffalo character 50p coins; the treasure hoard of William I and Harold II pennies found in Somerset or the ever increasing price of gold. Each one of these stories has made the mainstream media news at one time or another in the past few months (we know as we have been asked to comment on them) and this tells us a couple of things: firstly, that coins are of interest to a wider audience outside the relatively narrow confines of the coin collecting hobby and secondly there is probably no hobby or interest in the world that is quite as diverse as this one. Whether you are collecting Celtic staters, Norman Conquest era pennies, gold sovereigns for their metal content or Paddington at the Palace 50p pieces they all are part of the same great hobby, and, you will be glad to know, all are covered in this book!

The COIN YEARBOOK is, as its name suggests, an annual publication, a companion to the monthly magazine COIN NEWS and the new SPEND IT? SAVE IT guide to circulating decimal coins. Within these pages you will find a comprehensive price guide to all British Isles coins, from those used by the earliest Celtic tribes (and including the Roman coins used in Britain) right up to the current crop of new issues straight out of the Royal Mint. There are also handy hints and tips to help your collecting—because the hobby isn't just about the value, or cost, of coins, it is so much more rewarding than that if you take time to enjoy it.

We do realise that many people picking up this book will be doing so because they are new to the hobby, having started by collecting coins out of their change—and there is absolutely nothing wrong with that at all, it is how most collectors start and, after years of all coins being the same, and thus not very collectable, it is gratifying to see the new designs are encouraging new collectors. However, we do hope that at least some of you will, in time, look beyond the new issues. Yes, they are fun to collect and it is great to be able to search through your change for that elusive Peter Rabbit or Jemima Puddleduck that you just don't have yet but, as illustrated above, there is a depth and a breadth to coin collecting you just don't find in other hobbies. When you collect coins you actually connect with history in a way you rarely can with other things—if you pick up a Roman coin (and they are readily available and not anywhere near as expensive as you might think) you are holding something that a Roman centurion would have held 2,000 years ago. When you pick up a William the Conqueror penny or Charles I crown you know that you are handling something that represents a tumultuous period in English history so monumental and significant that it makes the current woes of Parliament look like a walk in the park. Add an Elizabethan shilling to your collection and you now own (or at least are custodian of for a while) something that may well have been used to buy entrance into the first showing of a new play by William Shakespeare. When you hold a George III guinea in your hand, like the one featured on this year's front cover, you know that that very coin would once have been used by a wealthy man or woman who may well have been worried about the King's health and unsettled by talk of the Prince Regent taking over. Coins are part of history, they have been around for thousands of years, fought over, spent, gambled, lost, hidden—they are history in themselves and to be able to hold them in our hands, touch them, own them today, is to become part of their history too. Coin collecting connects us to the past in a unique way and the fact that we are able to actually hold these things brings a very real dimension to them—these are not museum exhibits hidden away behind glass, these are things that are hundreds, if not thousands of years old that we can actually own—there's something pretty special about that that goes far beyond the simple pleasure of getting "one of everything".

Of course we aren't naïve and are aware that whilst the historical aspect of coin collecting does fascinate people, more often than not the reason stories about coins are found in the mainstream press is because there is a financial aspect to them—the story is invariably more about "what's it worth?" than "why's it important?" and that is why this YEARBOOK is more than a simple handbook for collecting, it's a price guide too.

It would be foolish of anyone to spend a fortune on any hobby without knowing the value of what they are buying and that is why guides like the COIN YEARBOOK are essential. We've all read the stories in the newspapers and websites that feature headlines such as "Is your coin worth £3,000? and then go on to talk about someone listing a Beatrix Potter 50p for some ludicrous price on eBay even though there were millions of them minted. Well rarely, if ever, do such coins sell (you can list whatever you like for however much you like, it doesn't mean you'll sell it and no, no British circulating coin is worth £3,000) but undoubtedly less ridiculous, but still crazily high, prices are paid by people who simply don't know what they are doing, which is why the YEARBOOK exists. It is here to help you the collectors, whether you're an old hand or just starting out, to get it right and not get caught out. In order to obtain the prices that feature in this book we look at dealers' lists and websites and auction results but we also enlist the help of a variety of experts in their respective fields and once again we are indebted to Chris Rudd and Elizabeth Cottam (Celtic), Mike Vosper (Roman), Stephen Mitchell of Studio Coins (Hammered), Roy Norbury of West Essex Coins (Milled), Nick Swabey (Maundy), David Fletcher (Decimal), David Stuart (Scottish), Del Parker (Irish), Charles Riley (Commemorative medals) and the numerous auction houses who allow us access to their archives for our illustrations, and of course, the Royal Mint for their invaluable help—all of which make the hobby an enjoyable experience.

At Token Publishing Ltd we are dedicated to helping the collector, so if you need anything such as accessories or books or have any queries or concerns about the hobby, don't hesitate to contact us and we will do our best to help. If you would like a free sample copy of our award-winning monthly magazine, COIN NEWS, simply ask. Our contact details are set out on page 9—we look forward to hearing from you.

COIN NEWS—a wealth of information every month

An exciting new guide
to the coins in your pocket

Most of us handle coins every day and nowadays there is a bewildering range of designs appearing in change. Some are worth just their face value, but others can be worth many times that! This has created an enthusiastic following, all seeking to complete their themes or sets, or simply hoping to make a fortune.

Spend It? Save It? is a simple guide to the many coins available, with hints and tips on what to look out for and how to pay the right price for the coins you want.

Fully illustrated · Up-to-date values · Lots of hints and tips · Handy coin check list · Suitable for all ages

An invaluable guide to the coins you come across every day.

Simply telephone: 01404 46972 or go to www.tokenpublishing.com to secure your copy.

RICHARD SESSIONS

Mystery Issues

The rare George V Pennies of 1922–26

The reign of King George V saw the issue of probably the most famous bronze penny—the legendary 1933 penny. Fewer than ten specimens are recorded and it is thought that just one is unaccounted for, leading to all sorts of fakes doing the rounds, and romantic dreams of finding that missing coin. The 1933 penny was even mentioned on a recent edition of the Antiques Roadshow and the last one to appear on the market fetched nearly £150,000 in 2016.

In fact, there are other pennies (apart from proofs or official patterns) produced during the reign of George V that are probably even rarer but will never attain the notoriety or desirability of the 1933 penny, since they are almost certainly unofficial "trial" strikings that somehow escaped from the Royal Mint. Unsurprisingly, these pennies were struck during the period from 1922 to 1926, a period when no pennies were struck with dates from 1923 to 1925 inclusive because there were sufficient numbers in circulation. It was also a period when the Royal Mint was experimenting with both obverse and reverse designs in an attempt to reduce the "ghosting" effect whereby a silhouette of the King's head would appear on the reverse of all previous coins (see figure 1).

The "common" coins of this period are the 1922 and 1926 penny, both struck with an obverse design first used on pennies dated 1921 and the reverse design used from 1913 to 1926. In 1926 a scarcer coin was struck with the same reverse but an obverse design aimed at reducing this ghosting, known as the "Modified Effigy" obverse and used for all 1927 pennies. The "Modified Effigy" obverse is recognisably different from the previous obverse by the fact that the engraver's initials (BM) are now without full stops and are positioned further to the right

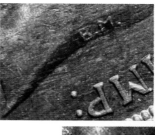

of the king's neck (see figure 2). Another differentiator, easier to spot on worn specimens, is that the words BRITT: and OMN: above the king's head are further apart on the "Modified Effigy".

Chris Peckris's splendid articles in Coin News (November 2015 to March 2016) on "The Coinage of George V" included some details of the rarities found in the pennies of 1922 and 1926 but also contained an error and a couple of omissions regarding the physical varieties found to date which I'd like to correct in this article. I do not propose to comment on Chris's explanations and theories on the origins of the various varieties but merely wish to correct the inventory of 1922–26 rarities.

In the February 2016 edition he focussed on the bronze coinage but incorrectly stated that a 1922 penny found with a "Modified Effigy" obverse was paired with the experimental reverse found on the very rare 1922 penny recorded by Michael Freeman as F192A. In fact, this penny was struck with the actual reverse used on pennies dated 1927 to 1936 inclusive. His article also did not mention a 1926 penny that was struck with a modified effigy obverse and an unrecorded reverse which appears to be a hybrid of

Fig. 1. The reverse "ghost" can be plainly seen on this 1920 penny.

Fig. 2 Left, the previous standard obverse and right, the "Modified effifgy" obverse, showing the difference between the designer's initials on the truncation.

two reverses. I will expand on all these varieties in this article.

The first great rarity of this period is the 1922 penny mentioned above (Freeman 192A). It is struck with the obverse used on pennies dated 1921 and 1922 but the reverse is strikingly different from that of the normal 1922 pennies. As Chris states in his article, Freeman refers to this reverse variety in his seminal publication, The Bronze Coinage of Great Britain, as "the reverse of 1927" but there are significant differences between this and the actual reverse used on pennies struck from 1927 to 1936. Although both designs feature a smaller figure of Britannia (with a noticeably shorter right thumb) such that her shield is now further from the border teeth, the exergue is shallower on F192A such that the date numerals almost touch the border teeth which are longer and there are fewer of them; 181 in fact, as opposed to the 184 on the true reverse of 1927. In fact, this unique reverse is the only obverse or reverse design of George V to feature 181 border teeth. Another distinguishing feature is Britannia's left hand which depicts a strangely thin and horizontal thumb (figure 3).

Fig. 4. The 1922 Freeman 192A, Gouby BP1922B with the unique "experimental" reverse (181 teeth).

Fig. 3. The horizontal thumb can be clearly seen.

Michael Gouby, in his equally seminal book, The British Bronze Penny 1860 to 1970 recognised and recorded the uniqueness of this reverse design, defining the coin's variety as BP1922B.

Although not as rare as the 1933 penny, this variety is still extremely rare with possibly fewer than 10 known specimens.

Interestingly, despite Freeman's inaccurate description of the above coin's reverse, there does actually exist a variety of 1922 penny with the strange and very rare die pairing of the 1920–21 obverse and the true reverse of 1927 (figure 5). It was struck to proof or specimen standard and included in sets from farthing to halfcrown with the other coins being dated 1924, probably to demonstrate the capabilities of the Royal Mint. It is thought that only two such sets were issued. This coin was not recorded by Freeman or Gouby and is so rare that Freeman almost certainly never saw one.As one can see from the picture above (figure 5), the coin has the true 1927 reverse with deeper exergue and normal left thumb (and 184 teeth).

Fig. 5. 1922 Proof or Specimen strike showing the 1927 reverse (184 border teeth) (photograph courtesy of the owner).

A possibly even rarer penny dated 1922 was sold at auction in 2006. Chris's article described it as having the "Modified Effigy" obverse first found on the scarcer pennies of 1926 but incorrectly stated that it was paired with the unique reverse of the F192A penny. In fact, like the proof penny above its reverse design with 184 border teeth is actually that first used on pennies dated 1927 and through to 1936. The fact that a penny dated 1922 but featuring obverse and reverse designs used extensively only from 1927 suggests that it is some sort of trial coin that somehow escaped the Royal Mint. Only a single specimen has been found to date (see figure 6).

The other potentially unique rarity, correctly described in Chris's article, is a penny dated 1926 which has the same die pairing as this 1922 penny, i.e. the "Modified Effigy" obverse and the true 1927 reverse (figure 7).

This penny was discovered by Michael Freeman himself who had it examined by the Royal Mint and several auction houses in order to authenticate it as not being an altered 1927 penny. In fact, the date, under high magnification, does appear to suggest some modification (probably of the die rather than the coin) and was actually slabbed by third party grading company PCGS as "Genuine— altered surface". However, both sides of this coin are considerably sharper than normal 1927 coins and suggest that it was struck from different, perhaps trial or even proof, dies. One auction house that examined the coin thought that the date figure "6" may have been altered but not from a 7. As with the 1922 penny above (figure 6), this may be some kind of trial strike for the forthcoming obverse and reverse designs of 1927. The written response from the Mint states that "we have consulted the die records for the 1920s and nothing has come to light to suggest that work was being carried out at the time in question which could have given rise to the striking of such a piece." Both Freeman and myself are surprised at this statement given the rare die pairings described in this article.

These two pennies are listed in the annual Spink publication Coins of England and the United Kingdom as "of the highest rarity" (reference 4054A) where Spink have now changed their description of the 1927 reverse at my suggestion to "Britannia sl. Smaller. Shorter right thumb".

Yet another potentially unique rarity was discovered in 2010, having been sold at auction at least twice previously as a normal 1926 Modified Effigy penny. However, it has an unrecorded reverse that appears to be a possible hybrid of the reverse found on pennies dated 1913 to 1926 inclusive (larger Britannia with 187 small border teeth) and the true 1927 reverse (smaller Britannia with 184 longer border teeth), as it has the larger Britannia but 184 longer border teeth. Under magnification it appears

Figure. 6. The unrecorded 1922 "Trial" with Modified Effigy obverse and 1927 reverse (184 border teeth).

Fig. 7. The unrecorded 1926 "Trial" 1—Modified Effigy obverse and 1927 reverse (184 border teeth).

Fig. 8. The unrecorded 1926 Trial 2 with Modified Effigy obverse and Hybrid reverse (184 border teeth) showing the trident prong touching the rim teeth.

The currently known inventory of pennies from 1922 to 1926 is therefore as follows:

Date	Obverse design	Reverse design	Rarity
1922	1921 obverse	1913-1926 reverse	Common
1922	1921 obverse	experimental reverse unique to 1922	Very rare
1922 Proof	1921 obverse	1927 reverse	2 known
1922	Modified Effigy obverse	1927 reverse	Unique ?
1923-25	No pennies issued		
1926	1921 obverse	1913-1926 reverse	Common
1926 Proof	1921 obverse	1913-1926 reverse	Very rare
1926	Modified Effigy obverse	1913-1926 reverse	Scarce
1926 Proof	Modified Effigy obverse	1913-1926 reverse	Very rare
1926	Modified Effigy obverse	1927 reverse	Unique ?
1926	Modified Effigy obverse	Trial/Hybrid reverse	Unique ?

that these longer teeth may have been re-engraved onto a 1913–26 reverse die as some sort of trial or experiment, as there is a possible guideline visible and the teeth appear to cover the right hand trident prong (figure 8). As Chris Peckris wrote in his original article, the real truth about the penny mysteries from 1922 to 1926 may never be officially resolved, but it does appear that an awful lot was going on at the Royal Mint at that time and there may be more mysteries and rarities to be discovered.

More details of these and other milled pennies can be found at my website www.pennyvarieties.co.uk.

References:
FREEMAN, Michael J., *The Bronze Coinage of Great Britain*, Spink, 2006.
GOUBY, Michael, *The British Bronze Penny 1860 to 1970*, 1986.
HOWARD, Emma, *The Coins of England & The United Kingdom*, Spink, 2018.

Museum
archive

Every month in COIN NEWS we are privileged to feature one of the rare items from the Royal Mint's Museum at Llantrisant. The collection represents one of the most impressive numismatic collections in the world, featuring outstanding rarities alongside the currency we all use in our everyday lives. Here we have chosen a few of the items we have featured, as a "snap shot" of the Museum's treasures.

A memento from the front line

With the centenary of the end of the First World War in mind, last month the focus was on a quantity of salvaged Mexican dollars that had been re-purposed into unofficial medals during the war. A related category of material might be seen as coins engraved by servicemen on the front line and illustrated here is an example from the Royal Mint Museum. Although crudely engraved, the design has been reasonably well worked out showing the cap badge of the Royal Garrison Artillery, reference to the Great War and the touching words "From a friend to a friend".

Shell cases were a favoured medium for this type of trench art, some elaborately conceived with figurative reliefs and decorative patterns, but in this instance the soldier chose to use a shilling of George V. The reverse has been worked smooth to take the engraved design and, compared to other such pieces, it is quite sophisticated. Coins were also hollowed out to conceal a message which may have had more relevance to the activities of spies than to a homesick infantryman. More often than not, though, souvenirs were being created of time spent in the trenches, a personalised piece to handle and provide reassurance.

The Last Sovereign

The Royal Mint site at Llantristant in South Wales was opened by the Queen in December 1968 but production continued at Tower Hill in London through the first half of the 1970s, albeit it on a reduced scale. After 1972 very few coins were struck in London, and with the commissioning of additional machinery in Llantrisant, there was little need for production of blanks and coins to continue at the old home of the Mint across from the Tower. On November 10, 1975 the last coin ever to be struck at Tower Hill was a gold sovereign dated 1974. The dwindling numbers of those still working there gathered around the press to see the ceremonial end of coin production some 160 years after it had all started with a coinage of copper pice of Penang for the East India Company.

The gold sovereign in question was retained and is in the collection of the Royal Mint Museum. In telling the story of where the Mint has been located over the last 1,000 years, it is a key object and consequently it is now on public display in the Royal Mint Experience. It was significant that of all the coins to have chosen, it was the sovereign. Far from being consigned to the demonetised cabinet of history, the sovereign had been given a new lease of life in the post-war world where gold played a part in providing stability for the international exchange rate mechanism. Millions of sovereigns were produced from 1957 through the 1960s and it was, therefore, an understandable choice as the last coin produced of the Tower Hill era.

SMS *Emden* "medals"

With the centenary of the end of the First World War it is timely to reflect on the influence war has had on money. Drawn broadly enough it can encompass a wide range of objects, one category of which is the way coins have been adapted during war. Changing the physical appearance of money is encountered in the Great War with soldiers engraving personal messages on coins. Then there is the story of coins found on board the SMS Emden, a German warship which was run aground in November 1914 off the Cocos Islands in the Indian Ocean.

Australian ship, HMAS Sydney, attacked and disabled the Emden and in the subsequent salvage a large quantity of Mexican dollars was found on board. The coins were being used as ready cash for buying supplies on account of their popularity in the region and several hundred of those seized from the ship were turned into a type of medal through the addition of an elaborate mount inscribed with the names of the two ships and the date of the action. In this form they were presented to the officers and crew of the Sydney as an informal recognition of the service they performed, while others were sold to members of the public. The sacrifice and stress of the time invested such items with emotional significance and they provide distinctive means through which war can be remembered.

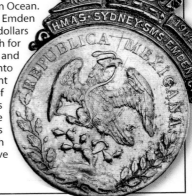

Living on the edge, the crown piece of 1818

The design development of the crown piece of 1818 was something of a saga. It brought out the best and sometimes the worst in the characters involved and, in particular, showed the Master of the Mint, William Wellesley Pole, as a perfectionist, setting admirably high standards that were not always easy to fulfil. Creating new designs for the obverse and reverse led to delays, and the complexity was compounded by Pole's insistence on a lettered edge. It was his original idea to have an incuse edge inscription, a point about which he was quite adamant. Tools were prepared for several edge designs, some of which, as illustrated here, are in the Royal Mint Museum collection, and amongst them we find variations on the theme of incuse lettering. In the Nobleman sale of 1922 there were pattern crowns dated 1817 and 1818 which were described as having edges incusely inscribed. This might have seemed strange given the tradition of crown pieces having raised lettered edges but recent precedents would have naturally suggested an incuse inscription. The Louis D'or gold coins of 1815 and the medal issued to commemorate the opening of the Waterloo Bridge in 1817 both had incuse lettered edges. The idea was ultimately dropped in favour of raised letters and, although the resulting coin was a masterpiece, this decision added further production difficulties to a coin whose passage through the Mint was fraught from start to finish.

Designs for the one pound coin

Stuart Devlin was one of the most gifted and energetic designers of his generation. He was most well known as a goldsmith and silversmith but his powers of creativity extended to architecture, furniture, sculpture and also into the realm of coins and medals. His designs for the Australian coinage released in 1966 were celebrated at the time and, like Percy Metcalfe's coinage for the Irish Free State in the 1920s, are rightly regarded as modern classics. Winning the competition transformed Devlin's life.

He went on to run a successful business in London as a silversmith with a large workshop, the output of which decorated the homes of the rich and famous, including Her Majesty the Queen. From a British perspective, though, the sadness is that it was not until towards the end of his career that he designed his first United Kingdom coin. The opportunity arose when he won a competition for a series of one pound coins to represent each of the four constituent parts of the United Kingdom. Devlin chose as the theme coats of arms of the capital cities. They were released in 2010 and 2011, and the drawings shown here demonstrate his masterly draughtsmanship and his commitment to the view that it was always possible to combine intricacy with elegance in coinage design.

Money and movies

The Royal Mint started producing twelve-sided nickel-brass threepences in earnest from 1937 and they became a much-loved part of the pre-decimal currency. The one illustrated here, dated 1943, looks in no way special but it does have a story because it was produced at Pinewood Studios during the Second World War. Lloyd's of London moved into the mansion house on the Pinewood site in Buckinghamshire a few days before hostilities started in September 1939 because of the risk to its central London location being bombed. The Royal Mint, or at least part of it, soon followed for the same reason.

The new auxiliary Mint began operations in June 1941 and being equipped with furnaces, rolling mills, blanking presses and eight Heaton coining presses, it was entirely self-sufficient. As well as lower denomination nickel-brass and bronze British coins, the temporary facility maintained the international profile of the Mint's commitments, making coins for Ireland, Iraq and Peru during the war. In recent years Pinewood Studios had been struggling and the joke went around that now it was no longer making any films it was finally making money. It was not true, though, to claim no films were being made at Pinewood. Wartime documentaries, like Frank Capra's *Tunisian Victory* (1944), were produced there and employees of the Mint found themselves sharing the site with an active film-making community, including a young Richard Attenborough, who was stationed at Pinewood between 1943 and 1946.

Frustratingly, no photographs seem to have survived of the Pinewood mint, perhaps because of the secrecy surrounding the operation.

Gold recoinage medal

In 1775 the medal illustrated here was produced to commemorate an extensive recoinage of gold that had been initiated a few years earlier. It was designed by John Kirk, a London medallist and gem engraver, who was responsible for a wide range of portrait and figurative medals in the second half of the 18th century. The idea of issuing a medal to commemorate a recoinage might seem somewhat obscure but there are other examples, one of the more significant being the medal struck to mark the restoration of the coinage by Elizabeth I following the debasement carried out by Henry VIII.

Both medals show a female figure holding a set of scales as a reference to the requirement to make coins to accurate standards and the 1770s recoinage medal emphasises this point further through its Latin inscriptions which translate as "the inviolable weight of gold" and "the coinage set right". The gold recoinage was undertaken from 1773 to 1777 and was required to improve the condition of guineas and half-guineas in circulation which had become worn through years of use and abuse. It is not a well-known reform of the currency but actually played a key role in establishing the gold standard in Britain 40 years before its formal adoption.

The
Royal
Mint ®

Don't just discover history, own it

Collector Services

The Royal Mint's Historic Coin Service

The Royal Mint has been striking British coins since AD 886. It's what we do. Trust us to be your source of expert advice for your next coin search and purchase, with assured authenticity.

With an extensive network of numismatic connections and in-house expert knowledge, we can source rare and special historic coins. Whether you're adding to your collection or looking for a memorable gift, our Historic Coin Finder Service can help.

If you know what you're looking for, send us the details of the coin you require and let us do the hard work sourcing it. If you are after a special coin or coins and are unsure of the exact details, or you would like some advice on the best coin to fit your requirements, get in touch with our specialist team.

Historic Coins

Authentication & Valuation

Care & Display

Secure Storage

Telephone: 0800 03 22 153
royalmint.com/historics

Follow us:

Treasure *for* Life®

Monarchs
of England

Here we list the Kings and Queens from Anglo-Saxon times to the present, with the dates of their rule. Before Eadgar became the King of all England the country had been divided up into small kingdoms, each with their own ruler.

ANGLO-SAXON KINGS

The Anglo-Saxon monarchs ruled over the various kingdoms which existed in England following the withdrawal of the Romans in the 5th century AD. The most prominent kingdoms in the land were Kent, Sussex, Wessex, Mercia and Northumbria. Each kingdom produced its own coinage but in 973 Eadgar introduced a new coinage that became the standard for the whole of the country.

Eadgar (959–975)
Edward the Martyr (975–978)
Aethelred II (978–1016)
Cnut (1016–1035)
Harold I (1035–1040)
Harthacanut (1035–1042)
Edward the Confessor (1042–1066)
Harold II (1066)

NORMAN KINGS

The Normans came to Britain from their native France following the establishment of a kingdom in Sicily and southern Italy. An expedition led by the powerful Duke William of Normandy culminated in the battle of Hastings in 1066 where he defeated Harold II and was proclaimed King of All England. Their influence spread from these new centres to the Crusader States in the Near East and to Scotland and Wales in Great Britain, and to Ireland. Today their influence can be seen in their typical Romanesque style of architecture.

William I (1066–1087)
William II (1087–1100)
Henry I (1100–1135)
Stephen (1135–1154)

PLANTAGENETS

The Plantagenet kings of England were descended from the first House of Anjou who were established as rulers of England through the Treaty of Wallingford, which passed over the claims of Eustace and William, Stephen of Blois's sons, in favour of Henry of Anjou, son of the Empress Matilda and Geoffrey V, Count of Anjou.

Henry II (1154–1189)
Richard I (1189–1199)
John (1199–1216)
Henry III (1216–1272)
Edward I (1272–1307)
Edward II (1307–1327)
Edward III (1327–1377)
Richard II (1377–1399)

HOUSE OF LANCASTER

The House of Lancaster, a branch of the English royal House of Plantagenet, was one of the opposing factions involved in the Wars of the Roses, the civil war which dominated England and Wales during the 15th century. Lancaster provided England with three Kings

Henry IV (1399–1413)
Henry V (1413–1422)
Henry VI (1422–1461) and again 1470

HOUSE OF YORK

The House of York was the other branch of the House of Plantagenet involved in the disastrous Wars of the Roses. Edward IV was descended from Edmund of Langley, 1st Duke of York, the fourth surviving son of Edward III.

Edward IV (1461–1483 and again 1471–83)
Richard III (1483–1485)

TUDORS

The House of Tudor was an English royal dynasty that lasted 118 years, from 1485 to 1603. The family descended from the Welsh courtier Owen Tudor (Tewdwr). Following the defeat of Richard III at Bosworth, the battle that ended the Wars of the Roses, Henry Tudor, 2nd Earl of Richmond, took the throne as Henry VII.

Henry VII (1485–1509)
Henry VIII (1509–1547)
Edward VI (1547–1553)
Mary (1553–1558)
Philip & Mary (1554–1558)
Elizabeth I (1558–1603)

STUARTS

The House of Stuart ruled Scotland for 336 years, between 1371 and 1707. Elizabeth I of England's closest heir was James VI of Scotland via her grandfather Henry VII of England, who was founder of the Tudor dynasty. On Elizabeth's death, James Stuart ascended the thrones of England and Ireland and inherited the English claims to the French throne. The Stuarts styled themselves "Kings and Queens of Great Britain", although there was no parliamentary union until the reign of Queen Anne, the last monarch of the House of Stuart.

James I (1603–1625)
Charles I (1625–1649)
The Commonwealth (1653–1658)
Charles II (1660–1685)
James II (1685–1688)
William III & Mary (1688–1694)
William III (1694–1702)
Anne (1702–1714)

HOUSE OF HANOVER

The House of Hanover was a Germanic royal dynasty which ruled the Duchy of Brunswick-Lüneburg and the Kingdom of Hanover. George Ludwig ascended to the throne of the Kingdom of Great Britain and Ireland through the female line from Princess Elizabeth, sister of Charles I.

George I (1714–1727)
George II (1727–1760)
George III (1760–1820)
George IV (1820–1830)
William IV (1830–1837)
Victoria (1837–1901)

HOUSES OF SAXE-COBURG-GOTHA AND WINDSOR

The name Saxe-Coburg-Gotha was inherited by Edward VII from his father Prince Albert, the second son of the Duke of Saxe-Coburg-Gotha and husband of Victoria. During World War I the name was changed to Windsor to avoid the Germanic connotatiion.

Edward VII (1901–1910)
George V (1910–1936)
Edward VIII (1936)
George VI (1936–1952)
Elizabeth II (1952–)

PUBLIC AUCTIONS
N THE NORTH OF ENGLAND
Coins, Medals & Banknotes

Coincraft

Sell Where the Dealers Sell !

Everyday we have dealers popping into Coincraft to sell their coins and banknotes. Why? Because selling to Coincraft is easy, pleasant and quick. Our experts look at your material and either pay you what you want or make you an attractive offer, 95% of which are accepted on the spot.

We need to buy and have collectors waiting for the latest issue of The Phoenix, which is published 17 times a year, that's every three weeks, so there is not a lot of waiting time to sell what we buy. We also publish a special listing, The BlueCard Flyer, for our more advanced collectors and that goes out 13 times a year. So we need material for our 30+ catalogues that we publish each year. You want to sell and we need to buy!

If you sell at auction, you have to wait for them to have a sale, which can sometimes be six months. Then you have to hope that everything gets sold, otherwise they return the unsold coins or banknotes to you. Then you have to wait until they get paid, because auction houses do not pay you, until they themselves have been paid. Sometimes auctions get more then a dealer is willing to pay and sometimes they get less, it is a gamble But most of the time, auction houses only want the cream and not the milk...

Dealers sell to Coincraft because they know that once we have agreed the price, we pay them out on the spot and that we will make an offer for almost everything. So there are no unsold or returned goods.

For more then 61 years Coincrat has been helping collectors find coins and banknotes for their collections. Let us help each other, you will get more money selling directly to Coincraft and we will be able to help more of our collectors, fill in those gaps in their collection.

Call in person at either of our two shops at 44 & 45 Great Russell Street, just across from the British Museum. Open Monday to Friday 9.30 to 5.00 and Saturday from 10.00 till 2.30.

Friendly, personal service and an interesting display of coins, banknotes, medallions, ancient coins and antiquities, to tempt and delight you.

Buy by post through Britain's only coin newspaper, The Phoenix, published every three weeks. It contains 24 tabloid sized pages of special offers and rare items, many not available anywhere else.

You can't buy a subscription, but you can get a complimentary copy free, just for the asking.

On the Internet Our website, www.coincraft.com is available 24 hours a day. There are many interesting features including a comprehensive numismatic glossary. Keep looking, more is being added every day.

We always need to buy Coincraft needs to buy: single items to entire collections, dealers inventories, hoards, accumulations, you name it and we will make you an offer. Over 90% of our offers are accepted. Sell where the dealers sell.

Find out why collectors say; Coincraft, nice people to do business with.

Coincraft
FRIENDLY PROFESSIONAL SERVICE SINCE 1955

45 Great Russel Street, London WC1B 3JL
(opposite the British Museum)

Tel 020 7636 1188
Fax 020 7323 2860
Web www.coincraft.com Email info@coincraft.com

Dates
on coins

The vast majority of modern coins bear the date prominently on one side. In most cases dates are expressed in modified Arabic numerals according to the Christian calendar and present no problem in identification. There have been a few notable exceptions to this general rule, however. Morocco, for example, has used European numerals to express dates according to the Moslem calendar, so that a coin dated 1321 actually signifies 1903. Dates are almost invariably written from left to right—even in Arabic script which writes words from right to left. An exception, however, occurred in the Philippines quarto of 1822 where the date appeared as 2281, and the "2"s back to front for good measure.

	ARABIC-TURKISH	CHINESE, JAPANESE KOREAN, ANNAMESE (ORDINARY)	CHINESE, JAPANESE KOREAN, ANNAMESE (OFFICIAL)	INDIAN	SIAMESE	BURMESE
1	١	一	壹	٩	๑	၁
2	٢	二	貳	٢	๒	၂
3	٣	三	叁	٣	๓	၃
4	٤	四	肆	٨	๔	၄
5	٥	五	伍	٤	๕	၅
6	٦	六	陸	٤	๖	၆
7	٧	七	柒	٥	๗	၇
8	٨	八	捌	٢	๘	၈
9	٩	九	玖	٩	๙	၉
0	٠			٥	๐	၀
10	١٠	十	拾		๑๐	
100	١٠٠	百			๑๐๐	
1000	١٠٠٠	千				

Dates in Roman numerals have been used since 1234 when this practice was adopted by the Danish town of Roskilde. Such Roman numerals were used sporadically throughout the Middle Ages and in later centuries and survive fitfully to this day. This was the system used in England for the first dated coins, the gold half-sovereigns of Edward VI struck at Durham House in 1548 (MDXLVIII). This continued till 1550 (MDL) but thereafter Arabic numerals were used, beginning with the half-crown of 1551. Notable exceptions of more recent times include the Gothic coinage of Queen Victoria (1847–87).

The first coin with the date in European numerals was a plappart of St Gallen, Switzerland dated 1424, but this was an isolated case. In 1477 Maria of Burgundy issued a guldiner which bore a date on the reverse, in the form of two pairs of digits flanking the crown at the top. The numerals in this instance were true Gothic, an interesting transition between true Arabic numerals and the modified Arabic figures now used in Europe. The Tyrolese guldengroschen of 1484–6 were the first coins to be regularly dated in European numerals and thereafter this custom spread rapidly.

For the numismatist, the problem arises when coins bear a date in the numerals of a different alphabet or computed according to a different era. Opposite is a table showing the basic numerals used in different scripts. The various eras which may be found in coin dates are as listed and explained opposite.

Hijra

The era used on Moslem coins dates from the flight of Mohammed from Mecca to Medina on July 15, 622 and is often expressed as digits followed by AH (Anno Hegirae). Moslems employ a lunar calendar of twelve months comprising 354 11/30 days. Tipu Sultan of Mysore in 1201 AH (the fifth year of his reign) introduced a new era dating from the birth of Mohammed in AD 570 and using a luni-solar system. Tipu also adopted the Hindu cycle of sixty years (the Tamil Brihaspate Cycle), but changed this two or three years later, from Hijra to Muludi.

Afghan coins used the lunar calendar until 1920 and during 1929–31, but at other times have used the solar calendar. Thus the Democratic Republic began issuing its coins in SH 1358 (1979).

To convert an AH date to the Christian calendar you must translate the Arabic into European numerals. Taking an Arabic coin dated 1320, for example, first deduct 3% (to convert from the Moslem lunar year to our solar year). This gives 39.6 which, rounded up to the nearest whole number, is 40. Deduct 40 from 1320 (1280), then add 622. The answer is 1902.

There have been a few notable exceptions. Thus the Khanian era of Ilkhan Ghazan Mahmud began on 1st Rajab 701 AH (1301). This era used a solar calendar, but was shortlived, being confined to coins of Mahmud and his nephew Abu Said down to year 34 (1333).

The era of Tarikh Ilahi was adopted by the Mughal emperor Akbar in the thirteenth year of his reign (922 AH). This era dated from his accession on 5th Rabi al-Sani 963 AH (February 19, 1556). The calendar had solar months and days but no weeks, so each day of the month had a different name. This system was used by Akbar, Jahangir and Shah Jahan, often with a Hijra date as well.

Saphar

The era of the Caesars began on January 1, 38 BC and dated from the conquest of Spain by Augustus. Its use on coinage, however, seems to have been confined to the marabotins of Alfonso VIII of Castile and was expressed in both Latin and Arabic.

Samvat

The era of Vikramaditya began in 57 BC and was a luni-solar system used in some Indian states. Coins may be found with both Samvat and Hijra dates. Conversion to the Christian date is simple; merely subtract 57 from the Samvat to arrive at the AD date.

Saka

This originated in the southwestern district of Northern India and began in AD 78. As it used the luni-solar system it converts easily by adding 78 to the Saka date.

Nepal

Nepalese coins have used four different date systems. All coins of the Malla kings were dated in Nepal Samvat (NS) era, year 1 beginning in 881. This system was also used briefly by the state of Cooch Behar. Until 1888 all coins of the Gurkha dynasty were dated in the Saka era (SE) which began in AD 78. After 1888 most copper coins were dated in the Vikram Samvat (VS) era from 57 BC. With the exception of some gold coins struck in 1890 and 1892, silver and gold coins only changed to the VS era in 1911, but now this system is used for all coins struck in Nepal. Finally, dates in the Christian era have appeared on some commemorative coins of recent years.

Ethiopian

This era dates from August AD 7, so that EE 1885 is AD 1892. Ethiopian dates are expressed in five digits using Amharic numerals. The first two are the digits of the centuries, the third is the character for 100, while the fourth and fifth are the digits representing the decade and year. On modern coins dates are rendered in Amharic numerals using the Christian era.

Thailand

Thai coins mainly use the Buddhist era (BE) which dates from 543 BC, but some coins have used dates from the Chula-Sakarat calendar (CS) which began in AD 638, while others use a Ratanakosind Sok (RS) date from the foundation of the Chakri dynasty in AD 1781.

Hebrew

The coins of Israel use the Jewish calendar dating from the beginning of the world (Adam and Eve in the Garden of Eden) in 3760 BC. Thus the year 1993 is rendered as 5753. The five millennia are assumed in dates, so that only the last three digits are expressed. 735 therefore equates with AD 1975. Dates are written in Hebrew letters, reading from right to left. The first two characters signify 400 and 300 respectively, totalling 700. The third letter denotes the decades (lamedh = 30) and the fourth letter, following the separation mark (") represents the final digit (heh = 5). The Jewish year runs from September or October in the Christian calendar.

Dates from the creation of the world

This system was also used in Russia under Ivan IV. The dating system Anno Mundi (AM) was established by the Council of Constantinople in AD 680 which determined that the birth of Christ had occurred in 5508 AM. Ivan's coins expressed the date as 7055 (1447).

Dynastic dates

The system of dating coinage according to regnal years is a feature of Chinese and Japanese coins. Chinese coins normally have an inscription stating that they are coins of such and such a reign period (not the emperor's name), and during the Southern Sung dynasty this was joined by the numeral of the year of the reign. This system was continued under the republic and survives in Taiwan to this day, although the coins of the Chinese Peoples Republic are dated in western numerals using the Christian calendar.

Early Japanese coins bore a reference to the era (the title assumed by each emperor on his accession) but, like Chinese coins, could not be dated accurately. From the beginning of the Meiji era (1867), however, coins have included a regnal number. The Showa era, beginning in 1926 with the accession of Hirohito, eventually ran to sixty-three (expressed in western numerals on some denominations, in Japanese ideograms on others) to denote 1988, although the rest of the inscription was in Japanese characters.

Dynastic dates were used on Korean milled coins introduced in 1888. These bore two characters at the top Kae Kuk (founding of the dynasty) followed by quantitative numerals. The system dated from the founding of the Yi dynasty in 1392. Curiously enough, some Korean banknotes have borne dates from the foundation of the first dynasty in 2333 BC.

Iran adopted a similar system in 1975, celebrating the 15th anniversary of the Pahlavi regime by harking back to the glories of Darius. The new calendar dated from the foundation of the Persian Empire 2535 years earlier, but was abolished only three years later when the Shah was overthrown.

··

Political eras

France adopted a republican calendar in 1793 when the monarchy was abolished. Coins were then inscribed L'AN (the year) followed by Roman numerals, but later Arabic numerals were substituted. This continued to the year 14 (1806) but in that year the Emperor Napoleon restored the Christian calendar. The French system was emulated by Haiti whose coins dated from the revolution of 1803. The date appeared as AN followed by a number until AN 31 (1834) on some coins; others had both the evolutionary year and the Christian date from 1828 until 1850 (AN 47). Coins with a date in the Christian calendar appeared only in 1807–9 and then from 1850 onwards.

Mussolini introduced the Fascist calendar to Italy, dating from the seizure of power in October 1922. This system was widely employed on documents and memorials, but was first used on silver 20 lire coins of 1927 and then only in addition to the Christian date and appearing discreetly as Roman numerals. Subsequently it was extended to gold 50 lire and 100 lire coins in 1931 and the subsidiary coinage in 1936, being last used in the year XXI (1943).

Coin
glossary

In this section we list all the terms commonly encountered in numismatics or in the production of coins.

Abbey Coins Medieval coins struck in the abbeys, convents and other great religious houses which were granted coinage rights. These coins were often used also by pilgrims journeying from one monastery to another.

Abschlag (German for "discount") A *restrike* from an original die.

Accolated Synonym sometimes used for *conjoined* or *jugate*, signifying two or more profiles overlapping.

Acmonital Acronym from *Aciaio Monetario Italiano*, a stainless steel alloy used for Italian coins since 1939.

Adjustment Reduction of metal in a *flan* or *blank* to the specified weight prior to striking, accomplished by filing down the face. Such file marks often survived the coining process and are occasionally met with in coins, especially of the 18th century.

Ae Abbreviation for the Latin *Aes* (bronze), used for coins made of brass, bronze or other copper alloys.

Aes Grave (Latin for heavy bronze) Heavy circular coins first minted at Rome in 269 BC.

Aes Rude (Latin for rough bronze) Irregular lumps of bronze which gradually developed into ingots of uniform shape and were the precursors of coins in Rome.

Aes Signatum (Latin for signed bronze) Bronze ingots of regular size and weight, bearing marks of authority to guarantee their weight (289–269 BC).

Agonistic (Greek) Term for coins issued to commemorate, or pertaining to, sporting events.

Alliance Coinage struck by two or more states acting together and having common features of design or inscription.

Alloy Coinage metal composed of two or more metallic elements.

Altered Deliberately changed, usually unofficially, with the aim of increasing the numismatic value of a coin, medal or note. This applies particularly to dates, where a common date may be altered to a rare date by filing or re-engraving one of the digits.

Aluminium (American *Aluminum*) Silvery lightweight metal, developed commercially in the late 19th century for commemorative medals, but used for tokens and emergency money during the First World War and since 1940 widely used in subsidiary coinage.

Aluminium-bronze Alloy of aluminium and copper. Hard-wearing and gold-coloured, it is widely used in tokens and subsidiary coinage.

Amulet Coin or medal believed to have talismanic qualities, such as warding off disease and bad luck. Many Chinese and Korean pieces come into this category. See also *Touchpiece*.

Androcephalous Heraldic term for creatures with a human head.

Anepigraphic Coins or medals without a legend.

Annealing Process of heating and cooling applied to metal to relieve stresses and prepare it for striking into coins.

Annulet Small circle often used as an ornament or spacing device in coin inscriptions.

Antimony Brittle white metal, chemical symbol *Sb*, virtually impractical as a coinage metal but used for the Chinese 10 cents of Kweichow, 1931. Alloyed with tin, copper or lead, it produces the white metal popular as a medallic medium.

Antoniniani Silver coins minted in Imperial Rome. The name derives from the Emperor Caracalla (Marcus Aurelius Antoninus) in whose reign they were first struck. The silver content was progressively reduced and by the last issue (AD 295) they were reduced to *billon*.

Ar Abbreviation for Latin *Argentum* (silver), used for coins struck in this metal.

Assay Mark Mark applied to a medal struck in precious metal by an assayer or assay office as a guarantee of the fineness of the metal.

Assignat Type of paper money used in France 1789–96, representing the land assigned to the holders.

Attribution Identification of a coin by characteristics such as issuing authority, date or reign, mint, denomination, metal, and by a standard reference.

Au Abbreviation for *aurum* (Latin for gold), denoting coins of this metal.

AU Abbreviation for "About Uncirculated", often found in catalogues and dealers' lists to describe the condition of a numismatic piece.

Autodollar Name given to the silver yuan issued by Kweichow, 1928, and having a contemporary motor car as the obverse motif.

Auxiliary Payment Certificate Form of paper money intended for use by American military personnel stationed in overseas countries. See also *Baf* and *Scrip*.

Babel Note Nickname given to the paper money of the Russian Socialist Federated Soviet Republic (1919) because it bore the slogan "workers of the world unite" in seven languages, a reference to the biblical tower of Babel.

BAF Acronym from British Armed Forces, the popular name for the vouchers which could only be exchanged for goods in service canteens from 1945 onwards.

Bag Mark Minor scratch or abrasion on an otherwise uncirculated coin, caused by coins in mint bags knocking together.

Banknote Form of paper money issued by banks and usually promising to pay the bearer on demand in coin of the realm.

Barbarous Imitation of Greek or Roman coins by the Celtic and Germanic tribes who lived beyond the frontiers of the civilised world.

Base Non-precious metals or alloys.

Bath Metal Inferior bronze alloy, named after the English city where it was used for casting cannon. Used by William Wood of Bristol for Irish and American tokens and by Amos Topping for Manx coins of 1733/4.

Beading Ornamental border found on the raised rim of a coin.

Behalfszahlungsmittel German term for auxiliary payment certificates used in occupied Europe from 1939 to 1945.

Bell Metal Alloy of copper and tin normally used for casting bells, but employed for the subsidiary coinage of the French Revolutionary period.

Billon Silver alloy containing less than 50 per cent fine silver, usually mixed with copper. In Spain this alloy was known as *vellon*.

Bi-metallic Coins struck in two separate metals or alloys. Patterns for such coins exist from the 19th century but actual coins with a centre of one metal surrounded by a ring of another did not appear till 1982 (Italy, San Marino and Vatican), since then many countries, including Great Britain, have introduced bi-metallic coins. See also *Clad, Plugged* and *Sandwich*.

Bi-metallism Monetary system in which two metals are in simultaneous use and equally available as legal tender, implying a definite ratio between the two. A double standard of gold and silver, with a ratio of 16:1, existed till the mid-19th century.

Bingle American term for a trade token, more specifically the US government issue of tokens for the Matacuska, Alaska colonization project, 1935.

Birthday Coins Coins celebrating the birthday of a ruler originated in Roman Imperial times, notably the reigns of Maximianus (286–305) and Constantinus I (307–37). Birthday talers were issued by many German states, and among recent examples may be cited coins marking the 70th, 80th and 90th birthdays of Gustaf Adolf VI of Sweden, 80th and 90th birthday coins from Great Britan and the British Commonwealth for Her Majesty the Queen, as well as the birthdays of other members of our Royal Family..

Bit Term denoting fragments of large silver coins, cut up and circulating as fractional values. Spanish dollars were frequently broken up for circulation in the American colonies and the West indies. Long bits and short bits circulated at 15 and 10 cents respectively, but the term came to be equated with the Spanish real or eighth peso, hence the American colloquialism "two-bit" signifying a quarter dollar.

Black Money English term for the debased silver deniers minted in France which circulated freely in England until they were banned by government decree in 1351.

Blank Piece of metal, cut or punched out of a roller bar or strip, and prepared for striking to produce coins. Alternate terms are *flan* and *planchet*.

Blundered Inscription Legend in which the lettering is jumbled or meaningless, indicating the illiteracy of the tribes who copied Greek and Roman coins.

Bonnet Piece Scottish gold coin, minted in 1539–40. The name is derived from the obverse portraying King James V wearing a large, flat bonnet.

Bon Pour French for "good for", inscribed on Chamber of Commerce brass tokens issued in 1920–7 during a shortage of legal tender coinage.

Bouquet Sou Canadian copper token halfpenny of 1837 deriving its name from the nosegay of heraldic flowers on the obverse.

Box Coin Small container formed by *obverse* and *reverse* of two coins, hollowed out and screwed together.

Bracteate (Latin *bractea*, a thin piece of metal) Coins struck on blanks so thin that the image applied to one side appears in reverse on the other. First minted in Erfurt and Thuringia in the 12th century, and later produced elsewhere in Germany, Switzerland and Poland till the 14th century.

Brass Alloy of copper and zinc, widely used for subsidiary coinage. The term was also formerly used for bronze Roman coins, known numismatically as first, second or third brass.

Breeches Money Derisive term given by the Royalists to the coinage of the Commonwealth, 1651, because the conjoined elongated oval shields on the reverse resembled a pair of breeches.

Brockage Mis-struck coin with only one design, normal on one side and *incuse* on the other. This occurs when a coin previously struck adheres to the die and strikes the next blank to pass through the press.

Broken Bank-note Note issued by a bank which has failed, but this is often applied more generally to banknotes which have actually been demonetised.

Bronze Alloy of copper and tin, first used as a coinage metal by the Chinese c. 1000 BC. Often used synonymously with copper, though it should be noted that bronze only superseded copper as the constituent of the base metal British coins in 1860.

Bull Neck Popular term for the coins of King George III, 1816–17.

Bullet Money Pieces of silver, *globular* in shape, bearing various *countermarks* and used as coins in Siam (Thailand) in the 18th and 19th centuries.

Bullion Precious metal in bars, ingots, strip or scrap (i.e. broken jewellery mounts, watch-cases and plate), its weight reckoned solely by weight and fineness, before being converted into coin.

Bullion Coin A coin struck in platinum, gold or silver, whose value is determined solely by the prevailing market price for the metal as a commodity. Such coins do not generally have a nominal face value, but include in their inscriptions their weight and fineness. Good examples of recent times include the Krugerrand (South Africa), the Britannia (UK), the Maple Leaf (Canada), the Libertad (Mexico), the Nugget (Australia) and the Eagle (USA).

Bun Coinage British coins of 1860–94 showing Queen Victoria with her hair in a bun.

Bungtown Coppers Derisive term (from Anglo-American slang *bung*, to swindle or bribe) for halfpence of English or Irish origin, often counterfeit, which circulated in North America towards the end of the colonial period.

Carat (American *Karat*) Originally a unit of weight for precious stones, based on carob seeds (ceratia), it also denotes the fineness or purity of gold, being 1/24th part of the whole. Thus 9 carat gold is .375 fine and 22 carat, the English sovereign standard, is .916 fine. Abbreviated as ct or kt.

Cartwheel Popular term for the large and cumbersome penny and twopenny pieces of 1797 weighing one and two ounces, struck by Matthew Boulton at the Soho Mint, Birmingham.

Cased Set   Set of coins in mint condition, housed in the official case issued by the mint. Formerly leather cases with blue plush or velvet lining were used, but nowadays many sets are encapsulated in plastic to facilitate handling.

Cash   (from Portuguese *caixa*, Hindi *kasu*). Round piece of bronze or brass with a square hole in the centre, used as subsidiary coinage in China for almost 2000 years, till the early 12th century. In Chinese these pieces were known as *Ch'ien* or *Li* and strung together in groups of 1000 were equivalent to a silver tael.

Cast Coins   Coins cast from molten metals in moulds. This technique, widespread in the case of early commemorative medals, has been used infrequently in coins, the vast majority of which are struck from *dies*. Examples include the Chinese cash coins and the Isle of Man coins of 1709.

Check   A form of *token* given as a means of identification, or issued for small amounts of money or for services of a specific nature.

Cheque   (American *Check*)   A written order directing a bank to pay money.

Chop   (Hindi, to seal). Countermark, usually consisting of a single character, applied by Chinese merchants to precious metal coins and ingots as a guarantee of their weight and fineness. Coins may be found with a wide variety of chop marks and the presence of several different marks on the same coin can sometimes enhances its interest and value. See also *Shroff mark*.

Christmas   Coins issued as Christmas gifts date from the Middle Ages when the Venetian Doges struck *Osselle* as presents for their courtiers. In modern times, however, the custom has developed only since the late 1970s with several countries having issued them since then.

Cistophori   (Greek for chest bearing) a generic term for the coins of Pergamum with an obverse motif of a chest showing a serpent crawling out of the half-opened lid. Cistophori became very popular all over Asia Minor in the 3rd and 2nd centuries BC and were struck also at mints in Ionia, Phrygia, Lydia and Mysia.

Clad Coins   Coins with a core of one alloy, covered with a layer or coating of another. US half dollars from 1965 to 1970, for example, had a core of 21 per cent silver and 79 per cent copper, bonded to outer layers of 80 per cent silver and 20 per cent copper. More recently, however, coins usually have a body in a cheap alloy, with only a thin cladding of a more expensive material, such as the British 1p and 2p coins of stainless steel with a copper cladding, introduced late in 1992.

Clash Marks   Mirror image traces found on a coin which has been struck from a pair of dies, themselves damaged by having been struck together without a blank between.

Clipped Coins   Precious metal coins from which small amounts have been removed by clipping the edges. It was to prevent this that *graining* and *edge inscriptions* were adopted.

Cob   Crude, irregularly shaped silver piece, often with little more than a vestige of die impressions, produced in the Spanish American mints in the 16th–18th centuries.

Coin   Piece of metal, marked with a device, issued by government authority and intended for use as money.

Collar   Retaining ring within which the *dies* for the *obverse* and *reverse* operate. When the *blank* is struck under high pressure between the dies the metal flows sideways and is formed by the collar, taking up the impression of *reeding* or *edge inscription* from it.

Commemorative   Coin, medal, token or paper note issued to celebrate a current event or the anniversary of a historic event or personality.

Communion Token   Token, cast in lead, but later struck in pewter, brass, bronze or white metal, issued to members of a congregation to permit them to partake of the annual communion service in the Calvinist and Presbyterian churches. John Calvin himself is said to have invented the communion token in 1561 but they were actually referred to in the minutes of the Scottish General Assembly in 1560. Later they were adopted by the Reformed churches in many parts of Europe. They survived in Scotland till the early years of this century. Each parish had its own tokens, often bearing the names or initials of individual ministers, with dates, symbols and biblical texts.

Conjoined   Term denoting overlapped profiles of two or more rulers (e.g. William and Mary).

Contact mark   Abrasion, dent or other imperfection caused by contact with other coins.

Contorniate   (from Italian *contorno*, edge). Late 4th and 5th century Roman bronze piece whose name alludes to the grooving on the edges.

Contribution Coins   Coins struck by Bamberg, Eichstatt, Fulda and other German cities in the

1790s during the First Coalition War against the French Republic. The name alludes to the fact that the bullion used to produce the coins necessary to pay troops was raised by contribution from the Church and the public.

Convention Money Any system of coinage agreed by neighbouring countries for mutual acceptance and interchange. Examples include the Amphictyonic coins of ancient Greece, and the Austrian and Bavarian talers and gulden of 1753–1857 which were copied by other south German states and paved the way for the German Monetary union.

Copper Metallic element, chemical symbol *Cu*, widely used as a coinage medium for 2,500 years. Pure or almost pure copper was used for subsidiary coinage in many countries till the mid-19th century, but has since been superseded by copper alloys which are cheaper and more durable: *bronze* (copper and tin), *brass* (copper and zinc), *Bath metal* or *bell metal* (low-grade copper and tin), *aluminium-bronze* (copper and aluminium), *potin* (copper, tin, lead and silver) or *cupro-nickel* (copper and nickel). Copper is also alloyed with gold to give it its reddish hue, and is normally alloyed with silver in coinage metals. When the copper exceeds the silver content the alloy is known as *billon*.

Copperhead Popular term for a copper *token* about the size and weight of an American cent which circulated in the USA during the Civil War (1861–65) during a shortage of subsidiary coinage. Many different types were produced, often of a political or patriotic nature.

Coppernose Popular name for the debased silver shillings of Henry VIII. Many of them were struck in copper with little more than a silver wash which tended to wear off at the highest point of the obverse, the nose on the full-face portrait of the king.

Counter A piece resembling a coin but intended for use on a medieval accountancy board or in gambling. See also *jeton*.

Counterfeit Imitation of a coin, token or banknote intended for circulation to deceive the public and defraud the state.

Countermark Punch mark applied to a coin some time after its original issue, either to alter its nominal value, or to authorise its circulation in some other country.

Cowrie Small shell (*Cypraea moneta*) circulating as a form of primitive currency from 1000 BC (China) to the present century (East and West Africa) and also used in the islands of the Indian and Pacific Oceans.

Crockard Debased silver imitation of English pennies produced in the Netherlands and imported into England in the late 13th century. Edward I tried to prevent their import then, in 1299, allowed them to pass current as halfpennies. As they contained more than a halfpennyworth of silver this encouraged their trading in to be melted down and they disappeared from circulation within a year. Sometimes known as *pollards*. See also *Lushbourne*.

Crown Gold Gold of 22 carat (.916) fineness, so called on account of its adoption in 1526 for the English gold crown. It has remained the British standard gold fineness ever since.

Cuirassed Monarch's bust or effigy shown wearing a breast plate of armour.

Cumberland Jack Popular name for a counter or medalet of sovereign size, struck unofficially in 1837 in brass. The figure of St George was replaced by the Duke of Cumberland on horseback with the inscription "To Hanover" a reference to the unpopular Duke of Cumberland, uncle of Queen Victoria, who succeeded to the Hanoverian throne since Victoria, as a female, was debarred by Salic law from inheritance.

Cupellation (Latin *cupella*, a little cup). Process by which gold and silver were separated from lead and other impurities in their ores. A cupel is a shallow cup of bone-ash or other absorbent material which, when hot, absorbs any molten material that wets its surface. Lead melts and oxidises with impurities into the cupel, whereas gold and silver remain on the cupel. Cupellation is also used in assaying the fineness of these precious metals.

Cupro-nickel Coinage alloy of 75 per cent copper and 25 per cent nickel, now widely used as a base metal substitute for silver. A small amount of zinc is added to the alloy in modern Russian coins.

Currency Coins, tokens, paper notes and other articles intended to pass current in general circulation as money.

Current Coins and paper money still in circulation.

Cut Money Coins cut into smaller pieces to provide correspondingly smaller denominations. The cross on many medieval coins assisted the division of silver pennies into halfpence and farthings. Spanish dollars were frequently divided into *bits* which themselves became units of currency in America and the West Indies.

Cowrie shells

Darlehnskassen (German for "state loan notes"). Paper money issued during the First World War in an abortive bid to fill the shortage of coinage in circulation. These low-denomination notes failed to meet demand and were superseded by local issues of small *Notgeld* in 1916.

Debasement The reduction in the precious metal content of the coinage, widely practised since time immemorial by governments for economic reasons. British coins, for example, were debased from sterling (.925 fine) silver to .500 in 1920 and from silver to cupro-nickel in 1947.

Decimalisation A currency system in which the principal unit is subdivided into ten, a hundred, or a thousand fractions. Russia was the first country to decimalise, in 1534 when the rouble of 100 kopeks was introduced, but it was not till 1792 that France adopted the franc of 100 centimes and 1793 when the USA introduced the dollar of 100 cents. Most European countries decimalised their currency in the 19th century. Britain toyed with the idea, introducing the florin or tenth of a pound in 1849 as the first step, but did not complete the process till 1971. The last countries to decimalise were Malta and Nigeria, in 1972 and 1973 respectively.

Demidiated Heraldic term to describe the junction of two armorial devices, in which only half of each is shown.

Demonetisation The withdrawal of coins or paper money from circulation and declaring them to be worthless.

Device Heraldic term for the pattern or emblem on coins or paper notes.

Die Hardened piece of metal bearing a mirror image of the device to be struck on one side of a coin or medal.

Die Proof An impression, usually pulled on soft carton or India paper, of an *intaglio* engraving of a banknote, usually taken during the progress of the engraving to check the detail. Banknote proofs of this nature usually consist of the portrait or some detail of the design, such as the border, rather than the complete motif.

Dodecagonal threepenny piece.

Dodecagonal Twelve-sided, as the nickel-brass threepence of Great Britain, 1937–67.

Dump Any primitive coin struck on a very thick *flan*, but more specifically applied to the circular pieces cut from the centre of Spanish dollars, countermarked with the name of the colony, a crown and the value, and circulated in New South Wales at 15 pence in 1813. See *Holey Dollar*.

Duodecimal Currency system based on units of twelve, i.e. medieval money of account (12 denarii = 1 soldo) which survived in Britain as 12 pence to the shilling as late as 1971.

Ecclesiastical Coins Coins struck by a religious authority, such as an archbishop, bishop, abbot, prior or the canons of a religious order. Such coins were common in medieval times but survived as late as the early 19th century, the bishops of Breslau (1817) and Gurk (1823) being the last prelates to exercise coinage rights. Coins were always struck by authority of the Pope at Rome till 1870 but since 1929 coinage has been struck at the Italian state mint on behalf of the Vatican.

Edge Inscription Lettering on the edge of a coin or medal to prevent clipping. Alluding to this, the Latin motto *Decus et Tutamen* (an ornament and a safeguard) was applied to the edge of English milled coins in the reign of Charles II.

Edge Ornament An elaboration of the *graining* found on many milled coins to prevent clipping, taking the form of tiny leaves, florets, interlocking rings, pellets and zigzag patterns. In some cases the ornament appears between layers of more conventional reeding.

EF Abbreviation for Extremely Fine.

Effigy An image or representation of a person, normally the head of state, a historical personage, or an allegorical figure, usually on the *obverse* or "heads" side of a coin or medal.

Electrotype A reproduction of a coin or medal made by an electrolytic process.

Electrum Alloy of gold and silver, sometimes called white gold, used for minting the staters of Lydia, 7th century BC, and other early European coins.

Elongated Coin An oval *medalet* created by passing a coin, such as an American cent, between rollers under pressure with the effect of squeezing it out and impressing on it a souvenir or commemorative motif.

Emergency Money Any form of money used in times of economic and political upheaval, when traditional kinds of currency are not available. Examples include the comparatively crude silver coins issued by the Royalists during the *Civil War* (1642–49), *obsidional* money, issued in time of siege, from Tyre (1122) to Mafeking (1900), the *Notgeld* issued by many German towns (1916–23), *encased money, fractional currency, guerrilla notes, invasion, liberation* and *occupation money* from the two World Wars and minor campaigns. Among the more recent examples may be cited the use of sweets and cheques in Italy (1976–77) and the issue of coupons and vouchers in many of the countries of the former Soviet Union pending the introduction of their own coins and notes.

Enamelled Coins Coins decorated by enamelling the obverse and reverse motifs in contrasting colours was an art practised by many jewellers in Birmingham and Paris in the 19th century, and revived in Europe and America in the 1970s.

Encased Money Postage and revenue stamps enclosed in small metal and mica-faced discs, circulated as small change in times of emergency. The practice was invented by John Gault, a Boston sewing-machine salesman, during the American Civil War (1862). The face of the stamp was visible through the transparent window, while the back of the disc was embossed with firms' advertisements. This practice was revived during and after the First World War when there was again a shortage of small coins. Encased stamps have also been recorded from France, Austria, Norway, Germany and Monaco.

Engrailing Technical term for the close serrations or vertical bars round the edge of a coin, applied as a security device.

Engraving The art of cutting lines or grooves in plates, blocks or dies. Numismatically this takes the form of engraving images into the face of the dies used in striking coins, a process which has now been almost completely superseded by *hubbing* and the use of *reducing machinery*. In the production of paper money, *intaglio* engraving is still commonly practised. In this process the engraver cuts the design into a steel die and the printing ink lies in the grooves. The paper is forced under great pressure into the grooves and picks up the ink, and this gives banknotes their characteristic ridged feeling to the touch. Nowadays many banknotes combine traditional intaglio engraving with multicolour lithography or photogravure to defeat the would-be counterfeiter.

Epigraphy The study of inscriptions, involving the classification and interpretation of coin legends, an invaluable adjunct to the study of a coin series, particularly the classical and medieval coins which, in the absence of dates and mintmarks, would otherwise be difficult to arrange in chronological sequence.

Erasion The removal of the title or effigy of a ruler from the coinage issued after his or her death.

This process was practised in imperial Rome, and applied to the coins of Caligula, Nero and Geta, as part of the more general practice of *damnatio memoriae* (damnation of the memory) ordered by the Senate.

Error Mistakes on coins and paper money may be either caused at the design or engraving stage, or as a result of a fault in the production processes. In the first category come mis-spellings in legends causing, in extreme cases, *blundered inscriptions*, or anachronisms or inaccuracies in details of the design. In the second, the most glaring error is the mule caused by marrying the wrong dies. Faulty alignment of dies can cause obverse and reverse to be out of true. Although many coins are issued with obverse and reverse upside down in relation to each other, this can also occur as an error in coins where both sides should normally be facing the same way up. Other errors caused at the production stage include striking coins in the wrong metal or with the wrong *collar* thus creating a different edge from the normal.

Essay (From the French *essai*, a trial piece). The term is applied to any piece struck for the purposes of examination, by parliamentary or financial bodies, prior to the authorisation of an issue of coins or paper money. The official nature of these items distinguishes them from *patterns*, which denote trial pieces often produced by mints or even private individuals bidding for coinage contracts.

Evasion Close copy or imitation of a coin, with sufficient deliberate differences in the design or inscription to avoid infringing counterfeit legislation. A good example is the imitation of Sumatran coins by European merchants, inscribed SULTANA instead of SUMATRA.

Exergue Lower segment of a coin or medal, usually divided from the rest of the *field* by a horizontal line, and often containing the date, value, ornament or identification symbols.

Exonumia Generic term for numismatic items not authorised by a government, e.g. *patterns, tokens, medalets* or *model coins*.

F Abbreviation for Fine.

Face The surface of a coin, medal or token, referred to as the *obverse* or the *reverse*. The corresponding faces of a paper note are more correctly termed *verso* and *recto*, but the coin terms are often used instead.

Facing Term for the portrait, usually on the obverse, which faces to the front instead of to the side (profile).

Fantasy Piece of metal purporting to be the coinage of a country which does not exist.

Recent examples include the money of Atlantis and the Hutt River Province which declared its independence of Western Australia.

FDC Abbreviation for *Fleur de Coin*, a term denoting the finest possible condition of a coin.

Fiat Money Paper notes issued by a government but not redeemable in coin or bullion.

Field Flat part of the surface of a coin or medal, between the *legend*, the *effigy* and other raised parts of the design.

Fillet Heraldic term for the ribbon or headband on the effigy of a ruler or allegorical figure.

Find Term applied to an archaeological discovery of one or more coins. A large quantity of such material is described as a *hoard*.

Flan Alternative name for *blank* or *planchet*, the piece of metal struck between dies to produce a coin or medal.

Forgery An unauthorised copy or imitation, made with the intention of deceiving collectors. Forgeries intended to pass current for real coins or banknotes are more properly called *counterfeits*.

Fractional Currency Emergency issue of small-denomonation notes by the USA in 1863–65, following a shortage of coins caused by the Civil War. This issue superseded the *Postage Currency* notes, but bore the inscription "Receivable for all US stamps", alluding to the most popular medium of small change at that time. Denominations ranged from 3c to 50c.

Franklinium Cupro-nickel alloy developed by the Franklin Mint of Philadelphia and used for coins, medals and gaming tokens since 1967.

Freak An *error* or *variety* of a non-recurring type, usually caused accidentally during production.

Frosting Matt surface used for the high relief areas of many proof coins and medals, for greater contrast with the mirrored surface of the field.

Funeral Money Imitations of banknotes, used in China and Latin America in funeral ceremonies.

Geat (Git) Channel through which molten metal is ducted to the mould. Cast coins often show tiny protrusions known as geat marks.

Ghost Faint image of the design on one side of a coin visible on the other. Good examples were the British penny and halfpenny of George V, 1911–27, the ghosting being eliminated by the introduction of a smaller effigy in 1928.

Globular Coins struck on very thick *dumps* with convex faces. Examples include some Byzantine coins, and the *bullet money* of Siam (Thailand)

Godless (or *Graceless*) Epithet applied to any coin which omits the traditional reference to the deity, e.g. the British florin of 1849 which omitted D.G. (*Dei Gratia*, "by the Grace of God").

Gold Precious metal, chemical symbol and numismatic abbreviation *Au*, from the *Latin Aurum*, used as a coinage medium from the 7th century BC till the present day. The purity of gold is reckoned in *carats* or a decimal system. Thus British gold sovereigns are 22 carat or .916 fine. Medieval coins were 23.5 carat or .995 fine, and some modern bullion coins are virtually pure gold, denoted by the inscription .999. Canadian maple leaves are now struck in "four nines" gold and bear the inscription .9999.

Goodfor Popular name for token coins and *emergency money* made of paper or card, from the inscription "Good for" or its equivalent in other languages (e.g. French *Bon pour* or Dutch *Goed voor*) followed by a monetary value. They have been recorded from Europe, Africa and America during times of economic crises or shortage of more traditional coinage.

Gothic Crown Popular name for the silver crown issued by the United Kingdom (1847–53), so-called on account of its script (more properly Old English, rather than Gothic).

Grain The weight of a single grain of wheat was taken as the smallest unit of weight in England. The troy grain was 1/5760 of a pound, while the avoirdupois grain was 1/7000 pound, the former being used in the weighing of precious metals and thus employed by numismatists in weighing coins. A grain is 1/480 troy ounce or 0.066 gram in the metric system.

Graining Term sometimes used as a synonym for the *reeding* on the edge of milled coins.

Gripped Edge Pattern of indentations found on the majority of American cents of 1797, caused by the milling process. Coins of the same date with a plain edge are rather scarcer.

Guerrilla Money Money issued in areas under the control of guerrillas and partisans during wartime range from the *veld ponds* of the Boers (1900–2) to the notes issued by the Garibaldi Brigade in Italy and the anti-fascist notes of Tito's forces in Yugoslavia. The most prolific issues were those produced in Luzon, Mindanao and Negros Occidental by the Filipino resistance during the Japanese occupation (1942–5).

Guilloche French term signifying the intricate pattern of curved lines produced by the rose engine and used as a security feature in the production of banknote, cheques and stocks .

Gun Money Emergency coinage of Ireland (1689 –91) minted from gunmetal, a type of bronze used in the casting of cannon. All denominations of James II, from the sixpence to the crown, normally struck in silver, were produced in this base metal.

Gutschein German word for voucher or coupon, denoting the paper money used aboard ships of the Imperial Navy during the First World War. The last issue was made at Scapa Flow, 1918–19, during the internment of the High Seas Fleet.

Hammered Term denoting coins produce by the traditional method of striking a *flan* laid on an anvil with a hammer. A characteristic of hammered coins is their uneven shape which tended to encourage *clipping*. This abuse was gradually eliminated by the introduction of the screw press in the 15th century and the mechanisation of coining processes in the course of the 16th and 17th centuries.

Hard Times Token Copper piece the size of the large cent, issued in the USA, 1834–44, during a shortage of coins caused by the collapse of the Bank of the United States, the panic of 1837 and the economic crisis of 1839, the landmarks in the period known as the Hard Times. Banks suspended *specie* payments and the shortage of coinage was filled by tradesmen's tokens. Many of these were more in the nature of satirical *medalets* than circulating pieces.

Hat Piece Alternative name for the *bonnet piece* of James VI of Scotland, 1591.

Hell Notes Imitation paper money used in Chinese funeral ceremonies and buried with the dead to pay for services in the next world.

Hoard Accumulation of coins concealed in times of economic or political upheaval and discovered, often centuries later. Under English common law, such hoards are subject to th law of *treasure trove* if they contain precious metal.

Hog Money Popular name for the early coinage of Bermuda, issued about 1616. The coins were minted in brass with a silver wash and circulated at various values from twopence to a shilling. They derived their name from the hog depicted on the obverse, an allusion to the pigs introduced to the island in 1515 by Juan Bermudez.

Holed Term denoting two different categories: (a) coins which have been pierced for suspension as a form of jewellery or talisman, and (b) coins which have a hole as part of their design. In the latter category come the Chinese *cash* with a square hole, and numerous issues of the 19th and 20th centuries from many countries, with the object of reducing weight and metal without sacrificing overall diameter.

Holey Dollar Spanish silver peso of 8 reales with the centre removed. The resultant ring was counter-marked "New South Wales" and dated 1813, with "Five Shillings" on the reverse, and placed into circulation during a shortage of British coin. The centre, known as a *dump*, was circulated at 15 pence.

Hub Heavy circular piece of steel on which the *die* for a coin or medal is engraved. The process of cutting the die and transferring the master die, by means of intermediary *punches*, to the die from which the coins are to be struck, is known as hubbing. Soft steel is used in the preliminary process, and after the design has been transferred, the hub is hardened by chemical action.

Hybrid Alternative name for a *mule*.

Imitation Money Also known as play money or toy money, it consists of coins and notes produced for games of chance (like Monopoly), children's toy shops and post offices, as tourist souvenirs, or for political satire (e.g. the shrinking pound or dollar). See also *funeral money*, *hell notes*, *model coins* and *skit notes*.

Imprint Inscription on a paper note giving the name of the printer.

Incuse Impression which cuts into the surface of a coin or medal, as opposed to the more usual raised relief. Many of the earliest coins, especially those with a device on one side only, bear an incuse impression often in a geometric pattern. An incuse impression appears on one side of the coins, reflecting the image on the other side. Few modern coins have had an incuse design, notable examples being the American half and quarter eagle gold coins of 1908–29 designed by Bela Pratt. Incuse inscriptions on a raised rim, however, are more common, and include the British *Cartwheel* coins of 1797 and the 20p coins since 1982.

Inflation Money Coins produced as a result of inflation date back to Roman times when bronze minimi, little bigger than a pinhead, circulated as denarii. Nearer the present day inflation has had devastating effects on the coinge and banknotes of Germany (1921–3),

Austria (1923), Poland (1923), Hungary (1945–6), Greece (1946) and many Latin American countries since the 1980s. Hungary holds the record for the highest value of any note ever issued — one thousand million adopengos, which is written as 20,000,000,000,000,000, 000,000,000,000 pengos.

Ingot   Piece of precious metal, usually cast in a mould, and stamped with the weight and fineness. A convenient method of storing bullion, ingots have been used as currency in many countries, notably Russia and Japan.

Inlay   Insertion into the surface of a coin or medal of another substance for decorative effect. e.g. Poland Amber Trade Routes 20zl (amber), Isle of Man Queen Mother centenery (pearl) and various coins incorporating rubies or diamonds.

Intaglio   Form of *engraving* in which lines are cut into a steel die for the recess-printing of banknotes.

Intrinsic   The net metallic value of a coin, as distinguished from the nominal or face value.

Iron   Metal, chemical symbol *Fe* (from Latin *Ferrum*), used as a primitive form of currency from classical times onwards. Iron spits (obeliskoi) preceded the obol as the lowest unit of Greek coinage, a handful of six spits being worth a drachma (from *drassomai*, "I grasp"). Cast iron coins were issued in China as a substitute for copper *cash*. Many of the emergency token issues of Germany during the First World War were struck in iron. Iron coins were issued by Bulgaria in 1943. See also *Steel*.

Ithyphallic   (Greek for "erect penis"). Term descriptive of coins of classical Greece showing a satyr.

Janiform   Double profiles back to back, after the Roman god Janus.

Jeton   (From French *jeter*, to throw). Alternative term for *counter*, and used originally on the chequerboard employed by medieval accountants. Nuremberg was the most important centre for the production of medieval jetons, often issued in lengthy portrait series. In modern parlance the term is often synonymous with *token*, though more specifically confined to pieces used in vending equipment, parking meters, laundromats, telephones and urban transport systems in many European countries. Apart from security, removing the temptation of vandals to break into the receptacles, the main advantage of such pieces is that they can be retariffed as charges increase, without any alteration in their design or composition, so far cheaper than altering costly equipment to take larger coins.

Jubilee Head   The effigy of Queen Victoria by Joseph Boehm adopted for British coinage after the 1887 Golden Jubilee.

Jugate   (From Latin *jugum*, a yoke). Alternative to *accolated* or *conjoined* to denote overlapping profiles of rulers.

Key Date   Term describing the rarest in a long-running series of coins with the dates changed at annual intervals.

Kipperzeit   German term meaning the time of clipped money, denoting the period during and after the Thirty Years War (1618–48) in which debased and clipped money was in circulation.

Klippe   Rectangular or square pieces of metal bearing the impression of a coin. Coins of this type were first struck in Sweden in the 16th century and were subsequently produced in many of the German states. The idea has been revived in recent years as a medium for striking commemorative pieces.

Knife Money   Cast bronze pieces, with an elongated blade and a ring at one end to facilitate stringing together in bunches, were used as currency in China from the 9th century BC until the 19th century.

Kreditivsedlar   (Swedish for "credit notes"). The name given to the first issue of paper money made in the western world. Paper money of this type was the brainchild of Johan Palmstruch at Riga in 1652, but nine years elapsed before it was implemented by the Stockholm Bank. The notes were redeemable in copper *platmynt*.

Laureate   Heraldic term for a laurel wreath, often framing a state emblem or shown, in the Roman fashion, as a crown on the ruler's forehead.

Leather Money   Pieces of leather embossed with an official device have been used as money on various occasions, including the sieges of Faenza and Leiden and in the Isle of Man in the 15th and 16th centuries. Several towns in Austria and Germany produced leather tokens during and after the First World War.

Legal Tender   Coins or paper money which are declared by law to be current money and which tradesmen and shopkeers are obliged to accept in payment for goods or services. (See *Money and the Law*).

Legend The inscription on a coin or medal.

Liberation Money Paper money prepared for use in parts of Europe and Asia, formerly under Axis occupation. Liberation notes were used in France, Belgium and the Netherlands in 1944–5, while various different Japanese and Chinese notes were overprinted for use in Hong Kong when it was liberated in 1945. Indian notes overprinted for use in Burma were issued in 1945–6 when that country was freed from Japanese occupation.

Ligature (From Latin *ligatus*, bound together). Term denoting the linking of two letters in a *legend*, e.g. Æ and Œ.

Long Cross Coinage Type of coinage introduced by King Henry III in 1247, deriving its name from the reverse which bore a cross whose arms extended right to the edge to help safeguard the coins against *clipping*. This remained the style of the silver penny, its fractions and multiples, till the reign of Henry VII, and vestiges of the long cross theme is seen in the silver coins throughout the remaining years of the Tudor period.

Love Token A coin which has been altered by smoothing one or both surfaces and engraving initials, dates, scenes, symbols of affection and messages thereon.

Lushbourne English word for base pennies made of inferior silver, said to have emanated from Luxembourg, from which the name derived. These coins were first minted under John the Blind who adopted the curious spelling of his name EIWANES in the hope that illiterate English merchants might confuse it with EDWARDVS and thus be accepted as coin issued in the name of Edward III. Lushbournes were also minted by Robert of Bethune, William I of Namur and the bishops of Toul during the mid-14th century.

Lustre The sheen or bloom on the surface of an uncirculated coin resulting from the centrifugal flow of metal caused by striking.

Magnimat Trade name used by VDM (*Verein Deutscher Metallwerke*) for a high-security alloy containing copper, nickel and magnetised steel. First used for the 5 deutschemark coin of 1975, it has since been adopted for other high-value coins in Germany and other countries.

Manillas

Manilla Copper, bronze or brass rings, sometimes shaped like horseshoes and sometimes open, with flattened terminals, used as currency in West Africa until recent years.

Matrix Secondary die for a coin or medal, produced from the master die by means of an intermediate punch. In this way dies can be duplicated from the original cut on the reducing machine.

Matt or Matte Finely granulated surface or overall satin finish to proof coins, a style which was briefly fashionable at the turn of the century. The Edward VII proof set of 1902 is a notable example. In more recent years many issues produced by the Franklin Mint have been issued with this finish.

Maundy Money Set of small silver coins, in denominations of 1, 2, 3 and 4 pence, distributed by the reigning British monarch to the poor and needy on Maundy Thursday. The custom dates back to the Middle Ages, but in its present form, of distributing pence to as many men and women as the years in the monarch's age, it dates from 1666. At first ordinary silver pennies and multiples were used but after they went out of everyday use distinctive silver coins were produced specifically for the purpose from the reign of George II (1727–60) onwards. For centuries the ceremony took place in Westminster Abbey but since 1955 other venues have been used in alternate years.

Medal (French *medaille*, Italian *medaglia*, from Latin *metallum*). A piece of metal bearing devices and legends commemorating an event or person, or given as an award. Military medals date from the 16th and 17th centuries, but were not generally awarded to all ranks till the 19th century. Commemora-tive medals can be traced back to Roman times, but in their present form they date from the Italian Renaissance when there was a fashion for large cast portrait medals.

Medalet A small medal, generally 25mm or less in diameter.

Medallion Synonym for medal, but usually confined to those with a diameter of 50mm or more.

Milling Process denoting the mechanical production of coins, as opposed to the handmade technique implied in *hammering*. It alludes to the use of watermills to drive the machinery of the screw presses and blank rollers developed in the 16th century. As the even thickness and diameter of milled coins permitted a security edge, the term milling is popularly, though erroneously, used as a synonym for *graining* or *reeding*.

Mint   The place in which coins and medals are produced. Mint condition is a term sometimes used to denote pieces in an uncirculated state.

Mint Set   A set of coins or medals in the package or case issued by the mint. See also *year set*.

Mintmark   A device appearing on a coin to denote the place of minting. Athenian coins of classical times have been recorded with up to 40 different marks, denoting individual workshops.   In the 4th century AD the Romans adopted this system to identify coins struck in provincial mints. This system was widely used in the Middle Ages and survives in France and Germany to this day. Initials and symbols are also used to identify mints, especially where the production of a coin is shared between several different mints. From 1351 onwards symbols were adopted in England to denote periods between trials of the *Pyx*, and thus assist the proper chronological sequence of coins, in an era prior to the adoption of dating. These mintmarks continued into the 17th century, but gradually died out as the use of dates became more widespread. See also *countermark* and *privy mark*.

Mionnet Scale   Scale of nineteen diameters covering all sizes of coins belonging to the classical period, devised by the French numismatist, Theodore-Edme Mionnet (1770–1842) during the compilation of his fifteen-volume catalogue of the numismatic collection in the Bibliotheque Nationale in Paris.

Mirror Finish   The highly polished surface of proof coins.

Misstrike   A coin or medal on which the impression has been struck off-centre.

Model Coin   Tiny pieces of metal, either reproducing the designs of existing coins (used as play money by children) or, more specifically, denoting patterns produced by Joseph Moore and Hyam Hyams in their attempts to promote an improved subsidiary coinage in 19th century Britain. These small coins were struck in bronze with a brass or silver centre and were designed to reduce the size of the existing cumbersome range of pence, halfpence and farthings.

Modified Effigy   Any coin in which the profile on the obverse has been subtly altered. Examples include minor changes in the Victorian Young Head and Old Head effigies and the George V profile by Sir Bertram Mackennal.

Money Order   Certificate for a specified amount of money, which may be transmitted by post and encashed at a money order office or post office. This system was pioneered by Britain and the United States in the early 19th century and is now virtually worldwide.   The term is now confined to certificates above a certain being used for similar certificates covering small amounts.

Mule   Coin whose obverse is not matched with its official or regular reverse. Mules include the erroneous combination of dies from different reigns, but in recent years such hybrids have arisen in mints where coins for several countries are struck.   Examples include the Coronation Anniversary crowns combining Ascension and Isle of Man dies and the 2 cent coins with Bahamas and New Zealand dies. *Restrikes* of rare American coins have been detected in which the dated die has been paired with the wrong reverse die, e.g. the 1860 restrike of the rare 1804 large cent.

Mute   An *anepigraphic* coin, identifiable only by the devices struck on it.

Nail Mark   Small indentation on ancient coins. The earliest coins of Asia Minor developed from the electrum *dumps* which merchants marked with a broken nail as their personal guarantee of value, the ancient counterpart of the *chop* marks used in China and Japan.

NCLT Coins   Abbreviation for "Non Circulating Legal Tender", a term devised by modern coin catalogues to denote coins which, though declared *legal tender*, are not intended for general circulation on account of their precious metal content or superior finish.

Nicked Coin   Coin bearing a tiny cut or nick in its edge. Silver coins were tested by this method, especially in the reign of Henry I (1100–35) when so many base silver pennies were in circulation. Eventually people refused to accept these nicked coins   a problem which was only overcome when the state decreed that all coins should have a nick in them.

Nickel   Metallic element, chemical symbol Ni, a hard white metal relatively resistant to tarnish, and extensively used as a cheap substitute for silver. It was first used for the American 5 cent coin in 1866, hence its popular name which has stuck ever since, although nowadays the higher denominations are minted in an alloy of copper and nickel. Although best known as a silver substitute, nickel was widely used in Jamaica (1869–1969) for halfpence and pennies and in British West Africa for the tiny 1/10th pennies (1908–57). Pure nickel was used for French francs and German marks, but usually it is alloyed with copper or zinc to produce *cupro-nickel* or nickel brass.

Notaphily   Hybrid word from Latin *nota* (note) and Greek *philos* (love), coined about 1970 to denote the branch of numismatics devoted to the study of paper money.

Notgeld   German word meaning emergency money, applied to the *tokens*, in metals, wood, leather and even ceramic materials, issued during the First World War when coinage disappeared from circulation. These tokens were soon superseded by low-denomination paper money issued by shops and businessmen in denominations from 10 to 50 pfennige and known as *kleine Notgeld* (small emergency money). These notes were prohibited in September 1922 but by that time some 50,000 varieties are thought to have been issued. Inflation raced out of control and the government permitted a second issue of local notes, known as *large Notgeld*, as the denominations were in thousands, and latterly millions, of marks. Some 3,600 types appeared in 1922 and over 60,000 in 1923. These ceased to circulate in 1924 when the currency was reformed.

Numismatics   The study of coins, medals and other related fields, a term derived from the Latin *numisma* and Greek *nomisma* (money).

Obsidional Currency   (From Latin *obsidium*, a siege). Term for *emergency money* produced by the defenders of besieged towns and cities. These usually took the form of pieces of silver plate, commandeered for the purpose, crudely marked with an official device and the value. Instances of such seige coinage have been recorded from the 12th to the 19th centuries.

Obverse   The "heads" side of a coin or medal, generally bearing the effigy of the head of state or an allegorical figure.

Off Metal   Term denoting a piece struck in a metal other than the officially authoriised or issued alloy. This originally applied to *patterns* which were often struck in lead or copper instead of gold and silver as trial pieces or to test the dies; but in recent years it has applied to collectors' versions, e.g. proofs in platinum, gold or silver of coins normally issued in bronze or cupro-nickel.

Overdate   One or more digits in a date altered by superimposing another figure. Alterations of this kind, by means of small hand punches, were made to dated dies so that they could be used in years other than that of the original manufacture. Coins with overdates invariably show traces of the original digit.

Overstrike   Coin, token or medal produced by using a previously struck pieces as a flan. The Bank of England dollar of 1804 was overstruck on Spanish pieces of eight, and examples showing traces of the original coins are worth a good premium.

Paduan   Name given to imitations of medals and bogus coins produced in Italy in the 16th century, and deriving from the city of Padua where forgeries of bronze sculpture were produced for the antique market.

Patina   Oxidation forming on the surface of metallic objects. So far as coins and medals are concerned, this applies mainly to silver, brass, bronze and copper pieces which may acquire oxidation from the atmosphere, or spectacular patination from salts in the ground in which they have been buried. In extreme forms patina leads to verdigris and other forms of rust which corrode the surface, but in uncirculated coins it may be little more than a mellowing of the original *lustre*. Coins preserved in blue velvet presentation cases often acquire a subtle toning from the dyes in the material.

Pattern   Piece resembling a coin or medal, prepared by the mint to the specifications or on the authorisation of the coin-issuing authority, but also applied to pieces produced by mints when tendering for coinage or medal contracts. Patterns may differ from the final coins as issued in the type of alloy used (*off metal*) but more often they differ in details of the design.

Pellet   Raised circular ornament used as a spacing device between words and abbreviations in the *legend* of coins and medals. Groups of pellets were also used as ornaments in the angles of the cross on the reverse of the early English silver pennies.

Piece de Plaisir   (French for "fancy piece"). Term given to coins struck in a superior precious metal, or to a superior finish, or on a much thicker flan than usual. See *off metal*, *piedfort* and *proof*.

Piedfort (Piefort)   Piece struck with coinage dies on a *flan* of much more than normal thickness. This practice originated in France in the late 16th century and continues to the present day. In recent years it has been adopted by mints in Britain and other countries as a medium for collectors' pieces.

Pile   Lower die incorporating the obverse motif, used in striking coins and medals.

Planchet French term used as an alternative for *blank* or *flan*.

Plaque or **Plaquette** Terms sometimes used for medals struck on a square or rectangular flan.

Plaster Cast taken from the original model for a coin or medal sculpted by an artist, and used in modern reducing machines in the manufacture of the master *die*.

Plated Coins Coins stuck in base metal but given a wash of silver or some other precious metal. This expedient was adopted in inflationary times, from the Roman Republic (91 BC) till the Tudor period. American cents of 1943 were struck in steel with a zinc coating, and more recently *clad* coins have produced similar results.

Platinum The noblest of all precious metals, platinum has a higher specific gravity than gold and a harder, brighter surface than silver. Until an industrial application was discovered in the mid-19th century, it was regarded as of little value, and was popular with counterfeiters as a cheap substitute for gold in their forgeries which, with a light gold wash, could be passed off as genuine. It was first used for circulating coins in Russia (the chief source of the metal since 1819) and 3, 6 and 12 rouble coins were mined at various times between 1828 and 1845. In recent years platinum has been a popular metal for limited-edition proof coins.

Platmynt (Swedish for "plate money"). Large copper plates bearing royal cyphers and values from half to ten dalers produced in Sweden between 1643 and 1768. They represented laudable attempts by a country rich in copper to produce a coinage in terms of its silver value, but the net result was far too cumbersome to be practical. The weight of the daler plate, for example, ranged from 766 grams to 1.1kg, and special carts had to be devised to transport them!

Plugged Coins Coins struck predominantly in one metal, but containing a small plug of another. This curious practice may be found in the farthings of Charles II (1684–85) and the halfpence or farthings of James II (1685–87), which were struck in tin, with a copper plug, to defeat forgers.

Porcelain Money Tokens made of porcelain circulated in Thailand from the late 18th century till 1868. The Meissen pottery struck tokens in 1920–22 as a form of small *Notgeld*, using reddish-brown Bottger stoneware and white *bisque* porcelain. These ceramic tokens circulated in various towns of Saxony.

Postage Currency Small paper notes in denominations of 5 (shown above), 10, 25 and 50 cents, issued by the US federal government in 1862–63, were thus inscribed and had reproductions of postage stamps engraved on them — five 5c stamps on the 25c and five 10c stamps on the 50c notes. The earliest issue even had perforations in the manner of stamps, but this unnecessary device was soon done away with. See also *stamp money*.

Postal Notes or Orders Low-value notes intended for transmission by post and encashable at post offices. Introduced by Britain in 1883, they were an extension of the earlier *money order* system, and are now issued by virtually every country.

Potin (French for pewter). Alloy of copper, tin, lead and silver used as a coinage metal by the Celtic tribes of eastern Gaul at the beginning of the Christian era.

Privy Mark Secret mark incorporated in the design of a coin or medal to identify the minter, or even the particular die used. The term is also used more loosely to denote any small symbol or initials appearing on a coin other than a *mint mark*, and is sometimes applied to the symbols associated with the trial of the *Pyx* found on English coins.

Prize Coins Coins of large size and value struck primarily as prizes in sporting contests. this principle dates from the late 5th century BC when Syracuse minted decadrachms as prizes in the Demareteian Games. The most notable example in modern times is the lengthy series of talers and five-franc coins issued by the Swiss cantons since 1842 as prizes in the annual shooting festivals, the last of which honoured the Lucerne contest of 1939.

Profile A side view of the human face, widely used as a coinage effigy.

Proof Originally a trial strike testing the *dies*, but now denoting a special collectors' version struck with dies that have been specially polished on *flans* with a mirror finish. Presses operating at a very slow speed, or multi-striking processes, are also used.

Propaganda Notes   Paper money containing a political slogan or a didactic element.   During the Second World War forgeries of German and Japanese notes were produced by the Allies and additionally inscribed or overprinted with slogans such as "Co-Prosperity Sphere—What is it worth?" (a reference to the Japanese occupied areas of SE Asia).   Forged dollars with anti-American propaganda were airdropped over Sicily by the Germans in 1943 and counterfeit pounds with Arabic propaganda over Egypt in 1942–43. Various anti-communist organisations liberated propaganda forgeries of paper money by balloon over Eastern Europe during the Cold War period.

Provenance Mark   Form of *privy mark* denoting the source of the metal used in coins. Examples include the plumes or roses on English coins denoting silver from Welsh or West of England mines, and the elephant or elephant and castle on gold coins denoting bullion imported by the African Company. Coins inscribed VIGO (1702–03) or LIMA (1745–46) denote bullion seized from the Spaniards by Anglo-Dutch privateers and Admiral Anson respectively. Other provenance marks on English coins include the letters EIC and SSC, denoting bullion imported by the East India Company or the South Sea Company.

Pseudo Coins   Derisory term coined in recent years to signify pieces of precious metal, often struck in *proof* versions only, aimed at the international investment market. Many of these pieces, though bearing a nominal face value, are not *legal tender* in the countries purporting to issue them and in many cases they go straight from the overseas mint where they are produced to coin dealers in America and western Europe, without ever appearing in the so-called country of origin.   See also *NCLT coins*.

Punch or Puncheon   Intermediate *die* whereby working dies can be duplicated from the master die, prior to the striking of coins and medals.

Pyx   Box in which a specimen from every 15 pounds troy weight of gold and every 60 pounds of silver minted in England is kept for annual trial by weight and assay. Many of the *mintmarks* on English coins of the 14th–17th centuries were in use from one trial to the next and still exist today and can therefore be used to date them.

Reducing Machinery   Equipment designed on the pantographic principle for transferring the image from a *plaster* to a *hub* and reducing it to the size of the actual coin or medal. The image is transferred by means of a stylus operating rather like a gramophone needle, but working from the centre to the outer edge.

Reeding   Security edging on coins, consisting of close vertical ridges. As a rule, this appears all round the edge but some coins, e.g. New Zealand's 50c (1967) and the Isle of Man's £1 (1978) have segments of reeding alternating with a plain edge, to help blind and partially sighted persons to identify these coins.

Re-issue   A coin or note issued again after an extended lapse of time.

Relief   Raised parts of the *obverse* and *reverse* of coins and medals, the opposite of *incuse*.

Remainder   A note from a bank or issuing authority which has never been circulated, due to inflation, political changes or bank failure. Such notes, some-times in partial or unfinished state (e.g. missing serial numbers or signatures), are generally unloaded on to the numismatic market at a nominal sum and provide a good source of inexpensive material for the beginner.

Restrike   Coin, medal or token produced from *dies* subsequent to the original use.   Usually restrikes are made long after the original and can often be identified by marks caused by damage, pitting or corrosion of the dies after they were taken out of service.

Retrograde   Term describing inscriptions running from right to left, or with the letters in a mirror image, thought to arise from unskilled die-cutters failing to realise that inscriptions have to be engraved in negative form to achieve a positive impression.   Retrograde inscriptions are common on ancient Greek coins, but also found on Roman and Byzantine coins.

Reverse   The side of a coin or medal regarded as of lesser importance; in colloquial parlance, the "tails" side.

Saltire   Heraldic term for a cross in the shape of an X.

Sandwich   Coin *blank* consisting of thin outer layers in one alloy bonded to a core in another. See *clad coins*.

Sceat   (Anglo-Saxon for "treasure", or German *Schatz*).   Money of account in Kent early in the 7th century as the twelfth part of a shilling or Merovingian gold tremissis.   As a silver coin, it dates from about AD 680–700 and weighed about 20 grains, putting it on par with the Merovingian denier or penny.   Sceats spread to other parts of England in the 8th century but tended to decline in weight and value, but from about 760 it was gradually superseded by the silver penny minted under Offa and his successors.

Scissel   The clippings of metal left after a *blank* has been cut. Occasionally one of these clippings accidentally adheres to the blank during the striking process, producing characteristic crescent-shaped flaws which are present on on the finished coin.

Scrip Paper money of restricted validity or circulation, e.g.*Bafs* and other military scrip used in canteens and post exchanges.

Scyphate (Greek *scypha*, a skiff or small boat). Byzantine coin with a concave *flan*.

Sede Vacante (Latin for "Vacant See"). Coins struck at *ecclesiastical mints* between the death of a prelate and the election of his successor are often thus inscribed. This practice originated at Rome in the 13th century.

Seignorage or Seigneurage Royalty or percentage paid by persons bringing *bullion* to a mint for conversion into coin, but nowadays synonymous with the royalty paid by mints in respect of the precious metal versions of coins sold direct to collectors. It arises from the medieval right of the king to a small portion of the proceeds of a mint, and amounted to a tax on moneying. It has also been applied to the money accruing to the state when the coinage is re-issued in an alloy of lesser fineness, as, for example, the debased sovereigns of Henry VIII in 20 instead of 23 carat gold, the king's treasury collecting the difference.

Series Term applied to sets of medals of a thematic character, which first became fashionable in the early 18th century. Jean Dassier pioneered the medallic series in the 1720s with his set of 72 medals portraying the rulers of France till Louis XV. The idea was developed by J. Kirk, Sir Edward Thomason, J. Mudie and A. J. Stothard in Britain, and by Moritz Fuerst and Amedee Durand in Europe. The fashion died out in the 19th century, but has been revived in America and Europe since 1964.

Serrated Having a notched or toothed edge, rather like a cogwheel. Coins of this type, struck in *electrum,* an alloy of silver and gold, are known from Carthage in the 2nd century BC, and some silver denarii of Rome in the 2nd century AD also come into this category.

Sexagesimal System Monetary system in which the principal unit is divided into 60 parts. The oldest system in the Western world was based on the gold talent of 60 minae and the mina of 60 shekels. In medieval Europe 60 groschen were worth a fine mark; in England from 1551, the silver coinage was based on the crown of 60 pence, and in the south German states till 1873 the gulden was worth 60 kreuzers.

Shin Plasters Derisory term originally applied to the Continental currency notes issued during the American War of Independence of 1776, the fractional currency of the Civil War period and also the low-denomination notes of Canada between 1870 and 1935, but often applied indiscriminately to any other low-denomination, small-format notes.

Short Cross Coinage Term for the silver coinage introduced by Henry II in 1180 and minted till 1247 at which time it was replaced by the *Long Cross* type. The termination of the arms of the cross on the reverse well within the circumference encouraged the dishonest practice of *clipping*.

Shroff Mark A *countermark* applied by Indian bankers or merchants to attest the full weight and purity of coins. See also *chop*.

Siege Money See *Obsidional Currency*

Silver Precious metal, chemical symbol *Ag*, numismatic abbreviation *Ar*, from Latin *Argentum*, widely used as a coinage metal from the 6th century BC to the present day.

Sterling silver denotes an alloy of .925 fine silver with .075 copper. Fine silver alloys used over the past 2,500 years have ranged from .880 to .960 fine, but base silver has also been all too common. British coins from 1920 to 1946 were struck in .500 fine silver, while alloys of lesser fineness are known as *billon* or *vellon*. Silver alloyed with gold produces a metal called *electrum*, used for the earliest coinage of the western world, the staters of Lydia in the 7th century BC. Since 1970 silver as a medium for circulating coinage has almost virtually disappeared, yet the volume of silver coins for sale to collectors has risen considerably in recent years.

Skit Note Piece of paper masquerading as a banknote. It differs from a *counterfeit* in that its design parodies that of a genuine note, often for political, satirical or advertising reasons. Others were produced as April Fools' Day jokes or a form of Valentine (e.g. the Bank of Lovers). In recent years they have been produced as advertising gimmicks, or as coupons permitting a discount off the list price of goods.

Slug Popular name for the $50 gold pieces produced by private mints in California in the mid-19th century. The term is also applied nowadays to *tokens* intended for use in gaming machine.

w**Spade Guinea** Name given to the guineas of George III issued between 1787 and 1799 because the shield on the reverse design resembled the shape of a spade. In Victorian times the spade guinea was extensively copied in brass for gaming counters.

Spade Money Cast bronze pieces resembling miniature spades and other agricultural implements, used as money and derived from the actual implements which had previously been used in barter. Often referred to as *Pu* or *Boo* money.

Specie Financial term denoting money in the form of precious metals (silver and gold), usually struck as coin, as opposed to money in the form of paper notes and bills of exchange. It occurs in the name of some European coins (e.g. *speciedaler*, *speciestaler* and *speciesducat*) to denote the use of fine silver or gold.

Specimen Generally used to denote a single piece, but more specifically applying to a coin in a special finish, less than *proof* in quality but superior to the general circulating version. It also denotes paper notes intended for circulation between banks or for press publicity and distinguished from the generally issued version by zero serial numbers, punch holes or a security endorsement.

Spintriae Metal tokens produced in Roman imperial times, with erotic motifs, thought to have been tickets of admission to brothels.

Spit Copper or iron rod used as a primitive form of currency in the Mediterranean area. The Greek word *belos* meant a spit, dart or bolt, and from this came the word *obolos* used for a coin worth a 6th of a drachma.

Stamp Money Both postage and revenue (fiscal) stamps have circulated as money during shortages of coins, from the American Civil War onwards. *Encased postage stamps* were used in the USA, 1861–62, before they were superseded by *Postage Currency* notes, but the same expedient was adopted by many countries during and immediately after the First World War. Stamps affixed to special cards have circulated as money in Rhodesia (now Zimbabwe) in 1900, the French colonies and Turkey during the First World War, in Spain during the Civil War (1936–39) and the Philippines during the Second World War. Stamps printed on thick card, with an inscription on the reverse signifying their parity with silver coins, were issued in Russia (1917–18) and also in Armenia, the Crimea and the Ukraine (1918–20). During the Second World War Ceylon (now Sri Lanka) and several Indian states issued small money cards with contemporary stamps printed on them.

Steel Refined and tempered from *iron*, and used in chromed or stainless versions as a coinage metal in the 20th century. Zinc-coated steel cents were issued by the USA (1943) but in the form known as *acmonital* (nickel steel) it has been extensively used by Italy since 1939. Other alloys of nickel and steel have been used for coins of the Philippines (1944–45) and Roumania since 1963. Chrome steel was used by France for 5 centime coins in 1961–64. Copper-clad steel is now extensively used for subsidiary coins formerly struck in bronze.

Sterling Word of uncertain origin denoting money of a standard weight and fineness, and hence the more general meaning of recognised worth. The traditionally accepted derivation from the Easterlings, north German merchants who settled in London in the 13th century and produced silver pennies of uniform fineness, is unlikely as the term has been found in documents a century earlier. A more plausible explanation is from Old English *steorling* ("little coin with a star"), alluding to Viking pennies with this device, or even as a diminutive of *stater*. Sterling silver denotes silver of .925 fineness.

Stone Money Primitive currency in the form of large stone discs, used in West Africa in the pre-colonial period, and in the Pacific island of Yap (now Micronesia) as recently as 1940.

Striation A pattern of alternate light and dark parallel marks or minute grooves on the surface of a coin or medal. In the latter case it is sometimes done for textural effect, but in coins it may result from faulty *annealing*. Deliberate ridging of the surface, however, was a distinctive feature of Japanese *koban* and *goryoban* coins of 1736–1862.

Styca Name given to the debased silver *sceats* of Northumbria in the 8th century.

Tael Chinese unit of weight corresponding to the European ounce and sometimes referred to as a liang. It was a measure of silver varying between 32 and 39 grams. In the 19th century it served as *money of account*, 100 British or Mexican trade dollars being worth 72 tael. The term has also been loosely applied to the Chinese silver yuan, although this was worth only .72 tael, or 7 mace and 2 candareens (10 candareens = 1 mace; 10 mace = 1 tael).

Thrymsa Early Anglo-Saxon gold coin based on the Merovingian tremissis or third-solidus, current in Kent, London and York around AD 63–75.

Tical Unit of weight in Thailand, first appearing as coins in the form of crudely shaped *bullet money* current from the 14th till the late 19th centuries. When European-style coins were introduced in 1860 the word was retained as a denomination (32 solot = 16 atts = 8 peinung or sio = 4 songpy or sik = 2 fuang= 1 salung or quarter-tical. The currency was decimalised in 1909 (100 satangs = 1 tical), and the tical was superseded by the baht about 1950.

Tin Metallic element, chemical symbol *Sn* (from Latin *Stannum*). Because of its unstable nature and tendency to oxidise badly when exposed to the atmosphere, it is unsatisfactory as a coinage metal, but has been used on several occasions, notably in Malaya, Thailand and the East Indies. In was also used for British halfpence and farthings, 1672–92.

Token Any piece of money whose nominal value is greater than its intrinsic value is, strictly speaking, a token or promise. Thus most of the coins issued since 1964 can be regarded in this light, but numismatists reserve the term for a piece of limited validity and circulation, produced by tradesmen, chambers of commerce and other organisations during times of a shortage of government coinage. The term is also loosely applied to metal tickets of admission, such as *communion tokens*, or *jetons* and *counters* intended for games of chance. Tokens with a nominal value may be produced for security reasons to lessen the possibility of theft from

milk bottles, vending machines, telephones, parking meters and transport facilities. Tokens exchangeable for goods have been issued by co-operative societies and used in prisons and internment camps in wartime. In addition to the traditional coinage alloys, tokens have been produced in ceramics, plastics, wood, stout card, leather and even rubber, in circular, square or polygonal shapes.

Tombac Type of brass alloy with a high copper content, used in coinage requiring a rich golden colour. It is, in fact, a modern version of the *aurichalcum* used by the Romans. It was used for the Canadian 5-cent coins of 1942–43, while 5- and 10-pfennig coins of Germany have a tombac cladding on a steel core.

Touchpiece Coin kept as a lucky charm, but more specifically the medieval gold angel of England which was worn round the neck as an antidote to scrofula, otherwise known as king's evil, from the belief that the reigning monarch possessed the power of healing by touch. The ceremony of touching for king's evil involved the suspension of an angel round the victim's neck, hence the prevalence of these coins pierced for suspension.

Trade Coins Coins widely used as a medium of international trade, often far beyond the boundaries of the country issuing them. The earliest examples were the Aiginetan turtles and Athenian tetrdrachms of the classical period. In the Middle Ages the English *sterling* was widely prized on account of its silver purity. Arab dinars and Italian florins were popular as gold coins in late-medieval times, while the British gold sovereign has been the preferred gold coin of modern times. The Maria Theresa silver thaler of Austria, with its date frozen at 1782, has been minted widely down to the present time for circulation in the Near and Middle East as a trade coin. Trade dollars were minted by Britain, the USA, the Netherlands and Japan to compete with the Spanish, and later the Mexican, peso or 8-reales coins as a trading medium in the Far East.

Transport Tokens Coin-like pieces of metal, plastic or card, issued by companies and corporations to employees and exchangeable for rides on municipal transport systems, date from the mid-19th century. In more recent times similar tokens have been used in many countries to activate turnstiles in buses, trams and rapid-transit railway systems.

Treasury Note Paper money worth 10 shillings or one pound, issued by the British Treasury on the outbreak of the First World War when *specie* payments were suspended, and continuing till 1928 when the Bank of England took over responsibility for note-issuing.

Treasure Trove Articles of precious metal concealed in times of economic or political upheaval and discovered years or centuries later deemed by law to be treasure trove (from the French word *trouve*, found). For further details see *Money and the Law*.

Trial Plate Plate of the same metal as the current coinage against which the fineness and quality of the coins produced are compared and tested.

Troy Weight System of weights derived from the French town of Troyes whose standard pound was adopted in England in 1526. It continued in Britain till 1879 when it was abolished, with the exception of the troy ounce and its decimal parts and multiples, which were retained for gold, silver, platinum and precious stones. The troy ounce of 480 grains is used for weighing coins.

Truncation Stylised cut at the base of a coinage effigy, sometimes containing a die number, engraver's initials or *mintmark*.

Trussel Reverse die in *hammered* coinage, the opposite of the *pile*.

Type Principal motif on a coin or medal, enabling numismatists to identify the issue.

Type Set A set of coins comprising one of each coin in a particular series, regardless of the actual date of issue.

Uncirculated Term used in grading coins to denote specimens in perfect condition, with original mint lustre. In recent years the term "Brilliant Uncirculated" has been adopted (abbreviated as BUnc or BU) both to indicate the condition of a coin, and, by The Royal Mint, to indicate the standard to which some coins are minted, being a standard between Circulation and Proof.

Uniface Coin with a device on one side only.

Vecture Term (mainly used in the US) for a *transport token*.

Veiled Head The effigy of Queen Victoria by Thomas Brock adopted for British coinage after 1893 – often referred to as the "Old Head" coinage.

Veld Pond (Dutch for "field pound"). Gold coin struck by the Boer guerrillas at Pilgrims Rest in 1902, in imitation of the British sovereign.

VF Standard abbreviation for Very Fine, used to describe the state of a coin or medal.

VG Abbreviation for Very Good, used to describe the state of a coin or medal, however, it is not a standard grade of a coin in the grading scale.

Vignette Strictly speaking the pictorial element of a paper note shading off into the surrounding unprinted paper rather than having a clearly defined border or frame; but nowadays applied generally to the picture portion of a banknote, as opposed to portrait, armorial or numeral elements.

Vis-à-Vis (French for "face to face"). Term describing coins with double portraits of rulers, their profiles or busts facing each other. A good example is the English coinage of Philip and Mary, 1554–58.

Wampum Barter currency of the North American Indians, composed of shells of *Venus mercenaria* strung together to form belts or "fathoms" worth 5 shillings. Wampum were tariffed variously from three to six to the English penny in the American colonies till 1704.

Wire Money Primitive currency of the Maldive Islands in the form of lengths of silver wire known as lari, from which the modern currency unit *laree* is derived. The term was also applied to English coins of the 18th century in which the numerals of value were exceptionally thin, resembling wire. Many Russian coins of the 17th/18th century were also made from pieces of wire cut from strips which were then roughly flattened, often in an oval shape. These blanks were then struck with round dies which often meant that parts of the wording and design was missed off.

Wooden Coins Thin pieces of wood used as tokens are known from many parts of China and Africa, and as small *Notgeld* from Austria and Germany during World War I. Wooden nickels is the name given to tokens of a commemorative nature, widely popular in the USA since 1930.

Young Head Profile of Queen Victoria sculpted by William Wyon for the Guildhall Medal of 1837 and subsequently utilised for British coins struck from 1837 to 1860 (copper) and 1887 (silver and gold).

Zinc Metallic element, chemical symbol *Zn*, widely used, with copper, as a constituent of brass. Alloyed with copper to form *tombac*, it was used for Canadian 5-cent coins (1942–43) and, coated on steel, it was used for American cents (1943). Zinc was used for *emergency coinage* in Austria, Belgium, Luxembourg and Germany (1915–18) and in Germany and German-occupied countries during World War II. Since then alloys of copper, nickel and zinc have been used for coinage in Eastern Europe.

Mintmarks
of the world

The following is a list of the initials and symbols denoting mints. In many cases, notably the Royal Mint, no mintmark was used on either British coins or those struck on behalf of other countries. Conversely many countries have only used one mintmark, that of one or other of the leading private mints.

It should be noted that the mintmarks of the main private mints have been recorded on the coins of the following countries:

H (Heaton, later the Birmingham Mint): Australia, Bolivia, British Honduras, British North Borneo, British West Africa, Bulgaria, Canada, Ceylon, Chile, Colombia, Costa Rica, Cyprus, Dominican Republic, East Africa, Ecuador, Egypt, El Salvador, Finland, French Indochina, Great Britain, Greece, Guatemala, Guernsey, Haiti, Hong Kong, Iran, Israel, Italy, Jamaica, Jersey, Liberia, Malaya and British Borneo, Mauritius, Mombasa, Mozambique, Newfoundland, Nicaragua, Poland, Roumania, Sarawak, Serbia, Siam, Straits Settlements, Uruguay and Venezuela.

FM (Franklin Mint, Philadelphia): Bahamas, Belize, British Virgin Islands, Cayman Islands, Cook Islands, Guyana, Jamaica, Liberia, Malaysia, Malta, Panama, Papua New Guinea, Philippines, Solomon Islands, Trinidad and Tobago.

PM (Pobjoy Mint, Sutton, Surrey): Ascension, Bosnia, Cook Islands, Gibraltar, Isle of Man, Liberia, Macau, Niue, Philippines, St Helena, Senegal, Seychelles, Tonga and Tristan da Cunha.

ALBANIA

L	London
R	Rome
V	Valona

ARGENTINA

BA	Buenos Aires
Bs	Buenos Aires
B.AS	Buenos Aires
JPP	Jose Policarpo Patino
M	Mendoza
PNP	Pedro Nolasco Pizarro
PP	Pedro Nolasco Pizarro
PTS	Potosi
R	Rioja
RA	Rioja
SE	Santiago del Estero
SoEo	Santiago del Estero
TN	Tucuman

AUSTRALIA

A	Perth
D	Denver
H	Heaton (1912–16)
I	Bombay (1942–43)
I	Calcutta (1916–18)
M	Melbourne
P	Perth
PL	Royal Mint, London
S	Sydney
S	San Francisco (1942–43)
Dot before and after PENNY and I on obverse	Bombay (1942–43)
Dot before and after HALFPENNY and I on obverse	Bombay (1942–43)
Dot before and after PENNY	Bombay (1942–43)
Dot after HALFPENNY	Perth
Dot before SHILLING	Perth (1946)
Dot above scroll on reverse	Sydney (1920)
Dot below scroll on reverse	Melbourne (1919–20)
Dot between designer's initials KG	Perth (1940–41)
Dot after AUSTRALIA	Perth (1952–53)

AUSTRIA

A	Vienna (1765–1872)
AH–AG	Carlsburg, Transylvania (1765–76)
AH–GS	Carlsburg (1776–80)
A–S	Hall, Tyrol (1765–74)
AS–IE	Vienna (1745)
AW	Vienna (1764, 1768)
B	Kremnitz (1765–1857)
B–L	Nagybanya (1765–71)
B–V	Nagybanya (1772–80)
C	Carlsburg (1762–64)
C	Prague (1766–1855)
C–A	Carlsburg (1746–66)
C–A	Vienna (1774–80)
CG–AK	Graz (1767–72)
CG–AR	Graz (1767)
C–K	Vienna (1765–73)
CM	Kremnitz (1779)
CVG–AK	Graz (1767–72)
CVG–AR	Graz (1767)
D	Graz (1765–72), Salzburg (1800–09)
E	Carlsburg (1765–1867)
EC–SK	Vienna (1766)
EvM–D	Kremnitz (1765–74)
EvS–AS	Prague (1765–73)
EvS–IK	Prague (1774–80)
F	Hall (1765–1807)
FH	Hall
G	Graz (1761–63)
G	Gunzburg (1764–79)
G	Nagybanya (1766–1851)
G–K	Graz (1767–72)
G–R	Graz (1746–67)
GTK	Vienna (1761)
H	Hall (1760–80)
H	Gunzburg (1765–1805)
H–A	Hall (1746–65)
H–G	Carlsburg (1765–77)
H–S	Carlsburg (1777–80)
IB–FL	Nagybanya (1765–71)
IB–IV	Nagybanya (1772–80)
IC–FA	Vienna (1774–80)
IC–IA	Vienna (1780)
IC–SK	Vienna (1765–73)
I–K	Graz (1765-67)
I–K	Vienna (1767)
IZV	Vienna (1763–65)
K	Kremnitz (1760–63)
K–B	Kremnitz (1619–1765)
K–D	Kremnitz (1765)
K–M	Kremnitz (1763–65)
M	Milan (1780–1859)
N	Nagybanya (1780)
N–B	Nagybanya (1630–1777, 1849)
O	Oravicza (1783–1816)
P	Prague (1760–63)
P–R	Prague (1746–67)
PS–IK	Prague (1774–80)
S	Hall (1765–80), Schmollnitz (1763–1816)
S–C	Gunzburg (1765–74)
SC–G	Gunzburg (1765)
S–F	Gunzburg (1775–80)
S–G	Gunzburg (1764–65)
S–IE	Vienna (1745)
SK–PD	Kremnitz (1774–80)
TS	Gunzburg (1762–88)
V	Venice (1805–66)
VC–S	Hall (1774–80)
VS–K	Prague (1774–80)
VS–S	Prague (1765–73)
W	Vienna (1748–63)
W–I	Vienna (1746–71)

BAHAMAS

FM	Franklin Mint
JP	John Pinches

BELGIUM

A	Vienna
B	Kremnitz
C	Prague
E	Carlsburg
F	Hall
G	Nagybanya
H	Gunzburg
hand	Antwerp
lion	Bruges

BELIZE (British Honduras)

FM	Franklin Mint
H	Heaton (1912–16)

BOLIVIA

H	Heaton (1892–1953)
P, PTR, PTS	Potosi

BRAZIL

A	Berlin (1913)
B	Bahia (1714–1831)
C	Cuiaba (1823–33)
G	Goias (1823–33)
M	Minas Gerais (1823–28)
P	Pernambuco
R	Rio de Janeiro (1703–1834)
RS	Rio de Janeiro (1869)
SP	Sao Paulo (1825–32)

BRITISH NORTH BORNEO (Sabah)

H	Heaton (1882–1941)

BRITISH WEST AFRICA

G	JR Gaunt, Birmingham
H	Heaton, Birmingham (1911–57)
K	King's Norton
KN	King's Norton
SA	Pretoria

BULGARIA

A	Berlin
BP	Budapest
Heaton	Heaton, Birmingham (1881–1923)
KB	Kormoczbanya
cornucopia	Paris
thunderbolt	Poissy

CANADA
C	Ottawa
H	Heaton (1871–1907)
maple leaf	Ottawa (on coins struck after the year inscribed on them)

CENTRAL AMERICAN REPUBLIC
CR	San Jose (Costa Rica)
G	Guatemala
NG	Guatemala
T	Tegucigalpa (Honduras)

CEYLON
H	Heaton (1912)

CHILE
A	Agustin de Infante y Prado (1768–72)
AJ	The above and Jose Maria de Bobadilla (1800–01)
D	Domingo Eizaguirre
DA	Domingo Eizaguirre and Agustin de Infante (1772–99)
BFF	Francisco Rodriguez Brochero
FJJF	Brochero and Jose Maria de Bobadilla (1803–17)
H	Heaton (1851)
J	Jose Larraneta (1749–67)
So	Santiago
VA	Val Distra

COLOMBIA
A	Paris
B	Bogota
BA	Bogota
B.B	Bogota
H	Heaton (1912)
M	Medellin
NR	Nuevo Reino
NoRo	Nuevo Reino
P	Popayan
PN, Pn	Popayan
SM	Santa Marta

COSTA RICA
CR	San Jose (1825–1947)
HBM	Heaton (1889–93)
S	San Domingo
SD	San Domingo

COURLAND
ICS	Justin Carl Schroder
IFS	Johan Friedrich Schmickert

CYPRUS
H	Heaton (1881–2)

DENMARK
FF	Altona
KM	Copenhagen Altona (1842)
crown	Copenhagen
heart	Copenhagen

orb	Altona (1839–48)

Other letters are the initials of mintmasters and moneyers

DOMINICAN REPUBLIC
HH	Heaton (1888–1919)

EAST AFRICA
A	Ackroyd & Best, Morley
H	Heaton (1910–64)
I	Bombay
K	Kynoch (IMI)
KN	King's Norton
SA	Pretoria

ECUADOR
BIRM^MH	Heaton (1915)
BIRMING-HAM	Heaton (1899–1900, 1928)
D	Denver
H	Heaton (1890, 1909, 1924–5)
HEATON BIRMING-HAM	Heaton (1872–95)
HF	Le Locle
LIMA	Lima
Mo	Mexico
PHILA	Philadelphia
QUITO	Quito
SANTIAGO	Santiago de Chile

EGYPT
H	Heaton (1904–37)

EL SALVADOR
CAM	Central American Mint, San Salvador
H	Heaton (1889–1913)
Mo	Mexico
S	San Francisco

FIJI
S	San Francisco

FINLAND
H	Heaton (1921)
heart	Copenhagen (1922). Since then coins have been struck at Helsinki without a mintmark.

Initials of mintmasters:
S	August Soldan (1864–85)
L	Johan Lihr (1885–1912)
S	Isaac Sundell (1915–47)
L	V. U. Liuhto (1948)
H	Uolevi Helle (1948–58)
S	Allan Soiniemi (1958–75)
SH	Soiniemi & Heikki Halvaoja (1967–71)
K	Timo Koivuranta (1977, 1979)
KN	Koivuranta and Antti Neuvonen (1978)
KT	Koivuranta and Erja Tielinen (1982)
KM	Koivuranta and Pertti Makinen (1983)
N	Reino Nevalainen (1983)

FRANCE

A	Paris (1768)
AA	Metz (1775–98)
B	Rouen (1786–1857)
B	Beaumont le Roger (1943–58)
BB	Strasbourg (1743–1870)
C	Castelsarrasin (1914, 1942–46)
CC	Genoa (1805)
CL	Genoa (1813–14)
D	Lyons (1771–1857)
G	Geneva (1796–1805)
H	La Rochelle (1770–1837)
L	Limoges (1766–1837)
K	Bordeaux (1759–1878)
L	Bayonne (1761–1837)
M	Toulouse (1766–1837)
MA	Marseilles (1787–1857)
N	Montpellier (1766–93)
O	Riom
P	Dijon
Q	Perpignan (1777–1837)
R	Royal Mint, London (1815)
R	Orleans (1780–92)
T	Nantes (1739–1835)
U	Turin (1814)
V	Troyes
W	Lille (1759–1857)
X	Amiens (1740)
&	Aix en Provence (1775)
9	Rennes
cow	Pau (1746–93)
flag	Utrecht (1811–14)
crowned R	Rome (1811–14)
thunderbolt	Poissy (1922-24)
star	Madrid (1916)

In addition, French coins include symbols denoting the privy marks of Engravers General (Chief Engravers since 1880) and Mint Directors.

GERMANY

The first name gives the location of the mint, and the second the name of the country or state issuing the coins.

A	Amberg, Bavaria (1763–94)
A	Berlin (1850)
A	Clausthal, Hannover (1832–49)
AE	Breslau, Silesia (1743–51)
AGP	Cleve, Rhineland (1742–43)
AK	Dusseldorf, Julich-Berg (1749–66)
ALS	Berlin (1749)
B	Bayreuth, Franconia (1796–1804)
B	Breslau, Silesia (1750–1826)
B	Brunswick, Brunswick (1850–60)
B	Brunswick, Westphalia (1809–13)
B	Dresden, Saxony (1861–72)
B	Hannover, Brunswick (1860–71)
B	Hannover, East Friesland (1823–25)
B	Hannover, Hannover (1821–66)
B	Hannover, Germany (1866-78)
B	Regensburg, Regensburg (1809)
B	Vienna, Germany (1938–45)

BH	Frankfurt (1808)
B–H	Regensburg, Rhenish Confederation (1802–12)
C	Cassel, Westphalia (1810–13)
C	Clausthal, Brunswick
C	Clausthal, Westphalia (1810–11)
C	Dresden, Saxony (1779–1804)
C	Frankfurt, Germany (1866–79)
CHI	Berlin (1749–63)
CLS	Dusseldorf, Julich-Berg (1767–70)
D	Aurich, East Friesland (1750–1806)
D	Dusseldorf, Rhineland (1816–48)
D	Munich, Germany (1872)
E	Dresden, Germany (1872–87)
E	Koenigberg, East Prussia (1750–98)
E	Muldenhutte, Germany (1887–1953)
EC	Leipzig, Saxony (1753–63)
EGN	Berlin (1725–49)
F	Dresden, Saxony (1845–58)
F	Magdeburg, Lower Saxony (1740–1806)
F	Cassel, Hesse-Cassel (1803–07)
F	Stuttgart, Germany (1872)
FW	Dresden, Saxony (1734–63)
G	Dresden, Saxony (1833–44, 1850–54)
G	Glatz, Silesia (1807–09)
G	Karlsruhe, Germany (1872)
G	Stettin, Pomerania (1750–1806)
GK	Cleve (1740–55)
GN	Bamberg, Bamberg
H	Darmstadt, Germany (1872–82)
H	Dresden, Saxony (1804–12)
HK	Rostock, Rostock (1862–64)
I	Hamburg, Germany (1872)
IDB	Dresden, Prussian occupation (1756–59)
IEC	Dresden, Saxony (1779–1804)
IF	Leipzig, Saxony (1763–65)
IGG	Leipzig, Saxony (1716–34, 1813–32)
J	Hamburg, Germany (1873)
J	Paris, Westphalia (1808–09)
L	Leipzig, Saxony (1761–62)
MC	Brunswick, Brunswick (1813–14, 1820)
PM	Dusseldorf, Julich-Berg (1771–83)
PR	Dusseldorf, Julich-Berg (1783–1804)
S	Dresden, Saxony (1813–32)
S	Hannover, Hannover (1839–44)
S	Schwabach, Franconia (1792–94)
SGH	Dresden, Saxony (1804–12)
ST	Strickling, Blomberg (1820–40)

GREAT BRITAIN

A	Ashby (1645)
B	Nicolas Briot (1631–39)
B	Bridgnorth (1646)
B	Bristol (1696)
Br	Bristol (1643–45)
C	Chester (1696)
CARL	Carlisle (1644–45)
CC	Corfe Castle (1644)
CHST	Chester (1644)
CR	Chester (1644)
E	Southwark (1547–49)

E	Exeter (1696)
E	Edinburgh (1707–13)
E*	Edinburgh (1707–09)
H	Heaton, Birmingham (1874–1919)
HC	Hartlebury Castle (1646)
K	London (1547–49)
KN	King's Norton
N	Norwich (1696)
OX	Oxford (1644–45)
OXON	Oxford (1644)
PC	Pontefract (1648–49)
SC	Scarborough (1644–45)
SOHO	Birmingham (1797–1806)
T	Canterbury (1549)
TC	Bristol (1549)
WS	Bristol (1547–49)
Y	Southwark (1551)
boar	Shrewsbury (1643–44)
book	Aberystwyth (1638–42)
bow	Durham House (1548–49)
castle	Exeter (1644–45)
crown	Aberystwyth Furnace (1648–49)
plume	Shrewsbury (1642)
plume	Oxford (1642–46)
plume	Bristol (1643–46)

Other symbols and marks on the hammered coins of Great Britain are usually referred to as Initial Marks. Complete listings of these marks appear in a number of specialist publications.

GREECE

A	Paris
B	Vienna
BB	Strasbourg
H	Heaton (1921)
K	Bordeaux
KN	King's Norton
owl	Aegina (1828–32)
owl	Athens (1838–55)
thunderbolt	Poissy

GUATEMALA

CG	Guatemala City (1733-76)
G	Guatemala City (1776)
H	Heaton (1894–1901)
NG	Nueva Guatemala (1777)

GUERNSEY

H	Heaton (1855–1949)

HAITI

A	Paris
HEATON	Heaton (1863)

HONDURAS

A	Paris (1869–71)
T	Tegucigalpa (1825–62)

HONG KONG

H	Heaton (1872–1971)
KN	King's Norton

HUNGARY

A	Vienna
B	Kremnitz
BP	Budapest
CA	Vienna
G	Nagybanya
GN	Nagybanya
GYF	Carlsburg
HA	Hall
K	Kremnitz
KB	Kremnitz
NB	Nagybanya
S	Schmollnitz
WI	Vienna

INDIA

B	Bombay (1835-1947)
C	Calcutta (1835-1947)
I	Bombay (1918)
L	Lahore (1943-45)
M	Madras (1869)
P	Pretoria (1943-44)
diamond	Bombay
dot in diamond	Hyderabad
split diamond	Hyderabad
star	Hyderabad

IRAN

H	Heaton (1928–29)

IRAQ

I	Bombay

ISRAEL

H	Heaton (1951–52)
star of David	Jerusalem

ITALY AND STATES

B	Bologna
B/I	Birmingham (1893–4)
FIRENZE	Florence
H	Heaton (1866–67)
KB	Berlin
M	Milan
N	Naples
OM	Strasbourg
R	Rome
T	Turin
V	Venice
ZV	Venice
anchor	Genoa
eagle head	Turin

JAMAICA

C	Ottawa
FM	Franklin Mint
H	Heaton (1882–1916)

JERSEY

H	Heaton (1877)

KENYA
C/M	Calcutta
H	Heaton (1911–64)

LIBERIA
B	Berne
FM	Franklin Mint
H	Heaton (1896–1906)
PM	Pobjoy Mint

LIECHTENSTEIN
A	Vienna
B	Berne
M	Munich

LUXEMBOURG
A	Paris
H	Gunzburg
anchor	Paris
angel	Brussels
caduceus	Utrecht
double eagle	Brussels
sword	Utrecht

MALAYSIA
B	Bombay
FM	Franklin Mint
H	Heaton (1955–61)
I	Calcutta (1941)
I	Bombay (1945)
KN	King's Norton
W	James Watt, Birmingham

MAURITIUS
H	Heaton (1877–90)
SA	Pretoria

MEXICO
A, As	Alamos
C, CN	Culiacan
CA, CH	Chihuahua
Ce	Real del Catorce
D, Do	Durango
Eo	Tlalpam
GA	Guadalajara
GC	Guadelupe y Calvo
Go	Guanajuato
Ho	Hermosillo
M, Mo	Mexico City
Mo	Morelos
MX	Mexico City
O, OA, OKA	Oaxaca
Pi	San Luis Potosi
SLPi	San Luis Potosi
TC	Tierra Caliente
Z, Zs	Zacatecas

MONACO
A	Paris
M	Monte Carlo
clasped hands	Cabanis
thunderbolt	Poissy

MOZAMBIQUE
H	Heaton (1894)
R	Rio

NETHERLANDS AND COLONIES
Austrian Netherlands (1700-93)
H	Amsterdam
S	Utrecht
W	Vienna
hand	Antwerp
head	Brussels
lion	Bruges

Kingdom of the Netherlands
B	Brussels (1821–30)
D	Denver (1943–45)
P	Philadelphia (1941–45)
S	Utrecht (1816–36)
S	San Francisco (1944–45)
Sa	Surabaya
caduceus	Utrecht

NICARAGUA
H	Heaton (1880–1916)
NR	Leon de Nicaragua

NORWAY
hammers	Kongsberg

PANAMA
CHI	Valcambi
FM	Franklin Mint

PERU
AREQ, AREQUIPA	Arequipa
AYACUCHO	Ayacucho
CUZCO, Co	Cuzco
L, LM, LR	Lima
LIMAE	Lima
PASCO	Pasco
Paz, Po	Pasco
P	Lima (1568-70)
P	Philadelphia
S	San Francisco

PHILIPPINES
BSP	Bangko Sentral Pilipinas
D	Denver (1944–45)
FM	Franklin Mint
M, MA	Manila
PM	Pobjoy Mint
S	San Francisco (1903–47)
5 point star	Manila

POLAND
AP	Warsaw (1772–74)
CI	Cracow (1765–68)
EB	Warsaw (1774–92)
EC	Leipzig (1758–63)
FF	Stuttgart (1916–17)
FH	Warsaw (1815–27)
FS	Warsaw (1765–68)
FWoF	Dresden (1734–64)
G	Cracow (1765–72)

H	Heaton (1924)
IB	Warsaw (1811–27)
IGS	Dresden (1716–34)
IP	Warsaw (1834–43)
IS	Warsaw (1768–74)
JGG	Leipzig (1750–53)
JS	Warsaw (1810–11)
KG	Warsaw (1829–34)
MV, MW	Warsaw
arrow	Warsaw (1925–39)
Dot after	
date	Royal Mint (1925)
8 torches	Paris (1924)

ROMANIA

B	Bucharest (1879–85)
C	Bucharest (1886)
H	Heaton (1867–1930)
HUGUENIN	Le Locle
J	Hamburg
KN	King's Norton
V	Vienna
W	Watt, Birmingham
thunderbolt	Poissy

RUSSIA

AM	Annensk (1762–96)
BM	Warsaw (1825–55)
bM	St Petersburg (1796)
C–M	Sestroretsk (1762–96)
CM	Souzan (1825–55)
E–M	Ekaterinburg (1762–1810)
KM	Kolpina (1810)
K–M	Kolyvan (1762–1810)
MM, M–M	Moscow (1730–96)
MMD	Moscow (1730–96)
MW	Warsaw (1842–54)
NM	Izhorsk (1811–21)
SP	St Petersburg (1798–1800)
SPB	St Petersburg (1724–1915)
SPM	St Petersburg (1825–55)
T–M	Feodosia (1762–96)

SAN MARINO

M	Milan
R	Rome

SIAM
(Thailand) H Heaton (1898)

SOUTH AFRICA

SA	Pretoria

SPAIN

B	Burgos
B, BA	Barcelona
Bo	Bilbao
C	Catalonia
C	Cuenca
C	Reus
CA	Zaragoza
G	Granada
GNA	Gerona
LD	Lerida

J, JA	Jubia
M, MD	Madrid
P	Palma de Majorca
PpP, PL, PA	Pamplona
S, S/L	Seville
Sr	Santander
T, To, Tole	Toledo
TOR:SA	Tortosa
V, VA, VAL	Valencia
crowned C	Cadiz
crowned M	Madrid
aqueduct	Segovia
crowned shield	Tarragona
pomegranate	Granada
quartered shield	Palma
scallop	Coruna
stars:	
3 points	Segovia
4 points	Jubia
5 points	Manila
6 points	Madrid
7 points	Seville (1833)
8 points	Barcelona (1838)
wavy lines	Valladolid

SURINAM

P	Philadelphia
S	Sydney
caduceus	Utrecht

SWITZERLAND

A	Paris
AB	Strasbourg
B	Berne
B	Brussels (1874)
BA	Basle
BB	Strasbourg
S	Solothurn

URUGUAY

H	Heaton (1869)

UNITED STATES OF AMERICA

C	Charlotte, North Carolina
Cc	Carson City, Nevada
D	Dahlonega, Georgia (1838–61)
D	Denver, Colorado (1906)
O	New Orleans
P	Philadelphia
S	San Francisco
W	West Point

VENEZUELA

A	Paris
H	Heaton (1852)
HEATON	Heaton (1852–63)

YUGOSLAVIA (including former Serbia)

A	Paris
H	Heaton (1883–84)
KOBHNUA, A.D.	Kovnica
V	Vienna
thunderbolt	Poissy

COLLECTORS' ALBUMS

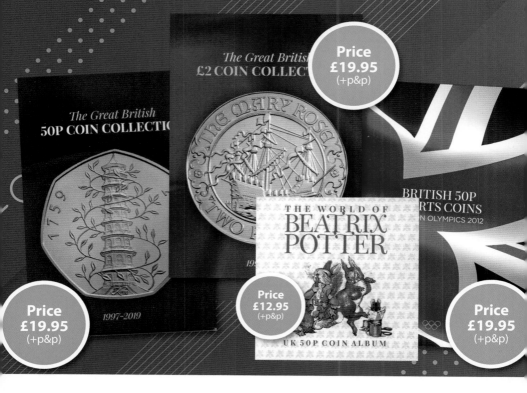

The Great British
£2 COIN COLLECT

**Price
£19.95**
(+p&p)

The Great British
50P COIN COLLECTION

BRITISH 50P
...RTS COINS
...N OLYMPICS 2012

THE WORLD OF
BEATRIX POTTER

UK 50P COIN ALBUM

**Price
£12.95**
(+p&p)

1997-2019

**Price
£19.95**
(+p&p)

**Price
£19.95**
(+p&p)

Are you hoarding Tiggy Winkles? Are your Puddle Ducks without a home? Would you like your Olympic numismatic souvenirs of the 2012 Games kept safe? Then look no further than the new Collectors' Albums—made especially to house your collectable coins.

Made from sturdy cardboard, each colourful folder opens out to reveal a safe slot to house each of your coins with an easy pictorial reference providing at-a-glance information on the coins you still need to find!

Coins not included!

 01404 46972 www.tokenpublishing.com Token Publishing Ltd., 40 Southernhay East, Exeter, Devon EX1 1PE

Coin
inscriptions

This alphabetical listing is confined to inscriptions found on coins, mainly in the form of mottoes or of a commemorative nature. Names of rulers are, for the most part, excluded. Where the inscription is in a language other than English a translation is given, followed by the name of the issuing country or authority in parentheses.

A Deo et Caesare   From God and the Emperor (Frankfurt).

A Domino Factum est Istud et est Mirabile in Oculis Nostris   This is the Lord's doing and it is marvellous in our eyes (England, Mary).

A Solo Iehova Sapientia   From God alone comes true wisdom (Wittgenstein).

Ab Inimicis Meis Libera Me Deus   Free me from enemies (Burgundy).

Ad Legem Conventionis   According to the law of the Convention (Furstenberg).

Ad Normam Conventionis   According to the standard of the Convention (Prussia).

Ad Palmam Pressa Laeturo Resurgo   Pressed to the palm I rise more joyfully (Wittgenstein).

Ad Usam Luxemburgi CC Vallati   For the use of the besieged Luxembourgers (Luxembourg siege coins).

Adiuva Nos Deus Salutaris Noster   Help us, O God, our Saviour (Lorraine).

Adventus Optimi Principis   The coming of the noblest prince (Papacy).

Aes Usibus Aptius Auro   Bronze in its uses is more suitable than gold (Brazil).

Aeternum Meditans Decus   An ornament intended for all time (Alencon).

Aliis Inserviendo Consumor   I spend my life devoted to others (Brunswick-Wolfenbuttel).

Alles Mit Bedacht   All with reflection (Brunswick).

Amor Populi Praesidium Regis   The love of the people is the king's protection (England, Charles I).

Ang Fra Dom Hib & Aquit   (King) of England and France, Lord of Ireland and Aquitaine (England, Edward III).

Anno Regni Primo   In the first year of the reign (Britain, edge inscription on crowns).

Apres les Tenebres la Lumiere   After the shadows, the light (Geneva).

Archangelus Michael   Archangel Michael (Italy, Grimoald IV).

Ardua ad Gloriam Via   Struggles are the way to glory (Waldeck).

Arte Mea Bis Iustus Moneta Lud Iust   By my art I am twice the just coin of King Louis (France, 1641).

Aspera Oblectant   Wild places delight (Nassau-Weilburg).

Aspice Pisas Sup Omnes Specio   Behold the coin of Pisa, superior to all (Pisa).

Audiatur Altera Pars   Let the other part be heard (Stavelot).

Auf Gott Trawe Ich   In God I trust (Brunswick).

Ausen Gefaesen der Kirchen und Burger   From the vessels of the Church and citizens (Frankfurt siege, 1796).

Auspicio Regis et Senatus Angliae   By authority of the king and parliament of England (East India Company).

Auxilio fortissimo Dei   With the strongest help of God (Mecklenburg).

Auxilium de Sanctio   Aid from the sanctuary (Papacy).

Auxilium Meum a Dno Qui Fecit Celum e Terram   My help comes from God who made heaven and earth (Portugal).

Beata Tranquillatis   Blessed tranquillity (Rome, Licinius II).

Beatus Qui Speravit in dom   Blessed is he who has hoped in the Lord (Mansfeld).

Benedic Haereditati Tuae   Blessings on your inheritance (Savoy).

Benedicta Sit Sancta Trinitas   Blessed be the Holy Trinity (Albon).

Benedictio Domini Divites Facit   The blessing of the Lord makes the rich (Teschen).

Benedictus Qui Venit in Nomine Domini   Blessed is he who comes in the name of the Lord (Flanders).

Beschaw das Ziel Sage Nicht Viel   Consider the matter but say little (Quedlinburg).

Besser Land und Lud Verloren als ein Falscher Aid Geschworn Better to lose land and wealth than swear a false oath (Hesse).

Bey Gott ist Rath und That With God is counsel and deed (Mansfeld).

Britanniarum Regina Queen of the Britains (Britain, Victoria).

Britt Omn Rex King of all the Britains (i.e. Britain and the overseas dominions) (Britain, 1902–52).

Cal et Car Com de Fugger in Zin et Norn Sen & Adm Fam Cajetan and Carl, Counts of Fugger in Zinnenberg and Nordendorf, Lords and Administrators of the Family (Empire, Fugger).

Candide et Constanter Sincerely and steadfastly (Hesse-Cassel).

Candide sed Provide Clearly but cautiously (Osterwitz).

Candore et Amore With sincerity and love (Fulda).

Candore et Constantia With sincerity and constancy (Bavaria).

Capit Cath Ecclesia Monasteriensis Chapter of the Cathedral Church of Munster (Munster).

Capit Eccle Metropolit Colon Chapter of the Metropolitan Church of Cologne (Cologne).

Capitulum Regnans Sede Vacante Chapter governing, the See being vacant (Eichstadt).

Carola Magna Ducissa Feliciter Regnante Grand Duchess Charlotte, happily reigning (Luxembourg).

Carolus a Carolo Charles (I) to Charles (II) (England).

Cedunt Prementi Fata The fates yield to him who presses (Ploen, Hese-Cassel).

Charitate et Candore With charity and sincerity (East Frisia).

Charta Magna Bavariae The Great Charter of Bavaria (Bavaria).

Christo Auspice Regno I reign under the auspices of Christ (England, Charles I).

Christus Spes Una Salutis Christ is our one hope of salvation (Cleve).

Chur Mainz Electoral Principality of Mainz (Mainz).

Circumeundo Servat et Ornat It serves and decorates by going around (Sweden).

Civibus Quorum Pietas Coniuratione Die III Mai MDCCXCI Obrutam et Deletam Libertate Polona Tueri Conabatur Respublica Resurgens To the citizens whose piety the resurgent commonwealth tried to protect Poland overturned and deprived of liberty by the conspiracy of the third day of May 1791 (Poland).

Civitas Lucemborgiensis Millesimum Ovans Expletannum Completing the celebration of a thousand years of the city of Luxembourg (Luxembourg).

Civium Industria Floret Civitas By the industry of its people the state flourishes (Festival of Britain crown, 1951).

Cluniaco Cenobio Petrus et Paulus Peter and Paul from the Abbey of Cluny (Cluny).

Comes Provincie Fili Regis Francie Court of Provence and son of the King of France (Provence).

Communitas et Senatus Bonon City and senate of Bologna (Bologna).

Concordia Fratrum The harmony of the brothers (Iever).

Concordia Patriae Nutrix Peace, the nurse of the fatherland (Waldeck).

Concordia Res Parvae Crescunt Little things increase through harmony (Batavian Republic).

Concordia Res Parvae Crescunt, Discordia Dilabuntur By harmony little things increase, by discord they fall apart (Lowenstein-Wertheim-Virneburg).

Concordia Stabili With lasting peace (Hildesheim).

Confidens Dno Non Movetur He who trusts in God is unmoved (Spanish Netherlands).

Confidentia in Deo et Vigilantia Trust in God and vigilance (Prussian Asiatic Company).

Confoederato Helvetica Swiss Confederation (Switzerland)

Conjuncto Felix Fortunate in his connections (Solms).

Conservator Urbis Suae Saviour of his city (Rome, 4th century).

Consilio et Aequitate With deliberation and justice (Fulda).

Consilio et Virtutis With deliberation and valour (Hesse-Cassel).

Constanter et Sincere Steadfastly and sincerely (Lautern).

Crescite et Multiplicamini Increase and multiply (Maryland).

Cristiana Religio Christian religion (Germany, 11th century).

Crux Benedicat May the cross bless you (Oldenburg).

Cuius Cruore Sanati Sumus By His sacrifice are we healed (Reggio).

Cultores Sui Deus Protegit God protects His followers (England, Charles I).

Cum Deo et Die (Jure) With God and the day (Wurttemberg).

Cum Deo et Jure With God and the law (Wurttemberg).

Cum Deo et Labore With God and work (Wittgenstein).

Cum His Qui Orderant Pacem Eram Pacificus With those who order peace I was peaceful (Zug).

Curie Bonthon to so Doulo Protect his servant, o Lord (Byzantine Empire).

Custos Regni Deus God is the guardian of the kingdom (Naples and Sicily).

Da Gloriam Deo et Eius Genitrici Marie Give glory to God and His mother Mary (Wurttemberg).

Da Mihi Virtutem Contra Hostes Tuos Give me valour against mine enemies (Netherlands, Charles V).

Dat Wort is Fleis Gworden   The word is made flesh (Muster).

Date Caesaris Caesari et Quae Sunt Dei Deo   Render unto Caesar the things that are Caesar's and unto God the things that are God's (Stralsund).

De Oficina . . .   From the mint of . . . (France, medieval).

Decreto Reipublicae Nexu Confoederationis Iunctae Die V Xbris MDCCXCII Stanislao Augusto Regnante   By decree of the state in conjunction with the joint federation on the fifth day of December 1792, Stanislaus Augustus ruling (Poland).

Decus et Tutamen   An ornament and a safeguard (Britain, pound).

Deducet Nos Mirabiliter Dextera Tua   Thy right hand will guide us miraculously (Savoy).

Denarium Terrae Mariae   Penny of Maryland (Maryland).

Deo Conservatori Pacis   To God, preserver of peace (Brandenburg-Ansbach).

Deo OM Auspice Suaviter et Fortiter sed Iuste nec Sibi sed Suis   Under the auspices of God, greatest and best, pleasantly and bravely but justly, not for himself but for his people (Speyer).

Deo Patriae et Subditio   For God, fatherland and neighbourhood (Mainz).

Der Recht Glaubt In Ewig Lebt   Who believes in right will live in eternity (Linange-Westerburg).

Der Rhein ist Deutschlands Strom Nicht Deutschlands Grenze   The Rhine is Germany's River not Germany's Frontier.

Deum Solum Adorabis   You will venerate God alone (Hesse).

Deus Constituit Regna   God establishes kingdoms (Nijmegen).

Deus Dat Qui Vult   God gives to him who wishes (Hanau-Munzenberg).

Deus et Dominus   God and Lord (Rome, 3rd century).

Deus in Adiutorium Meum Intende   God stretch out in my assistance (France).

Deus Providebit   God will provide (Lowenstein-Wertheim-Virneburg).

Deus Refugium Meum   God is my refuge (Cleve).

Deus Solatium Meum   God is my comfort (Sweden).

Dextera Domini Exaltavit Me   The right hand of God has raised me up (Modena, Spain).

Dextra Dei Exalta Me   The right hand of God exalts me (Denmark).

Dieu et Mon Droit   God and my right (Britain, George IV).

Dilexit Dns Andream   The Lord delights in St Andrew (Holstein).

Dilexit Dominus Decorem Iustitiae   The Lord is pleased with the beauty of justice (Unterwalden).

Dirige Deus Gressus Meos   O God, direct my steps (Tuscany, Britain, Una £5).

Discerne Causam Meam   Distinguish my cause (Savoy).

Divina Benedictiae et Caesarea Iustitia   Sacrifice of blessings and imperial justice (Coblenz).

Dn Ihs Chs Rex Regnantium   Lord Jesus Christ, King of Kings (Rome, Justinian II).

Dns Ptetor Ms Z Lib'ator Ms   The Lord is my protector and liberator (Scotland, David II).

Dominabitur Gentium et Ipse   He himself will also be lord of the nations (Austrian Netherlands).

Domine Conserva Nos in Pace   O Lord preserve us in peace (Basle, Mulhausen).

Domine Elegisti Lilium Tibi   O Lord Thou hast chosen the lily for Thyself (France, Louis XIV).

Domine ne in Furore Tuo Arguas Me   O Lord rebuke me not in Thine anger (England, Edward III).

Domine Probasti Me et Congnovisti Me   O Lord Thou hast tested me and recognised me (Mantua).

Domini est Regnum   The Kingdom is the Lord's (Austrian Netherlands).

Dominus Deus Omnipotens Rex   Lord God, almighty King (Viking coins).

Dominus Mihi Adiutor   The Lord is my helper (Spanish Netherlands).

Dominus Providebit   The Lord will provide (Berne).

Dominus Spes Populi Sui   The Lord is the hope of his people (Lucerne).

Donum Dei ex Fodinis Vilmariens   A gift of God from the Vilmar mines (Coblenz).

Duce Deo Fide et Justicia   By faith and justice lead us to God (Ragusa).

Dum Praemor Amplior   I increase while I die prematurely (Savoy).

Dum Spiro Spero   While I live, I hope (Pontefract siege coins).

Dum Totum Compleat Orbem   Until it fills the world (France, Henri II).

Dura Pati Virtus   Valour endures hardships (Saxe-Lauenburg).

Durae Necessitatis   Through force of necessity (Bommel siege, 1599).

Durum Telum Necessitas   Hardship is a weapon of necessity (Minden).

Dux et Gubernatores Reip Genu   Duke and governors of the republic of Genoa (Genoa).

E Pluribus Unum   One out of more (USA).

Eccl S. Barbarae Patronae Fodin Kuttenbergensium Duo Flor Arg Puri   The church of St Barbara, patron of the Kuttensberg mines, two florins of pure silver (Hungary).

Een en Ondelbaer Sterk   One and indivisible (Batavian Republic).

Eendracht Mag Macht   Unity makes strength (Belgium, South African Republic).

Einigkeit Recht und Freiheit   Union, right and freedom (Germany).

Electorus Saxoniae Administrator   Elector and administrator of Saxony (Saxony).

Elimosina Alms (France, Pepin).

Ep Fris & Ratisb Ad Prum Pp Coad Aug Bishop of Freising and Regensburg, administrator of Pruem, prince-provost, co-adjutant bishop of Augsburg (Trier).

Equa Libertas Deo Gratia Frat Pax in Virtute Tua et in Domino Confido I believe in equal liberty by the grace of God, brotherly love in Thy valour and in the Lord (Burgundy).

Equitas Iudicia Tua Dom Equity and Thy judgments O Lord (Gelderland).

Espoir Me Conforte Hope comforts me (Mansfeld).

Espreuve Faicto Par Lexpres Commandement du Roy Proof made by the express commandment of the King (France, piedforts).

Et in Minimis Integer Faithful even in the smallest things (Olmutz).

Ex Auro Argentes Resurgit From gold it arises, silver again (Sicily).

Ex Auro Sinico From Chinese gold (Denmark).

Ex Flammis Orior I arise from the flames (Hohenlohe-Neuenstein-Ohringen).

Ex Fodinis Bipontio Seelbergensibus From the Seelberg mines of Zweibrucken (Pfalz-Birkenfeld).

Ex Metallo Novo From new metal (Spain).

Ex Uno Omnis Nostra Salus From one is all our salvation (Eichstadt, Mulhouse).

Ex Vasis Argent Cleri Mogunt Pro Aris et Focis From the silver vessels of the clergy of Mainz for altars and for hearths (Mainz).

Ex Visceribus Fodinse Bieber From the bowels of the Bieber mine (Hanau-Munzenberg).

Exaltabitur in Gloria He shall be exalted in glory (England, quarter nobles).

Exemplum Probati Numismatis An example of a proof coin (France, Louis XIII piedforts).

Exemtae Eccle Passau Episc et SRI Princ Prince Bishop of the freed church of Passau, prince of the Holy Roman Empire (Passau).

Expectate Veni Come, o expected one (Roman Britain, Carausius).

Extremum Subidium Campen Kampen under extreme siege (Kampen, 1578).

Exurgat Deus et Dissipentur Inimici Eius Let God arise and let His enemies be scattered (England, James I).

Faciam Eos in Gentem Unam I will make them one nation (England, unites and laurels).

Faith and Truth I will Bear unto You (UK £5, 1993).

Fata Consiliis Potiora The fates are more powerful than councils (Hesse-Cassel).

Fata Viam Invenient The fates will find a way (Gelderland).

Fecit Potentiam in Brachio Suo He put power in your forearm (Lorraine).

Fecunditas Fertility (Naples and Sicily).

Fel Temp Reparatio The restoration of lucky times (Rome, AD 348).

Felicitas Perpetua Everlasting good fortune (Rome, Constantius II).

Felix coniunctio Happy Union (Brandenburg-Ansbach).

Fiat Misericordia Tua Dne Let Thy mercy be O Lord (Gelderland).

Fiat Voluntas Domini Perpetuo Let the goodwill of the Lord last for ever (Fulda).

Fidei Defensor Defender of the Faith (Britain).

Fidelitate et Fortitudine With fidelity and fortitude (Batthanyi).

Fideliter et Constanter Faithfully and steadfastly (Saxe-Coburg-Gotha).

Fidem Servando Patriam Tuendo By keeping faith and protecting the fatherland (Savoy).

Filius Augustorum Son of emperors (Rome, 4th century).

Fisci Iudaici Calumnia Sublata The false accusation of the Jewish tax lifted (Rome, Nerva).

Florent Concordia Regna Through harmony kingdoms flourish (England, Charles I and II).

Fortitudo et Laus Mea Dominu Fortitude and my praise in the Lord (Sardinia).

Free Trade to Africa by Act of Parliment *(Sic)* (Gold Coast).

Friedt Ernehrt Unfriedt Verzehrt Peace nourishes, unrest wastes (Brunswick).

Fulgent Sic Littora Rheni Thus shine the banks of the Rhine (Mannheim).

Fundator Pacis Founder of peace (Rome, Severus).

Gaudium Populi Romani The joy of the Roman people (Rome, 4th century).

Gen C Mar VI Dim Col USC & RAMAI Cons & S Conf M General field marshal, colonel of the only dragoon regiment, present privy councillor of both their sacred imperial and royal apostolic majesties, and state conference minister (Batthanyi).

Gerecht und Beharrlich Just and steadfast (Bavaria).

Germ Hun Boh Rex AAD Loth Ven Sal King of Germany, Hungary and Bohemia, Archduke of Austria, Duke of Lorraine, Venice and Salzburg (Austria).

Germ Jero Rex Loth Bar Mag Het Dux King of Germany, Jerusalem, Lorraine and Bar, Grand Duke of Tuscany (Austrian Netherlands).

Germania Voti Compos Germany sharing the vows (Brandenburg-Ansbach).

Gloria ex Amore Patriae Glory from love of country (Denmark).

Gloria in Excelsis Deo Glory to God in the highest (France, Sweden).

Gloria Novi Saeculi The glory of a new century (Rome, Gratian).

God With Us (England, Commonwealth).

Godt Met Ons God with us (Oudewater).

Gottes Freundt der Pfaffen Feindt God's friend, the Pope's enemy (Brunswick, Christian).

Gratia Dei Sum Id Quod Sum   By the grace of God, I am what I am (Navarre).

Gratia Di Rex   By the grace of God, king (France, 8th century).

Gratitudo Concivibus Exemplum Posteritati   Gratitude to fellow Citizens, an example to posterity (Poland).

Gud och Folket   God and the people (Sweden).

Hac Nitimur Hanc Tuemur   With this we strive, this we shall defend (Batavian Republic).

Hac Sub Tutela   Under this protection (Eichstadt).

Haec Sunt Munera Minerae S Antony Eremitae   These are the rewards of the mine of St Antony the hermit (Hildesheim).

Hanc Deus Dedit   God has given this (Pontefract siege coins).

Hanc Tuemur Hac Nitimur   This we defend, by this we strive (Batavian Republic).

Has Nisi Periturus Mihi Adimat Nemo   Let no one remove these (Letters) from me under penalty of death (Commonwealth, edge inscription).

Henricus Rosas Regna Jacobus   Henry (united) the roses, James the kingdoms (England and Scotland, James VI and I).

Herculeo Vincta Nodo   Bound by a Herculean fetter (Savoy).

Herr Nach Deinem Willen   O Lord Thy will be done (Palatinate, Erbach).

Herre Gott Verleich Uns Gnade   Lord God grant us grace (Brunswick).

Hic Est Qui Multum Orat Pro Populo   Here is he who prays a lot for the people (Paderborn).

Hir Steid te Biscop   Here is represented the bishop (Gittelde).

His Ventis Vela Levantur   By these winds the sails are raised up (Hesse-Cassel).

Hispaniarum Infans   Infante of Spain and its dominions (Spain).

Hispaniarum et Ind Rex   King of Spain and the Indies.

Hispaniarum Rex   King of Spain (Spain).

Hoc Signo Victor Eris   With this sign you will be victor (Rome, Vetranio).

Honeste et Decenter   Honestly and decently (Nassau-Idstein).

Honi Soit Qui Mal y Pense   Evil to him who evil thinks (Britain, George III).

Honni Soit Qui Mal y Pense   (Hesse-Cassel).

Hospitalis et S Sepul Hierusal   Hospital and Holy Sepulchre of Jerusalem (Malta).

Hun Boh Gal Rex AA Lo Wi et in Fr Dux   King of Hungary, Bohemia and Galicia, Archduke of Austria, Dalmatia, Lodomeria, Wurzburg and Duke in Franconia (Austria).

Hung Boh Lomb et Ven Gal Lod III Rex Aa   King of Hungary, Bohemia, Lombardo-Venezia, Galicia, Lodomeria, Illyria, Archduke (Austria).

Ich Dien   I serve (Aberystwyth 2d, UK 2p).

Ich Getrawe Got in Aller Noth   I trust in God in all my needs (Hesse-Marburg).

Ich Habe Nur Ein Vaterland und das Heisst Deutschland   I have only one fatherland and that is called Germany (Germany).

Ielithes Penniae   Penny of Gittelde (Gittelde, 11th century).

Iesus Autem Transiens Per Medium Illorum Ibat   But Jesus, passing through the midst of them, went His way (England, Scotland, Anglo-Gallic).

Iesus Rex Noster et Deus Noster   Jesus is our king and our God (Florence).

Ihs Xs Rex Regnantium   Jesus Christ, King of Kings (Byzantine Empire).

Ihsus Xristus Basileu Baslie   Jesus Christ, King of Kings (Byzantine Empire).

Imago Sanch Regis Illustris Castelle Legionis e Toleto   The image of Sancho the illustrious king of Castile, Leon and Toledo.

In Casus Per Vigil Omnes   In all seasons through vigil (Wertheim).

In Deo Meo Transgrediar Murum   In my God I shall pass through walls (Teschen).

In Deo Spes Mea   In God is my hope (Gelderland).

In Domino Fiducia Nostra   In the Lord is our trust (Iever).

In Equitate Tua Vivificasti Me   In thy equity Thou hast vivified me (Gelderland).

In God We Trust   (USA).

In Hoc Signo Vinces   In this sign shalt thou conquer (Portugal).

In Honore Sci Mavrici Marti   In honour of the martyr St Maurice (St Maurice, 8th century).

In Manibus Domini sortes Meae   In the hands of the Lord are my fates (Mainz siege, 1688–9).

In Memor Vindicatae Libere ac Relig   In memory of the establishment of freedom and religion (Sweden).

In Memoriam Conjunctionis Utriusque Burgraviatus Norice   In memory of the union of both burgraviates in peace (Brandenburg-Ansbach).

In Memorian Connub Feliciaes Inter Princ Her Frider Carol et Dub Sax August Louis Frider Rodas D 28 Nov 1780 Celebrati   In memory of the most happy marriage between the hereditary prince Friedrich Karl and the Duchess of Saxony Augusta Louisa Frederika, celebrated on 28 Nov 1780 (Schwarzburg-Rudolstadt).

In Memorian Felicisssimi Matrimonii   In memory of the most happy marriage (Wied).

In Memoriam Pacis Teschinensis   Commemorating the Treaty of Teschen (Brandenburg-Ansbach).

In Nomine Domini Amen   In the name of the Lord amen (Zaltbommel).

In Omnem Terram Sonus Eorum   In to all the land their shall go sound (Chateau Renault, Papal States).

In Silencio et Spe Fortitudo Mea   In silence and hope is my fortitude (Brandenburg-Kustrin).

In Spe et Silentio Fortitudo Mea   In hope and silence is my fortitude (Vianen).

In Te Domine Confido   In you O Lord I place my trust (Hesse).

In Te Domine Speravi   In You, O Lord, I have hoped (Gurk).

In Terra Pax   Peace in the land (Papacy).

In Via Virtuti Nulla Via   There is no way for virtue on the way. (Veldenz).

Ind Imp, Indiae Imperator, Imperatrix   Emperor (Empress) of India (Britain).

India Tibi Cessit   India has yielded to thee (Portuguese India).

Infestus Infestis   Hostile to the troublesome (Savoy).

Inimicos Eius Induam Confusione   As for his enemies, I shall clothe them in shame (Sardinia, England, Edward VI).

Insignia Capituli Brixensis   The badge of the chapter of Brixen (Brixen).

Isti Sunt Patres Tui Verique Pastores   These are your fathers and true shepherds (Papacy).

Iudicium Melius Posteritatis Erit   Posterity's judgment will be better (Paderborn).

Iure et Tempore   By right and time (Groningen).

Iusques a Sa Plenitude   As far as your plenitude (France, Henri II).

Iuste et Constanter   Justly and constantly (Paderborn).

Iustirt   Adjusted (Hesse-Cassel).

Iustitia et Concordia   Justice and harmony (Zurich).

Iustitia et Mansuetudine   By justice and mildness (Bavaria, Cologne).

Iustitia Regnorum Fundamentum   Justice is the foundation of kingdoms (Austria).

Iustitia Thronum Firmat   Justice strengthens the throne (England, Charles I).

Iustus Non Derelinquitur   The just person is not deserted (Brandenburg-Calenberg).

Iustus Ut Palma Florebit   The just will flourish like the palm (Portugal).

L Mun Planco Rauracorum Illustratori Vetustissimo   To L Municius Plancus the most ancient and celebrated of the Rauraci (Basle).

Landgr in Cleggov Com in Sulz Dux Crum   Landgrave of Klettgau, count of Sulz, duke of Krumlau (Schwarzburg-Sonderhausen).

Latina Emeri Munita   Latin money of Merida (Suevi).

Lege et Fide   By law and faith (Austria).

Lex Tua Veritas   Thy law is the truth (Tuscany).

Liberta Eguaglianza   Freedom and equality (Venice).

Libertad en la Ley   Freedom within the law (Mexico).

Libertas Carior Auro   Freedom is dearer than gold (St Gall).

Libertas Vita Carior   Freedom is dearer than life (Kulenberg).

Libertas Xpo Firmata   Freedom strengthened by Christ (Genoa).

Liberte, Egalite, Fraternite   Liberty, equality, fraternity (France).

Lucerna Pedibus Meis Verbum Est   Thy word is a lamp unto mine feet (England, Edward VI).

Lumen ad Revelationem Gentium   Light to enlighten the nations (Papacy).

L'Union Fait la Force   The union makes strength (Belgium).

Macula Non Est in Te   There is no sin in Thee (Essen).

Magnus ab Integro Saeculorum Nascitur Ordo   The great order of the centuries is born anew (Bavaria).

Mandavit Dominus Palatie hanc Monetam Fiert   The lord of the Palatine ordained this coin to be made (Balath).

Manibus Ne Laedar Avaris   Lest I be injured by greedy hands (Sweden).

Mar Bran Sac Rom Imp Arcam et Elec Sup Dux Siles   Margrave of Brandenburg, archchamberlain of the Holy Roman Empire and elector, senior duke of Silesia (Prussia).

Maria Mater Domini Xpi   Mary mother of Christ the Lord (Teutonic Knights).

Maria Unxit Pedes Xpisti   Mary washes the feet of Christ (France, Rene d'Anjou).

Mater Castrorum   Mother of fortresses (Rome, Marcus Aurelius).

Matrimonio Conjuncti   Joined wedlock (Austria).

Me Coniunctio Servat Dum Scinditur Frangor   The relationship serves me while I am being torn to pieces (Lowenstein-Wertheim).

Mediolani Dux   Duke of Milan (Milan).

Mediolani et Man   Duke of Mantua and Milan (Milan).

Memor Ero Tui Iustina Virgo   I shall remember you, o maiden Justina (Venice).

Merces Laborum   Wages of work (Wurzburg).

Mirabilia Fecit   He wrought marvels (Viking coinage).

Misericordia Di Rex   King by the mercy of God (France, Louis II).

Mo Arg Ord Foe Belg D Gel & CZ   Silver coin of the order of the Belgian Federation, duchy of Guelder-land, county of Zutphen (Guelderland).

Moneta Abbatis   Coin of the abbey (German ecclesiastical coins, 13th–14th centuries).

Moneta Argentiae Ord Foed Belgii Holl   Silver coin of the federated union of Belgium and Holland (Batavian Republic).

Mo No Arg Con Foe Belg Pro Hol   New silver coin of the Belgian Federation, province of Holland (Holland).

Mo No Arg Pro Confoe Belg Trai Holl   New silver coin of the confederated Belgian provinces, Utrecht and Holland (Batavian Republic).

Mon Lib Reip Bremens   Coin of the free state of Bremen (Bremen).

Mon Nova Arg Duc Curl Ad Norma Tal Alb   New silver coin of the duchy of Courland, according to the standard of the Albert thaler (Courland).

Mon Nov Castri Imp   New coin of the Imperial free city of . . . (Friedberg).

Moneta Bipont   Coin of Zweibrucken (Pfalz-Birkenfeld-Zweibrucken).

Monet Capit Cathedr Fuld Sede Vacante   Coin of the cathedral chapter of Fulda, the see being vacant (Fulda).

Moneta in Obsidione Tornacensi Cusa   Coin struck during the siege of Tournai (Tournai, 1709).

Moneta Livosesthonica   Coin of Livonia (Estonia).

Moneta Nov Arg Regis Daniae   New silver coin of the king of Denmark (Denmark).

Moneta Nova Ad Norman Conventionis   New coin according to the Convention standard (Orsini-Rosenberg).

Moneta Nova Domini Imperatoris   New coin of the lord emperor (Brunswick, 13th century).

Moneta Nova Lubecensis   New coin of Lubeck.

Moneta Nova Reipublicae Halae Suevicae   New coin of the republic of Hall in Swabia.

Moneta Reipublicae Ratisbonensis   Coin of the republic of Regensburg.

Nach Alt Reichs Schrot und Korn   According to the old empire's grits and grain (Hesse).

Nach dem Conventions Fusse   According to the Convention's basis (German Conventionsthalers).

Nach dem Frankf Schlus   According to the Frankfurt standard (Solms).

Nach dem Schlus der V Staend   According to the standard of the union (Hesse).

Navigare Necesse Est   It is necessary to navigate (Germany).

Nec Aspera Terrent   Nor do difficulties terrify (Brunswick).

Nec Cito Nec Temere   Neither hastily nor rashlly (Cambrai).

Nec Numina Desunt   Nor is the divine will absent (Savoy).

Nec Temere Nec Timide   Neither rashly nor timidly (Danzig, Lippe).

Necessitas Legem Non Habet   Necessity has no law (Magdeburg).

Nemo Me Impune Lacessit   No one touches me with impunity (UK, Scottish pound edge inscription).

Nihil Restat Reliqui   No relic remains (Ypres).

Nil Ultra Aras   Nothing beyond the rocks (Franque-mont).

No Nobis Dne Sed Noi Tuo Da Gloriam   Not to us, o Lord but to Thy name be glory given (France, Francis I).

Nobilissimum Dom Ac Com in Lipp & St   Most noble lord and count in Lippe and Sternberg (Schaumburg-Lippe).

Nomen Domini Turris Fortissima   The name of the Lord is the strongest tower (Frankfurt).

Non Aes Sed Fides   Not bronze but trust (Malta).

Non Est Mortale Quod Opto   What I desire is not mortal. (Mecklenburg).

Non Mihi Sed Populo   Not to me but to the people (Bavaria).

Non Relinquam Vos Orphanos   I shall not leave you as orphans (Papacy).

Non Surrexit Major   None greater has arisen (Genoa, Malta).

Nullum Simulatum Diuturnum Tandem   Nothing that is feigned lasts long (Wittgenstein).

Nummorum Famulus   The servant of the coinage (England, tin halfpence and farthings).

Nunquam Retrorsum   Never backwards (Brunswick-Wolfenbuttel).

O Crux Ave Spes Unica   Hail, o Cross, our only hope (England half-angels, France, Rene d'Anjou).

O Maria Ora Pro Me   O Mary pray for me (Bavaria).

Ob Cives Servatos   On account of the rescued citizens (Rome, Augustus).

Oculi Domini Super Iustos   The eyes of the Lord look down on the just (Neuchatel).

Omnia Auxiliante Maria   Mary helping everything (Schwyz).

Omnia Cum Deo   Everything with God (Reuss-Greiz).

Omnia cum Deo et Nihil Sine Eo   Everthing with God and nothing without Him (Erbach).

Omnis Potestas a Deo Est   All power comes from God (Sweden).

Opp & Carn Dux Comm Rittb SCM Cons Int & Compi Mareschal   Duke of Troppau and Carniola, count of Rietberg, privy councillor of his sacred imperial majesty, field marshal (Liechtenstein).

Opp & Carn . . . Aur Velleris Eques   Duke of Troppau . . . knight of the Golden Fleece (Liechtenstein).

Opportune   Conveniently (Savoy).

Optimus Princeps   Best prince (Rome, Trajan).

Opulentia Salerno   Wealthy Salerno (Siculo-Norman kingdom).

Pace et Iustitia   With peace and justice (Spanish Netherlands).

Pacator Orbis   Pacifier of the world (Rome, Aurelian).

Palma Sub Pondere Crescit   The palm grows under its weight (Waldeck).

Pater Noster   Our Father (Flanders, 14th century).

Pater Patriae   Farther of his country (Rome, Caligula).

Patria Si Dreptul Meu   The country and my right (Roumania).

Patrimon Henr Frid Sorte Divisum   The heritage of Heinrich Friedrich divided by lot (Hohenlohe-Langenberg).

Patrimonia Beati Petri   The inheritance of the blessed Peter (Papacy).

Patrona Franconiae   Patron Franconia (Wurzburg).

Pax Aeterna   Eternal peace (Rome, Marcus Aurelius).

Pax et Abundantia   Peace and plenty (Burgundy, Gelderland).

Pax Missa Per Orbem   Peace sent throughout the world (England, Anne).

Pax Petrus   Peace Peter (Trier, 10th century).

Pax Praevalet Armis   May peace prevail by force of arms (Mainz).

Pax Quaeritur Bello   Peace is sought by war (Commonwealth, Cromwell).

Pecunia Totum Circumit Orbem   Money goes round the whole world (Brazil).

Per Aspera Ad Astra   Through difficulties to the stars (Mecklenburg-Schwerin).

Per Angusta ad Augusta   Through precarious times to the majestic (Solms-Roedelheim, a pun on the name of the ruler Johan August).

Per Crucem Tuam Salva Nos Christe Redemptor   By Thy cross save us, O Christ our Redeemer (England, angels).

Per Crucem Tuam Salva Nos Xpe Redemt   By Thy cross save us, O Christ our Redeemer (Portugal, 15th century).

Perdam Babillonis Nomen   May the name of Babylon perish (Naples).

Perennitati Iustissimi Regis   For the duration of the most just king (France, Louis XIII).

Perennitati Principis Galliae Restitutionis   For the duration of the restoration of the prince of the Gauls (France, Henri IV).

Perfer et Obdura Bruxella   Carry on and stick it out, Brussels (Brussels siege, 1579–80).

Perpetuus in Nemet Vivar   Hereditary count in Nemt-Ujvar (Batthanyi).

Pietate et Constantia   By piety and constancy (Fulda).

Pietate et Iustitia   By piety and justice (Denmark).

Plebei Urbanae Frumento Constituto   Free distribu-tion of grain to the urban working-class established (Rome, Nerva).

Pleidio Wyf Im Gwlad   True am I to my country (UK, Welsh pound edge inscription).

Plus Ultra   Beyond (the Pillars of Hercules) (Spanish America).

Point du Couronne sans Peine   Point of the crown without penalty (Coburg).

Pons Civit Castellana   The bridge of the town of Castellana (Papacy).

Populus et Senatus Bonon   The people and senate of Bologna (Bologna).

Post Mortem Patris Pro Filio   For the son after his father's death (Pontefract siege coins).

Post Tenebras Lux   After darkness light (Geneva).

Post Tenebras Spero Lucem   After darkness I hope for light (Geneva).

Posui Deum Adiutorem Meum   I have made God my helper (England, Ireland, 1351–1603).

Praesidium et Decus   Protection and ornament (Bologna).

Prima Sedes Galliarum   First see of the Gauls (Lyon).

Primitiae Fodin Kuttenb ab Aerari Iterum Susceptarum   First results dug from the Kuttenberg mines in a renewed undertaking (Austria).

Princps Iuventutis   Prince of youth (Roman Empire).

Pro Defensione Urbis et Patriae   For the defence of city and country (France, Louis XIV).

Pro Deo et Patria   For God and the fatherland (Fulda).

Pro Deo et Populo   For God and the people (Bavaria).

Pro Ecclesia et Pro Patria   For the church and the fatherland (Constance).

Pro Fausio PP Reitur VS   For happy returns of the princes of the Two Sicilies (Naples and Sicily).

Pro Lege et Grege   For law and the flock (Fulda).

Pro maximo Dei Gloria et Bono Publico   For the greatest glory of God and the good of the people (Wurttemberg).

Pro Patria   For the fatherland (Wurzburg).

Propitio Deo Secura Ago   With God's favour I lead a secure life. (Saxe-Lauenburg).

Protector Literis Literae Nummis Corona et Salus   A protection to the letters (on the face of the coin), the letters (on the edge) are a garland and a safeguard to the coinage (Commonwealth, Cromwell broad).

Protege Virgo Pisas   Protect Pisa, O Virgin (Pisa).

Provide et Constanter   Wisely and firmly (Wurttem-berg).

Providentia et Pactis   Through foresight and pacts (Brandenburg-Ansbach).

Providentia Optimi Principis   With the foresight of the best prince (Naples and Sicily).

Proxima Fisica Finis   Nearest to natural end (Orciano).

Proxima Soli   Nearest to the sun (Modena).

Pulcra Virtutis Imago   The beautiful image of virtue (Genoa).

Pupillum et Viduam Suscipiat   May he support the orphan and the widow (Savoy).

Quae Deus Conjunxit Nemo Separet   What God hath joined let no man put asunder (England, James I).

Quem Quadragesies et Semel Patriae Natum Esse Gratulamur   Whom we congratulate for the forty-first time for being born for the fatherland (Lippe-Detmold).

Qui Dat Pauperi Non Indigebit   Who gives to the poor will never be in need (Munster).

Quid Non Cogit Necessitas   To what does Necessity not drive. (Ypres).

Quin Matrimonii Lustrum Celebrant   They celebrate their silver wedding (Austria, 1879).

Quocunque Gesseris (Jeceris) Stabit   Whichever way you throw it it will stand (Isle of Man).

Quod Deus Vult Hoc Semper Fit   What God wishes always occurs. (Saxe-Weimar).

Reconduntur non Retonduntur   They are laid up in store, not thundered back (Savoy).

Recta Tueri   Defend the right (Austria).

Recte Constanter et Fortiter   Rightly, constantly and bravely (Bavaria).

Recte Faciendo Neminem Timeas   May you fear no one in doing right. (Solms-Laubach).

Rector Orbis   Ruler of the world (Rome, Didius Julianus).

Rectus et Immotus   Right and immovable (Hesse).

Redde Cuique Quod Suum Est   Render to each that which is his own (England, Henry VIII).

Redeunt antiqui Gaudia Moris   There return the joys of ancient custom (Regensburg).

Reg Pr Pol et Lith Saxon Dux   Royal prince of Poland and Lithuania and duke of Saxony (Trier).

Regia Boruss Societas Asiat Embdae   Royal Prussian Asiatic Society of Emden (Prussia).

Regier Mich Her Nach Deinen Wort   Govern me here according to Thy word (Palatinate).

Regnans Capitulum Ecclesiae Cathedralis Ratisbonensis Sede Vacante   Administering the chapter of the cathedral church at Regensburg, the see being vacant (Regensburg).

Regni Utr Sic et Hier   Of the kingdom of the Two Sicilies and of Jerusalem (Naples and Sicily).

Religio Protestantium Leges Angliae Libertas Parliamenti   The religion of the Protestants, the laws of England and the freedom of Parliament (England, Royalists, 1642).

Relinquo Vos Liberos ab Utroque Homine   I leave you as children of each man (San Marino).

Restauracao da Independencia   Restoration of inde-pendence (Portugal, 1990).

Restitutor Exercitus   Restorer of the army (Rome, Aurelian).

Restitutor Galliarum   Restorer of the Gauls (Rome, Gallienus).

Restitutor Generis Humani   Restorer of mankind (Rome, Valerian).

Restitutor Libertatis   Restorer of freedom (Rome, Constantine).

Restitutor Orbis   Restorer of the world (Rome, Valerian).

Restitutor Orientis   Restorer of the east (Rome).

Restitutor Saeculi   Restorer of the century (Rome, Valerian).

Restitutor Urbis   Restorer of the city (Rome, Severus).

Rosa Americana Utile Dulci   The American rose, useful and sweet (American colonies).

Rosa Sine Spina   A rose without a thorn (England, Tudor coins).

Rutilans Rosa Sine Spina   A dazzling rose without a thorn (England, Tudor gold coins).

S Annae Fundgruben Ausb Tha in N Oe   Mining thaler of the St Anne mine in Lower Austria (Austria).

S Ap S Leg Nat Germ Primas   Legate of the Holy Apostolic See, born Primate of Germany (Salzburg).

S Carolus Magnus Fundator   Charlemagne founder (Munster).

S. Gertrudis Virgo Prudens Niviella   St Gertrude the wise virgin of Nivelles (Nivelles).

SI Aul Reg Her & P Ge H Post Mag   General hereditary postmaster, supreme of the imperial court of the hereditary kingdom and provinces (Paar).

S. Ian Bapt F. Zachari   St John the Baptist, son of Zachary (Florence).

S. Kilianus Cum Sociis Francorum Apostoli   St Kilian and his companions, apostles to the Franks (Wurzburg).

S. Lambertus Patronus Leodiensis   St Lambert, patron of Liege (Liege).

Sac Nupt Celeb Berol   For the holy matrimony celebrated at Berlin (Brandenburg-Ansbach).

Sac Rom Imp   Holy Roman Empire (German states).

Sac Rom Imp Provisor Iterum   Administrator of the Holy Roman Empire for the second time (Saxony).

Salus Generis Humani   Safety of mankind (Rome, Vindex).

Salus Patriae   Safety of the fatherland (Italy).

Salus Populi   The safety of the people (Spain).

Salus Provinciarum   Safety of the provinces (Rome, Postumus).

Salus Publica Salus Mea   Public safety is my safety (Sweden).

Salus Reipublicae   The safety of the republic (Rome, Theodosius II).

Salus Reipublicae Suprema Lex   The safety of the republic is the supreme law (Poland).

Salvam Fac Rempublicam Tuam   Make your state safe (San Marino).

Sanctus Iohannes Innoce   St John the harmless (Gandersheim).

Sans Changer   Without changing (Isle of Man).

Sans Eclat   Without pomp (Bouchain siege, 1711).

Sapiente Diffidentia   Wise distrust (Teschen).

Scutum Fidei Proteget Eum / Eam   The shield of faith shall protect him / her (England, Edward VI and Elizabeth I).

Secundum Voluntatem Tuam Domine   Your favourable will o Lord (Hesse).

Securitati Publicae   For the public safety (Brandenburg-Ansbach).

Sede Vacante   The see being vacant (Papal states, Vatican and ecclesiastical coinage).

Sena Vetus Alpha et W Principum et Finis   Old Siena alpha and omega, the beginning and the end (Siena).

Senatus Populus QR   Senate and people of Rome (Rome, 1188).

Si Deus Nobiscum Quis Contra Nos   If God is with us who can oppose us (Hesse).

Si Deus Pro Nobis Quis Contra Nos   If God is for us who can oppose us (Roemhild).

Sieh Deine Seeligkeit Steht Fest Ins Vaters Liebe   Behold thy salvation stands surely in thy Father's love (Gotha).

Signis Receptis   When the standards had been recovered (Rome, Augustus).

Signum Crucis   The sign of the cross (Groningen).

Sincere et Constanter   Truthfully and steadfastly (Hesse-Darmstadt).

Sit Nomen Domini Benedictum   Blessed be the name of the Lord (Burgundy, Strasbourg).

St T X Adiuto Reg Iste Domba   Let it be to you, o Christ, the assistant to the king of Dombes (Dombes).

Sit Tibi Xpe Dat q'tu Regis Iste Ducat   May this duchy which Thou rulest be given to Thee, O Christ (Venice, ducat).

Sit Unio Haec Perennis   May this union last for ever (Hohenlohe-Langenberg).

Sola Bona Quae Honesta   The only good things are those which are honest (Brunswick).

Sola Facta Deum Sequor   Through deeds alone I strive to follow God (Milan).

Soli Deo Honor et Gloria   To God alone be honour and glory (Nassau).

Soli Reduci   To him, the only one restored (Naples and Sicily).

Solius Virtutis Flos Perpetuus   The flower of Virtue alone is perpetual (Strasbourg).

Spes Confisa Deo Nunquam Confusa Recedit   Hope entrusted in God never retreats in a disorderly fashion (Lippe).

Spes Nr Deus   God is our hope (Oudenarde siege, 1582).

Spes Rei Publicae   The hope of the republic (Rome, Valens).

Strena ex Argyrocopeo Vallis S Christoph   A New Year's gift from the silver-bearing valley of St Christopher (Wurttemberg, 1625).

Sub His Secura Spes Clupeus Omnibus in Te Sperantibus   Under these hope is safe, a shield for all who reside hope in Thee (Bavaria).

Sub Pondere   Under weight (Fulda).

Sub Protectione Caesarea   Under imperial protection (Soragna).

Sub Tuum Praesidium Confug   We flee to Thy protection (Salzburg).

Sub Umbra Alarum Tuarum   Under the shadow of Thy wings (Iever, Scotland, James V).

Subditorum Salus Felicitas Summa   The safety of the subjects is the highest happiness (Lubeck).

Sufficit Mihi Gratia Tua Domine   Sufficient to me is Thy grace, o Lord (Ploen).

Supra Firmam Petram   Upon a firm rock (Papacy).

Susceptor Noster Deus   God is our defence (Tuscany).

Sydera Favent Industriae   The stars favour industry (Furstenberg).

Sylvarum Culturae Praemium   Prize for the culture of the forest (Brandenburg-Ansbach).

Tali Dicata Signo Mens Fluctuari Nequit   Consecrated by such a sign the mind cannot waver (England, Henry VIII George noble).

Tandem Bona Caus Triumphat   A good cause eventually triumphs (Dillenburg).

Tandem Fortuna Obstetrice   With good luck ultimately as the midwife (Wittgenstein).

Te Stante Virebo   With you at my side I shall be strong (Moravia).

Tene Mensuram et Respice Finem   Hold the measure and look to the end (Burgundy).

Tert Ducat Secular   Tercentenary of the duchy (Wurttemberg).

Thu Recht Schev Niemand   Go with right and fear no one (Saxe-Lauenburg).

Tibi Laus et Gloria   To Thee be praise and glory (Venice).

Timor Domini Fons Vitae   The fear of the Lord is a fountain of life (England, Edward VI shillings).

Tout Avec Dieu   Everything with God (Brunswick, 1626).

Traiectum ad Mosam   The crossing of the Maas (Maastricht).

Transvolat Nubila Virtus   Marriageable virtue soon flies past (Grueyeres).

Travail, Famille, Patrie   Work, family, country (Vichy France).

Triumphator Gent Barb   Victor over the barbarian people (Byzantine Empire, Arcadius).

Tueatur Unita Deus   May God guard these united (Kingdoms) (England, James I; Britain, 1847).

Turck Blegert Wien   Vienna besieged by the Turks (Vienna, 1531).

Tut Mar Gab Pr Vid de Lobk Nat Pr Sab Car et Aug Pr de Lobk   Regency of Maria Gabriela, widow of the prince of Lobkowitz, born princess of Savoy-Carignan, and August prince of Lobkowitz (Lobkowitz).

Tutela Italiae   The guardianship of Italy (Rome, Nerva).

Ubi Vult Spirat   He breathes where he will (Papacy).

Ubique Pax   Peace everywhere (Rome, Gallienus).

Union et Force   Union and strength (France).

Urbe Obsessa   The city under siege (Maastricht).

Urbem Virgo Tuam Serva   Protects thy city o virgin (Mary) (Strasbourg).

USC & RAM Cons Int Gen C Mar & Nob Praet H Turmae Capit   Privy councillor of both their holy imperial and royal apostolic majesties, general field marshal and captain of the noble praetorian Hungarian squadrons (Eszterhazy).

Veni Luumen Cordium   Come light of hearts (Vatican).

Veni Sancte Spiritus   Come Holy Ghost (Vatican).

Verbum Domini Manet in Aeternum   The word of the Lord abides forever (Hesse-Darmstadt, Veldenz).

Veritas Lex Tua   The truth is your law (Salzburg).

Veritas Temporis Filia   Truth is the daughter of time (England and Ireland, Mary Tudor).

Veritate et Labore   By truth and work (Wittgenstein).

Veritate et Iustitia   By truth and justice (German states).

Victoria Principum   The victory of princes (Ostrogoths).

Videant Pauperes et Laetentur   Let the poor see and rejoice (Tuscany).

Virgo Maria Protege Civitatem Savonae   Virgin Mary Protect the city of Savona (Savona).

Viribus Unitis   With united strength (Austria).

Virtute et Fidelitate   By virtue and faithfulness (Hesse-Cassel).

Virtute et Prudentia   With virtue and prudence (Auersperg).

Virtute Viam Dimetiar   I shall mark the way with valour (Waldeck).

Virtutis Gloria Merces   Glory is the reward of valour (Holstein-Gottorp).

Vis Unita Concordia Fratrum Fortior   United power is the stronger harmony of brothers (Mansfeld).

Visitavit Nos Oriens ex Alto   He has visited us arising on high (Luneburg).

Vivit Post Funera   He lives after death (Bremen).

Vota Optata Romae Fel   Vows taken for the luck of Rome (Rome, Maxentius).

Vox de Throno   A voice from the throne (Papacy).

Was Got Beschert Bleibet Unerwert   What God hath endowed leave undisturbed

Wider macht und List Mein Fels Gott Ist   Against might and trickery God is my rock (Hesse-Cassel).

Xpc Vincit Xpc Regnat   Christ conquers, Christ reigns (Scotland, Spain).

Xpc Vivet Xpc Regnat Xpc Impat   Christ lives, Christ reigns, Christ commands (Cambrai).

Xpe Resurescit   Christ lives again (Venice).

Xpistiana Religio   Christian religion (Carolingian Empire).

Xps Ihs Elegit me Regem Populo   Jesus Christ chose me as king to the people (Norway).

Zelator Fidei Usque ad Montem   An upholder of the faith through and through (Portugal).

Zum Besten des Vaterlands   To the best of the fatherland (Bamberg).

ABBREVIATIONS COMMONLY USED TO DENOTE METALLIC COMPOSITION	
Cu	Copper
Cu/Steel	Copper plated Steel
Ag/Cu	Silver plated copper
Ae	Bronze
Cu-Ni	Cupro-Nickel
Ni-Ag	Nickel Silver (note-does not contain silver)
Brass/Cu-Ni	Brass outer, Cupro-Nickel inner
Ni-Brass	Nickel-Brass
Ag	Silver
Au/Ag	Gold plated silver
Au	Gold
Pt	Platinum

Collectors' essentials
A fantastic range of coin accessories

- Coin albums
- Envelopes
- Description tickets
- Coin holders
- Magnifiers
- Scales

...and more

Care
of coins

There is no point in going to a great deal of trouble and expense in selecting the best coins you can afford, only to let them deteriorate in value by neglect and mishandling. Unless you give some thought to the proper care of your coins, your collection is unlikely to make a profit for you if and when you come to sell it. Housing your coins is the biggest problem of all, so it is important to give a lot of attention to this.

Storage

The ideal, but admittedly the most expensive, method is the coin cabinet, constructed of air-dried mahogany, walnut or rosewood *(never* oak, cedar or any highly resinous timber likely to cause chemical tarnish). These cabinets have banks of shallow drawers containing trays made of the same wood, with half-drilled holes of various sizes to accommodate the different denominations of coins. Such cabinets are handsome pieces of furniture but, being largely handmade, tend to be rather expensive. Occasionally good specimens can be picked up in secondhand furniture shops, or at the dispersal of house contents by auction, but the best bet is still to purchase a new cabinet, tailored to your own requirements. These collectors cabinets are hand-made using certified solid mahogany, as specified by leading museums, as mahogany does not contain any chemicals or resins that could result in the discolouration of the collection inside the cabinet. The polish used on the outside of the cabinets is based on natural oils and hand applied then finished with bees wax. The trays are left as untreated mahogany so as not to introduce any harmful contaminants. The coin trays are available as single thickness or double thickness for holding thicker coins, capsules or artifacts.

Peter Nichols Cabinets (telephone 0115 9224149, www.coincabinets.com) was established in 1967 and is now run by Geoff Skinner, Shirley Watts and Ben Skinner-Watts. Based in Nottingham, the family run business provides specialist and bespoke display and storage systems to suit every need from standard cabinets for the average collector all the way up to the massive 40-tray specials supplied to the British Museum. There are other makers of quality wooden coin cabinets such as **Rob Davis** of Ticknall, Derbyshire, who also provide a first-class bespoke product as well as a standard off-the-shelf range. All of these manufacturers use materials from sustainable sources and their products are exquisite examples of the cabinet maker's craft.

An excellent storage option is provided by a number of firms who manufacture coin trays in durable, felt-lined, man-made materials with shallow compartments to suit the various sizes of coins. Most of these trays interlock so that they build up into a cabinet of the desired size, and there are also versions designed as carrying cases, which are ideal for transporting coins.

For the coin connoisseur there are beautiful, hand-made mahogany cabinets such as this one from Peter Nichols Cabinets.

The popular and extensive **Lighthouse** range is available from Token Publishing Ltd (telephone 01404 46972, www.tokenpublishing.com). This range includes a wide variety of cases and albums for the general collector in basic or deluxe styles as required, as well as printed albums for the specialist. Their cases, including the popular aluminium range, are manufactured to the highest standards, lined with blue plush which displays any coin to its best advantage. The red-lined single

Adding to your collection with the stacking Lindner range is easy.

trays come in deep or standard size and make an ideal cabinet when stacked together or housed in their attractive aluminium case, which is available separately. The trays themselves come with a variety of compartments for every size of coin. Their complete range can be viewed on-line.

The extensive **Lindner** range is supplied in the UK by Prinz Publications of 3A Hayle Industrial Park, Hayle, Cornwall TR27 5JR (telephone 01736 751914, www.prinz.co.uk). Well-known for their wide range of philatelic and numismatic accessories, but these include a full array of coin boxes, capsules, carrying cases and trays. The basic Lindner coin box is, in fact, a shallow tray available in a standard version or a smoked glass version. These trays have a crystal clear frame, red felt inserts and holes for various diameters of coins and medals. A novel feature of these trays is the rounded insert which facilitates the removal of coins from their spaces with the minimum of handling. These boxes are designed in such a manner that they interlock and can be built up

into banks of trays, each fitted with a draw-handle and sliding in and out easily. Various types of chemically inert plastic capsules and envelopes have been designed for use in combination with plain shallow trays, without holes drilled. Lindner also manufacture a range of luxury cases lined in velvet and Atlas silk with padded covers and gold embossing on the spines, producing a most tasteful and elegant appearance.

Safe Albums of 16 Falcon Business Park, 38 Ivanhoe Road, Finchampstead, Berkshire RG40 4QQ (telephone 0118 932 8976, www.safealbums.co.uk) are the UK agents for the German Stapel-Element, a drawer-stacking system with clear plasticiser-free trays that fit into standard bookshelves. The sliding coin compartments, lined with blue velvet, can be angled for display to best advantage. Stackable drawers can be built up to any height desired. A wide range of drawer sizes is available, with compartments suitable for the smallest coins right up to four-compartment trays designed for very large artefacts such as card-cases or cigarette cases. The Mobel-Element cabinet is a superb specialised cabinet constructed of the finest timber with a steel frame and steel grip bars which can be securely locked.

There are also various other storage systems, such as the simple cardboard or plastic box which is made specifically to hold coins stored in see-through envelopes of chemically-inert plastic of various sizes, or white acid-free envelopes, usually 50mm square.

An alternative to these is the card coin holder which has a window made of inert cellophane-type see-through material. The card is folded over with the coin inside and is then stapled or stuck together with its own self-adhesive lining. The cards are a standard 50mm square with windows of various sizes from 15 to 39mm and fit neatly into the storage box or album page.

Coin Albums

When coin collecting became a popular hobby in the 1960s, several firms marketed ranges of coin albums. They had clear plastic sleeves divided into tiny compartments of various sizes and had the merit of being cheap and taking up little room on a bookshelf.

They had several drawbacks, however, not the least being the tendency of the pages to sag with the weight of the coins, or even, in extreme cases, to pull away from the pegs or rings holding them on to the spine. They required very careful handling as the coins could easily fall out of the top row as the pages were turned. The more expensive albums had little flaps that folded over the top of the coin to overcome this problem.

The Lighthouse range includes a wide selection of de luxe and printed albums.

Arguably the worst aspect of these albums was the use of polyvinyl chloride (PVC) in the construction of the sleeves. Collectors soon discovered to their horror that this reacted chemically with their coins, especially those made of silver and many fine collections were ruined as a result.

Fortunately the lesson has been learned and the coin albums now on the market are quite safe. Lighthouse and Lindner offer a wide range of albums designed to house coins, medals or banknotes. The old problem about sagging pages is overcome by the use of a multi-ring binding welded to a very stout spine, while the sleeves contain neither Styrol nor PVC and will not affect any metals at all. In addition to pages with pockets of uniform size, the Karat range of albums operates on a slide principle which enables the user to insert vertical strips of different sizes on the same page, so that the coins of one country or series, or perhaps a thematic display of coins from different countries, can be displayed side by side.

Safe Albums offer a wide range of albums in the Coinholder System and Coin-Combi ranges. These, too, offer the choice of fixed pages with uniform-sized pockets, or interchangeable sliding inserts for different sizes side by side.

The "slab"

In the United States in the past few decades one of the preferred methods for keeping coins in pristine condition is the use of "slabs"—these tough plastic rectangles cannot be easily broken into, meaning that the coin inside remains in exactly the same condition as when it was placed in there. This has led to the rise of professional grading and encapsulation companies who not only "slab" your coin but also grade it and guarantee that grade. This allows coins to be bought and sold with both vendor and purchaser knowing exactly what the grade is, thus taking out the subjectivity of dealer or collector—an issue that can mean a huge

difference in the value of the coin. Slabbing in this way is essentially a tool to help a coin maintain a grade and thus more easily guarantee its value, however, many collectors prefer it as a method of protecting their coins as it allows them to be stored or transported easily with no fear of damage.

The biggest companies in the United States for the encapsulation of coins are **PCGS** (Professional Coin Grading Service) and **NGC** (Numismatic Gauaranty Corporation). They have been in business for some years and in America the "slabbed" coin is a common sight. It is less common in the UK, with many collectors still unsure about the benefits of the "slab", but undoubtedly with the US companies opening offices and grading centres throughout the world more and more collectors are using the service and the "slab" is becoming accepted everywhere. However, anyone wishing to photograph a coin undoubtedly has a problem, as can be seen in many auction catalogues offering such items. The tell-tale grips that hold the coin obscure part of the edge of the coin.

Token Publishing Ltd stock a varied range of coin accessories from magnifying glasses to coin albums. To find out more, log onto www.tokenpublishing.com or call 01404 446972 for an up-to-date illustrated, colour catalogue.

Cleaning
coins

This is like matrimony—it should not be embarked on lightly. Indeed, the advice given by the magazine *Punch* in regard to marriage is equally sound in this case—don't do it! It is far better to have a dirty coin than an irretrievably damaged one. Every dealer has horror stories of handling coins that previous owners have cleaned, to their detriment. Probably the worst example was a display of coins found by a metal detectorist who "improved" his finds by abrading them in the kind of rotary drum used by lapidarists to polish gemstones. If you really must remove the dirt and grease from coins, it is advisable to practise on coins of little value.

Warm water containing a mild household detergent or washing-up liquid will work wonders in removing surface dirt and grease from most coins, but silver is best washed in a weak solution of ammonia and warm water—one part ammonia to ten parts water. Gold coins can be cleaned with diluted citric acid, such as lemon juice. Copper or bronze coins present more of a problem, but patches of verdigris can usually be removed by careful washing in a 20 per cent solution of sodium sesquicarbonate. Wartime coins made of tin, zinc, iron or steel can be cleaned in a 5 per cent solution

of caustic soda containing some aluminium or zinc foil or filings, but they must be rinsed afterwards in clean water and carefully dried. Cotton buds are ideal for gently prising dirt out of coin legends and crevices in the designs. Soft brushes (with animal bristles—*never* nylon or other artificial bristles) designed for cleaning silver are most suitable for gently cleaning coins.

Coins recovered from the soil or the sea bed present special problems, due to chemical reaction between the metals and the salts in the earth or sea water. In such cases, the best advice is to take them to the nearest museum and let the professional experts decide on what can or should be done.

There are a number of proprietary coin-cleaning kits and materials on the market suitable for gold, silver, copper and other metals but all of these should be used with caution and always read the instructions that come with them. When using any type of chemical cleaner rubber gloves should be worn and care taken to avoid breathing fumes or getting splashes of liquid in your eyes or on your skin. Obviously, the whole business of cleaning is a matter that should not be entered into without the utmost care and forethought.

POLISHING: A WARNING

If cleaning should only be approached with the greatest trepidation, polishing is definitely OUT! Beginners sometimes fall into the appalling error of thinking that a smart rub with metal polish might improve the appearance of their coins. Short of actually punching a hole through it, there can hardly be a more destructive act. Polishing a coin may improve its superficial appearance for a few days, but such abrasive action will destroy the patina and reduce the fineness of the high points of the surface.

Even if a coin is only polished once, it will never be quite the same again, and an expert can tell this a mile off.

Where money talks

Both print and digital subscriptions are available

COIN NEWS is Britain's biggest selling Coin and Banknote magazine. Every month it is crammed full with over 90 pages of news, views, articles and insights into the fascinating world of coin and banknote collecting. Every issue features all the latest numismatic news, auction results and comments on the hobby as well as a wealth of interesting articles on all things coin and banknote—from hammered to modern from treasury notes to polymers—all are covered!

For more information please call 01404 46972 or visit www.tokenpublishing.com

Come and watch the UKs coins being made

The Royal Mint
experience

THE EXPERIENCE OFFERS A GRAND DAY OUT FOR ALL THE FAMILY WHERE THE WORK AND ISSUES OF ONE OF THE OLDEST MINTS IN THE WORLD CAN BE EXPLORED AT IT'S PURPOSE-BUILT VISITORS' CENTRE IN LLANTRISANT.

Walk through Interactive Exhibition
....

Come and play games, do interactives and watch the `journey of a coin` film

Creating the Die
Creu'r Dei

The Master Tool
Yr Offeryn Meistr

Reducing
Lleihau

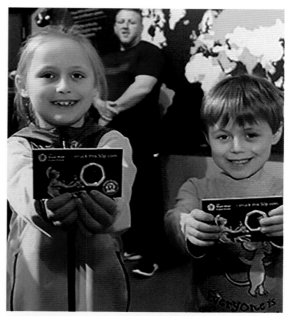

Strike your own coin

On the Royal Mint Experience tour you will learn more about the manufacturing process that goes into creating the coins in your pocket. As part of your tour, you will have the opportunity to strike your very own coin (the design of the coin alters, depending on what theme the Royal Mint are celebrating at the time of your visit. The opportunity is limited to one coin per person and can be purchased at check-in for £6.90 or pre-booked on-line. Pre-booking your tour is advisable—see the panel overleaf for booking details.

WANT TO VISIT see overleaf

I struck this 50p coin

SHERLOCK HOLMES

And finally

Do visit the Royal Mint Experience shop where you can purchase a memento of your day. At the shop, for collectors of the A-Z 10 pences, there is a chance to swap your normal "shield" 10p for one of those elusive "Great British Coin Hunt" 10 pences and fill those pesky gaps in your collection!

All in all, a great day out awaits for you at the Royal Mint Experience.

Remember to plan your visit by going online or telephoning the Royal Mint Experience and book your place on the a tour before setting off on a long journey—details appear below.

The Royal Mint is located 4 miles from Junction 34 of the M4. Drive past the main entrance to the Mint. The visitors' car park for The Royal Mint Experience is on the left opposite the Three Saints Hotel. The guided tour lasts 45 minutes, but allow a good couple of hours to explore the exhibits in the final exhibition hall. There are plenty of interactive exhibits to keep the children amused. There is a large cafeteria for visitors and a well-stocked shop selling souvenirs as well as coins.

Plan your visit

Admission Prices:	Door £	Online £
Adult (16+)	13.50	13.00
Child (5-15 years)	11.00	10.50
Child under 5 years	Free	Free
Senior Citizens	12.00	11.50
Students	12.00	11.50
Family (1 adult/3 children Or 2 adults/2 children)	40.00	38.50

There are restrictions on the number of wheelchair users in any one group. Wheelchair users, or others with special needs, should telephone 0333 241 2223. This number can also be used to book a tour. The tours run at regular intervals throughout the day from 10am to 4.30pm. Remember all children under 16 must be accompanied by an adult at all times.

The Royal Mint Experience is open daily from 9.30am to 6.30pm except December 25 and 26 and January 1.

To plan your visit to the Royal Mint Experience go online at www.royalmint.com.

Images courtesy of the Royal Mint.

Celtic
coinage of Britain

Pritanic coins were the first coins made in Britain. They were issued for a century and a half before the Roman invasion, and possibly a little later in some areas. They were minted by the rulers of thirteen tribal groups or administrative authorities situated on the southeast of a line from the Humber to the Severn. In this short article Pritanic specialist CHRIS RUDD introduces this increasingly popular series.

Most folk call them British Celtic or Celtic coins of Britain. But I'll begin by letting you into a little known secret: most folk may be wrong. You see, there is no ancient textual evidence—none whatsoever—that anyone in iron age Britain called themselves a Celt. Neither is there a hint—not a whisper—that anyone else in the ancient world ever referred to the Brits as Celts. The Greeks didn't, the Gauls didn't, the Romans didn't. The correct name for iron age Britons is Pritani—well formed people or people of the forms. How do we know? Because a sailor from Marseilles said so.

The first coins made in Britain were made like this

Molten tin-rich bronze was poured into clay moulds.

Coin designs were scribed onto clay strip-moulds with a stylus prior to firing. Tentative reconstruction.

and look like this

Cast bronze
c.120-100 BC

Cast potin
c.80-50 BC

Many Gaulish coins were imported to Britain, like this silver stater of the Coriosolites (ABC 70), typical of many in the huge Jersey hoard found in June 2012, containing an estimated 50,000 coins.

Around 330 BC an explorer, Pytheas of Marseilles, sailed to Britain in search of tin. His visit indicates early trade links with southern Gaul and that the Britons were called Pritani. Marseilles inspired Britain's first homemade coinage: potin coins cast in clay strip-moulds, with Apollo on one side and a bull on the other, plus MA for Massalia (Marseilles). Made in Kent c. 120–100 BC, these cast potins circulated alongside gold coins imported from Gaul. During the Gallic Wars (58–51 BC) many other Gaulish coins—gold, silver and bronze—came to Britain, some brought by refugees, others by British mercenaries, others by trade.

The most famous Gallic migrant was Commios "friend", a former ally of Caesar, who became king of the Regini and Atrebates in the south of England c. 50–25 BC. Commios was the first British ruler to place his name on coins. His three sons—Tincomarus (great in peace), Eppillus (little horse) and Verica (the high one), made the Commian dynasty one of the wealthiest and most powerful in Britain. Most of their coins adopted Roman imagery and archaeology indicates that they imported Roman luxury goods, especially Italian wine. Many coins of Verica show grapes, vine leaves and wine cups.

The main rivals of the Regini and Atrebates were the Catuvellauni of Hertfordshire. Their first known ruler was probably Cassivellaunos "bronze commander", leader of the British coalition against Caesar in 54 BC. Many of Britain's earliest gold coins were probably struck to fund resistance to Caesar and then to pay tribute to him. Cassivellaunos may have organised this war money. Addedomaros "great in chariots" (c. 45–25 BC) was the first ruler north of the Thames to inscribe his coins, perhaps copying Commios.

Thirteen possible tribal groups which were producing coins by c.50-40 BC (Cantiaci much earlier). By c.30 BC the Belgae, East Wiltshire and Berkshire group had apparently stopped minting independently.

Gold stater of Commios (ABC 1022) the first British king to place his name on coins. There are two hidden faces on the obverse.

Verica silver minim with wine cup (ABC 1331) and Verica gold stater with vine leaf (ABC 1193)—evidence of Britain's thirst for fine Italian wine and Roman silverware.

Catuvellaunian expansion continued under Tasciovanos "killer of badgers" whose coins became increasingly Roman in style. His son Cunobelinus "hound of Belenus"—Shakespeare's *Cymbeline*) was the most potent tribal king in Atlantic Europe. Suetonius called him "king of the Britons". During his thirty-year reign (c. AD 8–41) Cunobelinus may have minted well over a million gold staters, most of them displaying a corn ear and CAMV— short for *Camulodunon* (Colchester). When his brother Epaticcus "leader of horsemen" and his son Caratacus "the beloved"—both clad as Hercules on their silver coins—crossed the Thames and attacked the Atrebates, Verica fled to Claudius who invaded Britain in AD 43. The minting of tribal coins ceased shortly afterwards.

Other tribes that issued coins included the Cantiaci of Kent, the Belgae of Hampshire, the Durotriges of Dorset, the Dobunni of the West Midlands, the Trinovantes of Essex, the Iceni of East Anglia and the Corieltavi of Lincolnshire. However, only a minority of people in the British Isles used coins regularly—the moneyed minority in southeast England. Cornwall, Devon, Wales, northern England, Scotland and Ireland remained coinless. Which is why ancient British coins are relatively rare. For example, whereas Greek coins were minted for about 600 years, Roman for about 800 years and Gaulish for about 250 years, ancient British coins were produced for little more than 150 years, and often in much smaller runs.

Ancient British coins weren't minted for as long as Greek, Roman or Gaulish coins were. That's one of the reasons they are so scarce.

This century and a half of Pritanic (not Celtic) coin production generated a remarkable flowering of insular creativity and insular technology, unmatched by any other northern European nation of the period. Though initially influenced by Gallic minting techniques and Gallic iconography, ancient British coinage rapidly developed its own denominational systems, its own gold standards and its own highly distinctive coin designs—often inspired by Roman prototypes, but invariably modified to suit local needs. Between c. 110 BC and c. AD 45 around a thousand different coin types were minted in Britain. Many if not most of these thousand types displayed what might loosely be described as "religious" imagery. Not surprising, really, when one recalls that Caesar says that Druidism originated in Britain. Moreover, Tasciovanos struck coins in no fewer than five different denominations, whereas most Gaulish rulers issued no more than two or three.

The history of late iron age Britain, particularly the century prior to the Claudian conquest, has largely been rewritten with the help of ancient British coins. Most of the recent advances in our knowledge of this period have been due to amateur metal detecting. As a direct result of coin finds made by metal detectorists since the 1970s four new coin-issuing groups and maybe ten new rulers, previously unknown or unrecognised, have been identified. Not bad for barely forty years of unfunded, unofficial fieldwork.

Unlike Gaul, most of the British Isles was virtually coinless throughout the late iron age (and later). Coin production was confined to south-east Britain. That's why, overall, ancient British coins are much rarer than Gaulish coins.

What is it about ancient British coins that is making them increasingly popular with collectors all over the world? Having been involved with them for many years (I excavated my first in 1952) I'll tell you why they appeal to me.

I love the *primal antiquity* of Pritanic coins. They were the first coins made in Britain over two thousand years ago. When you see the flamboyant freedom of their designs you realise that they are the most boisterously British coins ever minted, unlike the unsmiling Roman, Anglo-Saxon and Norman series that marched soberly in their dancing footsteps.

I love the *anarchic regality* of Pritanic coins. Like the rumbustious tribal kings that issued them, their personality is wild, strong and highly irregular. These coins were made by the first British rulers known by name to us—unruly, quarrelsome, beer-swilling, tribal warlords such as Cassivellaunos who fought Julius Caesar in 54 BC and Caratacus, the British resistance leader who opposed Claudius in AD 43.

I love the *imaginative imagery* you find on Pritanic coins: all the different gods and goddesses, armed warriors, chariot wheels, hidden faces, decapitated heads, suns, moons, stars, thunderbolts, floral motifs, magic signs and phallic symbols. Plus an amazing menagerie of wild animals, birds and mythical beasts.

I love the *myths, mystery and mysticism* behind Pritanic coins. Look closely at this late iron age money of Albion and you'll catch glimpses

Ancient British denominations

There was no national currency in pre-Roman Britain and little consistency from region to region. Different tribes issued different mixtures of low, medium and high value coins. Here are the most common denominations used by the ancient Brits. The names are ours, not theirs. We've no idea what they called their coins, shown here actual size.

GOLD STATERS
Can also be silver, billon or bronze

Norfolk Wolf, ABC 1393

GOLD QUARTER STATERS
Can also be silver or billon

Irstead Smiler, ABC 1480

SILVER UNITS

Norfolk God, ABC 1567

SILVER HALF UNITS

Aunt Cost Half, ABC 1953

SILVER MINIMS

Verica Sphinx, ABC 1340

BRONZE UNITS

Cunobelinus Centaur, ABC 2957

BRONZE HALF UNITS

Tasciovanos Goat, ABC 2709

CAST POTIN UNITS

Nipples, ABC 174

of long-lost legends and ancient pagan rituals such as head-hunting, bull sacrificing and shape-shifting. You'll marvel at the plethora of occult signs and arcane symbols and you may even feel the secret power of the Druids.

I love the *palpitating unpredictability* of Pritanic coins. Even after sixty years of heart-racing intimacy they are constantly and delightfully surprising me. Attributions, names and dates are always being revised. Not long ago the Coritani were renamed Corieltavi and Tincommios was rechristened Tincomarus. Almost every month exciting new types and new variants keep leaping out of the ground, thanks to metal detectorists. For example, on September 4, 2010 the late

Bronze units of Cunobelinus, son of Tasciovanos, showing a bull being sacrificed (ABC 2972) and a man—perhaps a Druid priest?—carrying a severed human head (ABC 2987).

Danny Baldock discovered the first recorded coin of Anarevitos, a Kentish ruler previously unknown to history.

I love the *uncommon scarcity* of Pritanic coins. Ask any metdet how many so-called Celtic coins he or she has found and you'll immediately realise that they are rarer than Roman coins—at least a thousand times rarer on average—for the reasons stated above.

Finally I love the *galloping good value* of this horsey money (some Pritanic horses have three tails, some breathe fire, others have a human torso). Their greater rarity doesn't mean they are

Silver unit of freedom-fighter Caratacus (ABC 1376) who defied the Roman invaders for eight years until he was betrayed by Cartimandua, queen of the Brigantes.

costlier than other ancient coins. In fact, they are often cheaper because demand determines price and because there are far fewer collectors of ancient British coins than there are, say, of Greek or Roman coins. For example, a very fine British gold stater typically costs less than half the price—sometimes even a third the price of a Roman aureus or English gold noble of comparable quality and rarity. But the disparity is gradually diminishing as more and more canny collectors are appreciating the untamed beauty and undervalued scarcity of Pritanic coins.

Coin Yearbook provides a great guide to current prices of commoner Pritanic types, but because new types keep turning up and because big hoards are sometimes found (causing values to fluctuate temporarily) you'd be well advised to also keep an eye on dealers' catalogues and prices realised at auction. If you're buying in Britain, buy from people who are members of the BNTA (British Numismatic Trade Association). If you're buying overseas, check that your suppliers

A unique gold stater of Anarevitos, a previously unknown ruler of the Cantiaci, probably a son of Eppillus, king of Calleva (Silchester). Sold by Elizabeth Cottam of Chris Rudd for £21,000, a record price for an ancient British coin (Coin News, December 2010).

belong to the IAPN (International Association of Professional Numismatists). And, if you're a beginner, beware of dodgy traders on the internet, or you could end up with a fistful of fakes and no refund.

I'd also counsel you to spend a day at the British Museum. Its collection of almost 7,000 ancient British coins is the most comprehensive, publicly accessible collection of its kind in the world. As their curator, Ian Leins, says: "They're public coins . . . your coins, and they're here for you to see. So come and see them. We'll be pleased to show them to you". Access to the collection is free for everyone. But you'll need to make an appointment before you go, and take some photo ID and proof of address. Email: coins@thebritishmuseum.ac.uk or telephone: 020 7323 8607.

Before you buy coins—any coins of any period—it always pays to read about them first. As an old adman I'm not shy about blowing my own trumpet. The best little introduction to Pritanic coins is *Britain's First Coins* by Chris Rudd (expected late 2012) and the most comprehensive catalogue of the series is *Ancient British Coins* also by Chris Rudd (2010), known in the trade as ABC. If you have even half the fun I've had with ancient British coins (and am still having)—I can promise you that you'll be a very happy person indeed. Never bored, and never with a complete collection.

Collecting
ancient coins

Ancient coins differ from most other series which are collected in Britain in that every piece has spent the major part of the last two thousand years in the ground. As JOHN CUMMINGS, dealer in ancient coins and antiquities explains here, the effect that burial has had on the surface of the coin determines more than anything else the value of a particular piece. With more modern coins, the only things which affect price are rarity and grade. There may be a premium for coins exhibiting particularly fine tone, or with outstanding pedigrees, but an 1887 crown in "extremely fine" condition has virtually the same value as every other piece with the same grade and of the same date. With ancient coins the story is very different.

A large number of different criteria affect the price of an ancient coin. Factors affecting prices can be broken down into several categories:

Condition

The most important factor by far in determining price. Ancient coins were struck by hand and can exhibit striking faults. Value suffers if the coin is struck with the designs off-centre, is weakly struck, or if the flan is irregular in shape. Many of the Celtic tribes issued coins of varying fineness and those made from low quality gold or silver are worth less than similar specimens where the metal quality is better. Conversely, coins on exceptional flans, particularly well struck, or with fine patinas command a premium.

Many ancient coins have suffered during their stay in the ground. It must be borne in mind that the prices given in the price guide are for uncorroded, undamaged examples. A Roman denarius should be graded using the same criteria as those used for grading modern coins. The surfaces must be good, and the coin intact. The fact that the coin is 2,000 years old is irrelevant as far as grading is concerned. Coins which are not perfectly preserved are certainly not without value, however, the value for a given grade decreases with the degree of fault.

Rarity

As with all other series, rare coins usually command higher prices than common ones. A unique variety of a small fourth century Roman bronze coin, even in perfect condition, can be worth much less than a more worn and common piece from an earlier part of the empire. In the Celtic series, there is an almost infinite variety of minor types and a unique variety of an uninscribed type will rarely outbid an inscribed issue of a known king.

Historical and local significance

Types which have historical or local interest can command a price far above their scarcity value. Denarii of the emperor Tiberius are believed to have been referred to in the New Testament and command a far higher price than a less interesting piece of similar rarity. Similarly, pieces which have British reverse types such as the "VICT BRIT" reverse of the third century AD are more expensive than their scarcity would indicate. The 12 Caesars remain ever popular especially in the American market and this affects prices throughout the world. In the Celtic series, coins of Cunobelin or Boudicca are far more popular than pieces which have no historical interest but which may be far scarcer.

Reverse types

All Roman emperors who survived for a reasonable time issued coins with many different reverse types. The most common of these usually show various Roman gods. When a coin has an unusual reverse it always enhances the value. Particularly popular are architectural scenes, animals, references to Judaism, and legionary types.

Artistic merit

The Roman coinage is blessed with a large number of bust varieties and these can have a startling effect on price. For example, a common coin with the bust facing left instead of right can be worth several times the price of a normal specimen. Like many of the emperors, the coinage of Hadrian has a large number of bust varieties, some of which are extremely artistic and these, too, can command a premium.

The coinage used in Britain from the time of the invasion in AD 43 was the same as that introduced throughout the Empire by the emperor Augustus around 20 BC. The simple divisions of 2 asses equal to one dupondius, 2 dupondii equal to 1 sestertius, 4 sestertii equal to one denarius and 25 denarii equal to one aureus continued in use until the reformation of the coinage by Caracalla in AD 214.

Aureus (gold)

Denarius (silver)

Dupondius (copper)

Sestertius (bronze)

As (copper)

Hammered
coinage

The hammered currency of medieval Britain is among some of the most interesting coinage in the world. The turbulent history of these islands is reflected in the fascinating changes in size, design, fineness and workmanship, culminating in the many strange examples that emanated from the strife of the Civil War.

The Norman Conquest of England in 1066 and succeeding years had far-reaching effects on all aspects of life. Surprisingly, however, it had little impact on the coinage. William the Conqueror was anxious to emphasise the continuity of his reign, so far as the ordinary people were concerned, and therefore he retained the fabric, size and general design pattern of the silver penny. Almost 70 mints were in operation during this reign, but by the middle of the 12th century the number was reduced to 55 and under Henry II (1154–89) it fell to 30 and latterly to only eleven. By the early 14th century the production of coins had been centralised on London and Canterbury, together with the ecclesiastical mints at York and Canterbury. The silver penny was the principal denomination throughout the Norman period, pieces cut along the lines of the cross on the reverse continuing to serve as halfpence and farthings.

Eight types of penny were struck under William I and five under his son William Rufus, both profiles (left and right) and facing portraits being used in both reigns allied to crosses of various types. Fifteen types were minted under Henry I (1100–35), portraiture having now degenerated to crude caricature, the lines engraved on the coinage dies being built up by means of various punches. Halfpence modelled on the same pattern were also struck, but very sparingly and are very rare.

On Henry's death the succession was contested by his daughter Matilda and his nephew Stephen of Blois. Civil war broke out in 1138 and continued till 1153. Stephen controlled London and its mint, but Matilda and her supporters occupied the West Country and struck their own coins at Bristol. Several of the powerful barons struck their own coins, and there were distinct regional variants of the regal coinage. Of particular interest are the coins

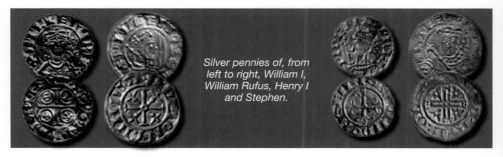

Silver pennies of, from left to right, William I, William Rufus, Henry I and Stephen.

struck from obverse dies with Stephen's portrait erased or defaced, believed to date from 1148 when the usurper was under papal interdict.

Peace was restored in 1153 when it was agreed that Matilda's son Henry should succeed Stephen. On the latter's death the following year, Henry II ascended the throne. Coins of Stephen's last type continued to be minted till 1158, but Henry then took the opportunity to overhaul the coinage which had become irregular and sub-standard during the civil war. The new "Cross Crosslet" coins, usually known as the Tealby coinage (from the hoard of over 5,000 pennies found at Tealby, Lincolnshire in 1807), were produced at 30 mints, but when the recoinage was completed this number was reduced to a dozen. The design of Henry's coins remained virtually the same throughout more than two decades, apart from minor variants. Then, in 1180, a new type, known as the Short Cross coinage, was introduced. This was a vast improvement over the poorly struck Cross Crosslet coins and continued without alteration, not only to the end of the reign of Henry II in 1189, but throughout the reigns of his sons Richard (1189–99) and John (1199–1216) and the first half of the reign of his grandson Henry III (1216–46). Throughout that 66 year period, however, there were minor variations in portraits and lettering which enable numismatists to attribute the HENRICUS coins to specific reigns and periods.

"Tealby" type penny (top), and
"Short Cross" penny of Henry II.

The style and workmanship of the Short Cross coinage deteriorated in the reign of Henry III. By the 1220s coin production was confined to the regal mints at London and Canterbury, the sole exception being the ecclesiastical mint maintained by the Abbot of Bury St Edmunds.

Halfpence and farthings were briefly struck in 1221–30, though halfpence are now extremely rare and so far only a solitary farthing has been discovered.

By the middle of this reign the coinage was in a deplorable state, being poorly struck, badly worn and often ruthlessly clipped. In 1247 Henry ordered a new coinage and in this the arms of the cross on the reverse were extended to the rim as a safeguard against clipping. This established a pattern of facing portrait and long cross on obverse and reverse respectively that was to continue till the beginning of the 16th century. Several provincial mints were re-activated to assist with the recoinage but they were all closed down again by 1250, only the regal mints at London and Canterbury and the ecclesiastical mints at Durham and Bury St Edmunds remaining active.

"Long Cross" pennies of Henry III (top),
and Edward I.

In 1257 Henry tentatively introduced a gold penny (worth 20 silver pence and twice the weight of a silver penny). The coin was undervalued and soon disappeared from circulation.

The Long Cross coinage of Henry III continued under Edward I till 1279 when the king introduced a new coinage in his own name. The penny continued the style of its predecessors, though much better designed and executed; but new denominations were now added. Henceforward halfpence and farthings became a regular issue and, at the same time, a fourpenny coin known as the groat (from French *gros*) was briefly introduced (minting ceased in 1282 and was not revived till 1351). Due to the centralisation of coin production the name of the moneyer was now generally dropped, although it lingered on a few years at Bury St Edmunds. The provincial mints were again revived in 1299–1302 to recoin the lightweight foreign imitations of pennies which had flooded in from the Continent.

The coinage of Edward II (1307–27) differed only in minor respects from that of his father, and a similar pattern prevailed in the first years of Edward III. In 1335 halfpence and farthings below the sterling fineness were struck. More importantly, further attempts were made to introduce gold coins. In 1344 the florin or double

Pre-Treaty Noble of Edward III which contained reference to France in the legend.

leopard of six shillings was introduced, along with its half and quarter. This coinage was not successful and was soon replaced by a heavier series based on the noble of 80 pence (6*s*. 8*d*.), half a mark or one third of a pound. The noble originally weighed 138.5 grains but it was successively reduced to120 grains, at which weight it continued from 1351. During this reign the protracted conflict with France known as the Hundred Years' War erupted. Edward III, through his mother, claimed the French throne and inscribed this title on his coins. By the Treaty of Bretigny (1361) Edward temporarily gave up his claim and the reference to France

Noble of Edward IV, issued before he was forced to abandon the throne of England.

was dropped from the coins, but when war was renewed in 1369 the title was resumed, and remained on many English coins until the end of the 18th century. The silver coinage followed the pattern of the previous reign, but in 1351 the groat was re-introduced and with it came the twopence or half-groat. Another innovation was the use of mintmarks at the beginning of the inscriptions. Seven types of cross and one crown were employed from 1334 onwards and their sequence enables numismatists to date coins fairly accurately.

The full range of gold (noble, half-noble and quarter-noble) and silver (groat, half-groat, penny, halfpenny and farthing) continued under Richard II (1377–99). Little attempt was made to alter the facing portrait on the silver coins, by now little more than a stylised caricature anyway.

Noble of Henry IV which was reduced in weight due to the shortage of gold.

Under Henry IV (1399–1413) the pattern of previous reigns prevailed, but in 1412 the weights of the coinage were reduced due to a shortage of bullion. The noble was reduced to 108 grains and its sub-divisions lightened proportionately. The penny was reduced by 3 grains, and its multiples and sub-divisions correspondingly reduced. One interesting change was the reduction of the fleur de lis of France from four to three in the heraldic shield on the reverse of the noble; this change corresponded with the alteration in the arms used in France itself. The Calais mint, opened by Edward III in 1363, was closed in 1411. There was no change in the designs used for the coins of Henry V (1413–22) but greater use was now made of mintmarks to distinguish the various periods of production. Coins were by now produced mainly at London, although the episcopal mints at Durham and York were permitted to strike pennies.

The supply of gold dwindled early in the reign of Henry VI and few nobles were struck after 1426. The Calais mint was re-opened in 1424 and struck a large amount of gold before closing finally in 1440. A regal mint briefly operated at York in 1423–24. Mintmarks were now much more widely used and tended to correspond more closely to the annual trials of the Pyx. The series of civil upheavals known as the Wars of the Roses erupted in this period.

In 1461 Henry VI was deposed by the Yorkist Earl of March after he defeated the Lancastrians at Mortimer's Cross. The Yorkists advanced on London where the victor was crowned Edward IV. At first he continued the gold series of his predecessor, issuing nobles and quarter-nobles, but in 1464 the weight of the penny was reduced to 12 grains and the value of the noble was raised to 100 pence (8s. 4d.). The ryal or rose-

Groat of Richard III (1483–85).

noble of 120 grains, together with its half and quarter, was introduced in 1465 and tariffed at ten shillings or half a pound. The need for a coin worth a third of a pound, however, led to the issue of the angel of 80 grains, worth 6s. 8d., but this was initially unsucessful and very few examples are now extant. The angel derived its name from the figure of the Archangel Michael on the obverse; a cross surmounting a shield appeared on the reverse.

In 1470 Edward was forced to flee to Holland and Henry VI was briefly restored. During this brief period (to April 1471) the ryal was discontinued but a substantial issue of angels and half-angels was made both at London and Bristol. Silver coins were struck at York as well as London and Bristol, the issues of the provincial mints being identified by the initials B or E (Eboracum, Latin for York). Edward defeated the Lancastrians at Tewkesbury and deposed the luckless Henry once more. In his

second reign Edward struck only angels and half-angels as well as silver from the groat to halfpenny. In addition to the three existing mints, silver coins were struck at Canterbury, Durham and the archiepiscopal mint at York. Mintmarks were now much more frequent and varied. Coins with a mark of a halved sun and rose are usually assigned to the reign of Edward IV, but they were probably also struck in the nominal reign of Edward V, the twelve-year-old prince held in the Tower of London under the protection of his uncle Richard, Duke of Gloucester. Coins with this mark on the reverse had an obverse mark of a boar's head, Richard's personal emblem. The brief reign of Richard III (1483–5) came to an end with his defeat at Bosworth and the relatively scarce coins of this period followed the pattern of the previous reigns, distinguished by the sequence of mint marks and the inscription RICAD or RICARD.

In the early years of Henry VII's reign the coinage likewise followed the previous patterns, but in 1489 the first of several radical changes was effected, with the introduction of the gold sovereign of 20 shillings showing a full-length portrait of the monarch seated on an elaborate throne. For reverse, this coin depicted a Tudor rose surmounted by a heraldic shield. A similar reverse appeared on the ryal of 10 shillings, but the angel and angelet retained previous motifs. The silver coins at first adhered to the medieval pattern, with the stylised facing portrait and long cross, but at the beginning of the 16th century a large silver coin, the testoon or shilling of 12 pence, was introduced and adopted a realistic profile of the king, allied to a reverse showing a cross surmounted by the royal arms. The same design was also used for the later issue of groat and half groat.

First coinage Angel of Henry VIII which retained the traditional 23.5 carat fineness.

This established a pattern which was to continue till the reign of Charles I. In the reign of Henry VIII, however, the coinage was subject to considerable debasement. This led to the eventual introduction of 22 carat (.916 fine) gold for the crown while the traditional 23 1/2 carat gold was retained for the angel and ryal. This dual system continued until the angel was discontinued at the outset of the Civil War in 1642; latterly it had been associated with the ceremony of touching for "King's Evil" or scrofula, a ritual used by the early Stuart monarchs to bolster their belief in the divine right of kings.

Under the Tudors and Stuarts the range and complexity of the gold coinage increased, but it was not until the reign of Edward VI that the silver series was expanded. In 1551 he introduced the silver crown of five shillings, the first English coin to bear a clear date on the obverse. Under Mary dates were extended to the shilling and sixpence.

The mixture of dated and undated coins continued under Elizabeth I, a reign remarkable for the range of denominations—nine gold and

The magnificent second coinage Rose-Ryal of James I (1603–25).

eight silver. The latter included the sixpence, threepence, threehalfpence and threefarthings, distinguished by the rose which appeared behind the Queen's head.

The coinage of James I was even more complex, reflecting the king's attempts to unite his dominions. The first issue bore the legend ANG: SCO (England and Scotland), but from 1604 this was altered to MAG: BRIT (Great Britain). This period witnessed new denominations, such as the rose-ryal and spur-ryal, the unite, the Britain crown and the thistle crown, and finally the laurel of 20 shillings and its sub-divisions.

In the reign of Elizabeth experiments began with milled coinage under Eloi Mestrell. These continued sporadically in the 17th century, culminating in the beautiful coins struck by Nicholas Briot (1631–39). A branch mint was established at Aberystwyth in 1637 to refine and coin silver from the Welsh mines. Relations between King and Parliament deteriorated in the reign of Charles I and led to the Civil War (1642). Parliament controlled London but continued to strike coins in the King's name. The Royalists struck coins, both in pre-war and new types, at Shrewsbury, Oxford, Bristol, Worcester, Exeter, Chester, Hereford and other Royalist strongholds, while curious siege pieces were pressed into service at Newark, Pontefract and Scarborough.

After the execution of Charles I in 1649 the Commonwealth was proclaimed and gold and silver coins were now inscribed in English instead of Latin. Patterns portraying Cromwell and a crowned shield restored Latin in 1656. Plans for milled coinage were already being considered before the Restoration of the monarchy in 1660. Hammered coinage appeared initially, resuming the style of coins under Charles I, but in 1662 the hand-hammering of coins was abandoned in favour of coins struck on the mill and screw press. The hammered coins of 1660–62 were undated and bore a crown mintmark, the last vestiges of medievalism in British coinage.

The Royal Mint®

Don't just discover history, own it

Collector Services

The Royal Mint's Historic Coin Service

The Royal Mint has been striking British coins since AD 886. It's what we do. Trust us to be your source of expert advice for your next coin search and purchase, with assured authenticity.

With an extensive network of numismatic connections and in-house expert knowledge, we can source rare and special historic coins. Whether you're adding to your collection or looking for a memorable gift, our Historic Coin Finder Service can help.

If you know what you're looking for, send us the details of the coin you require and let us do the hard work sourcing it. If you are after a special coin or coins and are unsure of the exact details, or you would like some advice on the best coin to fit your requirements, get in touch with our specialist team.

- Historic Coins
- Authentication & Valuation
- Care & Display
- Secure Storage

Telephone: 0800 03 22 153
royalmint.com/historics

Follow us:

Treasure for Life®

Coin
grading

Condition is the secret to the value of virtually anything, whether it be antiques, jewellery, horses or second-hand cars—and coins are certainly no exception. When collecting coins it is vital to understand the recognised standard British system of grading, i.e. accurately assessing a coin's condition or state of wear. Grading is an art which can only be learned by experience and so often it remains one person's opinion against another's, therefore it is important for the beginner or inexperienced collector to seek assistance from a reputable dealer or knowledgeable numismatist when making major purchases.

The standard grades as used in the Price Guide are as follows:	
UNC	**Uncirculated** A coin that has never been in circulation, although it may show signs of contact with other coins during the minting process.
EF	**Extremely Fine** A coin in this grade may appear uncirculated to the naked eye but on closer examination will show signs of minor friction on the highest surface.
VF	**Very Fine** A coin that has had very little use, but shows signs of wear on the high surfaces.
F	**Fine** A coin that has been in circulation and shows general signs of wear, but with all legends and date clearly visible.
Other grades used in the normal grading system are:	
BU	**Brilliant Uncirculated** As the name implies, a coin retaining its mint lustre.
Fair	A coin extensively worn but still quite recognisable and legends readable.
Poor	A coin very worn and only just recognisable.
Other abbreviations used in the Price Guide are:	
Obv	**Obverse**
Rev	**Reverse**
Other abbreviations, mintmarks, etc. can be identified under the appropriate section of this Yearbook.	

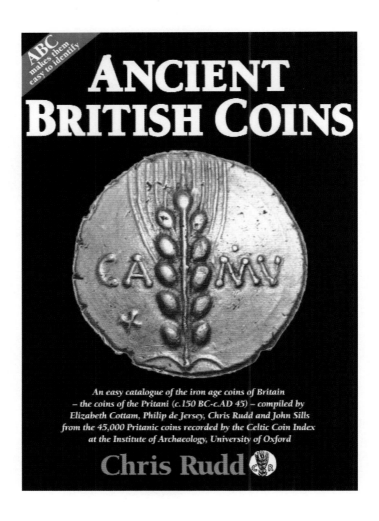

A SIMPLIFIED PRICE GUIDE TO
ANCIENT COINS USED IN BRITAIN

PART 1

Ancient British

The prices given in this section are those that you would expect to pay from a reputable dealer and not the prices at which you could expect to sell coins.

The list below, which has been generously provided by Celtic coin dealer Elizabeth Cottam of Chris Rudd, contains most of the commonly available types: a fully comprehensive guide is beyond the scope of this book. Prices are for coins with good surfaces which are not weakly struck or struck from worn dies. Examples which are struck from worn or damaged dies can be worth considerably less. Particularly attractive examples of bronze Celtic coins command a very high premium. Where a price is given for an issue of which there are many varieties, the price is for the most common type. The illustrations are representative examples only and are not shown actual size.

	F	VF	EF
UNINSCRIBED COINAGE			
GOLD STATERS			
Broad Flan	£700	£1775	£5750
Gallic War Uniface	£225	£300	£675
Remic types	£250	£400	£800
Wonersh types	£250	£450	£1900
Chute	£200	£300	£675
Cheriton	£250	£450	£975
Iceni (various types)	£300	£500	£1350
Norfolk "wolf" type			
fine gold	£250	£475	£1350
brassy gold	£175	£300	£695
very debased	£120	£200	£475
Corieltavi (various types)	£200	£400	£875
Dobunni	£250	£500	£1350
Whaddon Chase types	£275	£475	£1300

Cheriton Smiler gold stater

	F	VF	EF
GOLD QUARTER STATERS			
Gallic Imported Types	£80	£175	£395
Kent types	£200	£300	£550
Southern types	£125	£200	£375
Iceni	£150	£250	£450
Corieltavi	£125	£200	£475
Dobunni	£175	£300	£575
East Wiltshire	£300	£500	£1,000
Durotriges	£120	£225	£395
North Thames types	£220	£300	£550

	F	VF	EF
SILVER COINAGE			
Armorican billion staters	£125	£250	£500
Kent Types	£150	£300	£675
South Thames types	£120	£175	£375

Cranborne Chase silver stater

	F	VF	EF
Iceni ('crescent' types)............................	£35	£85	£185
Iceni ('Norfolk God' types)....................	£60	£100	£295
Corieltavi..	£50	£110	£225
Dobunni..	£85	£125	£295
Durotriges full stater			
fine silver..	£80	£175	£350
base silver..	£30	£55	£175
Durotriges quarter silver.......................	£25	£35	£95
(Note—most examples are for base coins as better quality items are appreciably higher)			
North Thames types.............................	£110	£195	£375

POTIN COINAGE

	F	VF	EF
Kent...	£25	£50	£135

Hengistbury cast bronze

BRONZE COINAGE

	F	VF	EF
Durotriges debased stater....................	£30	£75	£125
Durotriges cast bronze	£65	£125	£225
North Thames types. Various issues from:	£45	£110	£450

INSCRIBED CELTIC COINAGE

CANTIACI

Dubnovellaunos	F	VF	EF
stater..	£320	£600	£1500
silver unit...	£135	£220	£575
bronze unit..	£65	£175	£395
Vosenos			
stater..	£1100	£2500	£5200
quarter stater	£295	£585	£1250
silver unit...	£140	£300	£675
Sam			
stater (unique)	—	—	—
silver unit...	£185	£350	£800
bronze unit..	£110	£275	£550
Eppillus			
stater..	£1100	£2000	£4575
quarter stater	£150	£265	£575
silver unit...	£75	£145	£395
bronze unit..	£65	£125	£495
bronze minim....................................	£85	£175	£300
Anarevitos			
stater (unique)			—
Touto			
silver unit...	£200	£450	£875
Verica...			
silver unit...	£200	£350	£695
bronze unit..	£165	£300	£635
Sego			
stater..	£525	£1000	£3250
quarter stater	£220	£500	£1275
silver unit...	£150	£350	£675
silver minim......................................	£80	£200	£425
bronze unit..	£80	£165	£495
Amminus			
silver unit...	£175	£325	£695
silver minim......................................	£110	£215	£475
bronze unit..	£85	£175	£535
Solidus			
silver unit...	£535	£1100	£2350
silver minim......................................	£535	£1100	£1575

Vosenos gold quarter stater

Verica gold stater

	F	VF	EF
REGINI & ATREBATES			
Commios			
stater	£595	£1575	£3000
silver unit	£80	£160	£345
silver minim	£65	£125	£295
Tincomarus			
stater	£465	£895	£2250
quarter stater	£150	£250	£475
silver unit	£75	£145	£300
silver minim	£65	£125	£200
Eppillus			
stater	£1000	£2500	£6000
quarter stater	£160	£245	£575
silver unit	£80	£165	£345
Verica			
stater	£275	£575	£1300
quarter stater	£155	£275	£435
silver unit	£55	£160	£275
silver minim	£50	£120	£245
Epaticcus			
stater	£1000	£2000	£4250
silver unit	£50	£100	£275
silver minim	£55	£120	£295
Caratacus			
silver unit	£175	£320	£475
silver minim	£110	£220	£345

Tincomarus gold stater

VECTUARII			
Crab			
silver unit	£165	£325	£695
silver minim	£120	£295	£435

ICENI			
Cani Duro			
silver unit	£115	£275	£575
Antedios			
stater	£425	£1000	£2500
silver unit	£40	£65	£195
silver half unit	£45	£100	£150
Ecen			
stater	£425	£1200	£2575
silver unit	£45	£85	£195
silver half unit	£50	£100	£175
Saenu			
silver unit	£65	£125	£300
Aesu			
silver unit	£65	£125	£300
Ale Scavo			
silver unit	£275	£500	£1275
Esuprasto			
silver unit	£425	£1000	£2000

Ale Scavo silver unit

CORIELTAVI			
Cat			
silver unit	£400	£1100	£2200
silver half unit (unique)			—
VEPO			
stater	£450	£1000	£2600
silver unit	£85	£150	£350
Esuprasu			
stater	£350	£675	£1375
silver unit	£175	£325	£575

Vep CorF gold stater

	F	VF	EF
Aunt Cost			
stater	£275	£575	£1395
silver unit	£90	£195	£350
silver half unit	£90	£175	£325
Lat Ison			
stater	£1000	£2100	£4300
silver unit	£175	£425	£1175
silver half unit	£160	£300	£575
Dumnocoveros Tigirseno			
stater	£850	£2000	£3750
silver unit	£100	£195	£595
silver half unit	£100	£210	£625
Volisios Dumnocoveros			
stater	£350	£675	£1350
silver unit	£100	£185	£500
silver half unit	£100	£195	£495
Volisios Cartivellaunos			
stater	£1000	£2000	£4100
silver unit	£300	£675	£1200
Volisios Dumnovellaunos			
stater	£320	£765	£1675
silver half unit	£150	£325	£675

Catti gold stater

DOBUNNI

	F	VF	EF
Bodvoc			
stater	£1000	£2250	£3250
quarter stater (unique)			—
silver unit	£200	£500	£895
Corio			
stater	£275	£560	£1550
quarter stater	£200	£350	£675
Comux			
stater	£285	£560	£1550
Catti			
stater	£285	£565	£1600
Inamn			
plated stater (unique)			—
silver unit (unique)			—
Anted			
stater	£350	£700	£1600
silver unit	£60	£125	£325
Eisu			
stater	£450	£750	£1600
silver unit	£75	£125	£335

Dumno Tigir Seno gold stater

TRINOVANTES

	F	VF	EF
Dubnovellaunos			
stater	£275	£475	£1350
quarter stater	£175	£350	£650
silver unit	£75	£150	£375
silver half unit	£100	£200	£475
bronze unit	£65	£140	£295

CATUVELLAUNI

	F	VF	EF
Addedomaros			
stater	£300	£450	£1300
quarter stater	£300	£550	£675
silver unit	£100	£200	£420
silver half unit	£100	£200	£475
bronze unit	£35	£95	£295

Addedomaros gold stater

	F	VF	EF
Tasciovanos			
stater	£250	£475	£1650
quarter stater	£165	£250	£500
silver unit	£85	£175	£395
bronze unit	£60	£135	£275
bronze half unit	£60	£135	£295
Andoco			
stater	£350	£575	£1695
quarter stater	£200	£420	£775
silver unit	£155	£400	£775
bronze unit	£85	£225	£365
Dias			
silver unit	£100	£200	£425
bronze unit	£50	£150	£425
Rues			
bronze unit	£50	£150	£425
Cat			
plated silver unit (unique)			—

Tasciovanos gold stater

	F	VF	EF
CATUVELLAUNI & TRINOVANTES			
Cunobelinus			
stater	£250	£450	£1650
quarter stater	£150	£250	£495
silver unit	£85	£175	£495
bronze unit	£60	£145	£395
bronze half	£60	£145	£285
Trocc			
bronze unit	£50	£150	£550
Agr			
quarter stater	£125	£275	£895
silver unit	£100	£200	£525
bronze unit (only two)		(too rare to price)	
Dubn			
quarter stater (only three)	£1000	£3000	£7500

Cunobelinus gold stater

Illustrations by courtesy of Chris Rudd

The impressive Chawton hoard of Celtic coins discovered by a metal detectorists at Chawton Hampshire in 2012 and ʃe subject of a number of articles in COIN NEWS ring 2016. The Chawton hoard was originally reported as the "Vine Leaf Hoard".

BRITANNIA MEDAL FAIR

Sunday 17th November 2019
Sunday 26th April 2020
Sunday 15th November 2020
9:30am - 2:00pm

Carisbrooke Hall, The Victory Services Club, 63/79 Seymour Street, London, W2 2HF

FREE ENTRY

WE ARE PLEASED TO ANNOUNCE THAT THERE IS NO LONGER A CHARGE FOR VISITORS OR TRADE STANDS

Europe's largest independent medal bourse is now hosted by DNW

**Many leading medal dealers and auctioneers
from around the country will be in attendance**

and the popular Britannia Curry will be available from the canteen

*For further details please visit www.dnw.co.uk/britannia
or contact DNW on 020 7016 1700 or events@dnw.co.uk*

www.dnw.co.uk

16 Bolton Street Mayfair London W1J 8BQ
020 7016 1700 medals@dnw.co.uk

ANCIENT COINS USED IN BRITAIN

PART II

Roman Britain

The list below has been generously provided by coin dealer Mike Vosper. These prices are for the most common types unless otherwise noted. In most cases, especially with large bronze coins, the price for coins in extremely fine condition will be <u>much</u> higher than the price for the same coin in very fine condition as early bronze coins are seldom found in hoards and perfect, undamaged examples are rarely available.

The illustrations provided are a representative guide to assist with identification only.

REPUBLICAN COINAGE 280–41 BC

	FROM F	VF	EF
Republican			
Quadrigatus (or Didrachm) (Janus/Quadriga) £135		£450	£2000
Victoriatus (Jupiter/Victory)	£35	£105	£550
+Denarius (Roma/Biga)	£20	£80	£500
+Denarius (other types)	£30	£95	£575
Denarius (Gallic warrior—L.Hostilius Saserna)..	£400	£1150	£7650
Quinarius	£25	£85	£550
Cast Aes Grave, As	£400	£1150	—
Struck As/Semis/Litra	£60	£215	—
Struck Triens/Quadrands	£50	£160	—

Gnaeus Pompey Junior

IMPERATORIAL COINAGE 49–27 BC

Pompey the Great			
Denarius (Hd. of Pompilius/Prow)	£150	£475	£2850
Scipio			
Denarius (Jupiter/Elephant..............	£100	£310	£1800
Cato Uticensis			
Quinarius (Bacchus/Victory)	£45	£135	£750
Gnaeus Pompey Junior			
Denarius (Roma/Hispania)	£110	£350	£1850
Sextus Pompey			
Denarius (his bust)	£275	£785	£4950
Denarius (other types).....................	£190	£595	£3575
As..	£160	£595	—
Julius Caesar			
Aureus	£1200	£3450	£25,000
Denarius ("elephant" type)	£150	£500	£2750
Denarius (Ceasar portrait)	£450	£1450	£8250
Denarius (heads of godesses)..........	£115	£395	£2000

Julius Caesar

	FROM F	VF	EF
Brutus			
Denarius (his portrait/EID MAR)	£25,000	£73,500	£385,000
Denarius (others)	£150	£475	£2950
Cassius			
Denarius	£125	£425	£2000
Ahenobarbus			
Denarius	£450	£1300	£6750
Mark Antony			
Denarius ("Galley" type)	£75	£280	£2000
Denarius (with portrait)	£100	£395	£2375
Denarius (other types)	£70	£300	£2200
Mark Antony & Lepidus			
AR quinarius	£75	£195	£1200
Mark Antony & Octavian			
AR denarius	£175	£650	£3000
Quninarius	£50	£175	£1050
Mark Antony & Lucius Antony			
AR denarius	£345	£900	£4675
Mark Antony & Octavia			
AR Cistophorus	£225	£685	£3575
Cleopatra VII & Mark Antony			
AR denarius	£1400	£4600	£38,500
Fulvia			
AR quinarius	£125	£375	£2300
Octavian (later known as Augustus)			
Gold Aureus	£1200	£4200	£27,500
Denarius	£125	£375	£2500
Quinarius (ASIA RECEPTA)	£50	£135	£950
Octavian & Divos Julius Caesar			
AE sestertius	£275	£1575	—

Brutus

Mark Antony & Octavian

IMPERIAL COINAGE—Julio-Claudian Dynasty 27BC–AD 69

	FROM F	VF	EF
Augustus			
Gold Aureus (Caius & Lucius Caesar)	£1200	£3350	£18700
AR Cistophorus	£200	£685	£3500
Denarius (Caius & Lucius Caesar)	£65	£185	£1000
Denarius (other types)	£65	£225	£1375
AR quinarius	£50	£160	£965
Sestertius (large SC)	£135	£415	£2000
Dupondius or as (large SC)	£55	£170	£875
Quadrans	£20	£80	£300
Divus Augustus (struck under Tiberius)			
As	£70	£215	£1375
Augustus & Agrippa			
Dupondius (Crocodile rev)	£70	£220	£1375
Livia			
Sestertius or Dupondius	£200	£625	£4650
Gaius Caesar			
AR denarius	£375	£1425	£4500
Tiberius			
Aureus (Tribute penny)	£1000	£3000	£12,000
Denarius (Tribute penny)	£85	£245	£1200
Sestertius	£195	£625	£3650
Dupondius	£165	£585	£3000
As	£75	£245	£1200
Drusus			
Sestertius	£275	£950	£5000
As (Large S C)	£75	£215	£1450
Caligula			
Denarius (rev. portrait)	£450	£1365	£7500
Sestertius (PIETAS & Temple)	£300	£1900	£9500
As (VESTA)	£100	£300	£1650

Augustus

Tiberius

	FROM F	VF	EF
Agrippa (struck under Caligula)			
As..................................	£65	£180	£1250
Germanicus (struck under Caligula or Claudius)			
As (Large S C)	£65	£205	£1250
Agrippina Senior (struck under Caligula)			
Sestertius (Carpentum)....................	£500	£1500	£10000
Nero & Drusus (struck under Caligula)			
Dupondius (On horseback, galloping)	£195	£685	£4500
Claudius			
Aureus ("DE BRITANN" type)	£1650	£5000	£38,500
Denarius as above	£400	£1785	£10500
Didrachm as above	£375	£1250	£6750
Denarius other types	£375	£1000	£6700
Sestertius	£165	£525	£4500
Dupondius	£60	£240	£1700
As	£45	£150	£1250
Quadrans	£20	£55	£300
Irregular British Sestertius................	£30	£90	£550
Irregular British As	£20	£80	£430
Claudius & Agrippina Junior or Nero			
Denarius	£450	£1420	£8000
Nero Cludius Drusus (struck under Claudius)			
Sestertius	£250	£895	£6750
Antonia (struck under Claudius)			
Dupondius	£150	£475	£3200
Britannicus			
Sestertius	£6500	£29500	—
Nero			
Aureus	£1000	£3350	£18500
Denarius	£95	£275	£2040
Sestertius	£135	£575	£4000
Sestertius (Port of Ostia)	£1800	£6300	£66000
Dupondius	£85	£285	£1750
As	£50	£175	£1450
Semis...	£45	£135	£750
Quadrans	£20	£80	£385
Civil War			
Denarius	£190	£580	£3400
Galba			
Denarius	£110	£380	£2350
Sestertius	£170	£520	£3400
Dupondius	£180	£525	£3050
As	£110	£370	£2200
Otho			
Denarius	£195	£615	£4000
Vitellius			
Denarius	£100	£290	£2000
Sestertius	£1000	£2950	£21000
Dupondius	£350	£1000	£6250
As	£195	£525	£3500

IMPERIAL COINAGE—Flavian Dynasty AD 69–96

Vespasian			
Aureus	£850	£2650	£15300
Denarius	£30	£100	£575
Denarius (IVDAEA)	£80	£210	£1450
Sestertius	£195	£625	£5000
Dupondius	£70	£220	£1700
As	£55	£210	£1500
Titus			
Aureus	£900	£3000	£16500
Denarius as Caesar	£40	£120	£900
Denarius as Augustus	£45	£140	£1000

Caligula

Agrippina Senior

Claudius

Nero

Galba

	FROM F	VF	EF
Sestertius	£135	£475	£4000
Dupondius	£50	£195	£1450
As	£45	£170	£1450
As (IVDAEA CAPTA)	£170	£525	£3500
Julia Titi			
Denarious	£190	£600	£3500
Domitian			
Aureus	£950	£2500	£14500
Cistophorus	£125	£450	£2500
Denarius as Caesar	£35	£95	£550
Denarius as Augustus	£25	£85	£450
Sestertius	£95	£350	£2000
Dupondius	£35	£130	£1500
As	£35	£115	£850
Ae Semis	£30	£95	£600
Ae Quadrands.................................	£25	£80	£385
Domitia			
Cistophorus	£235	£730	£4000

Titus

IMPERIAL COINAGE—Adoptive Emperors AD 96–138

Nerva			
Aureus	£1850	£5880	£36300
Denarius	£50	£130	£900
Sestertius	£140	£550	£3650
Sestertius (Palm-tree)	£500	£1680	£1200
Dupondius	£70	£235	£1375
As	£65	£170	£1200
Trajan			
Aureus	£950	£2520	£14500
Denarius	£25	£65	£495
Denarius (Trajan's Column)	£40	£140	£900
Sestertius	£65	£240	£1700
Sestertius (Dacian rev.)	£75	£265	£1800
Dupondius or as	£35	£100	£715
Ae Quadrands	£25	£70	£450
Plotina, Marciana or Matidia			
Denarius	£425	£1350	£4750
Hadrian			
Aureus	£950	£2750	£16500
Cistophourus	£120	£525	£2000
Denarius (Provinces)	£45	£150	£950
Denarius other types	£25	£85	£600
Sestertius	£75	£250	£1650
Sestertius (RETITVTORI province types)	£135	£450	£3000
Sestertius (Britannia std)	£3000	£10500	–
Dupondius or As	£35	£125	£750
As (Britannia std)	£210	£685	–
Ae Semiis or Quadrands	£30	£100	£550
Eygpt, Alexandrian Billon Tetradrachm	£30	£100	£575
Sabina			
Denarius	£30	£90	£600
Sestertius	£115	£385	£2550
As or Dupondius	£70	£205	£1350
Aelius Ceasar			
Denarius	£70	£210	£1400
Sestertius	£145	£525	£3000
As or Dupondius	£65	£120	£1500

Domitian

Nerva

Trajan

Hadrian

	FROM F	VF	EF

IMPERIAL COINAGE—The Antonines AD 138–193

Antoninus Pius

Antoninus Pius

	FROM F	VF	EF
Aureus	£750	£2000	£11500
Denarius	£20	£55	£300
Sestertius Britannia seated	£500	£1500	£14000
Sestertius other types	£40	£160	£1000
As - Britannia rev.	£65	£200	£1650
Dupondius or As other types	£25	£100	£475

Antoninus Pius & Marcus Aurelius

	FROM F	VF	EF
Denarius (bust each side)	£30	£125	£635

Diva Faustina Senior

	FROM F	VF	EF
Denarius	£20	£50	£360
Sestertius	£45	£155	£905
As or Dupondius	£25	£85	£525

Marcus Aurelius

Marcus Aurelius

	FROM F	VF	EF
Aureus	£850	£2520	£14650
Denarius as Caesar	£22	£70	£440
Denarius as Augustus	£20	£55	£365
Sestertius	£45	£180	£120
As or Dupondius	£25	£80	£525

Faustina Junior

	FROM F	VF	EF
Denarius	£20	£70	£450
Sestertius	£40	£185	£1500
As or Dupondius	£30	£90	£600

Lucius Verus

	FROM F	VF	EF
Denarius	£25	£95	£525
Sestertius	£45	£200	£1500
As or Dupondius	£30	£105	£650

Faustina Junior

Lucilla

	FROM F	VF	EF
Denarius	£20	£70	£450
Sestertius	£65	£200	£1375
As or Dupondius	£30	£100	£650

Commodus

	FROM F	VF	EF
Aureus	£1050	£3000	£17600
Denarius as Caesar	£30	£80	£550
Denarius as Augustus	£20	£55	£450
Sestertius	£45	£170	£1350
Sestertius (VICT BRIT)	£150	£525	£3600
As or Dupondius	£25	£90	£580

Crispina

	FROM F	VF	EF
Denarius	£25	£85	£525
Sestertius	£70	£250	£1500
As or Dupondius	£35	£125	£775

IMPERIAL COINAGE—The Severan Dynasty AD 193–235

Pertinax

	FROM F	VF	EF
Denarius	£225	£700	£4500
Sestertius	£500	£2000	£14500

Didius Julianus

	FROM F	VF	EF
Denarius	£400	£1300	£9000
Sestertius or Dupondius	£325	£1000	£8000

Lucius Verus

Manlia Scantilla or Didia Clara

	FROM F	VF	EF
Denarius	£400	£1300	£9500

Pescennius Niger

	FROM F	VF	EF
Denarius	£275	£800	£5500

Clodius Albinus

	FROM F	VF	EF
Denarius as Caesar	£45	£150	£750
Denarius as Augustus	£85	£300	£1650
Sestertius	£275	£900	£6000
As	£85	£265	£1500

Commodus

121

	FROM F	VF	EF
Septimius Severus			
Aureus	£1000	£2650	£15500
Aureus (VICT BRIT)	£1200	£3675	£25000
+Denarius (Mint of Rome)	£15	£55	£300
+Denarius (Mints of Emesa & Laodicea)	£20	£50	£325
Denarius (LEG XIIII)	£30	£90	£585
Denarius (VICT BRIT)	£25	£105	£550
Sestertius other types	£75	£265	£1850
Sestertius (VICT BRIT)......................	£350	£1000	£8000
Dupondius or as	£50	£170	£1300
Dupondius or As (VICT BRIT)	£125	£385	£2500
Julia Domna			
Denarius	£15	£45	£310
Sestertius	£75	£245	£1750
As or Dupondius	£50	£170	£1100
Caracalla			
Aureus (VICT BRIT)	£1350	£3650	£25500
Denarius as Caesar	£15	£50	£350
Denarius as Augustus	£15	£45	£350
Denarius (VICT BRIT)	£30	£100	£600
Antoninianus	£25	£80	£525
Sestertius	£100	£310	£2000
Sestertius (VICT BRIT)......................	£300	£900	£7550
Dupondius or As	£50	£175	£1000
Dupondius or As (VICT BRIT)	£100	£315	£2000
Plautilla			
Denarius	£25	£80	£600
Geta			
Denarius as Caesar	£15	£50	£360
Denarius as Augustus	£25	£75	£550
Denarius (VICT BRIT)	£30	£100	£685
Sestertius	£125	£370	£2500
Sestertius (VICT BRIT)......................	£250	£810	£5250
Dupondius or as	£75	£245	£1650
As (VICT BRIT)	£120	£360	£2530
Macrinus			
Antoninianus	£90	£290	£1850
Denarius	£40	£135	£900
Sestertius	£175	£420	£3600
Diadumenian			
Denarius	£75	£205	£1200
Dupondius or As	£135	£415	£3000
Elagabalus			
Aureus	£1200	£3600	£20000
Antoninianus	£20	£70	£525
Denarius	£15	£40	£305
Sestertius	£100	£340	£2000
Dupondius or As	£60	£185	£1200
Julia Paula			
Denarius	£30	£120	£685
Aquilla Severa			
Denarius	£55	£195	£1400
Julia Soaemias			
Denarius	£30	£80	£550
Dupondius or As	£65	£250	£1500
Julia Maesa			
Denarius	£15	£50	£350
Sestertius	£80	£265	£2000
Severus Alexander			
Aureus	£1000	£2500	£15000
Denarius as Caesar	£65	£200	£1400
Denarius as Augustus	£15	£35	£300
Sestertius	£35	£100	£700
Dupondius or As	£25	£100	£600

Septimus Severus

Julia Domna

Geta

Macrinus

Elagabalus

Julia Maesa

	FROM F	VF	EF
Orbiana			
Denarius	£60	£200	£1400
As	£90	£345	£2000
Julia Mamaea			
Denarius	£15	£50	£350
Sestertius	£35	£115	£700

IMPERIAL COINAGE—Military Anarchy AD 235–270

Orbiana

Maximinus I			
Denarius	£15	£80	£350
Sestertius, Dupondius or As	£35	£135	£800
Diva Paula			
Denarius	£150	£450	£2850
Maximus Caesar			
Denarius	£70	£210	£1500
Sestertius	£65	£175	£1500
Gordian I & II, Africanus			
Denarius	£550	£1575	£7250
Sestertius	£550	£1850	£10000
Balbinus & Pupienus			
Antoninianus	£90	£265	£1575
Denarius	£80	£275	£1750
Gordian III			
Antoninianus	£10	£30	£200
Denarius	£15	£40	£250
Sestertius or As	£25	£90	£565
Tranquillina			
Common Colonial	£30	£115	£700
Philip I			
Antoninianus "Animal"			
Lion, stag, antelope, wolf & twins ...	£20	£65	£450
Other Antoninianus	£10	£30	£195
Sestertius, Dupondius or As	£25	£85	£565
Otacilla Severa			
Antoniniaus	£10	£30	£215
Antoninianus "Hipo"	£25	£85	£570
Sestertius	£25	£90	£550
Philip II			
Antoninianus	£10	£25	£200
Antoninianus "Goat"	£20	£70	£450
Sestertius, Dupondius or As	£30	£90	£565
Pacatian			
Antoninianus	£1500	£5000	—
Trajan Decius			
Antoninianus	£10	£35	£170
Antoninianus (DIVI series Augustus, Trajan etc)	£40	£135	£800
Double Sestertius	£260	£1000	£5000
Sestertius, Dupondius or As	£25	£90	£570
Herennius Etruscilla			
Antoninianus	£10	£40	£205
Sestertius, Dupondius or As	£30	£120	£775
Herennius Etruscus			
Antoninianus	£16	£60	£400
Sesterius, Dupondius or As	£55	£195	£1450
Hostilian			
Antoninianus as Caesar	£30	£120	£650
Antoninianus as Augustus	£70	£235	£1450
Trebonianus Gallus			
Antoninianus....................................	£10	£35	£195
Sestertius or As	£30	£120	£650
Volusian			
Antoninianus....................................	£10	£40	£300
Sestertius..	£30	£120	£1200

Julia Mamaea

Diva Paula

Gordian III

Trajan Decius

Hostilian

	FROM F	VF	EF
Aemilian			
Antoninianus	£45	£150	£850
Valerian I			
Antoninianus	£10	£30	£250
Sestertius & As	£45	£160	£1000
Diva Mariniana			
Antoninianus	£35	£135	£800
Gallienus			
Silver Antoninianus	£10	£35	£185
Ae Antoninianus	£5	£25	£165
Ae Antoninianus (Military bust)	£10	£30	£225
Ae Antoninianus (Legionary)	£75	£235	—
Ae Sestertius	£40	£150	£1250
Ae Denarius	£45	£135	£850
Saloninus			
Ae Antoninianus	£5	£25	£195
Valerian II			
Billon Antoninianus	£10	£40	£250
Saloninus			
Antoninianus	£15	£50	£2500
Macrianus & Quietus			
Billon Antoninianus	£45	£145	£850
Regalianus or Dryantilla			
Billon Antoninianus	£1850	£7500	—
Postumus			
Silver Antoninianus	£10	£25	£200
Ae Antoninianus	£5	£25	£140
Radiated sestertius	£45	£185	£1400
Laelianus			
Ae Antoninianus	£250	£800	£3600
Marius			
Ae Antoninianus	£40	£135	£770
Victorinus			
Ae Antoninianus	£5	£25	£165
Tetricus I & II			
Ae Antoninianus	£5	£25	£165
Claudius II Gothicus			
Ae Antoninianus	£5	£25	£195
Egypt, Alexandrian Billon tetradrachm	£5	£30	£195
DIVO Ae Antoninianus	£5	£30	£220
Quintillus			
Ae Antoninianus	£10	£35	£250

Postumus

Aurelian

Severina

IMPERIAL COINAGE—The Illyrian Emperors—AD 270–285

	FROM F	VF	EF
Aurelian			
Ae Antoninianus	£5	£45	£195
Ae Denarius	£20	£70	£475
Vabalathus & Aurelian			
Ae Antoninianus (bust both sides)	£20	£70	£450
Vabalathus			
Ae Antoninianus	£350	£1000	—
Severina			
Ae Antoninianus	£15	£50	£300
Ae As	£35	£110	£650
Zenobia			
Eygpt, Alexandrian Billon Tetradrachm	£700	£2750	—
Tacitus			
Ae Antoninianus	£15	£35	£250
Florian			
Ae Antoninianus	£25	£90	£550
Probus			
Gold Aureus	£1250	£3360	£18500
Ae Antoninianus	£10	£25	£200

Tacitus

Florian

	FROM F	VF	EF
Antoninianus (military or imp. Busts RIC G or H)	£10	£40	£250
Antoninianus			
(Other military or imp NOT BUSTS G or H)	£20	£70	£450
Antoninianus (VICTOR GERM rev.) ..	£10	£65	£225
Egypt, Alexandrian Billon tetradrachm	£5	£20	£115
Carus			
Ae Antoninianus	£15	£45	£300
Numerian			
Ae Antoninianus	£15	£45	£250
Carinus			
Ae Antoninianus	£10	£65	£250
Magna Urbica			
Ae Antoninianus	£95	£265	£1700
Julian of Pannonia			
Ae Antoninianus	£600	£2600	-

Carinus

Diocletian

IMPERIAL COINAGE—The Tetrarchy AD 285–307

Diocletian			
Gold Aureus	£1000	£2750	£16500
AR Argenteus	£100	£250	£1500
Ae Antoninianus & Radiates	£10	£30	£225
Ae Follis (London Mint)	£15	£50	£325
As above with LON mint mark	£100	£325	£1800
Ae Follis (other mints)	£10	£35	£195
Ae Follis (Imperial bust)....................	£25	£80	£450
Maximianus			
AR Argenteus	£100	£300	£1500
Ae Follis (London mint)	£15	£45	£300
Ae Follis (other mints)	£10	£35	£200
Ae Follis (MONETA rev.)	£10	£50	£250
Carausius			
Aureus	£8000	£26500	—
Denarius	£400	£1200	£7500
Ae Antoninianus (PAX)......................	£25	£100	£550
As above but full silvering	£35	£120	£800
Legionary Antoninianus	£75	£200	£2000
Expectate Veni Antoninianus	£100	£325	—
In the name of Diocletian or Maximian	£35	£130	£850
Allectus			
Aureus...	£11000	£34000	—
Ae Antoninianus	£25	£95	£700
As above but full silvering	£45	£155	£1000
Quinarius	£25	£95	£750
Constantius I			
AR Argenteus	£95	£300	£1500
Ae Follis (London Mint)	£15	£50	£325
Ae Follis (other mints)	£10	£35	£195
Ae Follis (SALVS rev.)	£15	£55	£300
Ae 4 (Lion or Eagle)	£10	£35	£200
Galerius			
Ae Follis (London mint)	£15	£40	£250
Ae Follis (other mints)	£10	£35	£175
Galeria Valeria			
Ae Follis	£30	£85	£500
Severus II			
Ae Follis (London mint)	£35	£100	£650
Ae Follis (other mints)	£30	£100	£500
Ae Radiate	£25	£50	£300
Ae Denarius	£25	£100	£500
Maximinus II			
Ae Follis (London mint)	£15	£45	£300
Ae Follis (other mints)	£5	£25	£150
Ae Radiate	£10	£35	£195

Maximianus

Carausius

Severus II

Maximinus II

	FROM F	VF	EF
Maxentius			
Ae Follis	£10	£35	£225
Romulus			
Ae Follis	£45	£145	£1500
Licinius I			
Billon Argenteus	£45	£165	£1000
Ae Follis (London mint)	£10	£30	£165
Ae Follis (other mints)	£10	£25	£140
AE3	£5	£20	£125
Licinius II			
AE3	£10	£30	£175
Alexander or Martinian			
AE	£1500	£4500	—

Licinius II

IMPERIAL COINAGE—Family of Constantine AD 307–350

	FROM F	VF	EF
Constantine I			
Billon Argenteus	£50	£170	£1000
Ae Follis (London mint)	£10	£30	£200
As above—helmeted bust	£15	£50	£300
Ae Follis (other mints) as Caesar ...	£15	£50	£350
Ae Follis (other mints) as Augustus	£5	£20	£120
AE3	£5	£20	£120
AE3 (London mint)	£10	£30	£195
AE3 (SARMATIA rev)	£10	£40	£250
Urbs Roma / Wolf & twins AE3/4..........	£5	£25	£140
Constantinopolis AE3/4	£5	£20	£130
Fausta & Helena			
AE3 (London mint)	£50	£165	£1000
AE3 (other mints)	£15	£75	£300
Theodora			
AE4	£10	£30	£200
Crispus			
AE3 (London mint)	£10	£35	£200
AE3	£10	£25	£135
Delmatius			
AE3/4	£15	£45	£250
Hanniballianus Rex			
AE4	£75	£240	£1350
Constantine II			
AE3 (London mint)	£10	£30	£205
AE3	£5	£30	£140
AE3/4	£5	£15	£110
Constans			
AE2 (centenionalis)	£10	£35	£200
AE3 (half centenionalis)	£5	£25	£180
AE4	£5	£20	£110
Constantius II			
Gold Solidus	£300	£800	£4500
Siliqua	£25	£100	£550
AE2 (or centenionalis)	£10	£30	£230
AE3 (or half centenionalis)	£5	£20	£135
AE3 (London mint)...........................	£15	£50	£275
AE3................................	£5	£15	£85

Constantine I

Constantine II

Magnentius

IMPERIAL COINAGE—Late period to the collapse of the Empire AD 350 to end

	FROM F	VF	EF
Magnentius			
Gold Solidus................................	£800	£2500	£13500
Silver Siliqua	£250	£835	£4500
Double centenionalis	£45	£195	£1300
Centenionalis	£15	£55	£345
Decentius			
Double centenionalis.......................	£70	£235	£1650
Centenionalis	£20	£65	£385
Vetranio			
AE2 (centenionalis)	£40	£135	£750
AE3 (half centenionalis)	£30	£100	£625

Vetranio

	FROM F	VF	EF
Nepotian			
AE2 (centenionalis)	£2000	£6825	—
Constantius Gallus			
AE2 (centenionalis)	£15	£40	£220
AE3 (half centenionalis)	£5	£30	£100
Julian II			
Siliqua	£28	£90	£550
AE1	£45	£135	£800
AE3 (helmeted bust)	£10	£30	£195
Anonymous, Serapis + Jupiter AE3	£195	£580	—
Jovian			
AE1	£65	£225	£1300
AE3	£15	£55	£220
Valentinian I			
Sold Solidus	£200	£550	£2500
Silver Milliarense............................	£165	£575	£3500
Siliqua	£25	£95	£550
AE3	£5	£20	£100
Valens			
Gold Solidus	£200	£525	£2500
Silver Milliarense............................	£190	£630	£3750
Siliqua	£25	£90	£550
AE3	£5	£20	£100
Procopius			
AE3	£45	£150	£850
Gratian			
Silver Milliarense............................	£165	£550	£2500
Siliqua	£25	£85	£500
AE3	£5	£30	£110
AE4	£5	£25	£100
Valentinian II			
Solidus	£220	£550	£2800
Siliqua	£25	£100	£550
AE2	£10	£30	£195
AE4	£2	£15	£95
Theodosius I			
Solidus	£225	£550	£2800
Siliqua	£30	£100	£635
AE2	£10	£45	£220
AE3	£10	£35	£220
Aelia Flaccilla			
AE2	£30	£115	£650
AE4...	£15	£50	£350
Magnus Maximus			
Solidus (AVGOB)	£4800	£13650	—
Solidus	£800	£2500	£15000
Siliqua	£40	£130	£850
Siliqua (AVGPS)	£700	£2350	—
AE2	£20	£70	£400
Flavius Victor			
Silver Sliqua	£140	£475	£2500
AE4	£30	£80	£445
Eugenius			
Silver Siliqua	£150	£500	£2500
Arcadius			
Gold Solidus...................................	£200	£525	£2500
Silver Siliqua	£25	£100	£550
Silver Half-siliqua	£150	£475	£2500
AE2	£10	£45	£200
AE4	£3	£15	£85

Julian II

Jovian

Valentinian I

Valens

Theodosius I

Arcadius

	FROM F	VF	EF
Eudoxia			
AE3	£25	£75	£450
Honorius			
Gold Solidus	£200	£500	£2500
Silver Siliqua	£30	£100	£575
AE4	£5	£20	£110
Constantine III			
Silver Siliqua	£145	£500	£2500
Theodosius II			
Gold Solidus	£200	£500	£2500
Johannes			
AE4	£115	£475	—
Valentinian III			
Gold Soldius..................................	£200	£520	£2500
AE4	£25	£85	£450

Honorius

Theodosius II

Ae = bronze; AE 1, 2, 3, 4 = bronze coins in descending order of size.

Coin illustrations by courtesy of Classical Numismatic Group/ Seaby Coins and Mike Vosper.

Finders of the Chew Valley Hoard, Lisa Grace and Adam Staples, unearthed some 2,528 coins with their metal detectors in the pouring rain in January 2019. Declared "hugely significant" and most certainly the find of a lifetime.

From the hoard, an Edward the Confessor penny (top), a William the Conqueror penny (left) and a Harold II penny (right).

ROMA NUMISMATICS LIMITED

Dealers and Auctioneers of English, World, Islamic and Ancient Coins

Victor Emmanuel II, 50 Lire 1864
Sold at auction by Roma Numismatics Ltd for £200,000

Contact us or visit www.RomaNumismatics.com/Selling for more information on how we help our consignors to realise the best possible sale prices for their coins, and to find out more about the bespoke sales options we can offer you.

20 FITZROY SQUARE
LONDON W1T 6EJ
+44 (0)20 7121 6518
INFO@ROMANUMISMATICS.COM

A SIMPLIFIED PRICE GUIDE TO

ENGLISH
HAMMERED COINS

PART I

780–1485

INTRODUCTION

We have taken our starting point for English hammered coin prices back to the middle Anglo-Saxon period. This time sees the country divided into separate kingdoms, the Viking divided areas and numismatically the introduction of the silver "penny" as the standard unit of currency (as well as a few struck halfpennies). This is a complicated time in our history and that is reflected numismatically. We have therefore listed only the commonest or most frequently found pieces or rulers within their kingdoms. For many later rulers the price is for the more common non-portait issue.

PRICING

The prices given in the following pages are intended to be used as a "Pocket book guide" to the values of the *most common* coins within any denomination of any one reign. The price quoted is what a collector may expect to pay for such a piece in the condition indicated. For more detailed information we recommend the reader to one of the many specialist publications.

GRADING

The prices quoted are generally for three different grades of condition: Fine (F), Very Fine (VF) and Extremely Fine (EF). A "Fine" coin is assumed to be a fairly worn, circulated, piece but with all or most of the main features and lettering still clear. "Very Fine" is a middle grade with a small amount of wear and most details fairly clear. For this edition we have included the prices for coins in Extremely Fine condition where appropriate, although very few hammered coins actually turn up in this grade (i.e. nearly mint state with hardly any wear). In some instances the prices quoted are theoretically based and are only included to provide a guide. It is important to note that on all hammered coins the very nature of striking, i.e. individually, by hand, means hammered coinage is rarely a straight grade and when listed by a dealer the overall condition will often be qualified by terms such as: *weak in parts, struck off-centre, cracked or chipped flan, double struck,* etc. When applicable the price should be adjusted accordingly.

HISTORY

Below the heading for each monarch we have given a few historical notes as and when they apply to significant changes in the coinage.

KINGS OF KENT

	F	VF
CUTHRED (798–807)	£900	£4000

(non portrait pieces may be not quite as highly priced)

ARCHBISHOPS OF CANTERBURY

WULFRED (805–832)	£800	£3350

COELNOTH (833–870)	£750	£3000

PLEGMUND (890–914) (non portrait)	£700	£2750

KINGS OF MERCIA

OFFA (757–796) (non portrait) .	£600	£2000
— — (portrait)	£800	£2500

COENWULF (796–821)	£400	£1300

BURGRED (852–874)	£350	£800

KINGS OF EAST ANGLIA

EDMUND (855–870)	£425	£1150

ST EDMUND (Danish E. Anglia 855–915)

(Many have crude lettering)	£250	£550

VIKING ISSUES OF YORK

	F	VF	
CNUT (READS CV N·NET·TI)	£225	£550	
ST PETER COINAGE (905–915)	£350	£900	

KINGS OF WESSEX (later all England)

ALFRED THE GREAT (871–99)	£600	£1850	
EDWARD THE ELDER (899–924)	£275	£600	
AETHELSTAN (924–39)	£400	£1150	
EADMUND (939–46)	£325	£725	
EADRED (946–55)	£325	£725	
EADWIG (955–59)	£750	£1900	

EDGAR (First King of All England) (959–975)

	F	VF	EF
Edgar Penny, non portrait (2 line inscription)	£250	£550	£1350

EDWARD THE MARTYR (975–978)

	F	VF	EF
Edward, Penny, Portrait	£1500	£4500	—

AETHELRED II (978–1016)

	F	VF	EF
Aethelred II, Penny (1st hand type illustrated)	£200	£450	£1250
Penny, last small cross type	£150	£250	£700

CNUT (1016–1035)

	F	VF	EF
Cnut, Penny (Quatrefoil type illustrated)	£150	£275	£600
Penny (short cross type)	£125	£250	£550

HAROLD I
(1035–40)

	F	VF	EF
Harold I, Penny (long cross type Illustrated)......£375		£900	£2000

HARTHACANUTE
(1035–42)

	F	VF	EF
Harthacanute, Penny, English Mint (in his own name) £1250		£4200	—
Harthacanute Penny (king's name given as "CNUT")......£650		£1750	—
Harthacanute, Penny, Danish type £325		£750	—

Danish type

EDWARD THE CONFESSOR
(1042–66)

	F	VF	EF
Edward the Confessor, Penny (helmet type illustrated)...... £180		£350	£1200
Edward the Confessor, Penny, facing bust type £140		£325	£900

HAROLD II
(1066)

	F	VF	EF
Harold II, Penny £1350		£3350	—

135

WILLIAM I
(1066–87)

The Norman Conquest had very little immediate effect on the coinage of England. The Anglo-Saxon standard of minting silver pennies was very high and the practice of the moneyer putting his name and mint town on the reverse continued as before, except with William's portrait of course. It is worth noting here that non-realistic, stylised portraits were used until the reign of Henry VII.

There are eight major types of pennies of which the last, the PAXS type, is by far the commonest.

	F	VF	EF
William I, Penny (PAXS type illustrated)	£300	£600	£1250

WILLIAM II
(1087–1100)

Very little change from his father's reign except that five new types were issued, most of which were much more crudely designed than previous, all are scarce.

	F	VF	EF
William II, Penny (cross in quatrefoil type illustrated)	£800	£2150	—

HENRY I
(1100–35)

There are fifteen different types of penny for this reign of which the last two are the most common. Most issues are of a very poor standard both in workmanship and metal, the prices reflect a poor quality of issue.

	F	VF	EF
Henry I, Penny type XV	£160	£475	—
Henry I, Penny type XIV (illustrated)	£225	£775	—
Halfpenny	£2000	£6000	—

STEPHEN
(1135–54)

This is historically a very complicated time for the coinage, mainly due to civil war and a consequential lack of central control in the country which resulted in very poor quality and deliberately damaged pieces. Coins were struck not only in the name of Stephen and his main rival claimant Matilda rare, but also by their supporters. The commonest issue is the "Watford" type; so named, as are many issues, after the area in which a hoard was found.

	F	VF	EF
Stephen, Penny ("Watford" type illustrated)	£250	£800	—

HENRY II
(1154–89)

There were two distinct issues struck during this reign. The first, Cross and Crosslets or "Tealby" coinage (named after Tealby in Lincolnshire, where a large hoard was found), continued to be very poorly made and lasted 20 years. However, in 1180 the new and superior "Short Cross" issue commenced, being issued from only twelve major towns.

	F	VF	EF
Henry II, Penny, Tealby	£100	£325	—

	F	VF	EF
Henry II, Penny, Short Cross	£45	£145	—

RICHARD I
(1189–1199)

There were no major changes during this reign, in fact pennies continued to be struck with his father Henry's name throughout the reign. The coins struck under Richard tend to be rather crude in style.

	F	VF	EF
Richard I, Penny	£60	£180	—

JOHN
(1199–1216)

As with his brother before him, there were no major changes during the reign of King John, and pennies with his father's name were struck throughout the reign, although they tended to be somewhat neater in style than those struck during the reign of Richard I.

	F	VF
John, Penny......................................	£45	£135

HENRY III
(1216–72)

The coinage during Henry III's reign continued as before with the short cross issue. However, in 1247 a new long cross design was introduced to prevent clipping. This design was to last in one form or another for many centuries. Late in the reign saw a brief appearance of the 1st English gold coin.

	F	VF	EF
Henry III, Penny, Short Cross	£25	£80	£275
Henry III, Penny, Long Cross...................	£25	£55	£200

EDWARD I
(1272–1307)

After a few years of issuing similar pieces to his father, and in his farther's name in 1279 Edward I ordered a major re-coinage. This consisted of well-made pennies, halfpennies and farthings in relatively large quantities, and for a brief period a groat (four pence) was produced. These were often mounted and gilded, the price is for an undamaged piece. The pennies are amongst the most common of all hammered coins.

	F	VF	EF
Edward I (and Edward II)			
Groat (often damaged) see below ...	£3250	£7500	—
Penny...	£20	£50	£250
Halfpenny...	£20	£60	—
Farthing..	£20	£55	—

Edward I penny

EDWARD II
(1307–1327)

	F	VF	EF
Edward II, long cross Pennies, Halfpennies and Farthings continued in very similar style to his father (Edward I)

	F	VF	EF
Pennies	£25	£70	—
Halfpennies	£40	£150	—
Farthings	£30	£120	—

EDWARD III
(1327–77)

This was a long reign which saw major changes in the coinage, the most significant being the introduction of a gold coinage (based on the Noble, valued at 6s 8d, and its fractions) and a regular issue of a large silver groat (and half groat). The provincial mints were limited to a few episcopal cities but coins of English type were also struck in the newly-acquired Calais Mint.

	F	VF	EF
Gold			
Noble	£800	£2650	£5250
Half Noble	£550	£1600	£3750
Quarter Noble	£300	£650	£1350
Silver			
Groat	£40	£140	£750
Half Groat	£30	£100	£425
Penny	£20	£80	£325
Half Penny	£15	£50	£250
Farthing	£25	£100	£300

Gold Noble

RICHARD II
(1377–1399)

The denominations continued during this reign much as before. However, coins are quite scarce mainly due to the lack of bullion gold and silver going into the mints, mainly because of an inbalance with European weights and fineness.

	F	VF	EF
Gold			
Noble	£1250	£4000	—
Half Noble	£1300	£4500	—
Quarter Noble	£450	£1250	—
Silver			
Groat	£500	£1750	—
Half Groat	£225	£800	—
Penny	£60	£300	—
Half Penny	£30	£100	—
Farthing	£125	£475	—

Gold Noble

139

HENRY IV
(1399–1413)

Because of the continuing problems with the scarcity of gold and silver the coinage was reduced by weight in 1412, towards the end of the reign. All coins of this reign are quite scarce.

	F	VF
Gold		
Noble, Light coinage....................	£2000	£6750
Half Noble, Light coinage...........	£2250	£7250
Quarter Noble, Light coinage	£700	£2100
Silver		
Groat, Light coinage....................	£2000	£6500
Half Groat, Heavy coinage..........	£750	£2350
Penny...	£450	£1200
Half Penny	£275	£800
Farthing......................................	£750	£2250

Noble

HENRY V
(1413–22)

Monetary reform introduced towards the end of his father's reign in 1412 improved the supply of bullion and hence coins of Henry V are far more common. All of the main denominations continued as before.

	F	VF	EF
Gold			
Noble	£1150	£3750	£6500
Half Noble	£900	£2750	—
Quarter Noble	£350	£750	£1750
Silver			
Groat, class "C"	£160	£475	—
Half Groat..............................	£125	£375	—
Penny......................................	£35	£150	—
Half Penny..............................	£25	£90	—
Farthing..................................	£350	£1000	—

Groat

HENRY VI
(1422–61 and again 1470–71)

Although there were no new denominations except for the Angel & Halfangel during the 2nd reign (see Edward IV below), Henry's first reign saw eleven different issues, each for a few years and distinguished by privy marks, i.e. annulets, pinecones, mascles, leaves etc.

HENRY VI *continued*

	F	VF	EF
Gold			
First reign—			
Noble, Annulet issue	£1000	£3350	£5500
Half Noble, Annulet issue	£750	£2150	£4500
Quarter Noble, Annulet issue	£350	£750	£1500
2nd reign—			
Angel	£2000	£5750	—
Half Angel	£4750	£13750	—
Silver			
Groat, Annulet issue	£50	£140	£375
Half Groat, Annulet issue	£30	£100	£325
Penny	£25	£70	£350
Half Penny, Annulet issue	£20	£50	£185
Farthing, Annulet issue	£100	£350	—

Noble

EDWARD IV
(1461–70 and again 1471–83)

The significant changes during these reigns were the replacement of the noble by the rose ryal (and revalued at 10 shillings) and the continuation of the angel at the old noble value. We also start to see mint-marks or initial marks appearing, usually at the top of the coin, they were used to denote the period of issue for dating purposes and often lasted for two to three years e.g. rose, lis, crown etc. Groats were issued at London, Bristol, Coventry, Norwich and York.

	F	VF	EF
Gold			
Noble and quarter noble (Heavy Coinage)			Very rare
Ryal	£900	£3000	£4750
"Flemish" copy of Ryal	£750	£2250	—
Half Ryal	£750	£2250	£4000
Quarter Ryal	£450	£1250	£2500
Angel, 2nd reign	£850	£2500	£3750
Half Angel, 2nd reign	£775	£2250	—
Silver			
Groat	£45	£125	£500
Half Groat Canterbury	£40	£140	£425
Penny	£30	£125	£350
Half Penny	£25	£80	—
Farthing, Heavy coinage	£350	£1000	—

Angel

RICHARD III
(1483–85)

The close of the Yorkist Plantagenet and Medieval period come together at this time. There are no new significant numismatic changes but most silver coins of Richard whilst not really rare, continue to be very popular and priced quite high. The smaller denominations are usually poor condition.

	F	VF	EF
Gold			
Angel	£5250	£17000	—
Half Angel	£8500	£27500	—
Silver			
Groat	£775	£2200	—
Half Groat	£1400	£4200	—
Penny	£400	£1100	—
Half Penny	£350	£1000	—
Farthing	£1650	£4750	—

Groat

PART II
1485–1663

Among the more significant features of the post-Renaissance period as it affected coinage is the introduction of realistic portraiture during the reign of Henry VII. We also have a much wider and varied number of new and revised denominations, for example eleven different gold denominations of Henry VIII and the same number of silver for Elizabeth I. Here we only mention the introduction or changes in the main denominations, giving a value for all of them, once again listing the commonest type.

HENRY VII
(1485–1509)

The gold sovereign of 20 shillings makes its first appearance in 1489 as does the testoon (later shilling) in about 1500. The silver penny was re-designed to a rather crude likeness of the sovereign, enthroned.

	F	VF	EF
Gold			
Sovereign	£30000	£100,000	—
Ryal	£35000	£135,000	—
Angel	£750	£2200	—
Half Angel	£700	£2000	—
Silver			
Testoon 1/-	£17500	£40,000	—
Groat, facing bust	£65	£185	£800
Half Groat	£30	£110	£400
Penny, sovereign type	£35	£100	£350
Half Penny	£25	£70	—
Farthing	£450	£1400	—

Profile Groat

HENRY VIII
(1509–47)

After a long initial period of very little change in the coinage, in 1526 there were many, with an attempt to bring the gold/silver ratio in line with the continental currencies. Some gold coins only lasted a short time and are very rare. The crown (in gold) makes its first appearance. Towards the end of the reign we see large issues of debased silver coins (with a high copper content) bearing the well-known facing portrait of the ageing King. These tend to turn up in poor condition and include the shilling in greater numbers. Similar posthumous issues were minted during early reign of Edward VI.

Gold			
Sovereign, 3rd coinage	£6500	£24000	—
Half Sovereign	£900	£3250	—
Angel	£850	£2400	£3500
Half Angel	£700	£2000	£3000
Quarter Angel	£800	£2400	—
George Noble	£11000	£37500	—
Half George Noble	£10000	£35000	—
Crown of the rose	£7250	£26500	—
Crown of the double rose	£750	£2400	—
Half Crown of the double rose	£600	£1650	—
Silver			
Testoon 1/-	£1000	£4500	—
Groat, 2nd coinage	£100	£265	£1250
Half Groat, 2nd coinage	£60	£160	£650
Penny	£35	£110	£425
Half Penny	£25	£80	—
Farthing	£300	£850	—

Gold Sovereign

EDWARD VI
(1547–53)

Some of the coins struck in the first few years of this short reign could really be called Henry VIII posthumous issues as there is continuity in both name and style from his father's last issue. However, overlapping this period are portrait issues of the boy King, particularly shillings (usually poor quality coins). This period also sees the first dated English coin (shown in Roman numerals) MDXLIX (1549). In 1551 however, a new coinage was introduced with a restored silver quality from the Crown (dated 1551) down to the new sixpence and threepence.

	F	VF	EF
Gold			
Sovereign (30s)	£7000	£25000	—
Half Sovereign	£1550	£6750	—
Crown	£2000	£7250	—
Half Crown	£1700	£5750	—
Angel	£14000	£40000	—
Half Angel	—	£45000	—
Sovereign (20s)	£6500	£20000	—
Silver			
Crown	£900	£2850	—
Half Crown	£600	£1750	—
Shilling	£125	£450	—
Sixpence	£135	£475	—
Groat	£750	£4250	—
Threepence	£225	£1150	—
Half Groat	£375	£1300	—
Penny	£60	£235	—
Half Penny	£225	£900	—
Farthing	£1250	£4250	—

Crowned bust half sovereign

MARY
(1553–54)

The early coins of Mary's sole reign are limited and continue to use some of the same denominations as Edward, except that the gold ryal was reintroduced.

	F	VF
Gold		
Sovereign (30s)	£8250	£27000
Ryal	£35000	—
Angel	£2250	£6500
Half Angel	£6000	£16000
Silver		
Groat	£175	£575
Half Groat	£700	£2400
Penny	£650	£2250

Groat

PHILIP & MARY
(1554–58)

After a very short reign alone, Mary married Philip of Spain and they technically ruled jointly (although not for very long in practise) until her death. After her marriage we see both her and Philip on the shillings and sixpences with both full Spanish and then English titles alone.

	F	VF
Gold		
Angel	£6500	£22000
Half Angel	£14000	—
Silver		
Shilling	£450	£1900
Sixpence	£450	£1750
Groat	£200	£650
Half Groat	£500	£1800
Penny	£65	£225

Shilling

ELIZABETH I
(1558–1603)

As might be expected with a long reign there are a number of significant changes in the coinage which include several new denominations—so many in silver that every value from the shilling downwards was marked and dated to distinguish them. Early on we have old base Edward VI shillings countermarked to a new reduced value (not priced here). Also due to a lack of small change and the expense of making a miniscule farthing we have a new threehalfpence and threefarthings. Finally we see the beginnings of a milled (machine produced) coinage for a brief period from 1561–71.

	F	VF	EF
Gold			
Sovereign (30s)	£7250	£20000	—
Ryal (15s)	£25000	£75000	—
Angel	£1150	£3250	—
Half Angel	£1050	£3100	—
Quarter Angel	£900	£2800	—
Pound (20s)	£3500	£13000	—
Half Pound	£1750	£5000	—
Crown	£1200	£3500	—
Half Crown	£1150	£3400	—
Silver			
Crown (mm l)	£1750	£5350	—
Half Crown (mm l)	£1000	£2750	—
Shilling	£80	£375	£1750
Sixpence	£55	£200	£1000
Groat	£60	£260	£750
Threepence	£40	£165	£450
Half Groat	£25	£80	£275
Threehalfpence	£40	£185	—
Penny	£20	£75	£225
Threefarthings	£65	£200	—
Half Penny	£30	£75	£135

Shilling

JAMES I
(1603–25)

Although the size of the gold coinage remains much the same as Elizabeth's reign, the name and weight or value of the denominations have several changes, i.e. Pound = Sovereign = Unite = Laurel. A new four shilling gold coin (thistle crown) was introduced. A number of the silver coins now have their value in Roman numerals on the coin. Relatively few angels were made from this period onwards and they are usually found pierced.

	F	VF	EF
Gold			
Sovereign (20s)	£3000	£13000	—
Unite	£700	£1750	£3750
Double crown/half unite	£475	£1300	£2850
Crown	£300	£800	£2000
Thistle Crown	£325	£750	£1850
Half Crown	£250	£550	—
Rose Ryal (30s)	£3250	£12000	—
Spur Ryal (15s)	£8000	£30000	—
Angel (pierced)	£700	£2200	—
Half Angel (Unpierced)	£1500	£5000	—
Laurel	£650	£1700	£3750
Half Laurel	£450	£1400	£3250
Quarter Laurel	£275	£700	£1750
Silver			
Crown	£750	£2100	—
Half Crown	£300	£800	—
Shilling	£75	£250	—
Sixpence	£55	£210	—
Half Groat	£20	£50	£150
Penny	£20	£45	£135
Half Penny	£10	£35	£100

Gold Unite, second bust

Silver Halfcrown

CHARLES I
(1625–49)

This reign is probably the most difficult to simplify as there are so many different issues and whole books have been produced on this period alone. From the beginning of the King's reign and throughout the Civil War, a number of mints operated for varying lengths of time, producing both regular and irregular issues. The Tower mint was taken over by Parliament in 1642 but before this a small quantity of milled coinage was produced alongside the regular hammered issues. The Court then moved to Oxford from where, for the next three years, large quantities of gold and silver were struck (including rare triple unites and large silver pounds). The most prolific of the provincial mints were those situated at Aberystwyth, York, Oxford, Shrewsbury, Bristol, Exeter, Truro, Chester and Worcester as well as some smaller mints mainly situated in the West Country. Among the more interesting coins of the period are the pieces struck on unusually-shaped flans at Newark and Pontefract whilst those towns were under siege. As many of the coins struck during the Civil War were crudely struck on hastily gathered bullion and plate, they provide a fascinating area of study. The prices indicated below are the minimum for the commonest examples of each denomination irrespective of town of origin.

	F	VF	EF
Gold			
Triple Unite (£3) (Oxford)	£12500	£35000	—
Unite	£700	£1850	—
Double crown/Half unite	£450	£1500	—
Crown	£300	£700	—
Angel (pierced)	£750	£2400	—
Angel (unpierced)	£2500	£8500	—
Silver			
Pound (20 shillings—Oxford)	£2750	£8500	—
Half Pound (Shrewsbury)	£1300	£3350	—
Crown (Truro, Exeter)	£400	£1200	—
Half Crown	£50	£200	—
Shilling	£40	£150	£900
Sixpence	£40	£140	£800
Groat (Aberystwyth)	£60	£175	£550
Threepence (Aberystwyth)	£55	£165	£500
Half Groat	£20	£60	£175
Penny	£20	£50	£160
Half Penny	£15	£30	£60

Triple unite

Oxford Halfcrown

Above: Newark siege shilling.

THE COMMONWEALTH
(1649–60)

After the execution of Charles I, Parliament changed the design of the coinage. They are simple non- portrait pieces with an English legend.

	F	VF	EF
Gold			
Unite	£2250	£5400	—
Double crown/Half unite	£1650	£4750	—
Crown	£1300	£3750	—
Silver			
Crown	£1300	£3000	£7000
Half Crown	£350	£850	£3350
Shilling	£275	£625	£2250
Sixpence	£225	£575	£2000
Half Groat	£45	£135	£350
Penny	£45	£140	£350
Halfpenny	£35	£85	£175

Crown

CHARLES II
(1660–85)

Although milled coins had been produced for Oliver Cromwell in 1656–58, after the Restoration of the monarchy hammered coins continued to be produced until 1663, when the machinery was ready to manufacture large quantities of good milled pieces.

	F	VF	EF
Gold			
Unite (2nd issue)	£1900	£5500	—
Double crown/Half unite	£1550	£4700	—
Crown (1st issue)	£1750	£5400	—
Silver			
Half Crown (3rd issue)	£235	£800	—
Shilling (3rd issue)	£140	£600	—
Sixpence (3rd issue)	£125	£475	—
Fourpence (3rd issue)	£40	£140	£275
Threepence (3rd issue)	£35	£125	£225
Twopence (3rd issue)	£20	£60	£160
Penny (3rd issue)	£35	£100	£200

Halfcrown

THE
UNITED KINGDOM
1656–2019

including

*England, Scotland,
Isle of Man,
Guernsey, Jersey, Alderney,
also Ireland*

When referring to this price guide one must bear a number of important points in mind. The points listed here have been taken into consideration during the preparation of this guide and we hope that the prices given will provide a true reflection of the market at the time of going to press. Nevertheless, the publishers can accept no liability for the accuracy of the prices quoted.

1. "As struck" examples with flaws will be worth less than the indicated price.
2. Any coin which is particularly outstanding, with an attractive natural toning or in superb state will command a much *higher* price than that shown.
3. These prices refer strictly to the British market, and do not reflect outside opinions.
4. Some prices given for coins not seen in recent years are estimates based on a knowledge of the market.
5. In the case of coins of high rarity, prices are not generally given.
6. In the listing, "—" indicates, where applicable, one of the following:
     a. Metal or bullion value only
     b. Not usually found in this grade
     c. Not collected in this condition
7. Proof coins are listed in FDC under the UNC column.
8. All prices are quoted in £ sterling, exclusive of VAT (where applicable).

FIFTY SHILLINGS

	F	VF	EF

OLIVER CROMWELL (1656–58)

	F	VF	EF
1656..	£25,000	£70,000	£170,000

Opinions differ as to whether the portrait coinage of Oliver Cromwell was ever meant for circulation but for the sake of completeness it has been decided to include it in this Yearbook. The fifty shillings gold coin is unique as it was only struck during Cromwell's time using the same dies that were used for the broad or 20 shillings coin but with a weight of approximately 2.5 times that of the broad.

FIVE GUINEAS

CHARLES II (1660–85)

Charles II

	F	VF	EF
1668 First bust	£4000	£11000	£40000
1668 — Elephant below bust	£4000	£10000	£40000
1669 —	£4000	£10000	—
1669 — Elephant...................................	£4000	£10000	—
1670 —	£4200	£10000	£40000
1670 Proof...	—	—	£160000
1671 —	£4000	£11000	£45000
1672 —	£4000	£10000	£44000
1673 —	£4000	£11000	£44000
1674 —	£4500	£12000	£50000
1675 —	£4000	£10000	£46000
1675 — Elephant...................................	£4200	£12000	—
1675 — Elephant & Castle below bust...	£4500	£11000	£45000
1676 —	£4000	£10000	£40000
1676 — Elephant & Castle	£4000	£10000	£45000
1677 —	£4000	£12000	£44000
1677/5 — Elephant................................	£4250	£12000	£46000
1677 — Elephant & Castle	£4200	£11000	£40000
1678/7 — 8 over 7..................................	£4000	£11000	£48000
1678/7 — Elephant & Castle	£4000	£11000	£50000
1678/7 Second Bust...............................	£4000	£10000	£40000
1679 —	£4400	£10000	£40000
1680 —	£4400	£10000	£40000
1680 — Elephant & Castle	£4200	£11000	£44000
1681 —	£4000	£10000	£40000
1681 — Elephant & Castle	£4000	£10000	£40000
1682 —	£4000	£10000	£40000
1682 — Elephant & Castle	£4000	£10000	£40000
1683 —	£4000	£10000	£42000
1683 — Elephant & Castle	£4000	£10000	£43000
1684 —	£4200	£12000	£50000
1684 — Elephant & Castle	£4200	£12000	£50000

JAMES II (1685–88)

	F	VF	EF
1686..	£4500	£13500	£50000
1687..	£4000	£13500	£45000
1687 Elephant & Castle..........................	£4000	£13500	£45000
1688	£4000	£13500	£45000
1688 Elephant & Castle..........................	£4800	£15000	£55000

	F	VF	EF

WILLIAM AND MARY (1688–94)

	F	VF	EF
1691..	£4000	£11000	£42000
1691 Elephant & Castle..........................	£4000	£11000	£42000
1692..	£4000	£11000	£42000
1692 Elephant & Castle..........................	£4250	£12000	£44000
1693..	£4000	£11000	£42000
1693 Elephant & Castle..........................	£4000	£11000	£42000
1694..	£4000	£11000	£40000
1694 Elephant & Castle..........................	£4000	£11000	£40000

WILLIAM III (1694–1702)

	F	VF	EF
1699 First bust	£4000	£12000	£42000
1699 — Elephant & Castle	£4200	£12500	£44000
1700 —	£4000	£12500	£42000
1701 Second bust "fine work"	£4000	£12500	£40000

(1701 "fine work" — beware recent forgeries)

ANNE (1702–14)

Pre-Union with Scotland

	F	VF	EF
1703 VIGO below bust	£60000	£120000	£400000
1705..	£6000	£20000	£60000
1706..	£6000	£20000	£55000

Post-Union (different shields)

	F	VF	EF
1706..	£4000	£12000	£50000
1709 Narrow shields..............................	£4000	£12000	£50000
1711 Broader shields	£4000	£12000	£50000
1713 —	£4000	£11000	£45000
1714 —	£4000	£12000	£45000
1714/3	£4200	£12000	£46000

William & Mary

GEORGE I (1714–27)

	F	VF	EF
1716..	£5000	£15000	£55000
1717..	£4800	£16000	£52000
1720..	£5000	£14000	£52000
1726..	£5000	£15000	£48000

GEORGE II (1727–60)

	F	VF	EF
1729 Young head	£3200	£10000	£40000
1729 — E.I.C. below head......................	£3400	£11000	£40000
1731 —	£4000	£11000	£42000
1735 —	£4000	£11000	£40000
1738 —	£4000	£11000	£40000
1741	£4000	£10000	£38000
1741/38 41 over 38	£3750	£10000	£38000
1746 Old head, LIMA	£3750	£10000	£38000
1748 —	£3750	£10000	£35000
1753 —	£3750	£10000	£35000

GEORGE III (1760–1820)

	F	VF	EF
1770 Patterns.......................................	—	—	£300000
1773..	—	—	£300000
1777..	—	—	£280000

Anne

151

TWO GUINEAS

	F	VF	EF

CHARLES II (1660–85)

	F	VF	EF
1664 First bust	£2200	£5000	£18000
1664 — Elephant	£1900	£4400	£13000
1665 —		Extremely rare	
1669 —		Extremely rare	
1671 —	£2600	£6000	£20000
1673 First bust		Extremely rare	
1675 Second bust	£2200	£5000	£14000
1676 —	£2000	£5000	£16000
1676 — Elephant & Castle	£2000	£5000	£16000
1677 —	£2000	£5000	£15000
1677 — Elephant & Castle		Extremely rare	
1678/7 —	£2200	£5000	£15000
1678 — Elephant		Extremely rare	
1678 — Elephant & Castle	£2000	£4000	£15000
1679 —	£2000	£4000	£12000
1680 —	£2000	£4500	£13000
1681 —	£2000	£4000	£12000
1682 — Elephant & Castle	£2000	£4000	£13000
1683 —	£2000	£3700	£12000
1683 — Elephant & Castle	£2000	£4500	£15000
1684 —	£1800	£4250	£12000
1684 — Elephant & Castle	£2000	£4750	£17000

Charles II

JAMES II (1685–88)

	F	VF	EF
1687	£2500	£6000	£24000
1688/7	£2800	£7000	£25000

WILLIAM AND MARY (1688–94)

	F	VF	EF
1691 Elephant & Castle		Extremely rare	
1693	£2200	£5500	£17000
1693 Elephant & Castle	£2400	£6000	£18000
1694 — 4 over 3	£2200	£5000	£17000
1694/3 Elephant & Castle	£2200	£5000	£17500

James II

WILLIAM III (1694–1702)

	F	VF	EF
1701 "fine work"	£2000	£5000	£18000

ANNE (1702–14)

	F	VF	EF
1709 Post Union	£1600	£4000	£15000
1711	£1550	£4000	£13000
1713	£1500	£3750	£13000
1714/3	£1800	£4000	£16000

GEORGE I (1714–27)

	F	VF	EF
1717	£1600	£4000	£12000
1720	£1600	£4000	£12500
1720/17	£1750	£4000	£12000
1726	£1500	£4000	£13000

Anne

	F	VF	EF
## GEORGE II (1727–60)			
1733 Proof only FDC		Extremely Rare	
1734 Young head 4 over 3	£2000	£4500	
1735 —	£1800	£5000	£11000
1738 —	£900	£2000	£3600
1739 —	£900	£1800	£3600
1739 Intermediate head	£900	£1700	£5000
1740 —	£900	£1800	£5200
1748 Old head	£950	£1850	£5500
1753 —	£1100	£2750	£6500

	F	VF	EF
## GEORGE III (1760–1820)			
1768 Patterns only	—	Extremely Rare	
1773 Patterns only	—	Extremely Rare	
1777 Patterns only	—	Extremely Rare	

George II

GUINEAS

	F	VF	EF
## CHARLES II (1660–85)			
1663 First bust	£3500	£12500	£50000
1663 — Elephant below	£3000	£8000	—
1663 Second bust	£3000	£9000	£35000
1664 Second bust	£3000	£8500	—
1664 — Elephant	£3600	£10000	£40000
1664 Third bust	£900	£3000	£15000
1664 — Elephant	£1800	£5000	£18000
1665 —	£900	£3000	£13000
1665 — Elephant	£1800	£5000	£20000
1666 —	£900	£3000	£12000
1667 —	£900	£3000	£12000
1668 —	£850	£3000	£12000
1668 — Elephant		Extremely rare	
1669 —	£900	£2850	£12500
1670 —	£900	£2700	£13000
1671 —	£900	£2700	£13000
1672 —	£900	£3200	£13000
1672 Fourth bust	£800	£2400	£8000
1673 Third bust	£900	£3000	£12000
1673 Fourth bust	£700	£2000	£9000
1674 —	£700	£2000	£9000
1674 — Elephant & Castle		Extremely rare	
1675 —	£750	£2500	£9000
1675 — CRAOLVS Error		Extremely rare	
1675 — Elephant & Castle	£850	£3200	£12500
1676 —	£700	£2200	£8500
1676/4 — 6 over 4	£700	£2200	£8500
1676 — Elephant & Castle	£800	£3200	£14000
1677 —	£700	£2200	£9000
1677 — GRATIR Error		Extremely rare	
1677/5 — Elephant 7 over 5		Extremely rare	
1677 — Elephant & Castle	£800	£2800	£12000
1678 —	£750	£2000	£8500
1678 — Elephant		Extremely rare	
1678 — Elephant & Castle	£800	£3000	£13000

Charles II, third bust

Charles II, fourth bust, elephant & castle below

	F	VF	EF
1679 —	£750	£2200	£9000
1679 — Elephant & Castle	£900	£3300	£13000
1680 —	£700	£2100	£8500
1680 — Elephant & Castle	£900	£3500	£12500
1681 —	£750	£2400	£9000
1681 — Elephant & Castle	£900	£3500	£13000
1682 —	£750	£2500	£9000
1682 — Elephant & Castle	£900	£3800	£14000
1683 —	£700	£2200	£9000
1683 — Elephant & Castle	£850	£3500	£13000
1684 —	£700	£2500	£10000
1684 — Elephant & Castle	£900	£3600	£13500

James II, first bust, elephant & castle below

JAMES II (1685–1688)

	F	VF	EF
1685 First bust	£800	£2700	£11000
1685 — Elephant & Castle	£900	£3200	£12500
1686 —	£800	£2600	£11000
1686 — Elephant & Castle		Extremely rare	
1686 Second bust	£750	£2400	£8500
1686 — Elephant & Castle	£900	£3500	£13000
1687 —	£750	£2300	£9000
1687 —Elephant & Castle	£900	£3500	£14000
1688 —	£700	£2400	£9000
1688 — Elephant & Castle	£850	£3200	£11500

James II, second bust

WILLIAM AND MARY (1688–94)

	F	VF	EF
1689..	£700	£2300	£10000
1689 Elephant & Castle....................	£750	£2400	£10500
1690..	£800	£2700	£10500
1690 GVLIFLMVS............................	£800	£2700	£10500
1690 Elephant & Castle....................	£900	£3000	£12000
1691..	£750	£2500	£9500
1691 Elephant & Castle....................	£800	£2500	£9500
1692..	£800	£2500	£9500
1692 Elephant	£950	£3000	£11000
1692 Elephant & Castle....................	£850	£2800	£11000
1693..	£750	£2600	£10000
1693 Elephant	£1100	£4000	£14000
1693 Elephant & Castle....................	£1000	£4000	£13500
1694..	£900	£2800	£10000
1694/3...	£900	£2800	£10000
1694 Elephant & Castle....................	£900	£3000	£10500
1694/3 Elephant & Castle.................	£900	£3000	£10500

(Please note there are several overstamp erros of this reign. Prices are similar to standard issues)

WILLIAM III (1694–1702)

	F	VF	EF
1695 First bust	£650	£2400	£8000
1695 — Elephant & Castle	£1200	£5000	£15000
1696 —	£700	£2600	£9000
1696 — Elephant & Castle		Extremely rare	
1697 —	£700	£3000	£9250
1697 Second bust	£650	£2500	£8500
1697 — Elephant & Castle	£1500	£6000	—
1698 —	£700	£2500	£7500
1698 — Elephant & Castle	£1200	£4000	£12000
1699 —	£700	£2300	£8000
1699 — Elephant & Castle		Extremely rare	
1700 —	£650	£2200	£8000
1700 — Elephant & Castle	£1200	£4750	—
1701 —	£725	£2500	£7500
1701 — Elephant & Castle		Extremely rare	
1701 Third bust "fine work"..............	£1400	£5000	£15000

William III, second bust

	F	VF	EF

ANNE (1702–1714)

	F	VF	EF
1702 (Pre-Union) First bust	£1200	£4000	£14000
1703 — VIGO below	£18000	£50000	£130000
1705 —	£1200	£4000	£13000
1706 —	£1200	£4000	£13000
1707 —	£1200	£4000	£13000
1707 — (Post-Union)	£750	£3000	£10000
1707 — Elephant & Castle	£1200	£5000	£15000
1707 Second bust	£700	£2800	£9000
1708 First bust	£750	£3000	£11000
1708 Second bust	£600	£2200	£7500
1708 — Elephant & Castle	£1000	£4000	£13000
1709 —	£800	£2000	£8000
1709 — Elephant & Castle	£900	£3500	£12000
1710 Third bust	£700	£1500	£5000
1711 —	£700	£1500	£5000
1712 —	£700	£1700	£5500
1713 —	£550	£1500	£4500
1714 —	£550	£1500	£4500
1714 GRΛTIΛ	£700	£1700	£5000

Anne, second bust

GEORGE I (1714–27)

	F	VF	EF
1714 First bust (Prince Elector)	£1600	£4250	£14000
1715 Second bust	£750	£1800	£5000
1715 Third bust	£500	£1500	£5200
1716 —	£600	£1500	£5500
1716 Fourth bust	£525	£1500	£5000
1717 —	£525	£1500	£5000
1718/7 — 8 over 7		Extremely rare	
1718 —		Extremely rare	
1719 —	£550	£1500	£4500
1720 —	£550	£1500	£4200
1721 —	£600	£1600	£5200
1721 — Elephant & Castle		Extremely rare	
1722 —	£550	£1600	£5000
1722 — Elephant & Castle		Extremely rare	
1723 —	£550	£1500	£5000
1723 Fifth bust	£550	£1500	£5000
1724 —	£550	£1500	£4750
1725 —	£550	£1500	£4750
1726 —	£525	£1400	£4500
1726 — Elephant & Castle	£2000	£7500	£22000
1727 —	£650	£1800	£5500

George I, third bust

GEORGE II (1727–60)

	F	VF	EF
1727 First young head, early large shield	£1000	£3000	£12000
1727 — Larger lettering, early small shield	£1000	£3200	£14000
1728 — —	£1100	£3500	£12500
1729 2nd young head E.I.C. below	£1100	£3500	£13000
1729 — Proof		Very Rare	
1730 —	£700	£1800	£6000
1731 —	£700	£2000	£7000
1731 — E.I.C. below	£1100	£3500	£12000
1732 —	£700	£2500	£8000
1732 — E.I.C. below	£900	£3000	£10000
1732 — Larger lettering obverse	£650	£1700	£6000
1732 — — E.I.C. below	£1200	£3000	£14000
1733 — —	£550	£1400	£4000
1734 — —	£550	£1400	£4000
1735 — —	£550	£1400	£4000
1736 — —	£550	£1500	£3850
1737 — —	£550	£1500	£3850

George II, 1759, old head, larger lettering

	F	VF	EF
1738 — —	£550	£1500	£4250
1739 Intermediate head	£500	£1400	£4000
1739 — E.I.C. below...........................	£1100	£3000	£11000
1740 —	£600	£1500	£5000
1741/39 —	£800	£2400	£7000
1743 —	£800	£2400	£7000
1745 — Larger lettering obv. Older bust	£500	£1400	£4750
1745 — LIMA below............................	£2000	£7000	£18000
1746 — (GEORGIVS) Larger lettering obv.	£550	£1500	£4000
1747 Old head, large lettering	£500	£1200	£3700
1748 —	£500	£1200	£3800
1749 —	£500	£1300	£3800
1750 —	£500	£1200	£3800
1751 — small lettering.....................	£450	£1100	£3800
1753 —	£450	£1100	£3800
1755 —	£450	£1200	£3750
1756 —	£450	£1100	£3800
1758 —	£450	£1100	£3800
1759 —	£450	£1100	£3800
1760 —	£450	£1100	£3600

George III first head

GEORGE III (1760–1820)

	F	VF	EF
1761 First head...................................	£2000	£5500	£11000
1763 Second head	£1600	£4000	£10000
1764 —	£1400	£4000	£11000
1764 – No stop above bust	£2000	£5000	£11000
1765 Third head	£450	£800	£2000
1766 —	£450	£800	£2000
1767 —	£500	£1000	£2500
1768 —	£450	£800	£2000
1769 —	£450	£800	£2100
1770 —	£1200	£2500	£7000
1771 —	£450	£650	£1700
1772 —	£450	£650	£1700
1773 —	£450	£650	£1800
1774 Fourth head	£400	£650	£1250
1775 —	£425	£650	£1400
1776 —	£425	£675	£1300
1777 —	£425	£600	£1300
1778 —	£750	£1200	£3250
1779 —	£450	£725	£1250
1781 —	£400	£650	£1400
1782 —	£400	£650	£1400
1783 —	£375	£625	£1400
1784 —	£375	£625	£1300
1785 —	£375	£625	£1300
1786 —	£450	£700	£1350
1787 Fifth head, "Spade" reverse	£400	£575	£1100
1788 —	£400	£575	£1100
1789 —	£400	£575	£1150
1790 —	£425	£650	£1300
1791 —	£400	£600	£1200
1792 —	£400	£600	£1200
1793 —	£400	£650	£1250
1794 —	£400	£650	£1200
1795 —	£400	£650	£1200
1796 —	£400	£650	£1200
1797 —	£400	£650	£1200
1798 —	£400	£650	£1200
1799 —	£475	£800	£1800
1813 Sixth head, "Military" reverse	£900	£2200	£5000

(Beware of counterfeits of this series—many dangerous copies exist)

Fourth head

Fifth head, Spade reverse

Sixth "Military" head

HALF GUINEAS

	F	VF	EF
CHARLES II (1660–85)			
1669 First bust	£450	£1500	£5500
1670 —	£450	£1500	£4750
1671 —	£550	£1700	£6000
1672 —	£500	£1500	£5250
1672 Second bust	£500	£1450	£4750
1673 —	£500	£1600	£5250
1674 —	£550	£1800	£5000
1675 —	£550	£1800	£5000
1676 —	£475	£1500	£4750
1676 — Elephant & Castle	£725	£3000	—
1677 —	£475	£1600	£4600
1677 — Elephant & Castle	£650	£2000	—
1678 —	£500	£1500	£4800
1678/7 —	£500	£1500	£4800
1678/7 — Elephant & Castle	£650	£1900	£7500
1679 —	£450	£1600	£4400
1680 —	£450	£2000	—
1680 — Elephant & Castle	£700	£2200	£7800
1681 —	£500	£1600	—
1682 —	£450	£1600	£4250
1682 — Elephant & Castle	£650	£2000	£8000
1683 —	£450	£1500	£4500
1683 — Elephant & Castle		Extremely rare	
1684 —	£450	£1450	£4500
1684 — Elephant & Castle	£650	£2100	£8000

Charles II, first bust

	F	VF	EF
JAMES II (1685–88)			
1686	£550	£1600	£5000
1686 Elephant & Castle	£900	£3750	£9000
1687	£550	£1700	£5500
1688	£525	£1700	£5500

	F	VF	EF
WILLIAM AND MARY (1688–94)			
1689 First busts	£600	£1850	£5000
1690 Second busts	£575	£2000	£5000
1691 —	£600	£1700	£5250
1691 — Elephant & Castle	£625	£2000	£6000
1692 —	£600	£1800	£6000
1692 — Elephant		Extremely rare	
1692 — Elephant & Castle	£650	£2200	£6250
1693 —		Extremely rare	
1694 —	£600	£1700	£5000

William & Mary, first busts

	F	VF	EF
WILLIAM III (1694–1702)			
1695	£400	£1200	£4000
1695 Elephant & Castle	£600	£2000	£6000
1696 —	£500	£1500	£5000
1697 Larger Harp rev.	£600	£1800	£6000
1698	£500	£1300	£4200
1698 Elephant & Castle	£600	£1700	£5250
1699		Extremely rare	
1700	£400	£1100	£4000
1701	£375	£1000	£3800

William III, elephant & castle below bust

	F	VF	EF

ANNE (1702–14)

	F	VF	EF
1702 (Pre-Union)	£850	£2800	£9000
1703 VIGO below bust	£8000	£22000	£60000
1705	£800	£2600	£8500
1707 (Post-Union)	£325	£1000	£3500
1708	£350	£1000	£3500
1709	£350	£1100	£3500
1710	£325	£850	£3300
1711	£325	£850	£3300
1712	£350	£900	£3500
1713	£300	£850	£3200
1714	£300	£850	£3200

Anne

GEORGE I (1714–27)

	F	VF	EF
1715 First bust	£750	£1500	£4500
1717 —	£400	£750	£3250
1718 —	£400	£750	£3250
1718/7 —	£400	£750	£3250
1719 —	£375	£750	£3250
1720 —	£400	£500	£3000
1721 —		Extremely rare	
1721 — Elephant & Castle		Extremely rare	
1722 —	£400	£800	£3350
1723 —	£450	£850	£3400
1724 —	£400	£850	£4000
1725 Second bust	£400	£750	£3000
1726 —	£400	£750	£3200
1727 —	£400	£800	£3400

George I, second bust

GEORGE II (1727–60)

	F	VF	EF
1728 Young head	£550	£1350	£4000
1729 —	£550	£1400	£3900
1729 — E.I.C.	£650	£1500	£5000
1730 —	£450	£1000	£3600
1730 — E.I.C.	£700	£2000	—
1731 —	£350	£1000	£3250
1731 — E.I.C.		Extremely rare	
1732 —	£350	£1000	£3250
1732 — E.I.C.		Extremely rare	
1733 —			Unknown
1734 —	£350	£850	£3200
1735 —			Unknown
1736 —	£350	£850	£3250
1737 —	£400	£900	£3500
1738 —	£350	£800	£3000
1739 —	£350	£800	£2800
1739 — E.I.C.		Extremely rare	
1740 Intermediate head	£400	£1000	£3250
1743 —		Extremely rare	
1745 —	£350	£1000	£3300
1745 — LIMA	£1250	£3750	£10000
1746 —	£325	£750	£2250
1747 Old head	£375	£750	£2600
1748 —	£325	£750	£2500
1749 —	£375	£850	£2500
1750 —	£350	£750	£2700
1751 —	£325	£750	£2400
1752 —	£325	£750	£2400
1753 —	£325	£750	£2400
1755 —	£325	£650	£2400
1756 —	£350	£600	£2300
1758 —	£300	£750	£2600
1759 —	£275	£700	£2200
1759/8	£280	£600	£2500
1760 —	£280	£700	£2200

George II, young head

George II, old head

GEORGE III (1760–1820)

	F	VF	EF
1762 First head	£700	£1900	£5200
1763 —	£750	£2500	£6500
1764 Second head	£275	£525	£1400
1765 —	£500	£1500	£4000
1766 —	£275	£500	£1700
1768 —	£275	£550	£1700
1769 —	£325	£600	£1750
1772 —		Extremely rare	
1773 —	£325	£700	£1900
1774 —	£350	£750	£2200
1774 Third head		Extremely rare	
1775 —	£1400	£4000	£10000
1775 Fourth head	£250	£425	£1050
1775 — Proof		Extremely rare	
1776 —	£275	£550	£1400
1777 —	£275	£550	£1100
1778 —	£275	£550	£1200
1779 —	£275	£550	£1300
1781 —	£275	£550	£1200
1783 —	£500	£1800	—
1784 —	£225	£500	£1000
1785 —	£225	£500	£950
1786 —	£225	£500	£950
1787 Fifth head, "Spade" rev.	£225	£375	£900
1788 —	£225	£375	£900
1789 —	£225	£375	£900
1790 —	£225	£375	£875
1791 —	£225	£375	£875
1792 —	£1500	£4000	—
1793 —	£225	£475	£900
1794 —	£225	£475	£850
1795 —	£225	£525	£1000
1796 —	£225	£475	£900
1797 —	£225	£475	£900
1798 —	£225	£475	£900
1800 —	£325	£900	£2500
1801 Sixth head, Shield in Garter rev.	£225	£350	£800
1802 —	£225	£350	£800
1803 —	£225	£350	£800
1804 Seventh head	£225	£350	£800
1805		Extremely rare	
1806 —	£225	£375	£800
1808 —	£225	£375	£800
1899 —	£225	£375	£800
1810 —	£225	£400	£800
1811 —	£325	£600	£1500
1813 —	£325	£600	£1200

George III, second head

George III, fifth head, "spade" reverse

THIRD GUINEAS

DATE	F	VF	EF
GEORGE III (1760–1820)			
1797 First head, date in legend	£150	£275	£625
1798 — —	£150	£275	£625
1799 — —	£400	£800	£1800
1800 — —	£150	£300	£725
1801 Date under crown	£170	£350	£775
1802 —	£170	£350	£775
1803 —	£170	£350	£725
1804 Second head	£140	£260	£650
1806 —	£140	£275	£650
1808 —	£140	£350	£700
1809 —	£140	£350	£700
1810 —	£140	£350	£700
1811 —	£525	£1300	£3000
1813 —	£300	£600	£1300

George III, date in legend

George III, date under crown

QUARTER GUINEAS

	F	VF	EF
GEORGE I (1714–27)			
1718	£150	£300	£725
GEORGE III (1760–1820)			
1762	£250	£500	£900

George I

FIVE POUNDS

DATE	Mintage	F	VF	EF	UNC
GEORGE III (1760–1820)					
1820 (pattern only)	—				Extremely rare
GEORGE IV (1820–30)					
1826 proof only	—	—	—	—	£65,000
VICTORIA (1837–1901)					
1839 Proof Only (Una & The Lion) Many Varieties FDC £175,000 upwards					
1887	53,844	£1400	£2000	£2800	£3800
1887 Proof	797	—	—	—	£20000
1887 S on ground on rev. (Sydney Mint)					Excessively rare
1893	20,405	£2000	£2800	£4750	£8000
1893 Proof	773	—	—	—	£16000
EDWARD VII (1902–10)					
1902	34,910	£1500	£2000	£2750	£4000
1902 Matt proof	8,066	—	—	—	£3500

DATE	MINTAGE	F	VF	EF	UNC
GEORGE V (1911–36)					
1911 Proof only	2,812	—	—	—	£8500
GEORGE VI (1937–52)					
1937 Proof only	5,501	—	—	—	£8000

Later issues are listed in the Decimal section.

TWO POUNDS

GEORGE III (1760–1820)

1820 (pattern only).............		—	—	—	Extremely rare

GEORGE IV (1820–30)

1823 St George reverse.....	—	£800	£1100	£2500	£4250
1826 Proof only, shield reverse	—	—	—	—	Extremely rare

WILLIAM IV (1830–37)

1831 Proof only	225	—	—	—	£18500

VICTORIA (1837–1901)

1887...................................	91,345	£675	£950	£1350	£1900
1887 Proof.........................	797	—	—	—	£3250
1887 S on ground of rev. (Sydney Mint)				Excessively rare	
1893...................................	52,212	£800	£1100	£2000	£3000
1893 Proof.........................	773	—	—	—	£5500

EDWARD VII (1902–10)

1902...................................	45,807	£650	£800	£1200	£2000
1902 Matt proof.................	8,066	—	—	—	£1800

GEORGE V (1911–36)

1911 Proof only	2,812	—	—	—	£2750

GEORGE VI (1937–52)

1937 Proof only	5,501	—	—	—	£2750

Later issues are listed in the Decimal section.

CROMWELL GOLD

	F	VF	EF
OLIVER CROMWELL (1656–58)			
1656 Fifty Shillings	£24,000	£70,000	£160,000
1656 Twenty Shillings.............................	£5,500	£15,000	£35,000

SOVEREIGNS

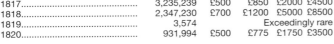

DATE	MINTAGE	F	VF	EF	UNC

GEORGE III (1760–1820)

	MINTAGE	F	VF	EF	UNC
1817	3,235,239	£500	£850	£2000	£4500
1818	2,347,230	£700	£1200	£5000	£8500
1819	3,574		Exceedingly rare		
1820	931,994	£500	£775	£1750	£3500

George III

GEORGE IV (1820–30)

	MINTAGE	F	VF	EF	UNC
1821 First bust, St George reverse	9,405,114	£500	£750	£180	—
1821 — Proof	incl. above	—	—	—	£10000
1822 —	5,356,787	£450	£750	£2000	£3000
1823 —	616,770	£1000	£2750	£8000	—
1824 —	3,767,904	£500	£900	£2250	£4000
1825 —	4,200,343	£700	£2000	£6000	£8500
1825 Second bust, shield reverse	incl. above	£425	£700	£1750	£2600
1826 —	5,724,046	£425	£700	£1500	£2600
1826 — Proof	—	—	—	—	£8000
1827 —	2,266,629	£475	£750	£1750	£3500
1828 —	386,182	£6000	£15000	£30000	—
1829 —	2,444,652	£475	£800	£2500	£3500
1830 —	2,387,881	£475	£800	£2500	£3500

George IV, shield reverse

WILLIAM IV (1830–37)

	MINTAGE	F	VF	EF	UNC
1831	598,547	£600	£1000	£3250	£5000
1831 Proof, plain edge	—	—	—	—	£12,000
1832	3,737,065	£500	£900	£2500	£3800
1833	1,225,269	£500	£900	£2500	£3800
1835	723,441	£500	£900	£2500	£3800
1836	1,714,349	£500	£900	£2000	£3800
1836 N. of Anno struck on shield	—	£6000	£11000	—	—
1837	1,172,984	£525	£950	£2000	£4200

William IV

Note—from the Victoria reign onwards, the prices of coins in lower grade will be subject to the bullion price of gold.

VICTORIA (1837–1901)

Many of the gold coins struck at the colonial mints found their way into circulation in Britain, for the sake of completeness these coins are listed here. These can easily be identified by a tiny initial letter for the appropriate mint which can be found below the base of the reverse shield or, in the case of the St George reverse, below the bust on the obverse of the Young Head issues, or on the "ground" below the horse's hoof on the later issues.

YOUNG HEAD ISSUES

Shield reverse
(Note—Shield back sovereigns in Fine/VF condition, common dates, are normally traded as bullion + a percentage)

	MINTAGE	F	VF	EF	UNC
1838	2,718,694	£750	£1400	£3750	£6000
1839	503,695	£1100	£2750	£4000	£8000
1839 Proof, plain edge	—	—	—	—	£18000
1841	124,054	£4750	£9500	£22000	—
1842	4,865,375	£300	£400	£1000	£2000
1843	5,981,968	£300	£400	£1000	£2000
1843 "Narrow shield" variety	incl. above	£5000	£10000	—	—
1843 Roman I in date not 1841	—	£750	£1500	—	—
1844	3,000,445	£300	£400	£1000	£1800
1845	3,800,845	£300	£400	£1000	£1800
1846	3,802,947	£300	£400	£1000	£1800

DATE	MINTAGE	F	VF	EF	UNC
1847	4,667,126	£295	£420	£1000	£1800
1848	2,246,701	£295	£420	£1000	£1800
1849	1,755,399	£295	£420	£1000	£1600
1850	1,402,039	£295	£420	£1000	£1600
1851	4,013,624	£295	£420	£750	£1600
1852	8,053,435	£295	£420	£850	£1600
1853	10,597,993	£295	£420	£750	£1600
1853 Proof...............................	—	—	—		—£20000
1854 Incuse WW	3,589,611	£295	£420	£750	£1750
1854 Surface raised WW	3,589,611	£295	£420	£750	£2000
1855	4,806,160	£295	£420	£750	£1750
1856	8,448,482	£295	£420	£750	£1750
1857	4,495,748	£295	£420	£750	£1750
1858	803,234	£295	£420	£750	£1750
1859	1,547,603	£295	£420	£750	£1750
1859 "Ansell" (additional line on lower part of hair ribbon)..........	—	£750	£1800	£9000	—
1860	2,555,958	£295	£310	£650	£1250
1861	7,624,736	£295	£310	£600	£1250
1862	7,836,413	£295	£310	£650	£1250
1863	5,921,669	£295	£310	£600	£1250
1863 Die No 827 on Truncation...				Extremely rare	
1863 with Die number below shield	incl. above	£295	£310	£600	£1100
1864 —	8,656,352	£295	£310	£650	£1100
1865 —	1,450,238	£295	£310	£650	£1100
1866 —	4,047,288	£295	£310	£600	£1100
1868 —	1,653,384	£295	£310	£550	£1100
1869 —	6,441,322	£295	£310	£550	£1000
1870 —	2,189,960	£295	£310	£550	£1100
1871 —	8,767,250	£295	£310	£500	£1100
1872 —	8,767,250	£295	£310	£500	£1000
1872 no Die number	incl. above	£295	£310	£500	£1000
1873 with Die number	2,368,215	£295	£310	£600	£1000
1874 —	520,713	£2000	£4000	£12,000	—

The mint initial appears below the shield, i.e. "S" indicates that the coin was struck at the Sydney Mint

M below reverse shield (Melbourne Mint)

1872..	748,180	£295	£310	£500	£1250
1873..	—		Extremely rare		
1874..	1,373,298	£295	£310	£350	£1250
1879..			Extremely rare		
1880..	3,053,454	£700	£1650	£3000	£5500
1881..	2,325,303	£295	£310	£350	£1600
1882..	2,465,781	£295	£310	£350	£1150
1883..	2,050,450	£295	£310	£600	£3200
1884..	2,942,630	£295	£310	£350	£1000
1885..	2,967,143	£295	£310	£350	£1000
1886..	2,902,131	£1800	£4000	£6500	£8000
1887..	1,916,424	£600	£1350	£3500	£5000

S below reverse shield (Sydney Mint)

1871	2,814,000	£295	£310	£340	£1300
1872..	1,815,000	£295	£310	£340	£1600
1873..	1,478,000	£295	£310	£340	£1300
1875..	2,122,000	£295	£310	£340	£1300
1877..	1,590,000	£295	£310	£340	£1300
1878..	1,259,000	£295	£310	£400	£1400
1879..	1,366,000	£295	£310	£350	£1300
1880..	1,459,000	£295	£310	£340	£1500
1881..	1,360,000	£295	£310	£350	£1500
1882..	1,298,000	£295	£310	£340	£1300
1883..	1,108,000	£295	£310	£340	£1100
1884..	1,595,000	£295	£310	£340	£1100
1885..	1,486,000	£295	£310	£340	£1100
1886..	1,667,000	£295	£310	£340	£1100
1887..	1,000,000	£295	£310	£340	£1500

> **IMPORTANT NOTE:**
> The prices quoted in this guide are set at September 2019 with the price of gold at £1,220 per ounce and silver £14.50 per ounce— market fluctuations can have a marked effect on the values of modern precious metal coins.

DATE	MINTAGE	F	VF	EF	UNC
St George & Dragon reverse					
1871	incl. above	£295	£310	£340	£500
1872	incl. above	£295	£310	£340	£500
1873	incl. above	£295	£310	£350	£500
1874	incl. above	£295	£310	£340	£500
1876	3,318,866	£295	£310	£340	£500
1878	1,091,275	£295	£310	£340	£500
1879	20,013	£600	£1500	£13,000	—
1880	3,650,080	£295	£310	£340	£500
1884	1,769,635	£295	£310	£340	£500
1885	717,723	£295	£310	£350	£500
M below bust on obverse (Melbourne Mint)					
1872	incl. above	£295	£500	£1150	£4200
1873..	752,199	£295	£310	£350	£500
1874..	incl. above	£295	£310	£350	£500
1875..	incl. above	£295	£310	£340	£500
1876..	2,124,445	£295	£310	£350	£550
1877..	1,487,316	£295	£310	£340	£500
1878..	2,171,457	£295	£310	£340	£500
1879..	2,740,594	£295	£310	£340	£500
1880..	incl. above	£295	£310	£340	£500
1881..	incl. above	£295	£310	£340	£500
1882..	incl. above	£295	£310	£340	£500
1883..	incl. above	£295	£310	£340	£500
1884..	incl. above	£295	£310	£340	£500
1885..	incl. above	£295	£310	£340	£500
1886..	incl. above	£295	£310	£340	£500
1887..	incl. above	£295	£310	£340	£500
S below bust on obverse (Sydney Mint)					
1871	2,814,000	£295	£310	£350	£500
1872..	incl. above	£295	£310	£340	£700
1873..	incl. above	£295	£310	£340	£500
1874..	1,899,000	£295	£310	£340	£500
1875..	inc above	£295	£310	£340	£500
1876..	1,613,000	£295	£310	£350	£500
1877..	—				Unknown
1879..	incl. above	£295	£310	£350	£500
1880..	incl. above	£295	£310	£350	£500
1881..	incl. above	£295	£310	£350	£500
1882..	incl. above	£295	£310	£340	£550
1883..	incl. above	£295	£310	£340	£500
1884..	incl. above	£295	£310	£340	£500
1885..	incl. above	£295	£310	£340	£500
1886..	incl. above	£295	£310	£340	£500
1887..	incl. above	£295	£310	£340	£500
JUBILEE HEAD ISSUES					
1887..	1,111,280	£295	£310	£340	£350
1887 Proof....................................	797	—	—	—	£3000
1888..	2,717,424	£295	£310	£350	£500
1889..	7,257,455	£295	£310	£340	£500
1890..	6,529.887	£295	£310	£340	£500
1891..	6,329,476	£295	£310	£340	£500
1892..	7,104,720	£295	£310	£340	£500
M on ground on reverse (Melbourne Mint)					
1887	940,000	£295	£310	£375	£500
1888..	2,830,612	£295	£310	£340	£450
1889..	2,732,590	£295	£310	£340	£450
1890..	2,473,537	£295	£310	£340	£450
1891..	2,749,592	£295	£310	£340	£450
1892..	3,488,750	£295	£310	£340	£450
1893..	1,649,352	£295	£310	£340	£450

M below bust indicates Melbourne Mint

S below bust indicates Sydney Mint

Jubilee head type

"M" below the horse's hoof above the date indicates that the coin was struck at the Melbourne Mint

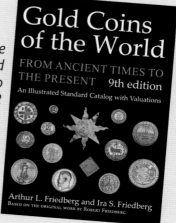

DATE	MINTAGE	F	VF	EF	UNC

S on ground on reverse (Sydney Mint)

1887	1,002,000	£295	£400	£1600	£2750
1888	2,187,000	£295	£310	£340	£500
1889	3,262,000	£295	£310	£340	£500
1890	2,808,000	£295	£310	£340	£500
1891	2,596,000	£295	£310	£340	£500
1892	2,837,000	£295	£310	£340	£500
1893	1,498,000	£295	£310	£340	£500

OLD HEAD ISSUES

1893	6,898,260	£295	£310	£340	£500
1893 Proof	773	—	—	—	£2600
1894	3,782,611	£295	£310	£340	£400
1895	2,285,317	£295	£310	£340	£400
1896	3,334,065	£295	£310	£340	£400
1898	4,361,347	£295	£310	£340	£400
1899	7,515,978	£295	£310	£340	£400
1900	10,846,741	£295	£310	£340	£400
1901	1,578,948	£295	£310	£340	£400

M on ground on reverse (Melbourne Mint)

1893	1,914,000	£295	£310	£340	£360
1894	4,166,874	£295	£310	£340	£360
1895	4,165,869	£295	£310	£340	£360
1896	4,456,932	£295	£310	£340	£360
1897	5,130,565	£295	£310	£340	£360
1898	5,509,138	£295	£310	£340	£360
1899	5,579,157	£295	£310	£340	£360
1900	4,305,904	£295	£310	£340	£360
1901	3,987,701	£295	£310	£340	£360

P on ground on reverse (Perth Mint)

1899	690,992	£295	£310	£500	£2500
1900	1,886,089	£295	£310	£340	£360
1901	2,889,333	£295	£310	£340	£360

S on ground on reverse (Sydney Mint)

1893	1,346,000	£295	£310	£340	£450
1894	3,067,000	£295	£310	£340	£360
1895	2,758,000	£295	£310	£340	£360
1896	2,544,000	£295	£310	£350	£500
1897	2,532,000	£295	£310	£340	£360
1898	2,548,000	£295	£310	£340	£360
1899	3,259,000	£295	£310	£340	£360
1900	3,586,000	£295	£310	£340	£360
1901	3,012,000	£295	£310	£340	£360

Old head type

EDWARD VII (1902–10)

1902	4,737,796	£295	£310	£340	£360
1902 Matt proof	15,123	—	—	—	£700
1903	8,888,627	£295	£310	£340	£360
1904	10,041,369	£295	£310	£340	£360
1905	5,910,403	£295	£310	£340	£360
1906	10,466,981	£295	£310	£340	£360
1907	18,458,663	£295	£310	£340	£360
1908	11,729,006	£295	£310	£340	£360
1909	12,157,099	£295	£310	£340	£360
1910	22,379,624	£295	£310	£340	£360

C on ground on reverse (Ottawa Mint)

1908 Satin finish Proof only	633			Extremely rare	
1909	16,300	£295	£310	£500	£800
1910	28,020	£295	£310	£500	£700

DATE	MINTAGE	F	VF	EF	UNC
M on ground on reverse (Melbourne Mint)					
1902	4,267,157	£295	£310	£340	£360
1903	3,521,780	£295	£310	£340	£360
1904	3,743,897	£295	£310	£340	£360
1905	3,633,838	£295	£310	£340	£360
1906	3,657,853	£295	£310	£340	£360
1907	3,332,691	£295	£310	£340	£360
1908	3,080,148	£295	£310	£340	£360
1909	3,029,538	£295	£310	£340	£360
1910	3,054,547	£295	£310	£340	£360
P on ground on reverse (Perth Mint)					
1902	3,289,122	£295	£310	£340	£360
1903	4,674,783	£295	£310	£340	£360
1904	4,506,756	£295	£310	£340	£360
1905	4,876,193	£295	£310	£340	£360
1906	4,829,817	£295	£310	£340	£360
1907	4,972,289	£295	£310	£340	£360
1908	4,875,617	£295	£310	£340	£360
1909	4,524,241	£295	£310	£340	£360
1910	4,690,625	£295	£310	£340	£360
S on ground on reverse (Sydney Mint)					
1902	2,813,000	£295	£310	£330	£280
1902 Proof	incl. above			Extremely rare	
1903	2,806,000	£295	£310	£340	£360
1904	2,986,000	£295	£310	£340	£360
1905	2,778,000	£295	£310	£340	£360
1906	2,792,000	£295	£310	£340	£360
1907	2,539,000	£295	£310	£340	£360
1908	2,017,000	£295	£310	£340	£375
1909	2,057,000	£295	£310	£340	£375
1910	2,135,000	£295	£310	£340	£375

> **IMPORTANT NOTE:** The prices quoted in this guide are set at September 2019 with the price of gold at £1,220 per ounce and silver £14.50 per ounce— market fluctuations can have a marked effect on the values of modern precious metal coins.

GEORGE V (1911–36)

(Extra care should be exercised when purchasing as good quality forgeries exist of virtually all dates and mintmarks)

DATE	MINTAGE	F	VF	EF	UNC
1911	30,044,105	£295	£310	£340	£350
1911 Proof	3,764	—	—	—	£1250
1912	30,317,921	£295	£310	£340	£360
1913	24,539,672	£295	£310	£340	£360
1914	11,501,117	£295	£310	£340	£360
1915	20,295,280	£295	£310	£340	£360
1916	1,554,120	£295	£310	£500	£750
1917	1,014,714	£1500	£5500	£20000	—
1925	4,406,431	£295	£310	£340	£360
C on ground on reverse (Ottawa Mint)					
1911	256,946	£295	£310	£500	£750
1913	3,715	£295	£375	£1750	—
1914	14,891	£295	£310	£1500	—
1916	6,111			Extremely rare	
1917	58,845	£295	£310	£600	£850
1918	106,516	£295	£310	£500	£650
1919	135,889	£295	£310	£500	£650
I on ground on reverse (Bombay Mint)					
1918	1,295,372	£295	£310	£340	—
M on ground on reverse (Melbourne Mint)					
1911	2,851,451	£295	£310	£340	£360
1912	2,469,257	£295	£310	£340	£360
1913	2,323,180	£295	£310	£340	£360
1914	2,012,029	£295	£310	£340	£360
1915	1,637,839	£295	£310	£340	£375
1916	1,273,643	£295	£310	£340	£375
1917	934,469	£295	£310	£500	£750
1918	4,969,493	£295	£310	£340	£360
1919	514,257	£295	£310	£350	£425

DATE	MINTAGE	F	VF	EF	UNC
1920	530,266	£1350	£2500	£4000	£6500
1921	240,121	£4000	£7000	£8000	£24000
1922	608,306	£4000	£7000	£7000	£23000
1923	510,870	£295	£310	£500	£750
1924	278,140	£295	£310	£500	£750
1925	3,311,622	£295	£310	£340	£450
1926	211,107	£295	£310	£340	£450
1928	413,208	£500	£900	£1700	£3800
1929	436,719	£900	£1000	£1700	£4750
1930	77,547	£295	£310	£500	£750
1931	57,779	£295	£310	£750	£1000

P on ground on reverse (Perth Mint)

1911	4,373,165	£295	£310	£340	£360
1912	4,278,144	£295	£310	£340	£360
1913	4,635,287	£295	£310	£340	£360
1914	4,815,996	£295	£310	£340	£360
1915	4,373,596	£295	£310	£340	£360
1916	4,096,771	£295	£310	£340	£375
1917	4,110,286	£295	£310	£340	£375
1918	3,812,884	£295	£310	£340	£360
1919	2,995,216	£295	£310	£340	£360
1920	2,421,196	£295	£310	£340	£360
1921	2,134,360	£295	£310	£340	£360
1922	2,298,884	£295	£310	£340	£360
1923	2,124,154	£295	£310	£340	£360
1924	1,464,416	£295	£310	£340	£360
1925	1,837,901	£295	£310	£500	£650
1926	1,313,578	£500	£900	£1500	£4000
1927	1,383,544	£295	£310	£500	£750
1928	1,333,417	£295	£310	£400	£575
1929	1,606,625	£295	£310	£340	£400
1930	1,915,352	£295	£310	£500	£675
1931	1,173,568	£295	£310	£340	£400

S on ground on reverse (Sydney Mint)

1911	2,519,000	£295	£310	£340	£360
1912	2,227,000	£295	£310	£340	£360
1913	2,249,000	£295	£310	£340	£360
1914	1,774,000	£295	£310	£340	£360
1915	1,346,000	£295	£310	£340	£375
1916	1,242,000	£295	£250	£340	£360
1917	1,666,000	£295	£310	£340	£360
1918	3,716,000	£295	£310	£340	£360
1919	1,835,000	£295	£310	£340	£360 ⇨

Melbourne Mint (M on ground)

Perth Mint (P on ground)

DATE	MINTAGE	F	VF	EF	UNC
1920...............................	—		Excessively rare		
1921...............................	839,000	£600	£900	£1750	£2750
1922...............................	578,000		Extremely rare		
1923...............................	416,000		Extremely rare		
1924...............................	394,000	£600	£1100	£1500	£2750
1925...............................	5,632,000	£295	£310	£340	£400
1926...............................	1,031,050		Extremely rare		

SA on ground on reverse (Pretoria Mint)

1923...............................	719	£800	£1850	£3500	£7500
1923 Proof..............................	655		Extremely rare		
1924...............................	3,184	—	£3000	£5000	—
1925...............................	6,086,264	£295	£310	£340	£360
1926...............................	11,107,611	£295	£310	£340	£360
1927...............................	16,379,704	£295	£310	£340	£360
1928...............................	18,235,057	£295	£310	£340	£360
1929...............................	12,024,107	£295	£310	£340	£360
1930...............................	10,027,756	£295	£310	£340	£360
1931...............................	8,511,792	£295	£310	£340	£360
1932...............................	1,066,680	£295	£310	£340	£375

Pretoria Mint (SA on ground)

GEORGE VI (1937–52)

1937 Proof only	5,501	—	—	£3750	£5500

ELIZABETH II (1952–   )

Pre Decimal Issues

1957..	2,072,000	£295	£310	£340	£360
1958..	8,700,140	£295	£310	£340	£360
1959..	1,358,228	£295	£310	£340	£360
1962..	3,000,000	£295	£310	£340	£360
1963..	7,400,000	£295	£310	£340	£360
1964..	3,000,000	£295	£310	£340	£360
1965..	3,800,000	£295	£310	£340	£360
1966..	7,050,000	£295	£310	£340	£360
1967..	5,000,000	£295	£310	£340	£360
1968..	4,203,000	£295	£310	£340	£360

Later issues are included in the Decimal section.

HALF SOVEREIGNS

GEORGE III (1760–1820)

1817..	2,080,197	£200	£370	£1000	£1750
1818..	1,030,286	£220	£400	£1000	£1750
1820..	35,043	£220	£400	£800	£1500

GEORGE IV (1820–30)

1821 First bust, ... ornate shield reverse	231,288	£600	£1600	£3750	£5000
1821 — Proof	unrecorded	—	—	—	£8000
1823 First bust, Plain shield rev..................................	224,280	£200	£280	£1000	£1750
1824 —	591,538	£200	£280	£850	£1500
1825 —	761,150	£200	£280	£750	£1200
1826 bare head, shield with full legend reverse............	344,830	£200	£320	£1000	£1500
1826 — Proof	unrecorded	—	—	—	£5000
1827 —	492,014	£200	£340	£1000	£1600
1828 —	1,224,754	£200	£350	£800	£1450

DATE	MINTAGE	F	VF	EF	UNC

WILLIAM IV (1830–37)

DATE	MINTAGE	F	VF	EF	UNC
1831 Proof only	unrecorded	—	—	—	£6000
1834	133,899	£300	£600	£1500	£2400
1835	772,554	£300	£600	£1000	£2000
1836	146,865	£250	£500	£1250	£2100
1836 obverse from 6d die	incl. above	£2500	£5000	£10000	—
1837	160,207	£275	£500	£1400	£2000

VICTORIA (1837–1901)

YOUNG HEAD ISSUES

Shield reverse

DATE	MINTAGE	F	VF	EF	UNC
1838	273,341	£170	£245	£1000	£1800
1839 Proof only	1,230	—	—	—	£6500
1841	508,835	£180	£260	£1250	£22000
1842	2,223,352	£160	£230	£1000	£1600
1843	1,251,762	£160	£230	£1000	£1600
1844	1,127,007	£160	£230	£850	£1150
1845	887,526	£320	£720	£3000	£5000
1846	1,063,928	£160	£200	£850	£1200
1847	982,636	£160	£200	£750	£1100
1848	410,595	£160	£200	£850	£1200
1849	845,112	£160	£200	£750	£1100
1850	179,595	£240	£620	£2500	£3500
1851	773,573	£160	£220	£700	£1100
1852	1,377,671	£160	£220	£700	£1100
1853	2,708,796	£160	£220	£700	£1100
1853 Proof	unrecorded	—	—	—	£12500
1855	1,120,362	£160	£200	£700	£1100
1856	2,391,909	£160	£200	£700	£1100
1857	728,223	£160	£200	£700	£1100
1858	855,578	£160	£200	£700	£1100
1859	2,203,813	£160	£200	£700	£1100
1860	1,131,500	£160	£200	£700	£1100
1861	1,130,867	£160	£200	£700	£1100
1862	unrecorded	£750	£2000	£10000	—
1863	1,571,574	£160	£200	£700	£1000
1863 with Die number	incl. above	£160	£200	£800	£1000
1864 —	1,758,490	£160	£200	£650	£1000
1865 —	1,834,750	£160	£200	£650	£1000
1866 —	2,058,776	£160	£200	£650	£1000
1867 —	992,795	£160	£200	£650	£1000
1869 —	1,861,764	£160	£200	£650	£1000
1870 —	1,159,544	£160	£200	£650	£1000
1871 —	2,062,970	£160	£200	£650	£1000
1872 —	3,248,627	£160	£200	£650	£1000
1873 —	1,927,050	£160	£200	£650	£1000
1874 —	1,884,432	£160	£200	£650	£1000
1875 —	516,240	£160	£200	£650	£1000
1876 —	2,785,187	£160	£200	£650	£1000
1877 —	2,197,482	£160	£200	£650	£1000
1878 —	2,081,941	£160	£200	£650	£1000
1879 —	35,201	£160	£200	£650	£1000
1880 —	1,009,049	£160	£200	£650	£1000
1880 no Die number	incl. above	£160	£200	£900	£1200
1883 —	2,870,457	£160	£200	£600	£950
1884 —	1,113,756	£160	£200	£650	£1000
1885 —	4,468,871	£160	£200	£600	£1000

M below shield (Melbourne Mint)

DATE	MINTAGE	F	VF	EF	UNC
1873	165,034	£150	£230	£1000	—
1877	80,016	£150	£280	£2000	—
1881	42,009	£150	£330	£2000	—
1882	107,522	£150	£225	£700	—
1884	48,009	£150	£225	£1750	—
1885	11,003	£150	£330	£3750	—
1886	38,008	£150	£280	£6000	—
1887	64,013	£170	£630	£10000	£16,000

Date	Mintage	F	VF	EF	UNC
S below shield (Sydney Mint)					
1871	180,000 (?)	£150	£210	£750	—
1872	356,000	£150	£210	£750	—
1875	unrecorded	£150	£210	£750	—
1879	94,000	£150	£210	£650	—
1880	80,000	£150	£230	£850	—
1881	62,000	£150	£280	£1000	—
1882	52,000		Extremely rare		
1883	220,000	£150	£210	£900	—
1886	82,000	£150	£180	£600	—
1887	134,000	£155	£230	£700	£4000

JUBILEE HEAD ISSUES

Date	Mintage	F	VF	EF	UNC
1887	871,770	£150	£160	£250	£350
1887 Proof	797	£150	£160	—	£2200
1890	2.266,023	£150	£160	£500	£750
1891	1,079,286	£150	£160	£300	£475
1892	13,680,486	£150	£160	£300	£475
1893	4,426,625	£150	£160	£300	£475
M below shield (Melbourne Mint)					
1887	incl. above	£150	£160	£400	£600
1893	110,024	£150	£160	£450	£750
S below shield (Sydney Mint)					
1887	incl. above	£150	£160	£300	£600
1889	64,000	£150	£280	£1500	—
1891	154,000	£150	£180	£1000	—

OLD HEAD ISSUES

Date	Mintage	F	VF	EF	UNC
1893	incl. above	£150	£160	£185	£250
1893 Proof	773	—	—	—	£2350
1894	3,794,591	£150	£160	£185	£250
1895	2,869,183	£150	£160	£185	£250
1896	2,946,605	£150	£160	£185	£250
1897	3,568,156	£150	£160	£185	£250
1898	2,868,527	£150	£160	£185	£250
1899	3,361,881	£150	£160	£185	£250
1900	4,307,372	£150	£160	£185	£250
1901	2,037,664	£150	£160	£185	£250
M on ground on reverse (Melbourne Mint)					
1893	unrecorded		Extremely rare		
1896	218,946	£150	£180	£450	—
1899	97,221	£150	£180	£550	—
1900	112,920	£150	£180	£600	—
P on ground on reverse (Perth Mint)					
1900	119,376	£150	£330	£550	—
S on ground on reverse (Sydney Mint)					
1893	250,000	£150	£180	£600	—
1897	unrecorded	£150	£180	£500	—
1900	260,00	£150	£180	£400	—

EDWARD VII (1902–10)

Date	Mintage	F	VF	EF	UNC
1902	4,244,457	£150	£155	£175	£150
1902 Matt proof	15,123	—	—	—	£600
1903	2,522,057	£150	£155	£175	£225
1904	1,717,440	£150	£155	£175	£225
1905	3,023,993	£150	£155	£175	£225
1906	4,245,437	£150	£155	£175	£225
1907	4,233,421	£150	£155	£225	£250
1908	3,996,992	£150	£155	£250	£250
1909	4,010,715	£150	£155	£275	£350
1910	5,023,881	£150	£155	£160	£200
M on ground on reverse (Melbourne Mint)					
1906	82,042	£145	£180	£750	£1100
1907	405,034	£145	£150	£250	£325
1908	incl. above	£145	£150	£250	£350
1909	186,094	£145	£150	£600	£750

DATE		F	VF	EF	UNC
P on ground on reverse (Perth Mint)					
1904..	60,030	£145	£180	£1000	—
1908..	24,668	£145	£180	£950	—
1909..	44,022	£145	£150	£500	—
S on ground on reverse (Sydney Mint)					
1902	84,000	£145	£155	£200	£325
1902 Proof..................................				Extremely rare	
1903..	231,000	£130	£150	£250	£325
1906..	308,000	£145	£155	£200	£300
1908..	538,000	£145	£150	£160	£300
1910..	474,000	£145	£150	£160	£300

GEORGE V (1911–36)

		F	VF	EF	UNC
1911..	6,104,106	£145	£150	£160	£175
1911 Proof..................................	3,764	—	—	—	£1000
1912..	6,224,316	£145	£150	£160	£175
1913..	6,094,290	£145	£150	£160	£175
1914..	7,251,124	£145	£150	£160	£175
1915..	2,042,747	£145	£150	£160	£175
M on ground on reverse (Melbourne Mint)					
1915..	125,664	£145	£150	£160	£200
P on ground on reverse (Perth Mint)					
1911	130,373	£145	£150	£250	£325
1915..	136,219	£145	£150	£250	£325
1918..	unrecorded	£205	£600	£2000	£3750
1919..	56,786				Rare
1920..	53,208				Rare
S on ground on reverse (Sydney Mint)					
1911	252,000	£145	£150	£160	£175
1912..	278,000	£145	£150	£160	£175
1914..	322,000	£145	£150	£160	£175
1915..	892,000	£145	£150	£160	£175
1916..	448,000	£145	£150	£160	£175
SA on ground on reverse (Pretoria Mint)					
1923 Proof only	655	—	—	—	£1400
1925..	946,615	£145	£150	£160	£175
1926..	806,540	£145	£150	£160	£175

GEORGE VI (1937–52)

		F	VF	EF	UNC
1937 Proof only	5,501	—	—	—	£950

Later issues are included in the Decimal section.

BALDWIN'S
ESTABLISHED 1872

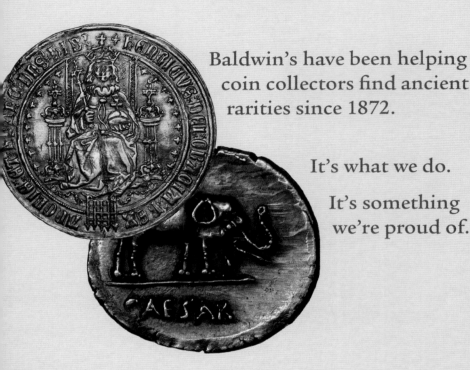

Baldwin's have been helping
coin collectors find ancient
rarities since 1872.

It's what we do.

It's something
we're proud of.

Discover a personal service with a team of world
renowned specialists to help you discover exquisite
items that have stood the test of time.

Visit www.baldwin.co.uk

To contact us:
PHONE: +44 (0) 2079 306879 | EMAIL: COINS@BALDWIN.CO.UK | WEB: www.baldwin.co.uk
VISIT: 399 STRAND, LONDON, WC2R 0LX

 /BaldwinsCoins   @BaldwinsCoins   @BaldwinsCoins   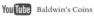 Baldwin's Coins

CROWNS

DATE	F	VF	EF	UNC

OLIVER CROMWELL

	F	VF	EF	UNC
1658 8 over 7 (always)	£1900	£3500	£7000	—
1658 Dutch Copy		Extremely rare		
1658 Patterns. In Various Metals		Extremely rare		

CHARLES II (1660–85)

	F	VF	EF	UNC
1662 First bust, rose (2 varieties)	£250	£800	£5000	—
1662 — no rose (2 varieties)	£250	£800	£5000	—
1663 —	£250	£800	£4750	—
1664 Second bust	£200	£800	£4500	—
1665 —	£1500	£4000	—	—
1666 —	£300	£1000	£5000	—
1666 — error RE.X for REX		Extremely rare		
1666 — Elephant below bust	£900	£3500	£20000	—
1667 —	£160	£500	£3000	—
1668/7 — 8 over 7	£170	£550	—	—
1668 —	£170	£550	£3500	—
1669/8 — 9 over 8	£350	£800	—	—
1669 —	£300	£1000	£5000	—
1670/69 — 70 over 69	£200	£1000	—	—
1670 —	£175	£600	£4000	—
1671	£170	£600	£3200	—
1671 Third bust	£170	£600	£3200	—
1672 —	£170	£500	£3200	—
1673 —	£170	£500	£3200	—
1674 —		Extremely rare		
1675 —	£700	£2200	—	—
1675/3 —	£700	£2200	—	—
1676 —	£175	£550	£3200	—
1677 —	£190	£600	£3500	—
1677/6 — 7 over 6	£200	£900	—	—
1678/7 —	£200	£900	—	—
1678/7 — 8 over 7	£275	£900	—	—
1679 —	£180	£600	£3500	—
1679 Fourth bust	£180	£600	£3200	—
1680 Third bust	£180	£900	£4000	—
1680/79 — 80 over 79	£200	£800	—	—
1680 Fourth bust	£180	£800	£5000	—
1680/79 — 80 over 79	£200	£1000	—	—
1681 —	£180	£600	£4000	—
1681 — Elephant & Castle below bust	£5500	£15000	—	—
1682/1 —	£180	£700	£3500	—
1682 — edge error QVRRTO for QVARTO	£400	—	—	—
1683 —	£400	£1100	£5000	—
1684 —	£400	£1300	—	—

JAMES II (1685–88)

	F	VF	EF	UNC
1686 First bust	£325	£1000	£6000	—
1686 — No stops on obv	£400	£1500	—	—
1687 Second bust	£300	£700	£4500	—
1688/7 — 8 over 7	£320	£850	—	—
1688 —	£280	£800	£4500	—

WILLIAM AND MARY (1688–94)

	F	VF	EF	UNC
1691	£750	£1750	£7000	—
1692	£750	£1850	£6500	—
1692 2 over upside down 2	£750	£1850	£6500	—

DATE	F	VF	EF	UNC

WILLIAM III (1694–1702)

	F	VF	EF	UNC
1695 First bust	£100	£340	£2000	—
1696 —	£90	£275	£1800	—
1696 — no stops on obv.	£225	£400	—	—
1996 — no stops obv./rev.	£250	£400	—	—
1696 — GEI for DEI	£750	£1800	—	—
1696 Second bust				Unique
1696 Third bust	£90	£275	£1900	—
1697 —	£2600	£10000	£25000	—
1700 Third bust variety edge year DUODECIMO	£140	£550	£2000	—
1700 — edge year DUODECIMO TERTIO..	£140	£550	£2000	—

ANNE (1702–14)

	F	VF	EF	UNC
1703 First bust, VIGO...................................	£350	£1200	£5500	—
1705 — Plumes in angles on rev.	£600	£1800	£7500	—
1706 — Roses & Plumes in angles on rev...	£200	£700	£2750	—
1707 — —	£200	£700	£2750	—
1707 Second bust, E below	£200	£700	£2750	—
1707 — Plain	£200	£700	£2750	—
1708 — E below	£200	£700	£2750	—
1708/7 — 8 over 7	£200	£800	—	—
1708 — Plain	£180	£700	£2750	—
1708 — — error BR for BRI........................			Extremely rare	
1708 — Plumes in angles on rev.	£200	£700	£3000	—
1713 Third bust, Roses & Plumes in angles on rev..	£200	£750	£3250	—

GEORGE I (1714–27)

	F	VF	EF	UNC
1716..	£750	£1800	£6500	—
1718 8 over 6...	£750	£1800	£6000	—
1720 20 over 18...	£750	£1800	£6000	—
1723 SSC in angles on rev. (South Sea Co.)	£750	£1800	£5750	—
1726	£750	£2000	£7500	—

GEORGE II (1727–60)

	F	VF	EF	UNC
1732 Young head, Plain, Proof	—	— £22,000		—
1732 — Roses & Plumes in angles on rev ..	£350	£700	£3500	—
1734 — —	£350	£700	£3500	—
1735 — —	£350	£700	£3500	—
1736 — —	£350	£700	£3500	—
1739 — Roses in angles on rev..................	£350	£600	£3500	—
1741 — —	£350	£600	£3000	—
1743 Old head, Roses in angles on rev.......	£350	£600	£2400	—
1746 — LIMA below bust	£350	£600	£2400	—
1746 — Plain, Proof	—	— £15,000		—
1750 — —	£500	£1400	£4500	—
1751 — —	£550	£1700	£5000	—

GEORGE III (1760–1820)

	F	VF	EF	UNC
Dollar with oval counterstamp......................	£175	£650	£1000	—
Dollar with octagonal counterstamp	£200	£600	£850	—
1804 Bank of England Dollar, Britannia rev.	£120	£275	£550	—
1818 LVIII..	£40	£100	£350	£900
1818 LIX	£40	£100	£350	£900
1819 LIX	£40	£100	£350	£900
1819 LIX 9 over 8	£45	£150	£500	—
1819 LIX no stops on edge	£60	£150	£400	£1000
1819 LX	£40	£100	£350	£1000
1820 LX	£35	£100	£350	£950
1820 LX 20 over 19	£35	£200	£600	—

DATE	MINTAGE	F	VF	EF	UNC

GEORGE IV (1820–30)

	MINTAGE	F	VF	EF	UNC
1821 First bust, St George rev.					
SECUNDO on edge	437,976	£45	£200	£700	£1500
1821 — — Proof...	—	—	—	£6000
1821 — — Proof TERTIO (error edge).........	—	—	—	£8000
1822 — — SECUNDO...................	124,929	£40	£200	£700	£1600
1822 — — TERTIO..................... Incl above	£40	£200	£700	£1600
1823 — — Proof only				Extremely rare
1826 Second bust, shield rev, SEPTIMO					
Proof only...	—	—		—£20000

WILLIAM IV (1830–37)

		F	VF	UNC
1831 Proof only W.W. on truncation............		—	—	£30000
1831 Proof only W. WYON on truncation....		—	—	£30000
1834 Proof only		—	—	—£45000

VICTORIA (1837–1901)

YOUNG HEAD ISSUES

	MINTAGE	F	VF	EF	UNC
1839 Proof only	—	—	—	—£25000
1844 Star stops on edge.............	94,248	£60	£300	£1400	£3250
1844 Cinquefoil stops on edge ...	incl. above	£60	£300	£1400	£3250
1845 Star stops on edge.............	159,192	£60	£300	£1400	£3250
1845 Cinquefoil stops on edge ...	incl. above	£60	£300	£1400	£3250
1847..	140,976	£70	£350	£1600	£5000

GOTHIC HEAD ISSUES (Proof only)

	MINTAGE	F	VF	EF	UNC
1847 mdcccxlvii UNDECIMO on edge	8,000	£900	£1750	£3000	£5000
1847 — Plain edge........................	—	—	—	£6000
1853 mdcccliii SEPTIMO on edge	460	—	—	—£20000
1853 — Plain edge.....................	—	—	—	—£40000

JUBILEE HEAD ISSUES

	MINTAGE	F	VF	EF	UNC
1887	173,581	£20	£30	£60	£160
1887 Proof...............................	1,084	—	—	—	£1800
1888 Narrow date.......................	131,899	£20	£35	£90	£270
1888 Wide date	incl above	£25	£60	£300	—
1889...	1,807,224	£20	£30	£60	£160
1890...	997,862	£20	£30	£70	£250
1891...	556,394	£20	£30	£70	£275
1892...	451,334	£20	£30	£80	£300

OLD HEAD ISSUES (Regnal date on edge in Roman numerals)

	MINTAGE	F	VF	EF	UNC
1893 LVI......................................	497,845	£20	£45	£150	£375
1893 LVII.....................................	incl. above	£20	£45	£220	£450
1893 Proof...................................	1,312	—	—	—	£2800
1894 LVII.....................................	144,906	£20	£45	£175	£475
1894 LVIII....................................	incl. above	£20	£45	£175	£475
1895 LVIII	252,862	£20	£45	£175	£475
1895 LIX	incl. above	£20	£45	£175	£475
1896 LIX	317,599	£20	£45	£175	£500
1896 LX	incl. above	£20	£45	£175	£475
1897 LX	262,118	£20	£45	£175	£475
1897 LXI	incl. above	£20	£45	£175	£500
1898 LXI	166,150	£20	£45	£175	£600
1898 LXII	incl. above	£20	£45	£175	£475
1899 LXII	166,300	£20	£45	£175	£475
1899 LXIII....................................	incl. above	£20	£45	£175	£475
1900 LXIII...................................	353,356	£20	£45	£175	£475
1900 LXIV	incl. above	£20	£45	£175	£475

Victoria, Jubilee head

DATE	MINTAGE	F	VF	EF	UNC

EDWARD VII (1901–10)

DATE	MINTAGE	F	VF	EF	UNC
1902	256,020	£75	£140	£220	£300
1902 "Matt Proof"	15,123	—	—	—	£320

GEORGE V (1910–36)

DATE	MINTAGE	F	VF	EF	UNC
1927 Proof only	15,030	—	£100	£170	£350
1928	9,034	£110	£160	£300	£500
1929	4,994	£110	£160	£300	£500
1930	4,847	£110	£160	£300	£525
1931	4,056	£110	£160	£300	£500
1932	2,395	£200	£400	£800	£1300
1933	7,132	£110	£160	£300	£525
1934	932	£800	£1600	£3500	£5500
1935 Jubilee issue. Incuse edge inscription	714,769	£15	£20	£30	£45
1935 — — error edge inscription	incl. above	—	—	—	£1500
1935 — Specimen in box	incl. above	—	—	—	£60
1935 — Proof	incl. above	—	—	—	£200
1935 — Proof. Raised edge inscription	2,500	—	—	£275	£600
1935 — — fine lettering	incl. above	—	—	—	£1000
1935 — — error edge inscription	incl. above	—	—	—	£1500
1935 — Gold proof	30	—	—	Extremely rare	
1936	2,473	£180	£350	£600	£1000

GEORGE VI (1936–52)

DATE	MINTAGE	F	VF	EF	UNC
1937 Coronation	418,699	£15	£22	£35	£55
1937 Proof	26,402	—	—	—	£65
1951 Festival of Britain, Proof-like	1,983,540	—	£3	£6	£8

ELIZABETH II (1952–   )

Pre-Decimal issues (Five Shillings)

DATE	MINTAGE	F	VF	EF	UNC
1953	5,962,621	—	—	£3	£6
1953 Proof	40,000	—	—	—	£25
1960	1,024,038	—	—	£3	£6
1960 Polished dies	70,000	—	—	—	£9
1965 Churchill	19,640,000	—	—	—	£1

Later issues are listed in the Decimal section.

DOUBLE FLORINS

VICTORIA (1837–1901)

DATE	MINTAGE	F	VF	EF	UNC
1887 Roman I	483,347	£15	£30	£50	£115
1887 Roman I Proof	incl. above	—	—	—	£600
1887 Arabic 1	incl. above	£15	£30	£50	£115
1887 Arabic 1 Proof	incl. above	—	—	—	£750
1888	243,340	£15	£40	£80	£150
1888 Second I in VICTORIA an inverted 1	incl. above	£25	£50	£100	£375
1889	1,185,111	£18	£30	£45	£140
1889 inverted 1	incl. above	£25	£50	£100	£400
1890	782,146	£15	£40	£60	£130

Patterns were also produced in 1911, 1914 and 1950 and are all extremely rare.

HALFCROWNS

DATE	MINTAGE	F	VF	EF	UNC

OLIVER CROMWELL

1656			Extremely rare		
1658		£1600	£2500	£5750	—
1658 Proof in Gold			Extremely rare		

CHARLES II (1660–1685)

1663 First bust		£170	£600	£3500	—
1663 — no stops on obv.		£200	£800	—	—
1664 Second bust		£250	£1200	£5000	—
1666 Third bust		£900	—	—	—
1666 — Elephant		£800	£3500		
1667/4 — 7 over 4			Extremely rare		
1668/4 — 8 over 4		£300	£1500	—	—
1669 —		£400	£1600	—	—
1669/4 — 9 over 4		£250	£900	—	—
1670 —		£140	£500	£2500	—
1670 — MRG for MAG		£300	£1000	—	—
1671 —		£150	£500	£2500	—
1671/0 — 1 over 0		£160	£600	£3000	—
1672 — Third bust			Extremely rare		
1672 Fourth bust		£150	£500	£2850	—
1673 —		£150	£500	£2500	—
1673 — Plumes both sides			Extremely rare		
1673 — Plume below bust		£6500	£18,000	—	—
1674 —		£150	£700	—	—
1675 —		£145	£400	£2200	—
1676 —		£145	£400	£2200	—
1676 — inverted 1 in date		£145	£400	£2200	—
1677 —		£145	£400	£1900	—
1678 —		£200	£800	—	—
1679 — GRATTA error			Extremely rare		
1679 —		£160	£440	£1900	—
1680 —		£175	£750	—	—
1681/0 — 1 over 0		£300	—	—	—
1681 —		£175	£600	£2850	—
1681 — Elephant & Castle		£3750	£12000	—	—
1682 —		£150	£500	£3400	—
1683 —		£150	£500	£3200	—
1683 — Plume below bust			Extremely rare		
1684/3 — 4 over 3		£325	£900	£4200	—

JAMES II (1685–1688)

1685 First bust		£220	£650	£3300	—
1686 —		£220	£650	£3500	—
1686/5 — 6 over 5		£220	£700	—	—
1686 — V over S		£225	£750	—	—
1687 —		£220	£675	£3300	—
1687/6 — 7 over 6		£300	£850	—	—
1687 Second bust		£200	£600	£3200	—
1688 —		£200	£600	£3000	—

WILLIAM AND MARY (1688–1694)

1689 First busts; first shield		£100	£350	£1600	—
1689 — — no pearls in crown		£100	£350	£1600	—
1689 — — FRA for FR		£160	£600	£2000	—
1689 — No stop on obv.		£100	£500	£1850	—
1689 — Second shield		£100	£350	£1600	—
1689 — — no pearls in crown		£100	£350	£1600	—
1690 — —		£160	£700	£2600	—
1690 — — error GRETIA for GRATIA		£550	£1600	£5500	—
1691 Second busts		£150	£450	£2200	—
1692 —		£150	£450	£2200	—

DATE	MINTAGE	F	VF	EF	UNC
1693 —		£170	£475	£2200	—
1693 — 3 over inverted 3		£180	£650	£2800	—

WILLIAM III (1694–1702)

DATE	MINTAGE	F	VF	EF	UNC
1696 First bust, large shields, early harp		£70	£240	£1000	—
1696 — — — B (Bristol) below bust		£70	£240	£1100	—
1696 — — — C (Chester)		£80	£325	£1200	—
1696 — — — E (Exeter)		£100	£400	£1400	—
1696 — — — N (Norwich)		£90	£400	£1400	—
1696 — — — y (York)		£80	£350	£1650	—
1696 — — — — Scottish arms at date				Extremely rare	
1696 — — ordinary harp		£80	£275	£1500	—
1696 — — — C		£110	£500	£1300	—
1696 — — — E		£100	£500	£1300	—
1696 — — — N		£150	£600	£2500	—
1696 — Small shields, ordinary harp		£70	£250	£1000	—
1696 — — — B		£90	£300	£1300	—
1696 — — — C		£90	£300	£1400	—
1696 — — — E		£100	£450	£2000	—
1696 — — — N		£110	£450	£1700	—
1696 — — — y		£100	£500	£1700	—
1696 Second bust				Only one known	
1697 First bust, large shields, ordinary harp		£75	£300	£1250	—
1697 — — — GRR for GRA				Extremely rare	
1697 — — — B		£80	£300	£1400	—
1697 — — — C		£80	£350	£1500	—
1697 — — — E		£90	£350	£1500	—
1697 — — — N		£100	£350	£1500	—
1697 — — — y		£90	£350	£1600	—
1698 — —		£100	£350	£1500	—
1698/7 — — 8 over 7				Extremely rare	
1699 — —		£150	£475	£2200	—
1699 — — Scottish arms at date				Extremely rare	
1700 — —		£140	£400	£2000	—
1701 — —		£145	£450	£2100	—
1701 — — No stops on rev		£160	£625	—	—
1701 — — Elephant & Castle below	Fair £2500				
1701 — — Plumes in angles on rev.		£230	£650	£3000	—

ANNE (1702–1714)

DATE	MINTAGE	F	VF	EF	UNC
1703 Plain (pre-Union)		£700	£2300	—	—
1703 VIGO below bust		£125	£400	£1400	—
1704 Plumes in angles on rev.		£175	£500	£1800	—
1705 —		£160	£600	£2000	—
1706 Roses & Plumes in angles on rev.		£90	£350	£1600	—
1707 —		£80	£300	£1100	—
1707 Plain (post-Union)		£80	£200	£900	—
1707 E below bust		£80	£200	£900	—
1707 — SEPTIMO edge				Extremely rare	
1708 Plain		£80	£250	£1000	—
1708 E below bust		£80	£250	£1100	—
1708 Plumes in angles on rev.		£90	£275	£1300	—
1709 Plain		£75	£275	£900	—
1709 E below bust		£260	£1100	—	—
1710 Roses & Plumes in angles on rev.		£80	£325	£1200	—
1712 —		£80	£325	£1200	—
1713 Plain		£80	£325	£1200	—
1713 Roses & Plumes in angles on rev.		£80	£325	£1150	—
1714 —		£80	£325	£1150	—
1714/3 4 over 3		£125	£500	—	—

GEORGE I (1714–1727)

DATE	MINTAGE	F	VF	EF	UNC
1715 Roses & Plumes in angles on rev.		£475	£950	£3200	—
1715 Plain edge				Extremely rare	
1717 —		£475	£950	£3300	—
1720 —		£450	£950	£3300	—
1720/17 20 over 17		£425	£850	£3200	—
1723 SSC in angles on rev.		£425	£850	£3000	—
1726 Small Roses & Plumes in angles on rev.		£4750	£14,000	—	—

DATE	MINTAGE	F	VF	EF	UNC

GEORGE II (1727–1760)

DATE	MINTAGE	F	VF	EF	UNC
1731 Young head, Plain, proof only..................	—	—	—	£9000	—
1731 — Roses & Plumes in angles on rev.........		£160	£400	£1800	—
1732 — —		£160	£400	£1800	—
1734 — —		£160	£400	£1850	—
1735 — —		£160	£400	£1850	—
1736 — —		£160	£400	£1850	—
1739 — Roses in angles on rev.		£150	£400	£1750	—
1741/39 — — 41 over 30		£160	£600	—	—
1741 — —		£150	£400	£1700	—
1743 Old head, Roses in angles on rev.		£85	£225	£1100	—
1745 — —		£85	£225	£1100	—
1745 — LIMA below bust................................		£70	£175	£650	—
1746 — —		£70	£175	£650	—
1746/5 — 6 over 5		£80	£220	£800	—
1746 — Plain, Proof		—	—	£6000	—
1750 — —		£225	£550	£2400	—
1751 — —		£250	£750	£2600	—

GEORGE III (1760–1820)

DATE	MINTAGE	F	VF	EF	UNC
1816 "Bull head"	—	£25	£80	£250	£500
1817 —	8,092,656	£25	£80	£250	£500
1817 "Small head"......................	incl. above	£25	£80	£250	£500
1818 —	2,905,056	£25	£80	£250	£500
1819/8 — 9 over 8......................	incl. above			Extremely rare	
1819 —	4,790,016	£25	£80	£250	£525
1820 —	2,396,592	£50	£140	£500	£1000

GEORGE IV (1820–30)

DATE	MINTAGE	F	VF	EF	UNC
1820 First bust, first reverse........	incl. above	£30	£80	£350	£675
1821 — —	1,435,104	£30	£80	£350	£675
1821 — — Proof.........................	incl. above	—	—	—	£4000
1823 — —	2,003,760	£1200	£4000	—	—
1823 — Second reverse..............	incl. above	£30	£80	£350	£650
1824 — —	465,696	£30	£90	£275	£700
1824 Second bust, third reverse .	incl. above			Extremely rare	
1825 — —	2,258,784	£30	£80	£200	£500
1826 — —	2,189,088	£30	£80	£200	£500
1826 — — Proof.........................	incl. above	—	—	—	£2500
1828 — —	49,890	£100	£275	£800	£2000
1829 — —	508,464	£70	£175	£500	£1050

WILLIAM IV (1830–37)

DATE	MINTAGE	F	VF	EF	UNC
1831..	—			Extremely rare	
1831 Proof (W.W. in script & block)	—	—	—	—	£3500
1834 W.W. in block.......................	993,168	£30	£80	£300	£850
1834 W.W. in script......................	incl. above	£30	£80	£300	£850
1835..	281,952	£35	£90	£300	£900
1836..	1,588,752	£30	£70	£300	£850
1836/5 6 over 5	incl. above	£60	£125	£600	—
1837..	150,526	£45	£160	£650	£1500

VICTORIA (1837–1901)

YOUNG HEAD ISSUES

DATE	MINTAGE	F	VF	EF	UNC
1839 (two varieties)	—	£1200	£4000	£10000	—
1839 Proof....................................	—	—	—	—	£6000
1840...	386,496	£60	£200	£700	£2000
1841...	42,768	£900	£2000	£4000	£7500
1842...	486,288	£55	£150	£700	£1700
1843...	454,608	£150	£450	£1100	£3500
1844...	1,999,008	£45	£110	£550	£1700
1845...	2,231,856	£45	£110	£550	£1700
1846...	1,539,668	£55	£140	£600	£1800
1848 Plain 8..................................	367,488	£150	£450	£1500	£4000
1848/6	incl. above	£120	£300	£900	£3000
1849...	261,360	£70	£160	£600	£1900
1849 Small date	incl. above	£90	£220	£850	£2200
1850...	484,613	£70	£200	£700	£2400
1853 Proof only	—	—	—	—	£7250

DATE	MINTAGE	F	VF	EF	UNC
1874	2,188,599	£25	£70	£300	£650
1875	1,113,483	£25	£70	£300	£600
1876	633,221	£30	£80	£280	£750
1876/5 6 over 5	incl. above	£35	£80	£280	£750
1876/6 6 over 6	incl. above	£75	£150	£450	—
1877	447,059	£25	£70	£250	£650
1878	1,466,323	£25	£70	£250	£650
1879	901,356	£35	£80	£280	£750
1880	1,346,350	£25	£70	£250	£600
1881	2,301,495	£25	£70	£250	£550
1882	808,227	£30	£70	£250	£600
1883	2,982,779	£25	£70	£250	£500
1884	1,569,175	£25	£70	£250	£500
1885	1,628,438	£25	£70	£250	£500
1886	891,767	£25	£70	£250	£500
1887	1,438,046	£25	£65	£275	£550
JUBILEE HEAD ISSUES					
1887	incl. above	£8	£14	£30	£75
1887 Proof	1,084	—	—	—	£550
1888	1,428,787	£12	£25	£50	£180
1889	4,811,954	£10	£20	£50	£160
1890	3,228,111	£12	£22	£70	£180
1891	2,284,632	£12	£22	£70	£180
1892	1,710,946	£12	£22	£75	£200
OLD HEAD ISSUES					
1893	1,792,600	£12	£25	£60	£110
1893 Proof	1,312	—	—	—	£1000
1894	1,524,960	£15	£35	£90	£250
1895	1,772,662	£12	£30	£70	£200
1896	2,148,505	£12	£22	£65	£190
1897	1,678,643	£12	£22	£65	£175
1898	1,870,055	£12	£22	£65	£175
1899	2,865,872	£12	£22	£65	£175
1900	4,479,128	£12	£22	£65	£175
1901	1,516,570	£12	£22	£65	£175

DATE	MINTAGE	F	VF	EF	UNC

EDWARD VII (1901–10)

DATE	MINTAGE	F	VF	EF	UNC
1902	1,316,008	£12	£30	£80	£170
1902 "Matt Proof"	15,123	—	—	—	£250
1903	274,840	£175	£550	£2200	£4500
1904	709,652	£60	£225	£500	£1500
1905	166,008	£500	£1400	£5000	£9000
1906	2,886,206	£12	£50	£200	£900
1907	3,693,930	£12	£50	£200	£900
1908	1,758,889	£20	£80	£400	£1300
1909	3,051,592	£12	£60	£340	£800
1910	2,557,685	£12	£45	£130	£475

GEORGE V (1910–36)

First issue

DATE	MINTAGE	F	VF	EF	UNC
1911	2,914,573	£15	£35	£80	£250
1911 Proof	6,007	—	—	—	£325
1912	4,700,789	£12	£25	£50	£200
1913	4,090,169	£12	£28	£75	£220
1914	18,333,003	£7	£12	£40	£70
1915	32,433,066	£7	£12	£35	£65
1916	29,530,020	£7	£12	£35	£65
1917	11,172,052	£8	£15	£45	£100
1918	29,079,592	£7	£12	£35	£70
1919	10,266,737	£7	£15	£45	£100

Second issue—debased silver

DATE	MINTAGE	F	VF	EF	UNC
1920	17,982,077	£4	£8	£22	£70
1921	23,677,889	£4	£8	£30	£65
1922	16,396,724	£5	£9	£24	£70
1923	26,308,526	£6	£8	£20	£45
1924	5,866,294	£15	£35	£90	£220
1925	1,413,461	£30	£75	£300	£1000
1926	4,473,516	£10	£25	£45	£180

Third issue—Modified effigy

DATE	MINTAGE	F	VF	EF	UNC
1926	incl. above	£6	£14	£40	£100
1927	6,837,872	£6	£12	£35	£75

Fourth issue—New shield reverse

DATE	MINTAGE	F	VF	EF	UNC
1927 Proof	15,000	—	—	—	£100
1928	18,762,727	£5	£8	£20	£35
1929	17,632,636	£5	£8	£20	£35
1930	809,051	£15	£60	£325	£900
1931	11,264,468	£5	£8	£20	£35
1932	4,793,643	£6	£10	£25	£90
1933	10,311,494	£5	£8	£20	£40
1934	2,422,399	£7	£12	£65	£185
1935	7,022,216	£5	£8	£18	£25
1936	7,039,423	£5	£8	£18	£20

George V, fourth issue, new shield reverse

GEORGE VI (1936–52)

DATE	MINTAGE	F	VF	EF	UNC
1937	9,106,440	—	£6	£9	£14
1937 Proof	26,402	—	—	—	£20
1938	6,426,478	£5	£6	£15	£25
1939	15,478,635	£5	£6	£9	£10
1940	17,948,439	£5	£6	£9	£10
1941	15,773,984	£5	£6	£9	£10
1942	31,220,090	£5	£6	£9	£10
1943	15,462,875	£5	£6	£9	£10
1944	15,255,165	£5	£6	£9	£10
1945	19,849,242	£5	£6	£9	£10
1946	22,724,873	£5	£6	£9	£10

Cupro-nickel

DATE	MINTAGE	F	VF	EF	UNC
1947	21,911,484	—	£1	£2	£4
1948	71,164,703	—	£1	£2	£4
1949	28,272,512	—	£1	£2	£6
1950	28,335,500	—	£1	£2	£6
1950 Proof	17,513	—	—	—	£35
1951	9,003,520	—	£1	£2	£6
1951 Proof	20,000	—	—	—	£10
1952				Only one known	

DATE	MINTAGE	F	VF	EF	UNC
ELIZABETH II (1952–)					
1953	4,333,214	—	—	£1	£3
1953 Proof	40,000	—	—	—	£8
1954	11,614,953	—	£1	£6	£40
1955	23,628,726	—	—	£1	£6
1956	33,934,909	—	—	£1	£6
1957	34,200,563	—	—	£1	£6
1958	15,745,668	—	£1	£6	£35
1959	9,028,844	—	£1	£9	£35
1960	19,929,191	—	—	£1	£3
1961	25,887,897	—	—	—	£2
1961 Polished dies	incl. above	—	—	£1	£2
1962	24,013,312	—	—	—	£1
1963	17,625,200	—	—	—	£1
1964	5,973,600	—	—	—	£2
1965	9,778,440	—	—	—	£1
1966	13,375,200	—	—	—	£1
1967	33,058,400	—	—	—	£1
1970 Proof	—	—	—	—	£8

FLORINS

VICTORIA (1837–1901)

YOUNG (CROWNED) HEAD ISSUES
"Godless" type (without D.G.— "Dei Gratia")

	MINTAGE	F	VF	EF	UNC
1848 "Godless" Pattern only plain edge	—		Very rare		
1848 "Godless" Pattern only milled edge	—		Extremely rare		
1849	413,820	£30	£70	£200	£400

(Beware of recent forgeries)

"Gothic" type i.e. date in Roman numerals in obverse legend
"brit." in legend. No die no.

	MINTAGE	F	VF	EF	UNC
1851 mdcccli Proof	1,540		Extremely rare		
1852 mdccclii	1,014,552	£30	£65	£220	£600
1853 mdcccliii	3,919,950	£30	£65	£220	£600
1853 — Proof	incl. above	—	—	—	£6000
1854 mdcccliv	550,413	£700	£2000	—	—
1855 mdccclv	831,017	£30	£70	£250	£700
1856 mdccclvi	2,201,760	£30	£70	£250	£700
1857 mdccclvii	1,671,120	£30	£65	£250	£750
1858 mdccclviii	2,239,380	£30	£65	£250	£700
1859 mdccclix	2,568,060	£30	£65	£250	£750
1860 mdccclx	1,475,100	£35	£90	£275	£850
1862 mdccclxii	594,000	£300	£650	£1500	£4250
1863 mdccclxiii	938,520	£1200	£2200	£5000	£11000

"brit" in legend. Die no. below bust

	MINTAGE	F	VF	EF	UNC
1864 mdccclxiv	1,861,200	£30	£60	£250	£650
1864 Gothic Piedfort flan	incl. above		Extremely rare		
1865 mdccclxv	1,580,044	£35	£70	£275	£650
1866 mdccclxvi	914,760	£35	£70	£275	£650
1867 mdccclxvii	423,720	£45	£130	£500	£1000
1867—only 42 arcs in border	incl. above		Extremely rare		

"Gothic" florin

"britt" in legend. Die no. below bust

	MINTAGE	F	VF	EF	UNC
1868 mdccclxviii	896,940	£30	£75	£325	£750
1869 mdccclxix	297,000	£35	£90	£400	£950
1870 mdccclxx	1,080,648	£30	£70	£275	£600
1871 mdccclxxi	3,425,605	£30	£70	£300	£550
1872 mdccclxxii	7,199,690	£30	£60	£225	£500
1873 mdccclxxiii	5,921,839	£30	£60	£240	£525
1874 mdccclxxiv	1,642,630	£30	£60	£240	£550
1874 — iv over iii in date	incl. above	£32	£70	£300	£700
1875 mdccclxxv	1,117,030	£32	£75	£240	£600
1876 mdccclxxvi	580,034	£50	£130	£500	£1000
1877 mdccclxxvii	682,292	£30	£65	£240	£550
1877 — 48 arcs in border no W.W.	incl. above	£30	£60	£220	£500
1877 — 42 arcs	incl. above	£30	£60	£220	£500
1877 — — no die number	incl. above		Extremely rare		
1878 mdccclxxviii with die number	1,786,680	£28	£60	£220	£500

DATE	MINTAGE	F	VF	EF	UNC
1879 mdccclxxix no die no	1,512,247			Extremely rare	
1879 — 48 arcs in border............	incl. above	£30	£60	£220	£500
1879 — no die number................	incl. above			Extremely rare	
1879 — 38 arcs, no W.W..	incl. above	£28	£60	£220	£500
1880 mdccclxxx Younger portrait	—			Extremely rare	
1880 — 34 arcs, Older portrait....	2,167,170	£30	£60	£200	£500
1881 mdccclxxxi — —	2,570,337	£28	£60	£200	£500
1881 — xxⱦi broken puncheon ...	incl. above	£35	£70	£200	£550
1883 mdccclxxxiii — —	3,555,667	£28	£65	£200	£500
1884 mdccclxxxiv — —	1,447,379	£28	£60	£200	£500
1885 mdccclxxxv — —	1,758,210	£28	£60	£200	£500
1886 mdccclxxxvi — —	591,773	£28	£60	£200	£500
1887 mdccclxxxvii — —	1,776,903	£50	£120	£325	£700
1887 — 46 arcs	incl. above	£50	£120	£350	£800

JUBILEE HEAD ISSUES

1887	incl. above	£7	£16	£30	£60
1887 Proof..............................	1,084	—	—	—	£500
1888.......................................	1,547,540	£7	£15	£45	£120
1889.......................................	2,973,561	£8	£18	£50	£140
1890.......................................	1,684,737	£10	£25	£80	£275
1891.......................................	836,438	£22	£60	£200	£550
1892.......................................	283,401	£35	£110	£325	£850

VICTORIA—OLD HEAD ISSUES

1893.......................................	1,666,103	£8	£16	£40	£110
1893 Proof..............................	1,312	—	—	—	£700
1894.......................................	1,952,842	£10	£25	£70	£300
1895.......................................	2,182,968	£10	£28	£70	£290
1896.......................................	2,944,416	£8	£25	£60	£200
1897.......................................	1,699,921	£8	£25	£60	£190
1898.......................................	3,061,343	£8	£25	£60	£180
1899.......................................	3,966,953	£8	£25	£60	£180
1900.......................................	5,528,630	£8	£25	£60	£180
1901.......................................	2,648,870	£8	£25	£60	£180

EDWARD VII (1901–10)

1902.......................................	2,189,575	£10	£22	£60	£140
1902 "Matt Proof"	15,123	—	—	—	£250
1903.......................................	1,995,298	£12	£35	£120	£550
1904.......................................	2,769,932	£14	£40	£150	£500
1905.......................................	1,187,596	£65	£175	£600	£1600
1906.......................................	6,910,128	£12	£40	£140	£550
1907.......................................	5,947,895	£12	£35	£130	£525
1908.......................................	3,280,010	£20	£55	£350	£900
1909.......................................	3,482,829	£15	£50	£240	£700
1910.......................................	5,650,713	£14	£35	£100	£320

GEORGE V (1910–36)

First issue

1911.......................................	5,951,284	£7	£12	£40	£90
1911 Proof..............................	6,007	—	—	—	£250
1912.......................................	8,571,731	£7	£15	£35	£130
1913.......................................	4,545,278	£10	£25	£50	£180
1914.......................................	21,252,701	£7	£18	£30	£65
1915.......................................	12,367,939	£7	£18	£28	£65
1916.......................................	21,064,337	£7	£18	£28	£65
1917.......................................	11,181,617	£7	£22	£35	£65
1918.......................................	29,211,792	£7	£18	£30	£90
1919.......................................	9,469,292	£9	£20	£45	£110

Second issue —*debased silver*

1920.......................................	15,387,833	£4	£12	£40	£85
1921.......................................	34,863,895	£4	£12	£40	£65
1922.......................................	23,861,044	£4	£12	£40	£65
1923.......................................	21,546,533	£4	£10	£30	£60
1924.......................................	4,582,372	£12	£35	£95	£250
1925.......................................	1,404,136	£30	£75	£300	£800
1926.......................................	5,125,410	£10	£25	£60	£170

Fourth issue—*new reverse*

1927 Proof only	101,497	—	—	—	£110
1928.......................................	11,087,186	£4	£7	£15	£40

DATE	MINTAGE	F	VF	EF	UNC
1929	16,397,279	£4	£7	£16	£35
1930	5,753,568	£4	£7	£20	£50
1931	6,556,331	£4	£7	£18	£35
1932	717,041	£15	£35	£250	£600
1933	8,685,303	£4	£7	£18	£40
1935	7,540,546	£4	£7	£14	£30
1936	9,897,448	£4	£7	£14	£30

GEORGE VI (1936–52)

1937	13,006,781	£4	£5	£7	£12
1937 Proof	26,402	–	–	–	£25
1938	7,909,388	£6	£8	£15	£30
1939	20,850,607	£4	£5	£8	£10
1940	18,700,338	£4	£5	£7	£12
1941	24,451,079	£4	£5	£7	£9
1942	39,895,243	£4	£5	£7	£9
1943	26,711,987	£4	£5	£7	£9
1944	27,560,005	£4	£5	£7	£9
1945	25,858,049	£4	£5	£7	£9
1946	22,300,254	£4	£5	£7	£9

Cupro-nickel

1947	22,910,085	–	–	£1	£3
1948	67,553,636	–	–	£1	£3
1949	28,614,939	–	–	£1	£5
1950	24,357,490	–	–	£2	£7
1950 Proof	17,513	–	–	£1	£9
1951	27,411,747	–	–	£2	£8
1951 Proof	20,000	–	–	–	£9

ELIZABETH II (1952–)

1953	11,958,710	–	–	–	£2
1953 Proof	40,000	–	–	–	£6
1954	13,085,422	–	–	£6	£40
1955	25,887,253	–	–	£1	£3
1956	47,824,500	–	–	£1	£3
1957	33,071,282	–	–	£4	£25
1958	9,564,580	–	–	£4	£35
1959	14,080,319	–	–	£4	£32
1960	13,831,782	–	–	£1	£4
1961	37,735,315	–	–	£1	£2
1962	35,147,903	–	–	£1	£2
1963	26,471,000	–	–	£1	£2
1964	16,539,000	–	–	£1	£2
1965	48,163,000	–	–	–	£1.50
1966	83,999,000	–	–	–	£1.50
1967	39,718,000	–	–	–	£1.50
1970 Proof	–	–	–	–	£10

SHILLINGS

OLIVER CROMWELL

1658		£1000	£2200	£4250	–
1658 Dutch Copy				Extremely rare

CHARLES II (1660–85)

1663 First bust	£125	£500	£1600	–
1663 — GARTIA error			Extremely rare	
1663 — Irish & Scottish shields transposed	£300	£800	–	–
1666 — Elephant below bust	£500	£1500	£6000	–
1666 "Guinea" head, elephant	£1800	£4500	–	–
1666 Second bust			Extremely rare	
1668 —	£120	£400	£1600	–
1668/3 — 8 over 3	£150	£500	–	–
1668 Second bust	£120	£450	£1600	–
1669/6 First bust variety			Extremely rare	
1669			Extremely rare	

DATE	F	VF	EF	UNC
			Extremely rare	
1669 Second bust	£150	£500	£2100	—
1670 —	£150	£500	£2100	—
1671 —	£450	£1000	£4500	—
1671 — Plume below, plume in centre rev.	£150	£550	£2100	—
1672 —	£150	£550	£2100	—
1673 —	£500	£1200	£5000	—
1673 — Plume below, plume in centre rev.	£175	£600	—	—
1673/2 — 3 over 2	£150	£550	—	—
1674/3 — 4 over 3	£150	£500	£2100	—
1674 —	£400	£1600	£5000	—
1674 — Plume below bust, plume in centre rev.	£700	£2000	£5000	—
1674 — Plume rev. only	£450	£1600	—	—
1674 Third bust	£200	£800	—	—
1675 Second bust	£220	£850	—	—
1675/4 — 5 over 4	£450	£1250	£5500	—
1675 — Plume below bust, plume in centre rev.	£350	£1300	—	—
1675 Third bust	£300	£1100	—	—
1675/3 — 5 over 3	£125	£450	£1800	—
1676 Second bust	£160	£550	—	—
1676/5 — 6 over 5	£450	£1600	£5250	—
1676 — Plume below bust, plume in centre rev.	£130	£500	£2000	—
1677 —	£1200	£3000	£9000	—
1677 — Plume below bust	£140	£500	£2000	—
1678 —	£160	£700	—	—
1678/7 — 8 over 7	£140	£500	£2200	—
1679 —	£450	£1200	£6000	—
1679 — Plume below bust, plume in centre rev.	£700	£2500	£6000	—
1679 — Plume below bust	£160	£600	—	—
1679 — 9 over 7			Extremely rare	
1680 —	£1100	£3000	£6500	—
1680 — Plume below bust, plume in centre rev.	£850	£2500	—	—
1680/79 — — 80 over 79	£300	£850	£3000	—
1681 —	£375	£900	£3250	—
1681 — 1 over 0	£3000	£9000	—	—
1681/0 Elephant & Castle below bust	£1000	£3300	—	—
1682/1 — 2 over 1			Extremely rare	
1683 —	£250	£800	£2700	—
1683 Fourth (Larger) bust	£250	£800	£2700	—
1684 —				

Charles II

JAMES II (1685–88)

	F	VF	EF	UNC
1685	£200	£500	£2000	—
1685 Plume in centre rev. rev			Extremely rare	
1685 No stops on rev.	£220	£650	—	—
1686	£220	£550	£2300	—
1686/5 6 over 5	£225	£600	£2250	—
1687	£200	£600	£2200	—
1687/6 7 over 6	£200	£550	£2300	—
1688	£200	£600	£2500	—
1688/7 last 8 over 7	£220	£550	£2300	—

James II

WILLIAM & MARY (1688–94)

	F	VF	EF	UNC
1692	£180	£500	£2400	—
1692 inverted 1	£210	£550	£2450	—
1693	£180	£500	£2400	—

WILLIAM III (1694–1702)

Provincially produced shillings carry privy marks or initials below the bust:
B: Bristol. C: Chester. E: Exeter. N: Norwich. Y or y: York.

	F	VF	EF	UNC
1695 First bust	£40	£120	£600	—
1696 —	£40	£100	£450	—
1696 — no stops on rev.	£60	£140	£750	—
1696 — MAB for MAG			Extremely rare	
1696 — 1669 error			Extremely rare	
1696 — 1669 various GVLELMVS errors			Extremely rare	
1696 — B below bust	£60	£150	£900	—
1696 — C	£55	£150	£900	—
1696 — E	£60	£160	£950	—

William & Mary

DATE	F	VF	EF	UNC
1696 — N	£55	£150	£825	—
1696 — y	£55	£150	£825	—
1696 — Y	£55	£150	£825	—
1696 Second bust			Only one known	
1696 Third bust C below	£160	£400	£1500	—
1696 — Y			Extremely rare	
1697 First bust	£50	£110	£400	—
1697 — GRI for GRA error			Extremely rare	
1697 — Scottish & Irish shields transposed			Extremely rare	
1697 — Irish arms at date			Extremely rare	
1697 — no stops on rev	£60	£180	£700	—
1697 — GVLELMVS error			Extremely rare	
1697 — B	£60	£150	£950	—
1697 — C	£60	£150	£950	—
1697 — E	£60	£150	£950	—
1697 — N	£60	£150	£900	—
1697 — — no stops on obv			Extremely rare	
1697 — y	£60	£150	£900	—
1697 — — arms of France & Ireland transposed			Extremely rare	
1697 — Y	£50	£150	£725	—
1697 Third bust	£50	£125	£550	—
1697 — B	£60	£150	£750	—
1697 — C	£60	£150	£800	—
1697 — — Fr.a error	£150	£500	—	—
1697 — — no stops on obv	£90	£300	—	—
1697 — — arms of Scotland at date			Extremely rare	
1697 — E	£60	£150	£850	—
1697 — N	£60	£150	£950	—
1697 — y	£60	£150	£800	—
1697 Third bust variety	£60	£140	£575	—
1697 — B	£60	£150	£1000	—
1697 — C	£120	£650	—	—
1698 —	£90	£275	£1150	—
1698 — Plumes in angles of rev.	£200	£550	£2200	—
1698 Fourth bust "Flaming hair"	£150	£600	£2200	—
1699 —	£110	£450	£1500	—
1699 Fifth bust	£100	£325	£1250	—
1699 — Plumes in angles on rev.	£150	£450	£2200	—
1699 — Roses in angles on rev.	£160	£500	£2100	—
1700 —	£70	£140	£600	—
1700 — Small round oo in date	£70	£140	£600	—
1700 — no stop after DEI			Extremely rare	
1700 — Plume below bust	£2750	£10000	—	—
1701 —	£80	£275	£1000	—
1701 — Plumes in angles on rev.	£160	£650	£2100	—

William III First bust

ANNE (1702–14)

	F	VF	EF	UNC
1702 First bust (pre-Union with Scotland)	£80	£300	£700	—
1702 — Plumes in angles on rev.	£100	£300	£850	—
1702 — VIGO below bust	£70	£220	£700	—
1702 — — colon before ANNA			Extremely rare	
1703 Second bust, VIGO below	£65	£200	£800	—
1704 — Plain	£500	£1800	—	—
1704 — Plumes in angles on rev.	£80	£240	£850	—
1705 — Plain	£75	£220	£750	—
1705 — Plumes in angles on rev.	£80	£240	£800	—
1705 — Roses & Plumes in angles on rev.	£70	£200	£700	—
1707 — —	£60	£180	£650	—
1707 Second bust (post-Union) E below bust	£50	£140	£550	—
1707 — E* below bust	£70	£200	£750	—
1707 Third bust, Plain	£35	£100	£450	—
1707 — Plumes in angles on rev.	£50	£180	£800	—
1707 — E below bust	£40	£90	£500	—
1707 "Edinburgh" bust, E* below			Extremely rare	
1708 Second bust, E below	£50	£100	£450	—
1708 — E* below bust	£55	£165	£700	—
1708/7 — — 8 over 7			Extremely rare	

Anne, VIGO below bust

DATE	MINTAGE	F	VF	EF	UNC
1708 — Roses & Plumes in angles on rev.........		£80	£275	£650	—
1708 Third bust, Plain		£45	£140	£475	—
1708 — Plumes in angles on rev.		£80	£220	£700	—
1708 Third bust, E below bust		£60	£175	£650	—
1708/7 — — 8 over 7		£200	£450	—	—
1708 — Roses & Plumes in angles on rev.........		£70	£180	£625	—
1708 "Edinburgh" bust, E* below		£60	£170	£550	—
1709 Third bust, Plain		£50	£160	£500	—
1709 "Edinburgh" bust, E* below		£50	£170	£650	—
1709 — E no star (filled in die?)........................		£70	£160	£550	—
1710 Third bust, Roses & Plumes in angles......		£60	£140	£675	—
1710 Fourth bust, Roses & Plumes in angles ...		£60	£150	£675	—
1711 Third bust, Plain		£70	£160	£475	—
1711 Fourth bust, Plain		£30	£75	£250	—
1712 — Roses & Plumes in angles on rev.........		£60	£130	£475	—
1713 — —		£60	£130	£450	—
1713/2 — 3 over 2...		£70	£230	—	—
1714 — —		£60	£110	£375	—
1714/3 —				Extremely rare	

GEORGE I (1714–27)

DATE	MINTAGE	F	VF	EF	UNC
1715 First bust, Roses & Plumes in angles on rev.		£80	£200	£900	£3000
1716 — —		£150	£500	£2000	—
1717 — —		£90	£300	£1400	—
1718 — —		£75	£225	£800	—
1719 — —		£120	£500	£2200	—
1720 — —		£75	£180	£475	—
1720/18 — —		£150	£500	£1450	—
1720 — Plain		£40	£100	£450	—
1721 — Roses & Plumes in angles on rev.........		£100	£350	£1750	—
1721/0 — — 1 over 0		£70	£250	£1000	—
1721 — Plain		£120	£450	£1500	—
1721/19 — — 21 over 19		£125	£400	—	—
1721/18 21 over 18 error, Plumes & Roses.......		£500	£1800	—	—
1722 — Roses & Plumes in angles on rev.........		£80	£240	£1100	—
1723 — —		£90	£275	£1200	—
1723 — SSC rev., Arms of France at date		£100	£300	£800	—
1723 — SSC in angles on rev		£35	£110	£275	—
1723 Second bust, SSC in angles on rev.		£50	£170	£550	—
1723 — Roses & Plumes in angles		£100	£270	£1100	—
1723 — WCC (Welsh Copper Co) below bust ..		£1000	£2200	£7000	—
1724 — Roses & Plumes in angles on rev.........		£80	£200	£800	—
1724 — WCC below bust..................................		£1000	£2200	£7000	—
1725 — Roses & Plumes in angles on rev.........		£80	£200	£1000	—
1725 — — no stops on obv..............................		£90	£225	£1100	—
1725 — WCC below bust..................................		£1000	£2200	£8000	—
1726 — — Roses & Plumes		£700	£1800	£7000	—
1726 — WCC below bust..................................		£1050	£2250	£8250	—
1727 — —				Extremely rare	
1727 — — no stops on obv..............................				Extremely rare	

George I Fir... bust with S... in angles or... reverse

GEORGE II (1727–60)

DATE	MINTAGE	F	VF	EF	UNC
1727 Young head, Plumes in angles on rev.......		£75	£300	£950	—
1727 — Roses & Plumes in angles on rev.........		£60	£180	£650	—
1728 — —		£65	£180	£650	—
1728 — Plain..		£75	£220	£700	—
1729 — Roses & Plumes in angles on rev.........		£60	£200	£750	—
1731 — —		£70	£200	£700	—
1731 — Plumes in angles on rev.		£100	£400	£1250	—
1732 — Roses & Plumes in angles on rev.........		£65	£200	£750	—
1734 — —		£65	£200	£700	—
1735 — —		£65	£200	£700	—
1736 — —		£65	£200	£700	—
1736/5 — — 6 over 5		£70	£200	£800	—
1737 — —		£65	£200	£650	—
1739 — Roses in angles on rev.		£50	£160	£475	—
1739/7 — — 9 over 7				Extremely rare	
1741 — —		£50	£160	£475	—
1741/39 — — 41 over 39				Extremely rare	
1743 Old head, Roses in angles on rev.............		£30	£80	£325	—
1745 — —		£30	£80	£325	—

George II Young hea... roses and plumes reverse typ...

DATE	MINTAGE	F	VF	EF	UNC
1745 — — LIMA below bust	£35	£90	£325	—
1745/3 — — — 5 over 3	£60	£175	£400	—
1746 — — —	£50	£175	£650	—
1746/5 — — — 6 over 5	£100	£300		—
1746 — Plain, Proof	—	—	£4000	—
1747 — Roses in angles on rev.	£45	£100	£425	—
1750 — Plain	£40	£140	£425	—
1750/6 — — 0 over 6	£60	£150	£500	—
1751 — —	£140	£600	£1750	—
1758 — —	£20	£50	£140	—

*George II
Old head,
plain reverse*

GEORGE III (1760–1820)

	MINTAGE	F	VF	EF	UNC
1763 "Northumberland" bust		£450	£800	£1600	—
(Beware recent counterfeits)					
1787 rev. no semée of hearts in 4th shield		£20	£35	£100	—
1787 — No stop over head		£25	£40	£120	—
1787 — No stop at date		£45	£75	£150	—
1787 — No stops on obv		£100	£250	£850	—
1787 rev. with semée of hearts in shield		£35	£65	£125	—
1798 "Dorrien Magens" bust		—	—	—£30,000	

NEW COINAGE—shield in garter reverse

	MINTAGE	F	VF	EF	UNC
1816	—	£12	£25	£75	£160
1817	3,031,360	£12	£35	£85	£180
1817 GEOE for GEOR	incl. above	£120	£250	£700	—
1818	1,342,440	£25	£45	£150	£400
1819	7,595,280	£15	£35	£100	£220
1819/8 9 over 8	incl. above	£20	£50	£150	—
1820	7,975,440	£15	£30	£100	£220

*George III
New coinage
Shield reverse
type*

GEORGE IV (1820–30)

	MINTAGE	F	VF	EF	UNC
1821 First bust, first reverse	2,463,120	£15	£40	£160	£490
1821 — — Proof	incl. above	—	—	—	£1800
1823 — Second reverse	693,000	£50	£90	£250	£600
1824 — —	4,158,000	£15	£45	£160	£400
1825 — —	2,459,160	£20	£50	£160	£550
1825/3 — — 5 over 3	incl. above		Extremely rare		
1825 Second bust, third reverse	incl. above	£10	£25	£60	£200
1825 — — Roman I	incl. above		Extremely rare		
1826 — —	6,351,840	£10	£25	£60	£200
1826 — — Proof	incl. above	—	—	—	£800
1827 — —	574,200	£30	£70	£200	£500
1829 — —	879,120	£20	£60	£175	£450

WILLIAM IV (1830–37)

	MINTAGE	F	VF	EF	UNC
1831 Proof only	—	—	—	—	£1750
1834	3,223,440	£15	£35	£170	£400
1835	1,449,360	£15	£35	£170	£400
1836	3,567,960	£15	£35	£170	£400
1837	478,160	£20	£60	£200	£550

VICTORIA (1837–1901)

YOUNG HEAD ISSUES
First head

	MINTAGE	F	VF	EF	UNC
1838 WW on truncation	1,956,240	£20	£50	£200	£450
1839 —	5,666,760	£20	£50	£200	£450

Second head

	MINTAGE	F	VF	EF	UNC
1839 WW on truncation, Proof only	incl. above	—	—	—	£1750
1839 no WW	incl. above	£20	£50	£180	£450
1840	1,639,440	£20	£50	£180	£450
1841	875,160	£22	£50	£180	£450
1842	2,094,840	£20	£45	£170	£475
1843	1,465,200	£20	£50	£180	£475
1844	4,466,880	£15	£40	£150	£420
1845	4,082,760	£15	£40	£150	£420
1846	4,031,280	£15	£40	£150	£420
1848 last 8 of date over 6	1,041,480	£80	£160	£650	£1500

*Victoria
Second head
type*

DATE	MINTAGE	F	VF	EF	UNC
1849	845,480	£30	£75	£240	£700
1850	685,080	£800	£1500	£3000	£7000
1850/49	incl. above	£800	£1500	£5000	—
1851	470,071	£45	£110	£450	£900
1852	1,306,574	£15	£35	£125	£400
1853	4,256,188	£15	£35	£125	£400
1853 Proof...............................	incl. above	—	—	—	£1800
1854	552,414	£250	£650	£1500	£4000
1854/1 4 over 1	incl. above	£200	£900	—	—
1855	1,368,400	£12	£30	£110	£300
1856	3,168,000	£12	£30	£110	£300
1857	2,562,120	£12	£30	£110	£300
1857 error F:G with inverted G ...	incl. above	£200	£600	—	—
1858	3,108,600	£12	£30	£110	£300
1859	4,561,920	£12	£30	£110	£300
1860	1,671,120	£12	£30	£110	£350
1861	1,382,040	£15	£40	£150	£500
1862	954,360	£70	£180	£500	£1500
1863	859,320	£140	£400	£900	£2200
1863/1 3 over 1				Extremely rare	
Die no. added above date up to 1879					
1864	4,518,360	£10	£30	£110	£250
1865	5,619,240	£10	£30	£110	£250
1866	4,984,600	£10	£30	£110	£250
1866 error BBITANNIAR	incl. above	£80	£250	£800	—
1867	2,166,120	£10	£35	£110	£275
Third head—with die no					
1867	incl. above	£100	£450	—	—
1868	3,330,360	£12	£40	£110	£275
1869	736,560	£20	£55	£140	£375
1870	1,467,471	£14	£40	£100	£275
1871	4,910,010	£12	£40	£100	£250
1872	8,897,781	£12	£40	£100	£250
1873	6,489,598	£12	£40	£100	£250
1874	5,503,747	£14	£40	£100	£250
1875	4,353,983	£12	£40	£100	£250
1876	1,057,487	£14	£45	£120	£450
1877	2,989,703	£12	£40	£100	£275
1878	3,127,131	£12	£40	£100	£275
1879	3,611,507	£20	£70	£220	£550
Fourth head—no die no					
1879 no Die no.	incl. above	£10	£28	£75	£190
1880	4,842,786	£10	£28	£75	£190
1881	5,255,332	£10	£28	£75	£190
1882	1,611,786	£25	£80	£200	£550
1883	7,281,450	£10	£28	£65	£180
1884	3,923,993	£10	£28	£65	£180
1885	3,336,526	£10	£28	£65	£180
1886	2,086,819	£10	£28	£65	£180
1887	4,034,133	£10	£28	£65	£180
JUBILEE HEAD ISSUES					
1887	incl. above	£4	£8	£15	£40
1887 Proof...............................	1,084	—	—	—	£350
1888..	4,526,856	£6	£10	£25	£70
1889..	7,039,628	£35	£90	£300	—
1889 Large bust (until 1892)........	incl. above	£6	£12	£45	£80
1890..	8,794,042	£6	£12	£45	£80
1891..	5,665,348	£6	£12	£45	£85
1892..	4,591,622	£6	£12	£45	£110
OLD HEAD ISSUES					
1893..	7,039,074	£5	£10	£30	£70
1893 small lettering	incl. above	£5	£10	£30	£70
1893 Proof................................	1,312	—	—	—	£270
1894..	5,953,152	£9	£25	£60	£170
1895..	8,880,651	£9	£25	£55	£160
1896..	9,264,551	£7	£15	£40	£90
1897..	6,270,364	£7	£12	£40	£85
1898..	9,768,703	£7	£12	£40	£80
1899..	10,965,382	£7	£12	£40	£80
1900..	10,937,590	£7	£12	£40	£85
1901..	3,426,294	£7	£12	£40	£80

Victoria Jubilee head

Victoria Old or Veiled head

DATE	MINTAGE	F	VF	EF	UNC

EDWARD VII (1901–10)

DATE	MINTAGE	F	VF	EF	UNC
1902	7,809,481	£5	£15	£45	£80
1902 Proof matt	13,123	—	—	—	£140
1903	2,061,823	£10	£35	£150	£500
1904	2,040,161	£8	£35	£130	£475
1905	488,390	£110	£300	£1100	£3500
1906	10,791,025	£5	£12	£40	£130
1907	14,083,418	£5	£12	£40	£140
1908	3,806,969	£10	£25	£150	£500
1909	5,664,982	£9	£22	£110	£400
1910	26,547,236	£5	£10	£45	£100

GEORGE V (1910–36)

First issue

DATE	MINTAGE	F	VF	EF	UNC
1911	20,065,901	£5	£9	£22	£55
1911 Proof	6,007	—	—	—	£150
1912	15,594,009	£6	£11	£25	£80
1913	9,011,509	£7	£20	£50	£150
1914	23,415,843	£4	£7	£25	£55
1915	39,279,024	£4	£7	£25	£55
1916	35,862,015	£4	£7	£25	£55
1917	22,202,608	£4	£7	£25	£60
1918	34,915,934	£4	£7	£25	£55
1919	10,823,824	£5	£8	£30	£65

Second issue—debased silver

DATE	MINTAGE	F	VF	EF	UNC
1920	22,825,142	£2	£4	£20	£45
1921	22,648,763	£2	£4	£20	£45
1922	27,215,738	£2	£4	£20	£45
1923	14,575,243	£2	£4	£20	£45
1924	9,250,095	£7	£15	£50	£150
1925	5,418,764	£6	£10	£40	£120
1926	22,516,453	£3	£8	£30	£110

George V First obverse

Third issue—Modified bust

DATE	MINTAGE	F	VF	EF	UNC
1926	incl. above	£2	£4	£25	£55
1927 —	9,247,344	£2	£4	£25	£55

Fourth issue—large lion and crown on rev., date in legend

DATE	MINTAGE	F	VF	EF	UNC
1927	incl. above	£2	£4	£20	£40
1927 Proof	15,000	—	—	—	£60
1928	18,136,778	£2	£4	£15	£40
1929	19,343,006	£2	£4	£15	£40
1930	3,172,092	£2	£4	£20	£50
1931	6,993,926	£2	£4	£15	£40
1932	12,168,101	£2	£4	£15	£45
1933	11,511,624	£2	£4	£15	£35
1934	6,138,463	£2	£4	£18	£50
1935	9,183,462	—	£4	£10	£22
1936	11,910,613	—	£4	£9	£20

GEORGE VI (1936–52)

George V Second obverse

E = England rev. (lion standing on large crown). S = Scotland rev. (lion seated on small crown holding sword and mace)

DATE	MINTAGE	F	VF	EF	UNC
1937 E	8,359,122	—	£2	£4	£6
1937 E Proof	26,402	—	—	—	£20
1937 S	6,748,875	—	£2	£4	£6
1937 S Proof	26,402	—	—	—	£20
1938 E	4,833,436	—	£3	£10	£20
1938 S	4,797,852	—	£3	£10	£20
1939 E	11,052,677	—	£2	£4	£6
1939 S	10,263,892	—	£2	£4	£6
1940 E	11,099,126	—	—	£4	£7
1940 S	9,913,089	—	—	£4	£7

DATE	MINTAGE	F	VF	EF	UNC
1941 E	11,391,883	—	—	£4	£6
1941 S	8,086,030	—	—	£4	£5
1942 E	17,453,643	—	—	£4	£5
1942 S	13,676,759	—	—	£4	£5
1943 E	11,404,213	—	—	£4	£6
1943 S	9,824,214	—	—	£4	£5
1944 E	11,586,751	—	—	£4	£5
1944 S	10,990,167	—	—	£4	£5
1945 E	15,143,404	—	—	£4	£6
1945 S	15,106,270	—	—	£4	£5
1946 E	16,663,797	—	—	£4	£5
1946 S	16,381,501	—	—	£4	£5
Cupro-nickel					
1947 E	12,120,611	—	—	—	£2
1947 S	12,283,223	—	—	—	£2
1948 E	45,576,923	—	—	—	£2
1948 S	45,351,937	—	—	—	£2
1949 E	19,328,405	—	—	—	£5
1949 S	21,243,074	—	—	—	£5
1950 E	19,243,872	—	—	—	£5
1950 E Proof	17,513	—	—	—	£20
1950 S	14,299,601	—	—	—	£5
1950 S Proof	17,513	—	—	—	£20
1951 E	9,956,930	—	—	—	£5
1951 E Proof	20,000	—	—	—	£20
1951 S	10,961,174	—	—	—	£6
1951 S Proof	20,000	—	—	—	£20

English reverse

Scottish reverse

ELIZABETH II (1952–)

E = England rev. (shield with three lions). S = Scotland rev. (shield with one lion).

DATE	MINTAGE	F	VF	EF	UNC
1953 E	41,942,894	—	—	—	£1
1953 E Proof	40,000	—	—	—	£4
1953 S	20,663,528	—	—	—	£1
1953 S Proof	40,000	—	—	—	£4
1954 E	30,262,032	—	—	—	£2
1954 S	26,771,735	—	—	—	£2
1955 E	45,259,908	—	—	—	£2
1955 S	27,950,906	—	—	—	£2
1956 E	44,907,008	—	—	—	£10
1956 S	42,853,639	—	—	—	£10
1957 E	42,774,217	—	—	—	£1
1957 S	17,959,988	—	—	—	£10
1958 E	14,392,305	—	—	—	£10
1958 S	40,822,557	—	—	—	£1
1959 E	19,442,778	—	—	—	£1
1959 S	1,012,988	£1	£3	£10	£50
1960 E	27,027,914	—	—	—	£1
1960 S	14,376,932	—	—	—	£1
1961 E	39,816,907	—	—	—	£1
1961 S	2,762,558	—	—	—	£3
1962 E	36,704,379	—	—	—	£1
1962 S	17,475,310	—	—	—	£1
1963 E	49,433,607	—	—	—	£1
1963 S	32,300,000	—	—	—	£1
1964 E	8,590,900	—	—	—	£1
1964 S	5,239,100	—	—	—	£1
1965 E	9,216,000	—	—	—	£1
1965 S	2,774,000	—	—	—	£2
1966 E	15,002,000	—	—	—	£1
1966 S	15,604,000	—	—	—	£1
1970 E Proof	—				£10
1970 S Proof	—				£10

English reverse

Scottish reverse

SIXPENCES

DATE	F	VF	EF	UNC

OLIVER CROMWELL

1658 Patterns by Thos. Simon & Tanner
Four varieties .... Extremely rare

CHARLES II (1660–85)

	F	VF	EF	UNC
1674..	£70	£300	£1000	—
1675..	£70	£300	£1100	—
1675/4 5 over 4	£80	£300	£1100	—
1676..	£80	£300	£1000	—
1676/5 6 over 5	£85	£300	£1000	—
1677..	£70	£300	£1000	—
1678/7	£70	£300	£1100	—
1679..	£75	£300	£1000	—
1680..	£100	£500	£1300	—
1681..	£80	£300	£1050	—
1682/1	£80	£300	£1100	—
1682..	£100	£320	£1200	—
1683..	£75	£300	£1000	—
1684..	£85	£300	£1000	—

JAMES II (1685–88)

	F	VF	EF	UNC
1686 Early shields	£140	£425	£1000	—
1687 Ealy Shields........................	£150	£475	£1300	—
1687/6 — 7 over 6........................	£150	£450	£1100	—
1687 Late shields........................	£150	£450	£1350	—
1687/6 — 7 over 6	£150	£475	£1150	—
1688 —	£150	£450	£1250	—

WILLIAM & MARY (1688–94)

	F	VF	EF	UNC
1693	£130	£450	£1100	—
1693 error inverted 3	£200	£500	£1400	—
1694...	£130	£450	£1100	—

WILLIAM III (1694–1702)

Provincially produced sixpences carry privy marks or initials below the bust:
B: Bristol. C: Chester. E: Exeter. N: Norwich. Y or y: York.

	F	VF	EF	UNC
1695 First bust, early harp in 4th shield on rev.	£35	£100	£400	—
1696 — ...	£35	£100	£325	—
1696 — — French arms at date	Extremely rare			
1696 — — Scottish arms at date	Extremely rare			
1696 — — DFI for DEI....................................	Extremely rare			
1696 — — No stops on obv.	£50	£140	£500	—
1696 — — B..	£40	£100	£425	—
1696 — — — B over E	Extremely rare			
1696 — — C..	£40	£100	£450	—
1696 — — E..	£50	£110	£450	—
1696 — — N..	£45	£100	£450	—
1696 — — y..	£40	£110	£550	—
1696 — — Y..	£50	£200	£600	—
1696 — Later harp	£50	£175	£400	—
1696 — — B	£70	£225	£600	—
1696 — — — no stops on obv........................	£80	£275	£550	—
1696 — — C..	£100	£400	£1000	—
1696 — — N..	£70	£325	—	—
1696 Second bust..	£300	£800	£2200	—
1697 First bust, later harp	£30	£75	£300	—
1697 — — Arms of France & Ireland transposed	Extremely rare			

DATE	MINTAGE	F	VF	EF	UNC
1697 — — B..		£50	£110	£450	—
1697 — — C..		£70	£200	£500	—
1697 — — — Irish shield at date			Extremely rare		
1697 — — E..		£70	£200	£500	—
1697 — — — error GVLIEMVS............................			Extremely rare		
1697 — — y..		£60	£125	£475	—
1697 — — — Irish shield at date			Extremely rare		
1697 Second bust		£220	£550	£1750	—
1697 Third bust		£35	£75	£300	—
1697 — error GVLIEMVS..................................			Extremely rare		
1697 — B..		£50	£110	£450	—
1697 — — IRA for FRA			Extremely rare		
1697 — C..		£75	£220	£550	—
1697 — E..		£75	£200	£550	—
1697 — Y..		£60	£200	£550	—
1698 —		£60	£190	£500	—
1698 — Plumes in angles on rev.		£80	£220	£750	—
1699 —		£90	£250	£800	—
1699 — Plumes in angles on rev.		£70	£250	£850	—
1699 — Roses in angles on rev.		£70	£250	£850	—
1699 — — error GⱯLIELMVS			Extremely rare		
1700 —		£45	£110	£400	—
1700 — Plume below bust		£2000	—	—	—
1701 —		£65	£160	£525	—

ANNE (1702–14)

1703 VIGO below bust Before Union with Scotland	£40	£140	£450	—
1705 Plain..	£60	£170	£525	—
1705 Plumes in angles on rev............................	£50	£160	£525	—
1705 Roses & Plumes in angles in rev.	£60	£150	£525	—
1707 Roses & Plumes in angles on rev.	£50	£150	£450	—
1707 (Post-Union), Plain....................................	£40	£85	£350	—
1707 E (Edinburgh) below bust	£40	£85	£320	—
1707 Plumes in angles on rev............................	£45	£120	£350	—
1708 Plain..	£45	£100	£400	—
1708 E below bust	£50	£100	£350	—
1708 E* below bust	£60	£140	£400	—
1708 "Edinburgh" bust E* below	£50	£140	£400	—
1708 Plumes in angles on rev............................	£55	£150	£500	—
1710 Roses & Plumes in angles on rev.	£35	£110	£450	—
1711 Plain..	£25	£70	£250	—

GEORGE I (1714–27)

1717 Roses & Plumes in angles on rev.	£90	£300	£800	—
1717 Plain edge..		Extremely rare		
1720 —	£90	£300	£725	—
1723 SSC in angles on rev.	£30	£70	£200	—
1723 Larger lettering	£30	£70	£200	—
1726 Small Roses & Plumes in angles on rev. ..	£80	£225	£650	—

GEORGE II (1727–60)

1728 Young head, Plain......................................	£70	£240	£525	—
1728 — Proof	—	—	£4000	—
1728 — Plumes in angles on rev.	£40	£140	£400	—
1728 — Roses & Plumes in angles on rev.........	£35	£125	£350	—
1731 — —	£40	£140	£375	—
1732 — —	£35	£130	£375	—
1734 — —	£40	£140	£375	—
1735 — —	£35	£140	£375	—
1735/4 5 over 4	£45	£150	£425	—
1736 — —	£45	£150	£400	—
1739 — Roses in angles on rev.	£30	£110	£350	—
1741 —	£30	£110	£325	—
1743 Old head, Roses in angles on rev.............	£25	£75	£250	—
1745 — —	£25	£75	£250	—

DATE	MINTAGE	F	VF	EF	UNC
1745 — — 5 over 3		£30	£85	£275	—
1745 — Plain, LIMA below bust........................		£30	£80	£275	—
1746 — — —		£30	£80	£275	—
1746 — — Proof...	—	—	£1800	—
1750 — —		£30	£120	£325	—
1751 — —		£35	£150	£375	—
1757 — —		£18	£35	£95	—
1758 — —		£18	£35	£95	—

GEORGE III (1760–1820)

1787 rev. no semée of hearts on 4th shield	£15	£35	£80	£110
1787 rev. with semée of hearts..........................	£15	£35	£80	£110

NEW COINAGE

1816..	—	£7	£15	£40	£100
1817..	10,921,680	£7	£15	£40	£100
1818..	4,284,720	£10	£25	£80	£175
1819..	4,712,400	£8	£15	£40	£90
1819 very small 8 in date.............	incl. above	£12	£22	£60	£140
1820..	1,488,960	£8	£15	£50	£120

GEORGE IV (1820–30)

1821 First bust, first reverse	863,280	£12	£30	£120	£350
1821 error BBRITANNIAR............		£100	£300	£950	—
1821 — — Proof.........................	incl. above	—	—	—	£1200
1824 — Second (garter) reverse..	633,600	£10	£30	£100	£325
1825 — —	483,120	£12	£30	£100	£300
1826 — —	689,040	£40	£100	£250	£550
1826 Second bust, third (lion on crown) reverse	incl. above	£10	£30	£100	£220
1826 — — Proof.........................	incl. above	—	—	—	£700
1827 — —	166,320	£40	£100	£300	£700
1828 — —	15,840	£20	£50	£150	£350
1829 — —	403,290	£15	£45	£125	£350

WILLIAM IV (1830–37)

1831..	1,340,195	£15	£40	£125	£300
1831 Proof, milled edge	incl. above	—	—	—	£800
1834..	5,892,480	£15	£40	£125	£300
1835..	1,552,320	£15	£40	£125	£300
1836..	1,987,920	£15	£45	£150	£350
1837..	506,880	£20	£45	£220	£500

VICTORIA (1837–1901)

YOUNG HEAD ISSUES
First head

1838..	1,607,760	£15	£40	£130	£350
1839	3,310,560	£15	£40	£130	£350
1839 Proof....................................	incl. above	—	—	—	£1500
1840..	2,098,800	£15	£40	£130	£350
1841..	1,386,000	£18	£45	£140	£400
1842..	601,920	£15	£40	£130	£350
1843..	3,160,080	£15	£40	£130	£350
1844..	3,975,840	£15	£30	£140	£350
1844 Large 44 in date.................	incl. above	£18	£40	£130	£400
1845..	3,714,480	£15	£35	£90	£350
1846..	4,226,880	£15	£35	£90	£350
1848..	586,080	£50	£110	£340	£475
1848/6 final 8 over 6....................	incl. above	£50	£120	£400	—
1850..	498,960	£15	£40	£120	£425
1850/3 0 over 3	incl. above	£18	£40	£110	£400
1851..	2,288,107	£10	£30	£100	£375
1852..	904,586	£10	£30	£150	£370
1853..	3,837,930	£10	£30	£150	£370

DATE	MINTAGE	F	VF	EF	UNC
1853 Proof	incl above	—	—	—	£1400
1854	840,116	£200	£600	£1200	3250
1855	1,129,684	£10	£30	£120	£250
1855/3 last 5 over 3	incl. above	£15	£45	£140	£300
1856	2,779,920	£10	£40	£120	£300
1857	2,233,440	£10	£40	£120	£280
1858	1,932,480	£10	£40	£120	£280
1859	4,688,640	£10	£40	£120	£280
1859/8 9 over 8	incl. above	£12	£40	£120	£400
1860	1,100,880	£10	£35	£120	£325
1862	990,000	£100	£200	£600	£1800
1863	491,040	£70	£150	£475	£1300

Die no. added above date from 1864 to 1879

DATE	MINTAGE	F	VF	EF	UNC
1864	4,253,040	£10	£25	£110	£250
1865	1,631,520	£10	£25	£100	£250
1866	4,140,080	£10	£25	£100	£250
1866 no Die no.	incl. above		Extremely Rare		

Jubilee head, shield reverse

Second head

DATE	MINTAGE	F	VF	EF	UNC
1867	1,362,240	£10	£30	£120	£300
1868	1,069,200	£10	£30	£110	£270
1869	388,080	£10	£30	£110	£280
1870	479,613	£10	£30	£110	£270
1871	3,662,684	£8	£30	£75	£220
1871 no Die no.	incl. above	£8	£30	£75	£230
1872	3,382,048	£8	£30	£75	£230
1873	4,594,733	£8	£30	£75	£230
1874	4,225,726	£8	£30	£80	£250
1875	3,256,545	£8	£30	£75	£220
1876	841,435	£8	£30	£75	£220
1877	4,066,486	£8	£30	£75	£220
1877 no Die no	incl. above	£8	£30	£75	£220
1878	2,624,525	£8	£30	£75	£250
1878 Dritanniar Error	incl. above	£125	£300	£1000	—
1879	3,326,313	£8	£25	£80	£220
1879 no Die no	incl. above	£8	£25	£80	£220
1880 no Die no	3,892,501	£8	£25	£75	£220

Jubilee head, wreath reverse

Third head

DATE	MINTAGE	F	VF	EF	UNC
1880	incl above	£8	£20	£80	£200
1881	6,239,447	£8	£20	£80	£200
1882	759,809	£15	£50	£150	£475
1883	4,986,558	£8	£20	£70	£160
1884	3,422,565	£8	£20	£70	£160
1885	4,652,771	£8	£20	£70	£160
1886	2,728,249	£8	£20	£70	£150
1887	3,675,607	£8	£20	£70	£150

JUBILEE HEAD ISSUES

DATE	MINTAGE	F	VF	EF	UNC
1887 Shield reverse	incl. above	£6	£10	£15	£30
1887 — Proof	incl. above	—	—	—	£200
1887 Six Pence in wreath reverse	incl. above	£6	£8	£18	£35
1888 —	4,197,698	£8	£12	£35	£60
1889 —	8,738,928	£8	£12	£35	£70
1890 —	9,386,955	£8	£12	£35	£70
1891 —	7,022,734	£8	£12	£35	£70
1892 —	6,245,746	£8	£12	£35	£80
1893 —	7,350,619	£800	£1500	£4000	—

OLD HEAD ISSUES

DATE	MINTAGE	F	VF	EF	UNC
1893	incl. above	£7	£12	£22	£50
1893 Proof	1,312	—	—	—	£250
1894	3,467,704	£8	£18	£50	£140
1895	7,024,631	£8	£18	£45	£110
1896	6,651,699	£7	£15	£35	£65
1897	5,031,498	£7	£15	£35	£65
1898	5,914,100	£7	£15	£35	£65
1899	7,996,80	£7	£15	£35	£55
1900	8,984,354	£7	£15	£35	£55
1901	5,108,757	£7	£15	£35	£55

DATE	MINTAGE	F	VF	EF	UNC
EDWARD VII (1901–10)					
1902	6,367,378	£5	£10	£30	£60
1902 "Matt Proof"	15,123	—	—	—	£140
1903	5,410,096	£7	£20	£50	£170
1904	4,487,098	£15	£50	£175	£500
1905	4,235,556	£8	£20	£70	£220
1906	7,641,146	£7	£12	£40	£110
1907	8,733,673	£7	£12	£45	£120
1908	6,739,491	£10	£30	£110	£350
1909	6,584,017	£8	£18	£50	£175
1910	12,490,724	£5	£8	£25	£55

GEORGE V (1910–36)

First issue

DATE	MINTAGE	F	VF	EF	UNC
1911	9,155,310	£3	£7	£15	£40
1911 Proof	6,007	—	—	—	£120
1912	10,984,129	£3	£7	£20	£65
1913	7,499,833	£3	£8	£22	£80
1914	22,714,602	£3	£7	£10	£35
1915	15,694,597	£3	£7	£12	£45
1916	22,207,178	£3	£7	£10	£35
1917	7,725,475	£8	£25	£60	£150
1918	27,553,743	£3	£7	£12	£30
1919	13,375,447	£3	£7	£12	£40
1920	14,136,287	£3	£7	£10	£35

George V first reverse

Second issue—debased silver

DATE	MINTAGE	F	VF	EF	UNC
1920	incl. above	£1	£3	£10	£40
1921	30,339,741	£1	£3	£10	£40
1922	16,878,890	£1	£3	£10	£30
1923	6,382,793	£4	£10	£45	£110
1924	17,444,218	£1	£5	£10	£35
1925	12,720,558	£1	£3	£10	£35
1925 Broad rim	incl. above	£1	£3	£10	£35
1926 —	21,809,621	£1	£3	£10	£35

Third issue—Modified bust

DATE	MINTAGE	F	VF	EF	UNC
1926	incl. above	£1	£2	£10	£35
1927	8,924,873	—	£2	£10	£35

Fourth issue—New design (oakleaves)

DATE	MINTAGE	F	VF	EF	UNC
1927 Proof only	15,000	—	—	—	£35
1928	23,123,384	£1	£2	£8	£25
1929	28,319,326	£1	£2	£8	£25
1930	16,990,289	£1	£2	£8	£30
1931	16,873,268	£1	£2	£8	£30
1932	9,406,117	£1	£2	£8	£40
1933	22,185,083	£1	£2	£8	£25
1934	9,304,009	£1	£2	£12	£35
1935	13,995,621	£1	£2	£6	£15
1936	24,380,171	£1	£2	£6	£15

George V second reverse (fourth issue)

GEORGE VI (1936–52)

First type

DATE	MINTAGE	F	VF	EF	UNC
1937	22,302,524	—	—	£1	£5
1937 Proof	26,402	—	—	—	£10
1938	13,402,701	—	£2	£5	£18
1939	28,670,304	—	—	£1	£5
1940	20,875,196	—	—	£1	£5
1941	23,086,616	—	—	£1	£5
1942	44,942,785	—	—	£1	£4
1943	46,927,111	—	—	£1	£4
1944	36,952,600	—	—	£1	£4
1945	39,939,259	—	—	£1	£3
1946	43,466,407	—	—	£1	£3

Cupro-nickel

DATE	MINTAGE	F	VF	EF	UNC
1947	29,993,263	—	—	£1	£3
1948	88,323,540	—	—	£1	£3

George VI first reverse

Second type—new cypher on rev.

DATE	MINTAGE	F	VF	EF	UNC
1949	41,335,515	—	—	£1	£3

George VI second reverse

DATE	MINTAGE	F	VF	EF	UNC
1950	32,741,955	—	—	£1	£3
1950 Proof	17,513	—	—	—	£7
1951	40,399,491	—	—	£1	£3
1951 Proof	20,000	—	—	—	£7
1952	1,013,477	£7	£22	£50	£140

ELIZABETH II (1952–)

1953	70,323,876	—	—	—	£2
1953 Proof	40,000	—	—	—	£4
1954	105,241,150	—	—	—	£3
1955	109,929,554	—	—	—	£1
1956	109,841,555	—	—	—	£1
1957	105,654,290	—	—	—	£1
1958	123,518,527	—	—	—	£3
1959	93,089,441	—	—	—	£1
1960	103,283,346	—	—	—	£3
1961	115,052,017	—	—	—	£3
1962	166,483,637	—	—	—	25p
1963	120,056,000	—	—	—	25p
1964	152,336,000	—	—	—	25p
1965	129,644,000	—	—	—	25p
1966	175,676,000	—	—	—	25p
1967	240,788,000	—	—	—	25p
1970 Proof	—				£8

GROATS OR FOURPENCES

DATE	MINTAGE	F	VF	EF	UNC

The earlier fourpences are included in the Maundy oddments section as they are generally considered to have been issued for the Maundy ceremony.

WILLIAM IV (1831–37)

1836	—	£8	£18	£40	£90
1837	962,280	£8	£18	£40	£95

VICTORIA (1838–1901)

1837	Extremely Rare Proofs or Patterns only				
1838	2,150,280	£7	£15	£40	£90
1838 over last 8 on its side		£10	£20	£60	£120
1839	1,461,240	£7	£16	£50	£100
1839 Proof	incl. above				Rare
1840	1,496,880	£7	£15	£50	£100
1840 Small 0 in date	incl. above	£7	£15	£50	£100
1841	344,520	£7	£15	£50	£100
1842/1 2 over 1	incl. above	£7	£15	£50	£100
1842	724,680	£7	£15	£45	£100
1843	1,817640	£8	£16	£50	£120
1843 4 over 5	incl. above	£7	£15	£50	£120
1844	855,360	£7	£15	£50	£110
1845	914,760	£7	£15	£50	£110
1846	1,366,200	£7	£15	£50	£100
1847 7 over 6	225,720	£15	£35	£125	—
1848	712,800	£7	£15	£50	£90
1848/6 8 over 6	incl. above	£30	£110	—	—
1848/7 8 over 7	incl. above	£8	£20	£60	£110
1849	380,160	£7	£15	£50	£100
1849/8 9 over 8	incl. above	£8	£20	£70	£135
1851	594,000	£35	£80	£250	£450
1852	31,300	£55	£130	£425	—
1853	11,880	£80	£170	£600	—
1853 Proof Milled Rim	incl. above	—	—	—	£1100
1853 Plain edge Proof		Extremely rare			
1854	1,096,613	£7	£15	£40	£90
1855	646,041	£7	£15	£40	£90
1857 Proofs only		Extremely rare			
1862 Proofs only		Extremely rare			
1888 Jubilee Head	—	£12	£25	£50	£110

THREEPENCES

DATE	MINTAGE	F	VF	EF	UNC

The earlier threepences are included in the Maundy oddments section.

WILLIAM IV (1830–37)
(issued for use in the West Indies)

DATE	MINTAGE	F	VF	EF	UNC
1834		£12	£22	£90	£240
1835		£10	£20	£80	£225
1836		£10	£20	£85	£225
1837		£12	£28	£120	£275

VICTORIA (1837–1901)

DATE	MINTAGE	F	VF	EF	UNC
1838 BRITANNIAB error			Extremely rare		
1838	—	£10	£25	£80	£240
1839	—	£10	£28	£80	£250
1840	—	£10	£25	£80	£250
1841	—	£12	£30	£90	£280
1842	—	£10	£25	£70	£240
1843	—	£10	£25	£60	£200
1843/34 43 over 34	—	£10	£25	£90	£250
1844	—	£12	£25	£80	£225
1845	1,319,208	£12	£25	£70	£225
1846	52,008	£25	£70	£250	£525
1847	4,488		Extremely rare		
1848	incl. above		Extremely rare		
1849	131,208	£12	£25	£80	£240
1850	954,888	£12	£25	£60	£200
1851	479,065	£12	£30	£70	£220
1851 5 over 8	incl. above	£25	£50	£220	—
1852	4,488	£80	£220	£700	£1100
1853	36,168	£60	£140	£300	£700
1854	1,467,246	£8	£25	£60	£200
1855	383,350	£12	£30	£70	£230
1856	1,013,760	£10	£25	£65	£200
1857	1,758,240	£10	£25	£70	£220
1858	1,441,440	£10	£25	£65	£200
1858 BRITANNIAB error	incl. above		Extremely rare		
1858/6 final 8 over 6	incl. above	£10	£30	£125	—
1858/5 final 8 over 5	incl. above	£10	£30	£125	—
1859	3,579,840	£8	£20	£50	£180
1860	3,405,600	£12	£28	£65	£235
1861	3,294,720	£10	£25	£60	£180
1862	1,156,320	£10	£25	£60	£180
1863	950,400	£30	£70	£125	£320
1864	1,330,560	£7	£22	£50	£170
1865	1,742,400	£7	£22	£50	£170
1866	1,900,800	£7	£22	£50	£170
1867	712,800	£7	£22	£50	£170
1868	1,457,280	£7	£22	£50	£180
1868 RRITANNIAR error	incl. above		Extremely rare		
1869	—	£90	£140	£275	£550
1870	1,283,218	£5	£16	£50	£140
1871	999,633	£5	£16	£40	£120
1872	1,293,271	£5	£16	£40	£110
1873	4,055,550	£5	£16	£40	£110
1874	4,427,031	£5	£16	£40	£120
1875	3,306,500	£5	£16	£40	£110
1876	1,834,389	£5	£16	£40	£110
1877	2,622,393	£5	£16	£40	£110
1878	2,419,975	£5	£16	£40	£140
1879	3,140,265	£5	£16	£40	£110
1880	1,610,069	£5	£16	£40	£100
1881	3,248,265	£5	£16	£40	£90
1882	472,965	£8	£25	£70	£190
1883	4,369,971	£5	£10	£30	£65

Victoria first type

DATE	MINTAGE	F	VF	EF	UNC
1884	3,322,424	£5	£12	£30	£75
1885	5,183,653	£5	£12	£30	£70
1886	6,152,669	£5	£12	£30	£60
1887	2,780,761	£5	£12	£30	£65

JUBILEE HEAD ISSUES

1887	incl. above	£2	£4	£14	£28
1887 Proof	incl. above	—	—	—	£250
1888	518,199	£2	£5	£20	£45
1889	4,587,010	£2	£5	£20	£50
1890	4,465,834	£2	£5	£20	£50
1891	6,323,027	£2	£5	£20	£50
1892	2,578,226	£2	£5	£20	£50
1893	3,067,243	£15	£50	£175	£400

*Victoria
Jubilee head*

OLD HEAD ISSUES

1893	incl. above	£2	£4	£15	£30
1893 Proof	incl. above	—	—	—	£220
1894	1,608,603	£3	£6	£25	£70
1895	4,788,609	£2	£5	£22	£60
1896	4,598,442	£2	£5	£18	£40
1897	4,541,294	£2	£5	£18	£40
1898	4,567,177	£2	£5	£18	£40
1899	6,246,281	£2	£5	£18	£40
1900	10,644,480	£2	£5	£18	£40
1901	6,098,400	£2	£5	£15	£30

*Victoria
Old or Veiled
head*

EDWARD VII (1901–10)

1902	8,268,480	£2	£3	£7	£15
1902 "Matt Proof"	incl. above	—	—	—	£60
1903	5,227,200	£2	£4	£20	£50
1904	3,627,360	£3	£10	£45	£110
1905	3,548,160	£2	£4	£25	£65
1906	3,152,160	£3	£8	£40	£85
1907	4,831,200	£2	£4	£20	£55
1908	8,157,600	£2	£3	£20	£50
1909	4,055,040	£2	£4	£20	£55
1910	4,563,380	£2	£4	£18	£40

GEORGE V (1910–36)

First issue

1911	5,841,084	—	—	£3	£10
1911 Proof	incl. above	—	—	—	£70
1912	8,932,825	—	—	£3	£12
1913	7,143,242	—	—	£3	£12
1914	6,733,584	—	—	£3	£12
1915	5,450,617	—	—	£3	£15
1916	18,555,201	—	—	£3	£10
1917	21,662,490	—	—	£3	£10
1918	20,630,909	—	—	£3	£10
1919	16,845,687	—	—	£3	£10
1920	16,703,597	—	—	£3	£10

Second issue—debased silver

1920	incl. above	—	—	£3	£12
1921	8,749,301	—	—	£3	£12
1922	7,979,998	—	—	£3	£40
1925	3,731,859	—	—	£5	£25
1926	4,107,910	—	—	£7	£30

*George V
second issue*

Third issue—Modified bust

1926	incl. above	—	—	£8	£22

Fourth issue—new design (oakleaves)

1927 Proof only	15,022	—	—	—	£110
1928	1,302,106	£4	£10	£30	£65
1930	1,319,412	£2	£4	£10	£40
1931	6,251,936	—	—	£2	£7
1932	5,887,325	—	—	£2	£7
1933	5,578,541	—	—	£2	£7
1934	7,405,954	—	—	£2	£7
1935	7,027,654	—	—	£2	£7
1936	3,328,670	—	—	£2	£7

*George V,
fourth issue
oak leaves
design reverse*

DATE	MINTAGE	F	VF	EF	UNC

GEORGE VI (1936–52)

Silver

DATE	MINTAGE	F	VF	EF	UNC
1937	8,148,156	—	—	£1	£4
1937 Proof	26,402	—	—	—	£15
1938	6,402,473	—	—	£1	£4
1939	1,355,860	—	—	£4	£15
1940	7,914,401	—	—	£1	£3
1941	7,979,411	—	—	£1	£3
1942	4,144,051	£2	£5	£12	£35
1943	1,397,220	£2	£5	£12	£35
1944	2,005,553	£7	£15	£40	£90
1945				Only one known	

George VI small silver 3d

Nickel brass

DATE	MINTAGE	F	VF	EF	UNC
1937	45,707,957	—	—	£1	£4
1937 Proof	26,402	—	—	—	£18
1938	14,532,332	—	—	£1	£18
1939	5,603,021	—	—	£3	£40
1940	12,636,018	—	—	£3	£30
1941	60,239,489	—	—	£1	£8
1942	103,214,400	—	—	£1	£8
1943	101,702,400	—	—	£1	£8
1944	69,760,000	—	—	£1	£8
1945	33,942,466	—	—	£4	£20
1946	620,734	£6	£25	£240	£850
1948	4,230,400	—	—	£7	£55
1949	464,000	£6	£28	£250	£900
1950	1,600,000	—	£2	£20	£140
1950 Proof	17,513	—	—	—	£25
1951	1,184,000	—	£3	£30	£150
1951 Proof	20,000	—	—	—	£25
1952	25,494,400	—	—	—	£10

George VI "Thrift" design of the nickel brass 3d

ELIZABETH II (1952–)

DATE	MINTAGE	F	VF	EF	UNC
1953	30,618,000	—	—	—	£1
1953 Proof	40,000	—	—	—	£6
1954	41,720,000	—	—	—	£5
1955	41,075,200	—	—	—	£5
1956	36,801,600	—	—	—	£6
1957	24,294,500	—	—	—	£6
1958	20,504,000	—	—	—	£9
1959	28,499,200	—	—	—	£6
1960	83,078,400	—	—	—	£2
1961	41,102,400	—	—	—	£1
1962	51,545,600	—	—	—	£1
1963	39,482,866	—	—	—	£1
1964	44,867,200	—	—	—	—
1965	27,160,000	—	—	—	—
1966	53,160,000	—	—	—	—
1967	151,780,800	—	—	—	—
1970 Proof	—				£6

TWO PENCES

GEORGE III (1760–1820)

		F	VF	EF	UNC
1797 "Cartwheel"	722,972	£30	£80	£425	£1100
1797 Copper Proofs		Many types from £800+			

VICTORIA (1837–1901)

For use in the Colonies

		F	VF	EF	UNC
1838		£4	£10	£18	£40
1848		£4	£12	£20	£45

Earlier issues of the small silver two pences are listed in the Maundy section.

THREE-HALFPENCES

DATE		F	VF	EF	UNC

WILLIAM IV (1830–37)

For use in the Colonies

DATE	F	VF	EF	UNC
1834	£6	£16	£35	£85
1835	£10	£25	£75	£210
1835 over 4	£6	£16	£40	£100
1836	£8	£18	£45	£100
1837	£15	£35	£110	£325

VICTORIA (1837–1901)

For use in the Colonies

DATE	F	VF	EF	UNC
1838	£6	£15	£35	£75
1839	£6	£15	£35	£75
1840	£8	£20	£60	£140
1841	£6	£15	£35	£80
1842	£6	£18	£40	£100
1843	£6	£15	£30	£70
1860	£10	£25	£80	£180
1862	£15	£35	£90	£220

PENNIES

DATE	MINTAGE	F	VF	EF	UNC

The earlier small silver pennies are included in the Maundy oddments section.

GEORGE III (1760–1820)

DATE	MINTAGE	F	VF	EF	UNC
1797 "Cartwheel", 10 laurel leaves	43,969,204	£25	£60	£300	£1000

Numerous proofs in different metals are known for this issue—all are rare.

1797 — 11 laurel leaves	incl. above	£25	£60	£300	£1000
1806 Fourth issue	19,355,480	£7	£18	£75	£300
1807	11,290,168	£7	£18	£75	£300
1808	—				Unique

GEORGE IV (1820–30)

1825	1,075,200	£14	£45	£250	£650
1826 (varieties)	5,913,600	£14	£45	£250	£650
1826 Proof	—	—	—	—	£1000
1827	1,451,520	£250	£900	£4500	—

WILLIAM IV (1830–37)

1831 (varieties)	806,400	£28	£70	£425	£1200
1831 Proof	—	—	—	—	£1200
1834	322,560	£30	£70	£400	£1300
1837	174,720	£65	£200	£800	£3000

VICTORIA (1837–1901)

YOUNG HEAD ISSUES

Copper

1839 Proof	unrecorded	—	—	—	£3250
1841	913,920	£10	£50	£300	£800
1841 No colon after REG	incl. above	£8	£20	£175	£550
1843	483,840	£100	£350	£2000	£5000
1844	215,040	£12	£30	£200	£600
1845	322,560	£15	£35	£240	£800
1846	483,840	£15	£25	£200	£725
1846 FID: DEF colon spaced	incl. above	£15	£25	£200	£725
1846 FID:DEF colon close	incl. above	£16	£30	£210	£750
1847	430,080	£12	£25	£180	£600
1848	161,280	£12	£25	£160	£525

George III "Cartwheel" penny

Note: Mintage figures for the Soho Mint strikings are from the on-line thesis, "Matthew Boulton and the Soho Mint—Copper to Customer", by Sue Tungate, Birmingham University, October 2011 (information supplied by Dennis Onions)

DATE	MINTAGE		F	VF	EF	UNC
1848/7 final 8 over 7	incl. above	£9	£22	£150	£475	
1848/6 final 8 over 6	incl. above	£20	£120	£525	—	
1849	268,800	£225	£600	£2500	—	
1851	268,800	£15	£45	£220	£800	
1853	1,021,440	£7	£15	£100	£200	
1853 Proof	—	—	—	—	£3500	
1854	6,720,000	£8	£22	£110	£250	
1854/3 4 over 3	incl. above	£15	£50	£200	—	
1855	5,273,856	£8	£20	£100	£250	
1856 Plain trident close colon DEF:	1,212,288	£110	£250	£1100	£3000	
1856 Orn trident far colon DEF: ..	—	£120	£270	£1100	£3200	
1857 Plain trident	752,640	£7	£18	£80	£300	
1857 Ornamental trident	incl. above	£6	£18	£70	£300	
1858/7 final 8 over 7	incl. above	£7	£18	£80	£325	
1858/6 final 8 over 6	—	£40	£120	£500	—	
1858/3 final 8 over 3	incl. above	£25	£90	£400	—	
1858	1,599,040	£7	£16	£100	£340	
1859	1,075,200	£8	£25	£170	£500	
1860/59	32,256	£900	£2200	£4000	£7000	

Note all are 60/59. All have a prominent die flan under Victoria's chin.

Victoria copper penny

Bronze

Prices of bronze Victoria Young "bun" head pennies are for the common types. There are many known varieties which are listed in detail in other more specialised publications. Prices for coins in mint with full lustre will be considerably higher.

DATE	MINTAGE		F	VF	EF	UNC
1860 Beaded border	5,053,440	£30	£75	£200	£850	
1860 Toothed border	incl. above	£10	£25	£75	£375	
1860 — Piedfort flan	—		Extremely rare			
1861	36,449,280	£8	£15	£50	£350	
1862	50,534,400	£8	£15	£50	£300	
1862 8 over 6	incl. above		Extremely rare			
1863	28,062,720	£8	£15	£50	£300	
1863 Die no below date	incl. above		Extremely rare			
1864 Plain 4	3,440,640	£30	£175	£700	£3200	
1864 Crosslet 4	incl. above	£35	£185	£800	£3500	
1865	8,601,600	£8	£20	£60	£400	
1865/3 5 over 3	incl. above	£45	£150	£550	—	
1866	9,999,360	£8	£25	£80	£500	
1867	5,483,520	£8	£25	£100	£850	
1868	1,182,720	£18	£75	£275	£2250	
1869	2,580,480	£150	£500	£2000	£6000	
1870	5,695,022	£15	£75	£175	£775	
1871	1,290,318	£45	£130	£500	£2500	
1872	8,494,572	£8	£25	£75	£300	
1873	8,494,200	£8	£25	£75	£300	
1874	5,621,865	£8	£25	£75	£300	
1874 H	6,666,240	£8	£25	£85	£350	
1874 Later (older) bust	incl. above	£15	£45	£120	£500	

Victoria Young or "Bun" head bronze penny

DATE	MINTAGE	F	VF	EF	UNC
1875................................	10,691,040	£8	£25	£75	£350
1875 H.............................	752,640	£35	£125	£900	£2500
1876 H.............................	11,074,560	£8	£15	£65	£320
1877................................	9,624,747	£8	£15	£65	£300
1878................................	2,764,470	£8	£15	£65	£300
1879................................	7,666,476	£6	£18	£60	£300
1880................................	3,000,831	£6	£18	£60	£325
1881................................	2,302,362	£8	£18	£60	£300
1881 H.............................	3,763,200	£10	£18	£60	£300
1882 H.............................	7,526,400	£8	£18	£60	£300
1882 no H........................	—		Extremely Rare		
1883................................	6,237,438	£8	£18	£60	£260
1884................................	11,702,802	£8	£18	£55	£250
1885................................	7,145,862	£8	£18	£55	£250
1886................................	6,087,759	£8	£18	£55	£250
1887................................	5,315,085	£8	£18	£55	£250
1888................................	5,125,020	£8	£18	£60	£300
1889................................	12,559,737	£8	£18	£50	£350
1890................................	15,330,840	£8	£18	£50	£250
1891................................	17,885,961	£8	£15	£50	£250
1892................................	10,501,671	£10	£20	£100	£350
1893................................	8,161,737	£8	£15	£55	£250
1894................................	3,883,452	£15	£45	£160	£500

OLD HEAD ISSUES

DATE	MINTAGE	F	VF	EF	UNC
1895 Trident 2mm from P(ENNY)	5,395,830	£20	£90	£300	£850
1895 Trident 1mm from P............	incl. above	—	£2	£18	£75
1896................................	24,147,156	—	£2	£18	£65
1897................................	20,756,620	—	£2	£15	£60
1897 Raised dot after O of ONE (O·NE)		£150	£275	£900	—
1898................................	14,296,836	—	£3	£18	£60
1899................................	26,441,069	—	£3	£16	£55
1900................................	31,778,109	—	£3	£16	£45
1901................................	22,205,568	—	£3	£10	£30

EDWARD VII (1901–10)

DATE	MINTAGE	F	VF	EF	UNC
1902................................	26,976,768	—	£1	£8	£30
1902 "Low tide" to sea line	incl. above	£4	£15	£60	£225
1903................................	21,415,296	—	£3	£15	£85
1904................................	12,913,152	—	£4	£25	£190
1905................................	17,783,808	—	£3	£15	£80
1906................................	37,989,504	—	£3	£15	£70
1907................................	47,322,240	—	£3	£15	£70
1908................................	31,506,048	—	£3	£18	£125
1909................................	19,617,024	—	£3	£20	£150
1910................................	29,549,184	—	£3	£15	£60

GEORGE V (1910–36)

DATE	MINTAGE	F	VF	EF	UNC
1911................................	23,079,168	—	£3	£12	£65
1912................................	48,306,048	—	£3	£12	£60
1912 H.............................	16,800,000	—	£4	£40	£230
1913................................	65,497,812	—	£3	£15	£75
1914................................	50,820,997	—	£3	£18	£75
1915................................	47,310,807	—	£3	£20	£85
1916................................	86,411,165	—	£3	£15	£65
1917................................	107,905,436	—	£3	£15	£60
1918................................	84,227,372	—	£3	£12	£55
1918 H.............................	3,660,800	£1	£15	£110	£525
1918 KN...........................	incl. above	£8	£80	£600	£2400
1919................................	113,761,090	—	£2	£15	£55
1919 H.............................	5,209,600	£1	£15	£200	£700
1919 KN...........................	incl. above	£15	£110	£750	£3000
1920................................	124,693,485	—	£2	£12	£30
1921................................	129,717,693	—	£2	£12	£40
1922................................	16,346,711	—	£3	£28	£160
1922 with reverse of 1927 (see article on p. 17)				Very rare	
1926................................	4,498,519	—	£6	£25	£150
1926 Modified effigy..................	incl above	£25	£150	£800	£2500
1927................................	60,989,561	—	£2	£10	£40

DATE	MINTAGE	F	VF	EF	UNC
1928	50,178,00	—	£2	£10	£35
1929	49,132,800	—	£2	£10	£40
1930	29,097,600	—	£2	£20	£70
1931	19,843,200	—	£2	£10	£50
1932	8,277,600	—	£2	£15	£100
1933		Only 7 examples known			
1934	13,965,600	—	£2	£25	£100
1935	56,070,000	—	—	£2	£14
1936	154,296,000	—	—	£2	£12

GEORGE VI (1936–52)

1937	88,896,000	—	—	—	£4
1937 Proof	26,402	—	—	—	£14
1938	121,560,000	—	—	—	£6
1939	55,560,000	—	—	—	£15
1940	42,284,400	—	—	£8	£25
1944 Mint Dark	42,600,000	—	—	—	£8
1945 Mint Dark	79,531,200	—	—	—	£8
1946 Mint Dark	66,855,600	—	—	—	£8
1947	52,220,400	—	—	—	£5
1948	63,961,200	—	—	—	£5
1949	14,324,400	—	—	—	£8
1950	240,000	£8	£16	£30	£50
1950 Proof	17,513	—	—	—	£25
1951	120,000	£20	£26	£50	£75
1951 Proof	20,000	—	—	—	£40

ELIZABETH II (1952–)

1953	1,308,400	—	—	£2	£5
1953 Proof	40,000	—	—	—	£10
1954		Only one known			
1961	48,313,400	—	—	—	£2
1962	143,308,600	—	—	—	50p
1963	125,235,600	—	—	—	50p
1964	153,294,000	—	—	—	50p
1965	121,310,400	—	—	—	50p
1966	165,739,200	—	—	—	50p
1967	654,564,000	—	—	—	—
1970 Proof	—				£8

Later issues are included in the Decimal section.

HALFPENNIES

CHARLES II (1660–85)

1672	£70	£300	£1350	—
1672 CRAOLVS error		Extremely rare		
1673	£70	£300	£1350	—
1673 CRAOLVS error		Extremely rare		
1673 No rev. stop	£100	£600	—	—
1673 No stops on obv.		Extremely rare		
1675	£65	£500	£1500	—
1675 No stops on obv.	£80	£550	—	—
1675/3 5 over 3	£175	£650	—	—

JAMES II (1685–88)

1685 (tin)	£250	£750	£4000	—
1686 (tin)	£300	£750	£4200	—
1687 (tin)	£325	£800	£4000	—

WILLIAM & MARY (1688–94)

Tin

1689 Small draped busts, edge dated		Extremely rare		
1690 Large cuirassed busts, edge dated	£200	£750	£3500	—
1691 — date on edge and in exergue	£180	£700	£3200	—
1692 — —	£200	£750	£3400	—

*Copper halfpenny
of William & Mary*

DATE	F	VF	EF	UNC

Copper

	F	VF	EF	UNC
1694 Large cuirassed busts, date in exergue	£80	£300	£1200	—
1694 — — GVLIEMVS error			Extremely rare	
1694 — — MΛRIΛ error			Extremely rare	
1694 — — No stops on rev.			Extremely rare	

WILLIAM III (1694–1702)

	F	VF	EF	UNC
1695 First issue (date in exergue)....................	£50	£200	£1100	—
1695 — No stop after BRITANNIA on rev.			Extremely rare	
1696 —	£40	£180	£1000	—
1696 — TERTVS error			Extremely rare	
1697 —	£50	£180	£1000	—
1697 — No stop after TERTIVS on obv.	£55	£325	—	—
1698 —	£50	£200	£1000	—
1698 Second issue (date in legend)	£55	£200		—
1698 — No stop after date.............................	£50	£200		—
1699 —	£55	£220	£1100	—
1699 — No stop after date.............................	£250	—	—	—
1699 Third issue (date in exergue) (Britannia with right hand on knee)..	£40	£200	£900	—
1699 — No stop after date.............................			Extremely rare	
1699 — BRITΛNNIΛ error	£225	—	—	—
1699 — TERTVS error			Extremely rare	
1699 — No stop on rev.................................			Extremely rare	
1699 — No stops on obv...............................	£90	£375	—	—
1700 —	£50	£200	£1000	—
1700 — No stops on obv...............................	£100	£350	—	—
1700 — No stops after GVLIELMUS	£100	£350	—	—
1700 — BRITVANNIA error............................			Extremely rare	
1700 — GVIELMS error...............................	£100	£350	—	—
1700 — GVLIEEMVS error............................	£100	£350	—	—
1701 —	£45	£200	£950	—
1701 — BRITΛNNIΛ error	£80	£300	—	—
1701 — No stops on obv...............................			Extremely rare	
1701 — inverted As for Vs.............................	£90	£350	—	—

William III first issue

GEORGE I (1714–27)

	F	VF	EF	UNC
1717 "Dump" issue	£45	£250	£800	
1718 —	£35	£225	£775	—
1719 "Dump" issue. Patterns..........................				Rare
1719 Second issue..	£40	£200	£800	—
1720 —	£35	£160	£600	—
1721 —	£35	£150	£600	—
1721 — Stop after date..................................	£45	£160	—	—
1722 —	£35	£140	£650	—
1722 — inverted A for V on obv.			Extremely rare	
1723 —	£35	£160	£650	—
1723 — No stop on rev...................................	£110	£500	—	—
1724 —	£40	£160	£650	—

GEORGE II (1727–60)

	F	VF	EF	UNC
1729 Young head	£30	£100	£470	—
1729 — No stop on rev..................................	£30	£100	£470	—
1730 —	£22	£100	£475	—
1730 — GEOGIVS error................................	£80	£240	£800	—
1730 — Stop after date.................................	£30	£130	£475	—
1730 — No stop after REX on obv.	£35	£160	£500	—
1731 —	£25	£120	£450	—
1731 — No rev. stop......................................	£28	£125	£450	—
1732 —	£25	£110	£440	—
1732 — No rev. stop......................................	£28	£140	£500	—
1733 —	£25	£100	£475	—
1734/3 — 4 over 3...	£35	£220	—	—
1734 — No stop on obv.	£35	£220	—	—

George I "Dump" type

DATE	MINTAGE	F	VF	EF	UNC
1735 —		£24	£90	£450	—
1736 —		£24	£90	£450	—
1737 —		£24	£95	£470	—
1738 —		£24	£90	£400	—
1739 —		£20	£70	£375	—
1740 Old head		£20	£75	£350	—
1742 —		£20	£75	£350	—
1742/0 — 2 over 0		£25	£150	£480	—
1743 —		£18	£75	£370	—
1744 —		£18	£75	£380	—
1745 —		£18	£75	£390	—
1746 —		£18	£75	£350	—
1747 —		£18	£75	£350	—
1748 —		£18	£75	£350	—
1749 —		£18	£75	£350	—
1750 —		£18	£75	£350	—
1751 —		£18	£75	£350	—
1752 —		£18	£75	£350	—
1753 —		£18	£75	£350	—
1754 —		£18	£75	£350	—

George II "Old" head

GEORGE III (1760–1820)

First type—Royal Mint

1770		£18	£50	£300	—
1770 No stop on rev.		£25	£70	£350	—
1771		£12	£50	£280	—
1771 No stop on rev.		£20	£65	£300	—
1772 Error GEORIVS		£80	£250	£800	—
1772		£12	£50	£225	—
1772 No stop on rev		£20	£65	£280	—
1773		£10	£45	£280	—
1773 No stop after REX		£35	£100	£425	—
1773 No stop on rev.		£20	£70	£300	—
1774		£12	£40	£220	—
1775		£12	£40	£220	—

Second type—Soho Mint

1799	42,481,116	£5	£12	£55	£120

Third type

1806	87,993,526	£5	£12	£60	£110
1807	41,394,384	£5	£12	£60	£110

George III second type

GEORGE IV (1820–30)

1825	215,040	£12	£45	£190	£380
1826 (varieties)	9,031,630	£12	£45	£190	£380
1826 Proof	—	—	—	—	£700
1827	5,376,000	£12	£45	£160	£350

WILLIAM IV (1830–37)

1831	806,400	£12	£30	£130	£325
1831 Proof	—	—	—	—	£750
1834	537,600	£12	£30	£130	£325
1837	349,440	£12	£30	£130	£325

VICTORIA (1837–1901)

Copper

1838	456,960	£8	£20	£80	£320
1839 Proof	268,800	—	—	—	£800
1841	1,075,200	£6	£18	£70	£260
1843	967,680	£40	£70	£250	£1000
1844	1,075,200	£12	£40	£180	£375

William IV

DATE	MINTAGE	F	VF	EF	UNC
1845..	1,075,200	£250	£550	£2200	—
1846..	860,160	£12	£25	£85	£280
1847..	725,640	£12	£22	£85	£280
1848..	322,560	£12	£22	£80	£280
1848/7 final 8 OVER 7	incl. above	£15	£35	£110	£300
1851..	215,040	£7	£18	£75	£270
1852..	637,056	£10	£22	£80	£280
1853..	1,559,040	£5	£10	£40	£120
1853/2 3 over 2	incl. above	£15	£30	£60	£250
1853 Proof...............................	—	—	—	—	£1200
1854..	12,354,048	£5	£9	£40	£140
1855..	1,455,837	£5	£9	£40	£140
1856..	1,942,080	£12	£28	£90	£320
1857..	1,820,720	£6	£18	£50	£160
1858..	2,472,960	£5	£12	£50	£150
1858/7 final 8 over 7	incl. above	£5	£12	£50	£150
1858/6 final 8 over 6................	incl. above	£5	£12	£50	£160
1859..	1,290,240	£8	£24	£80	£275
1859/8 9 over 8	incl. above	£8	£25	£70	£300
1860..	unrecorded	£1800	£3500	£7000	£12500

Bronze

	MINTAGE	F	VF	EF	UNC
1860 Beaded border	6,630,400	£3	£10	£50	£200
1860 Toothed border...............		£4	£12	£70	£300
1861..	54,118,400	£4	£10	£40	£200
1862 Die letter A, B or C to left of lighthouse				Extremely rare	
1862..	61,107,200	£3	£9	£40	£170
1863..	15,948,800	£3	£9	£75	£160
1864..	537,600	£3	£10	£50	£180
1865..	8,064,000	£4	£18	£75	£300
1865/3 5 over 3	incl. above	£50	£120	£450	—
1866..	2,508,800	£5	£15	£70	£270
1867..	2,508,800	£5	£15	£60	£250
1868..	3,046,400	£5	£15	£70	£300
1869..	3,225,600	£30	£100	£400	£1600
1870..	4,350,739	£5	£15	£60	£250
1871..	1,075,280	£75	£100	£500	£1600
1872..	4,659,410	£4	£10	£50	£220
1873..	3,404,880	£4	£10	£50	£220
1874..	1,347,655	£6	£25	£110	£320
1874 H.....................................	5,017,600	£3	£10	£60	£270
1875..	5,430,815	£3	£8	£60	£220
1875 H.....................................	1,254,400	£5	£12	£60	£220
1876 H.....................................	5,809,600	£5	£12	£70	£280
1877..	5,209,505	£3	£10	£60	£200
1878..	1,425,535	£6	£20	£100	£375
1878 Wide date		£100	£200	£550	—
1879..	3,582,545	£3	£10	£40	£200
1880..	2,423,465	£4	£12	£60	£210
1881..	2,007,515	£4	£12	£50	£180
1881 H.....................................	1,792,000	£3	£10	£50	£200
1882 H.....................................	4,480,000	£3	£10	£50	£220
1883..	3,000,725	£3	£12	£60	£240
1884..	6,989,580	£3	£10	£45	£160
1885..	8,600,574	£3	£10	£45	£160
1886..	8,586,155	£3	£10	£45	£160
1887..	10,701,305	£3	£10	£45	£160
1888..	6,814,670	£3	£10	£45	£160
1889..	7,748,234	£3	£10	£45	£160
1889/8 9 over 8	incl. above	£30	£60	£250	—
1890..	11,254,235	£3	£10	£40	£120
1891..	13,192,260	£3	£10	£35	£120
1892..	2,478,335	£3	£10	£50	£150

Victoria copper halfpenny

Victoria bronze halfpenny

DATE	MINTAGE	F	VF	EF	UNC
1893	7,229,344	£3	£10	£35	£140
1894	1,767,635	£5	£12	£80	£320

OLD HEAD ISSUES

1895	3,032,154	£2	£8	£25	£80
1896	9,142,500	£1	£4	£10	£55
1897	8,690,315	£1	£4	£10	£55
1898	8,595,180	£1	£5	£12	£65
1899	12,108,001	£1	£4	£10	£50
1900	13,805,190	£1	£4	£10	£40
1901	11,127,360	£1	£3	£8	£35

EDWARD VII (1901–10)

1902	13,672,960	£2	£4	£8	£30
1902 "Low tide"	incl. above	£22	£90	£180	£450
1903	11,450,880	£2	£5	£20	£75
1904	8,131,200	£2	£6	£25	£95
1905	10,124,800	£2	£5	£20	£70
1906	16,849,280	£2	£5	£25	£85
1907	16,849,280	£2	£5	£20	£85
1908	16,620,800	£2	£5	£20	£85
1909	8,279,040	£2	£5	£20	£85
1910	10,769,920	£2	£5	£20	£55

GEORGE V (1910–36)

1911	12,570,880	£1	£4	£15	£40
1912	21,185,920	£1	£3	£15	£35
1913	17,476,480	£1	£3	£15	£40
1914	20,289,111	£1	£3	£15	£40
1915	21,563,040	£2	£3	£20	£55
1916	39,386,143	£1	£2	£15	£40
1917	38,245,436	£1	£2	£15	£35
1918	22,321,072	£1	£2	£15	£35
1919	28,104,001	£1	£2	£15	£35
1920	35,146,793	£1	£2	£15	£40
1921	28,027,293	£1	£2	£15	£40
1922	10,734,964	£1	£4	£25	£45
1923	12,266,282	£1	£2	£15	£35
1924	13,971,038	£1	£2	£15	£30
1925	12,216,123	—	£2	£15	£30
1925 Modified effigy	incl. above	£4	£10	£50	£90
1926	6,172,306	—	£2	£10	£40
1927	15,589,622	—	£2	£10	£40
1928	20,935,200	—	£2	£8	£35
1929	25,680,000	—	£2	£8	£35
1930	12,532,800	—	£2	£8	£35
1931	16,137,600	—	£2	£8	£35
1932	14,448,000	—	£2	£8	£35
1933	10,560,000	—	£2	£8	£35
1934	7,704,000	—	£2	£12	£45
1935	12,180,000	—	£1	£6	£20
1936	23,008,800	—	£1	£5	£15

GEORGE VI (1936–52)

1937	24,504,000	—	—	£1	£5
1937 Proof	26,402	—	—	—	£20
1938	40,320,000	—	—	£1	£6
1939	28,924,800	—	—	£1	£5
1940	32,162,400	—	—	£2	£10

DATE	MINTAGE	F	VF	EF	UNC
1941	45,120,000	—	—	£1	£8
1942	71,908,800	—	—	£1	£5
1943	76,200,000	—	—	£1	£5
1944	81,840,000	—	—	£1	£5
1945	57,000,000	—	—	£1	£5
1946	22,725,600	—	—	£1	£6
1947	21,266,400	—	—	£1	£6
1948	26,947,200	—	—	£1	£4
1949	24,744,000	—	—	£1	£4
1950	24,153,600	—	—	£1	£5
1950 Proof	17,513	—	—	—	£18
1951	14,868,000	—	—	£1	£6
1951 Proof	20,000	—	—	—	£18
1952	33,784,000	—	—	£1	£4

ELIZABETH II (1952–)

1953	8,926,366	—	—	—	£1
1953 Proof	40,000	—	—	—	£4
1954	19,375,000	—	—	—	£3
1955	18,799,200	—	—	—	£3
1956	21,799,200	—	—	—	£3
1957	43,684,800	—	—	—	£1
1957 Calm sea	incl. above	—	—	£10	£30
1958	62,318,400	—	—	—	£1
1959	79,176,000	—	—	—	£1
1960	41,340,000	—	—	—	£1
1962	41,779,200	—	—	—	£1
1963	45,036,000	—	—	—	20p
1964	78,583,200	—	—	—	20p
1965	98,083,200	—	—	—	20p
1966	95,289,600	—	—	—	20p
1967	146,491,200	—	—	—	10p
1970 Proof	—				£5

Later issues are included in the Decimal section.

FARTHINGS

DATE		F	VF	EF	UNC

OLIVER CROMWELL

Undated (copper) Draped bust, shield rev. Variations — Extremely rare

CHARLES II (1660–85)

Copper

	F	VF	EF	UNC
1672	£45	£225	£800	—
1672 No stops on obv.	£70	£300	£900	
1673	£50	£250	£850	—
1673 CAROLA for CAROLO error	£150	£550	—	—
1673 No stops on obv.			Extremely rare	
1673 No stop on rev.			Extremely rare	
1674	£50	£270	£900	—
1675	£45	£240	£850	—
1675 No stop after CAROLVS			Extremely rare	
1679	£60	£300	£1000	—
1679 No stop on rev.	£70	£340		

Tin

	F	VF	EF	UNC
1684 with date on edge	£250	£900	—	—
1685 —			Extremely rare	

Charles II copper issue

DATE	F	VF	EF	UNC

JAMES II (1685–88)

	F	VF	EF	UNC
1684 (tin) Cuirassed bust			Extremely rare	
1685 (tin) —	£180	£700	£2750	—
1686 (tin) —	£190	£700	£2750	—
1687 (tin) —			Extremely rare	
1687 (tin) Draped bust	£250	£1000	—	—

WILLIAM & MARY (1688–94)

	F	VF	EF	UNC
1689 (tin) Small draped busts	£300	£700	—	—
1689 (tin) — with edge date 1690			Extremely rare	
1690 (tin) Large cuirassed busts	£170	£650	£3000	—
1690 (tin) — with edge date 1689			Extremely rare	
1691 (tin) —	£200	£700	—	—
1692 (tin) —	£200	£700	£3000	—
1694 (copper) —	£70	£275	£1000	—
1694 No stop after MARIΛ			Extremely rare	
1694 No stop on obv.			Extremely rare	
1694 No stop on rev.			Extremely rare	
1694 Unbarred As in BRITANNIA			Extremely rare	

WILLIAM III (1694–1702)

	F	VF	EF	UNC
1695 First issue (date in exergue)	£45	£250	£900	—
1695 — GVLIELMV error			Extremely rare	
1696 —	£45	£225	£900	—
1697 —	£45	£225	£900	—
1697 — GVLIELMS error			Extremely rare	
1698 —	£220	£750	—	—
1698 Second issue (date in legend)	£50	£275	£950	—
1699 First issue	£40	£240	£900	—
1699 Second issue	£40	£240	£900	—
1699 — No stop after date	£50	£325	—	—
1700 First issue	£35	£150	£750	—
1700 — error RRITANNIA			Extremely rare	

Queen Anne

ANNE (1702–14)

	F	VF	EF	UNC
1714	£425	£675	£1500	—

GEORGE I (1714–27)

	F	VF	EF	UNC
1717 First small "Dump" issue	£200	£650	£1250	—
1718 1 Known				
1719 Second issue	£40	£175	£600	—
1719 — No stop on rev.	£70	£375	—	—
1719 — No stops on obv.	£70	£325	—	—
1720 —	£30	£160	£600	—
1721 —	£25	£160	£600	—
1721/0 — Last 1 over 0	£40	£170	—	—
1722 —	£35	£140	£550	—
1723 —	£35	£140	£570	—
1723 — R over sideways R in REX			Extremely rare	
1724 —	£35	£160	£575	—

George I, first "Dump" type

GEORGE II (1727–60)

	F	VF	EF	UNC
1730 Young head	£15	£60	£350	—
1731 —	£15	£60	£350	—
1732 —	£15	£75	£400	—
1733 —	£15	£80	£425	—
1734 —	£15	£65	£400	—
1734 — No stop on obv.	£30	£110	£450	—

George I second type

DATE	MINTAGE	F	VF	EF	UNC
1735 —		£15	£70	£400	—
1735 — 3 over 5		£25	£110	£450	—
1736 —		£15	£60	£375	—
1737 —		£15	£60	£350	—
1739 —		£15	£60	£350	—
1741 Old Head		£15	£50	£340	—
1744 —		£15	£50	£340	—
1746 —		£15	£50	£320	—
1746 — V over LL in GEORGIVS				Extremely rare	
1749 —		£16	£65	£330	—
1750 —		£15	£55	£285	—
1754 —		£10	£30	£200	—
1754 — 4 over 0		£28	£120	£350	—

*George II
Young head*

GEORGE III (1760–1820)

1771 First (London) issue		£20	£65	£300	—
1773 —		£12	£40	£220	—
1773 — No stop on rev		£20	£60	£250	—
1773 — No stop after REX		£25	£80	£320	—
1774 —		£12	£40	£220	—
1775 —		£12	£40	£220	—
1797 Second (Soho Mint) issue				Patterns only	
1799 Third (Soho Mint) issue	4,225,428	£2	£8	£40	£100
1806 Fourth (Soho Mint) issue	4,833,768	£2	£8	£40	£100
1807 —	1,075,200	£2	£8	£40	£100

*George III,
third (Soho
Mint) issue*

GEORGE IV (1820–30)

1821 First bust (laureate, draped), first reverse (date in exergue)	2,688,000	£3	£10	£60	£130
1822 —	5,924,350	£3	£10	£60	£130
1823 —	2,365,440	£4	£10	£60	£130
1823 I for 1 in date	incl. above	£25	£75	£300	£600
1825 —	4,300.800	£4	£10	£60	£140
1826 —	6,666,240	£4	£10	£60	£130
1826 Second bust (couped, date below), second reverse (ornament in exergue)	incl. above	£4	£10	£60	£130
1826 — Proof	—	—	—	—	£700
1827 —	2,365,440	£4	£12	£60	£160
1828 —	2,365,440	£4	£12	£60	£160
1829 —	1,505,280	£4	£12	£60	£160
1830 —	2,365,440	£4	£12	£60	£160

*George III,
fourth (Soho
Mint) issue*

WILLIAM IV (1830–37)

1831	2,688,000	£5	£12	£45	£150
1831 Proof	—	—	—	—	£700
1834	1,935,360	£5	£12	£50	£160
1835	1.720,320	£5	£12	£50	£160
1836	1,290.240	£5	£12	£55	£160
1837	3.010,560	£5	£12	£55	£200

VICTORIA (1837–1901)
FIRST YOUNG HEAD (COPPER) ISSUES

1838	591,360	£5	£15	£50	£200
1839	4,300,800	£5	£15	£50	£200
1839 Proof	—	—	—	—	£800
1840	3,010,560	£4	£15	£40	£180
1841	1,720,320	£4	£15	£40	£190
1841 Proof				Extremely rare	
1842	1,290,240	£12	£40	£110	£400
1843	4,085,760	£5	£14	£40	£190

George IV

DATE	MINTAGE	F	VF	EF	UNC
1843 I for 1 in date		£90	£425	£900	—
1844..........................	430,080	£80	£220	£800	£2200
1845..........................	3,225,600	£6	£10	£50	£170
1846..........................	2,580,480	£7	£20	£55	£220
1847..........................	3,879,720	£5	£12	£50	£175
1848..........................	1,290,240	£5	£12	£50	£175
1849..........................	645,120	£50	£100	£350	£900
1850..........................	430,080	£5	£10	£40	£160
1851..........................	1,935,360	£8	£20	£80	£250
1851 D over sideways D in DEI ...	incl. above	£80	£110	£450	—
1852..........................	822,528	£10	£20	£80	£275
1853..........................	1,028,628	£4	£7	£30	£70
1853 Proof..............................	—	—	—	—	£1200
1854..........................	6,504,960	£4	£10	£35	£110
1855..........................	3,440,640	£4	£10	£35	£120
1856..........................	1,771,392	£10	£25	£80	£300
1856 R over E in VICTORIA........	incl. above	£20	£50	£250	—
1857..........................	1,075,200	£4	£10	£40	£100
1858..........................	1,720,320	£4	£10	£40	£100
1859..........................	1,290,240	£12	£25	£90	£350
1860..........................	unrecorded	£1600	£3750	£7000	—

Victoria Young Head first (copper) issue

SECOND YOUNG OR "BUN" HEAD (BRONZE) ISSUES

1860 Toothed border	2,867,200	£2	£5	£40	£120
1860 Beaded border	incl. above	£3	£7	£40	£130
1860 Toothed/Beaded border mule	incl. above			Extremely rare	
1861..	8,601,600	£2	£5	£35	£120
1862..	14,336,000	£1	£5	£35	£120
1862 Large 8 in date..................	incl. above			Extremely rare	
1863..	1,433,600	£40	£80	£300	£700
1864..	2,508,800	£1	£5	£30	£110
1865..	4,659,200	£1	£5	£30	£110
1865 5 over 2...........................	incl. above	£10	£20	£70	—
1866..	3,584,000	£1	£5	£25	£120
1867..	5,017,600	£1	£5	£25	£120
1868..	4,851,210	£1	£5	£25	£120
1869..	3,225,600	£2	£10	£50	£200
1872..	2,150,400	£1	£5	£25	£100
1873..	3,225,620	£1	£5	£25	£100
1874 H	3,584,000	£1	£5	£25	£130
1874 H both Gs over sideways G	incl. above	£150	£350	£1000	—
1875..	712,760	£4	£12	£40	£140
1875 H	6,092,800	£1	£5	£20	£85
1876 H	1,175,200	£5	£18	£70	£230
1878..	4,008,540	£1	£4	£20	£80
1879..	3,977,180	£1	£4	£20	£80
1880..	1,842,710	£1	£4	£20	£80
1881..	3,494,670	£1	£4	£20	£80
1881 H	1,792,000	£1	£4	£20	£80
1882 H	1,792,000	£1	£5	£25	£100
1883..	1,128,680	£5	£20	£70	£170
1884..	5,782,000	£1	£4	£20	£50
1885..	5,442,308	£1	£4	£20	£50
1886..	7,707,790	£1	£4	£20	£50
1887..	1,340,800	£1	£4	£20	£50
1888..	1,887,250	£1	£4	£20	£50
1890..	2,133,070	£1	£4	£20	£50
1891..	4,959,690	£1	£4	£20	£50
1892..	887,240	£4	£15	£60	£170
1893..	3,904,320	£1	£4	£20	£45
1894..	2,396,770	£1	£4	£20	£45
1895..	2,852,852	£10	£30	£90	£300

Victoria Young Head second (bronze) issue

DATE	MINTAGE	F	VF	EF	UNC
OLD HEAD ISSUES					
1895 Bright finish	incl. above	£1	£2	£16	£40
1896 —	3,668,610	£1	£2	£16	£30
1897 —	4,579,800	£1	£2	£16	£30
1897 Dark finish	incl. above	£1	£2	£16	£30
1898 —	4,010,080	£1	£2	£16	£30
1899 —	3,864,616	£1	£2	£16	£30
1900 —	5,969,317	£1	£2	£16	£30
1901 —	8,016,460	£1	£2	£10	£28

Victoria Old head

EDWARD VII (1901–10)

1902	5,125,120	50p	£1	£10	£16
1903	5,331,200	50p	£1	£12	£20
1904	3,628,800	£2	£5	£20	£45
1905	4,076,800	£1	£2	£12	£40
1906	5,340,160	50p	£1	£12	£30
1907	4,399,360	50p	£1	£10	£25
1908	4,264,960	50p	£1	£10	£25
1909	8,852,480	50p	£1	£10	£25
1910	2,298,400	£5	£10	£30	£80

GEORGE V (1910–36)

1911	5,196,800	50p	£1	£6	£14
1912	7,669,760	50p	£1	£8	£14
1913	4,184,320	50p	£1	£6	£14
1914	6,126,988	50p	£1	£5	£14
1915	7,129,255	50p	£1	£5	£16
1916	10,993,325	50p	£1	£5	£14
1917	21,434,844	25p	50p	£4	£10
1918	19,362,818	25p	50p	£4	£10
1919	15,089,425	25p	50p	£4	£10
1920	11,480,536	25p	50p	£4	£8
1921	9,469,097	25p	50p	£4	£8
1922	9,956,983	25p	50p	£4	£8
1923	8,034,457	25p	50p	£4	£8
1924	8,733,414	25p	50p	£4	£8
1925	12,634,697	25p	50p	£4	£8
1926 Modified effigy	9,792,397	25p	50p	£4	£8
1927	7,868,355	25p	50p	£4	£8
1928	11,625,600	25p	50p	£4	£8
1929	8,419,200	25p	50p	£4	£8
1930	4,195,200	25p	50p	£4	£8
1931	6,595,200	25p	50p	£4	£8
1932	9,292,800	25p	50p	£4	£8
1933	4,560,000	25p	50p	£4	£8
1934	3,052,800	25p	50p	£4	£8
1935	2.227,200	£1	£3	£10	£25
1936	9,734,400	25p	50p	£3	£6

GEORGE VI (1936–52)

1937	8,131,200	—	—	50p	£1
1937 Proof	26,402	—	—	—	£8
1938	7,449,600	—	—	£1	£6
1939	31,440,000	—	—	50p	£1
1940	18,360,000	—	—	50p	£1
1941	27,312,000	—	—	50p	£1
1942	28,857,600	—	—	50p	£1
1943	33,345,600	—	—	50p	£1
1944	25,137,600	—	—	50p	£1
1945	23,736,000	—	—	50p	£1

DATE	MINTAGE	F	VF	EF	UNC
1946	24,364,800	—	—	50p	£1
1947	14,745,600	—	—	50p	£1
1948	16,622,400	—	—	50p	£1
1949	8,424,000	—	—	50p	£1
1950	10,324,800	—	—	50p	£1
1950 Proof	17,513	—	—	50p	£8
1951	14,016,000	—	—	50p	£1
1951 Proof	20,000	—	—	50p	£8
1952	5,251,200	—	—	50p	£1

ELIZABETH II (1952–   )

1953	6,131,037	—	—	—	£1
1953 Proof	40,000	—	—	—	£8
1954	6,566,400	—	—	—	£2
1955	5,779,200	—	—	—	£2
1956	1,996,800	—	£1	£2	£6

HALF FARTHINGS

DATE	MINTAGE	F	VF	EF	UNC

GEORGE IV (1820–30)

1828 (two different obverses) (issued for Ceylon)	7,680,000	£10	£22	£60	£225
1830 (large or small date) (issued for Ceylon)	8,766,320	£10	£22	£60	£210

WILLIAM IV (1830–37)

1837 (issued for Ceylon)	1,935,360	£25	£75	£200	£400

VICTORIA (1837–1901)

1839	2,042,880	£5	£10	£35	£100
1842	unrecorded	£4	£8	£30	£100
1843	3,440,640	£3	£6	£25	£70
1844	6,451,200	£3	£6	£15	£55
1844 E over N in REGINA	incl. above	£10	£45	£100	—
1847	3,010,560	£6	£12	£40	£120
1851	unrecorded	£6	£12	£40	£150
1851 5 over 0	unrecorded	£8	£20	£60	£180
1852	989,184	£6	£12	£45	£160
1853	955,224	£6	£15	£50	£175
1853 Proof	incl. above	—	—	—	£800
1854	677,376	£9	£30	£80	£220
1856	913,920	£9	£30	£80	£220
1868 Proof	unrecorded			Very Rare	

THIRD FARTHINGS

DATE   MINTAGE   F   VF   EF   UNC

GEORGE IV (1820–30)

DATE	MINTAGE	F	VF	EF	UNC
1827 (issued for Malta)	unrecorded	£8	£20	£50	£125

WILLIAM IV (1830–37)

1835 (issued for Malta)	unrecorded	£8	£24	£55	£160

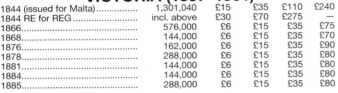

VICTORIA (1837–1901)

1844 (issued for Malta)	1,301,040	£15	£35	£110	£240
1844 RE for REG	incl. above	£30	£70	£275	—
1866	576,000	£6	£15	£35	£75
1868	144,000	£6	£15	£35	£70
1876	162,000	£6	£15	£35	£90
1878	288,000	£6	£15	£35	£80
1881	144,000	£6	£15	£35	£80
1884	144,000	£6	£15	£35	£80
1885	288,000	£6	£15	£35	£80

EDWARD VII (1902–10)

1902 (issued for Malta)	288,000	£5	£10	£25	£45

GEORGE V (1911–36)

1913 (issued for Malta)	288,000	£5	£10	£25	£45

QUARTER FARTHINGS

DATE   MINTAGE   F   VF   EF   UNC

VICTORIA (1837–1901)

DATE	MINTAGE	F	VF	EF	UNC
1839 (issued for Ceylon)	3,840,000	£50	£80	£150	£300
1851 (issued for Ceylon)	2,215,680	£50	£80	£150	£300
1852 (issued for Ceylon)	incl. above	£50	£80	£150	£300
1853 (issued for Ceylon)	incl. above	£50	£80	£150	£320
1853 Proof	—	—	—	—	£1500

EMERGENCY ISSUES

DATE	F	VF	EF	UNC

GEORGE III (1760–1820)

To alleviate the shortage of circulating coinage during the Napoleonic Wars the Bank of England firstly authorised the countermarking of other countries' coins, enabling them to pass as English currency. The coins, countermarked with punches depicting the head of George III, were mostly Spanish American 8 reales of Charles III. Although this had limited success it was later decided to completely overstrike the coins with a new English design on both sides—specimens that still show traces of the original host coin's date are avidly sought after by collectors. This overstriking continued for a number of years although all the known coins are dated 1804. Finally, in 1811 the Bank of England issued silver tokens which continued up to 1816 when a completely new regal coinage was introduced.

DOLLAR

Oval countermark of George III

	F	VF	EF	UNC
On "Pillar" type 8 reales	£200	£750	£1200	—
*On "Portrait" type.............	£200	£350	£1000	—

Octagonal countermark of George III

	F	VF	EF	UNC
On "Portrait" type	£200	£600	£1100	—

HALF DOLLAR

Oval countermark of George III

	F	VF	EF	UNC
On "Portrait" type 4 reales	£200	£425	£1000	—

FIVE SHILLINGS OR ONE DOLLAR

These coins were overstruck on Spanish-American coins

	F	VF	EF
1804.....................................	£120	£300	£700

— With details of original coin still visible add from 10%.

BANK OF ENGLAND TOKENS

THREE SHILLINGS

	F	VF	EF	UNC
1811 Draped bust..............	£35	£70	£250	—
1812 —	£35	£70	£275	—
1812 Laureate bust	£35	£60	£175	—
1813 —	£35	£60	£175	—
1814 —	£35	£60	£175	—
1815 —	£35	£60	£175	—
1816 —	£250	£600	£1800	—

ONE SHILLING AND SIXPENCE

	F	VF	EF	UNC
1811 Draped bust..............	£20	£45	£100	£180
1812 —	£20	£45	£100	£180
1812 Laureate bust	£20	£45	£100	£180
1812 Proof in platinum				Unique
1813 —	£20	£40	£75	£180
1813 Proof in platinum				Unique
1814 —	£20	£35	£75	£180
1815 —	£20	£35	£75	£180
1816 —	£20	£35	£75	£180

NINEPENCE

1812 Pattern (three types)	from £3000

MAUNDY SETS

DATE	F	VF	EF	UNC

Sets in contemporary dated boxes are usually worth a higher premium. For example approximately £30 can be added to sets from Victoria to George VI in contemporary undated boxes and above £40 for dated boxes.

GEORGE I (1714–27)

DATE	F	VF	EF	UNC
1723	£260	£450	£775	—
1727	£240	£435	£750	—

GEORGE II (1727–60)

	F	VF	EF	UNC
1729	£195	£325	£675	—
1731	£195	£335	£675	—
1732	£190	£320	£650	—
1735	£190	£320	£650	—
1737	£190	£325	£640	—
1739	£190	£320	£625	—
1740	£175	£300	£585	—
1743	£300	£445	£825	—
1746	£170	£300	£565	—
1760	£185	£325	£595	—

GEORGE III (1760–1820)

	F	VF	EF	UNC
1763	£170	£290	£480	—
1763 Proof	—			£18000
1766	£215	£325	£550	—
1772	£185	£300	£525	—
1780	£225	£350	£600	—
1784	£190	£320	£500	—
1786	£195	£310	£515	—
1792 Wire	£260	£450	£650	£850
1795	£115	£200	£325	£405
1800	£115	£200	£300	£395
New Coinage				
1817	£135	£210	£290	£425
1818	£135	£205	£280	£415
1820	£140	£220	£285	£420

GEORGE IV (1820–30)

	F	VF	EF	UNC
1822	—	£160	£245	£415
1823	—	£155	£255	£400
1824	—	£160	£260	£405
1825	—	£150	£250	£380
1826	—	£145	£245	£380
1827	—	£145	£255	£385
1828	—	£150	£250	£400
1828 Proof	—	—	—	£3750
1829	—	£150	£250	£385
1830	—	£150	£240	£375

WILLIAM IV (1830–37)

	F	VF	EF	UNC
1831	—	£170	£280	£450
1831 Proof	—	—	—	£1850
1831 Proof Gold	—	—		£38000
1832	—	£195	£315	£465
1833	—	£170	£275	£410
1834	—	£175	£280	£410
1835	—	£160	£265	£400
1836	—	£175	£285	£425
1837	—	£190	£315	£450

CHARLES II (1660–85)

	F	VF	EF	UNC
Undated	£240	£370	£800	—
1670	£225	£370	£750	—
1671	£260	£425	£850	—
1672	£230	£375	£735	—
1673	£225	£350	£720	—
1674	£225	£340	£735	—
1675	£210	£325	£715	—
1676	£230	£365	£755	—
1677	£195	£310	£690	—
1678	£280	£460	£830	—
1679	£225	£360	£750	—
1680	£225	£345	£730	—
1681	£250	£370	£775	—
1682	£230	£360	£715	—
1683	£230	£360	£725	—
1684	£250	£385	£775	—

JAMES II (1685–88)

	F	VF	EF	UNC
1686	£230	£375	£730	—
1687	£230	£370	£750	—
1688	£245	£400	£775	—

WILLIAM & MARY (1688–94)

	F	VF	EF	UNC
1689	£825	£1250	£1850	—
1691	£675	£875	£1500	—
1692	£710	£925	£1700	—
1693	£625	£900	£1800	—
1694	£470	£735	£1300	—

WILLIAM III (1694–1702)

	F	VF	EF	UNC
1698	£245	£480	£900	—
1699	£485	£675	£1575	—
1700	£265	£490	£925	—
1701	£245	£440	£875	—

ANNE (1702–14)

	F	VF	EF	UNC
1703	£225	£440	£750	—
1705	£245	£450	£775	—
1706	£200	£375	£675	—
1708	£600	£900	£1800	—
1709	£250	£475	£850	—
1710	£275	£485	£825	—
1713	£240	£435	£725	—

DATE	MINTAGE	EF	UNC

VICTORIA (1837–1901)

YOUNG HEAD ISSUES

DATE	MINTAGE	EF	UNC
1838	4,158	£240	£425
1838 Proof	unrecorded		£3400
1838 Proof Gold			£37000
1839	4,125	£300	£525
1839 Proof	unrecorded	£650	£1800
1840	4,125	£300	£445
1841	2,574	£395	£650
1842	4,125	£425	£600
1843	4,158	£260	£410
1844	4,158	£345	£550
1845	4,158	£225	£400
1846	4,158	£495	£750
1847	4,158	£575	£925
1848	4,158	£525	£900
1849	4,158	£365	£535
1850	4,158	£250	£415
1851	4,158	£305	£460
1852	4,158	£600	£900
1853	4,158	£625	£950
1853 Proof	unrecorded		£1850
1854	4,158	£260	£395
1855	4,158	£300	£465
1856	4,158	£235	£375
1857	4,158	£265	£405
1858	4,158	£240	£375
1859	4,158	£215	£325
1860	4,158	£240	£375
1861	4,158	£205	£375
1862	4,158	£245	£390
1863	4,158	£260	£425
1864	4,158	£240	£345
1865	4,158	£240	£350
1866	4,158	£225	£340
1867	4,158	£220	£345
1867 Proof	unrecorded	—	£2800
1868	4,158	£200	£315
1869	4,158	£240	£385
1870	4,458	£190	£290
1871	4,488	£185	£280
1871 Proof	unrecorded	—	£2600
1872	4,328	£180	£280
1873	4,162	£180	£270
1874	4,488	£185	£275
1875	4,154	£180	£265
1876	4,488	£190	£270
1877	4,488	£180	£255
1878	4,488	£185	£255
1878 Proof	unrecorded	—	£2500
1879	4,488	£190	£245
1879 Proof	unrecorded	—	£2850
1880	4,488	£185	£240
1881	4,488	£180	£240
1881 Proof	unrecorded	—	£2350
1882	4,146	£215	£285
1882 Proof	unrecorded	—	£2550
1883	4,488	£160	£225
1884	4,488	£160	£225
1885	4,488	£160	£225
1886	4,488	£165	£225
1887	4,488	£180	£255

JUBILEE HEAD ISSUES

1888	4,488	£160	£230
1888 Proof	unrecorded	—	£2100
1889	4,488	£155	£240
1890	4,488	£160	£230
1891	4,488	£160	£230
1892	4,488	£170	£245

OLD HEAD ISSUES

1893	8,976	£100	£185
1894	8,976	£130	£200
1895	8,976	£115	£190
1896	8,976	£115	£195
1897	8,976	£115	£185
1898	8,976	£115	£190
1899	8,976	£115	£190
1900	8,976	£100	£180
1901	8,976	£100	£180

EDWARD VII (1902–110)

1902	8,976	£95	£175
1902 Matt proof	15,123	—	£200
1903	8,976	£100	£170
1904	8,976	£110	£180
1905	8,976	£110	£180
1906	8,800	£100	£170
1907	8,760	£100	£175
1908	8,769	£90	£165
1909	1,983	£165	£265
1910	1,440	£195	£285

GEORGE V (1911–136)

1911	1,786	£150	£240
1911 Proof	6,007	—	£325
1912	1,246	£160	£250
1913	1,228	£155	£250
1914	982	£185	£275
1915	1,293	£165	£265
1916	1,128	£160	£250
1917	1,237	£160	£250
1918	1,375	£165	£255
1919	1,258	£160	£260
1920	1,399	£160	£250
1921	1,386	£160	£255
1922	1,373	£165	£260
1923	1,430	£165	£260
1924	1,515	£165	£260
1925	1,438	£150	£245
1926	1,504	£150	£245
1927	1,647	£155	£255
1928	1,642	£155	£250
1929	1,761	£160	£255
1930	1,724	£150	£240
1931	1,759	£150	£240
1932	1,835	£145	£245
1933	1,872	£140	£240
1934	1,887	£140	£240
1935	1,928	£155	£255
1936	1,323	£200	£300

GEORGE VI (1936–52)

1937	1,325	£140	£175
1937 Proof	20,900	£140	£200
1938	1,275	£170	£255
1939	1,234	£175	£260
1940	1,277	£170	£255
1941	1,253	£180	£260
1942	1,231	£170	£255
1943	1,239	£175	£260
1944	1,259	£170	£255

DATE	MINTAGE	EF	UNC
1945	1,355	£170	£255
1946	1,365	£175	£255
1947	1,375	£180	£275
1948	1,385	£180	£280
1949	1,395	£185	£280
1950	1,405	£185	£285
1951	1,468	£190	£290
1952	1,012	£200	£305
1952 Proof (copper)			£13000

ELIZABETH II (1952–   )

DATE AND PLACE OF ISSUE	MINTAGE	UNC
1953 St. Paul's Cathedral	1,025	£950
1953 Proof in gold	unrecorded	Ex. rare
1953 Proof Matt		Very rare
1954 Westminster Abbey	1,020	£200
1955 Southwark Cathedral	1,036	£200
1955 Proof Matt		£3250
1956 Westminster Abbey	1,088	£205
1957 St. Albans Cathedral	1,094	£205
1958 Westminster Abbey	1,100	£205
1959 St. George's Chapel, Windsor	1,106	£205
1960 Westminster Abbey	1,112	£205
1961 Rochester Cathedral	1,118	£205
1962 Westminster Abbey	1,125	£205
1963 Chelmsford Cathedral	1,131	£205
1964 Westminster Abbey	1,137	£205
1965 Canterbury Cathedral	1,143	£205
1966 Westminster Abbey	1,206	£205
1967 Durham Cathedral	986	£220
1968 Westminster Abbey	964	£225
1969 Selby Cathedral	1,002	£220
1970 Westminster Abbey	980	£220
1971 Tewkesbury Abbey	1,018	£215
1972 York Minster	1,026	£220
1973 Westminster Abbey	1,004	£215
1974 Salisbury Cathedral	1,042	£215
1975 Peterborough Cathedral	1,050	£215
1976 Hereford Cathedral	1,158	£220
1977 Westminster Abbey	1,138	£225
1978 Carlisle Cathedral	1,178	£215
1979 Winchester Cathedral	1,188	£215

DATE AND PLACE OF ISSUE	MINTAGE	UNC
1980 Worcester Cathedral	1,198	£215
1981 Westminster Abbey	1,178	£215
1982 St David's Cathedral	1,218	£220
1983 Exeter Cathedral	1,228	£215
1984 Southwell Minster	1,238	£215
1985 Ripon Cathedral	1,248	£215
1986 Chichester Cathedral	1,378	£225
1987 Ely Cathedral	1,390	£225
1988 Lichfield Cathedral	1,402	£220
1989 Birmingham Cathedral	1,353	£220
1990 Newcastle Cathedral	1,523	£220
1991 Westminster Abbey	1,384	£220
1992 Chester Cathedral	1,424	£225
1993 Wells Cathedral	1,440	£225
1994 Truro Cathedral	1,433	£225
1995 Coventry Cathedral	1,466	£225
1996 Norwich Cathedral	1,629	£230
1997 Birmingham Cathedral	1,786	£230
1998 Portsmouth Cathedral	1,654	£230
1999 Bristol Cathedral	1,676	£230
2000 Lincoln Cathedral	1,686	£220
2000 Silver Proof	13,180	£195
2001 Westminster Abbey	1,132	£250
2002 Canterbury Cathedral	1,681	£215
2002 Gold Proof	2,002	£2250
2003 Gloucester Cathedral	1,608	£235
2004 Liverpool Cathedral	1,613	£240
2005 Wakefield Cathedral	1,685	£240
2006 Guildford Cathedral	1,937	£240
2006 Silver Proof	6,394	£195
2007 Manchester Cathedral	1,822	£275
2008 St Patrick's Cathedral (Armagh)	1,833	£675
2009 St. Edmundsbury Cathedral	1,602	£600
2010 Derby Cathedral	1,617	£550
2011 Westminster Abbey	1,734	£525
2012 York Minster	1,633	£600
2013 Christ Church Cathedral Oxford	1,627	£640
2014 Blackburn Cathedral	1,693	£680
2015 Sheffield Cathedral	1,721	£650
2016 St. George's Chapel, Windsor	1,940	£615
2017 Leicester Cathedral		£700
2018 St. George's Chapel, Windsor		£700
2019 St. George's Chapel, Windsor		£725

Despite the decimalisation of the coinage in 1971, in keeping with ancient tradition the Royal Maundy sets are still made up of four silver coins (4p, 3p, 2p and 1p). The designs for the reverse of the coins are a crowned numeral in a wreath of oak leaves—basically the same design that has been used for Maundy coins since George IV.

MAUNDY ODDMENTS
SINGLE COINS

FOUR PENCE
CHARLES II (1660–85)

DATE	F	VF	EF
Undated	£70	£120	£190
1670	£70	£130	£230
1671	£100	£180	£285
1672/1	£80	£110	£185
1673	£75	£110	£180
1674	£70	£105	£170
1674 7 over 6	£75	£130	£205
1675	£60	£100	£165
1675/4	£70	£115	£190
1676	£65	£100	£185
1676 7 over 6	£80	£120	£200
1677	£55	£95	£160
1678	£55	£95	£160
1678 8 over 6	£60	£100	£165
1678 8 over 7	£65	£115	£175
1679	£55	£85	£150
1680	£55	£95	£160
1681	£55	£100	£170
1682	£60	£90	£180
1682/1	£65	£95	£190
1683	£60	£90	£180
1684	£70	£110	£200
1684 4 over 3	£85	£120	£215

JAMES II (1685–88)

DATE	F	VF	EF
1686	£65	£110	£200
1686 Date over crown	£75	£125	£215
1687	£60	£105	£180
1687 7 over 6	£75	£115	£190
1687 8 over 7	£75	£115	£200
1688	£80	£120	£210
1688 1 over 8	£90	£140	£225

WILLIAM & MARY (1688–94)

DATE	F	VF	EF
1689	£60	£110	£175
1689 GV below bust	£70	£120	£190
1689 GVLEELMVS	£140	£260	£325
1690	£60	£115	£210
1690 6 over 5	£90	£130	£230
1691	£80	£130	£225
1691 1 over 0	£90	£150	£230
1692	£125	£175	£275
1692 MAR·IA	£215	£265	£350
1692 2 over 1	£130	£160	£260
1693	£125	£240	£360
1693 3 over 2	£140	£255	£385
1694	£80	£135	£225
1694 small lettering	£85	£140	£230

WILLIAM III (1694–1702)

DATE	F	VF	EF
1698	£80	£140	£215
1699	£70	£125	£210
1700	£90	£155	£245
1701	£85	£135	£225
1702	£80	£130	£225

ANNE (1702–14)

DATE	F	VF	EF
1703	£80	£130	£215
1704	£60	£105	£185

It is nowadays considered that the early small denomination silver coins 4d–1d were originally struck for the Maundy ceremony although undoubtedly many subsequently circulated as small change—therefore they are listed here under "Maundy silver single coins".

Charles II

William & Mary

Queen Anne

DATE	F	VF	EF	UNC
1705.............................	£130	£205	£285	—
1706.............................	£70	£115	£175	—
1708.............................	£75	£120	£205	—
1709.............................	£80	£125	£205	—
1710.............................	£60	£100	£165	—
1713.............................	£75	£125	£190	—

GEORGE I (1714–27)

	F	VF	EF	UNC
1717.............................	£65	£110	£180	—
1721.............................	£65	£110	£185	—
1723.............................	£90	£140	£210	—
1727.............................	£90	£135	£215	—

George I

GEORGE II (1727–60)

	F	VF	EF	UNC
1729.............................	£75	£120	£170	—
1731.............................	£60	£110	£160	—
1732.............................	£65	£110	£160	—
1735.............................	£55	£95	£150	—
1737.............................	£70	£115	£170	—
1739.............................	£55	£100	£155	—
1740.............................	£50	£95	£140	—
1743.............................	£135	£195	£305	—
1743 3 over 0................	£145	£220	£325	
1746.............................	£55	£85	£135	—
1760.............................	£65	£115	£160	—

George II

GEORGE III (1760–1820)

	F	VF	EF	UNC
1763 Young head	£55	£95	£135	—
1763 Proof	—	—	Extremely rare	
1765.............................	£450	£700	£1100	—
1766.............................	£65	£100	£140	—
1770.............................	£165	£240	£370	—
1772.............................	£80	£130	£200	—
1776.............................	£65	£120	£170	—
1780.............................	£50	£95	£135	—
1784.............................	£50	£95	£130	—
1786.............................	£65	£120	£170	—
1792 Older head, Thin 4........	£90	£160	£225	£325
1795.............................	—	£55	£100	£140
1800.............................	—	£50	£90	£125
1817 New coinage.................	—	£60	£90	£140
1818.............................	—	£60	£90	£140
1820.............................	—	£50	£80	£130

George III

GEORGE IV (1820–30)

	F	VF	EF	UNC
1822.............................	—	—	£80	£150
1823.............................	—	—	£75	£135
1824.............................	—	—	£70	£135
1826.............................	—	—	£65	£120
1827.............................	—	—	£70	£130
1828.............................	—	—	£65	£120
1829.............................	—	—	£60	£115
1830.............................	—	—	£60	£115

George IV

WILLIAM IV (1830–37)

	F	VF	EF	UNC
1831–37..............................	—	—	£75	£145
1831 Proof	—	—	£300	£525

VICTORIA (1837–1901)

	F	VF	EF	UNC
1838 Proof	—	—	—	£850
1839 Proof	—	—	—	£575
1853 Proof	—	—	—	£600
1838–87 (Young Head)	—	—	£40	£60
1841	—	—	£50	£75
1888–92 (Jubilee Head)..........	—	—	£35	£55
1893–1901 (Old Head)............	—	—	£30	£50

Victoria

DATE	F	VF	EF	UNC

EDWARD VII (1901–10)

	F	VF	EF	UNC
1902–08	—	—	£30	£50
1902 Proof	—	—	£35	£55
1909 & 1910	—	—	£60	£90

GEORGE V (1910–36)

	F	VF	EF	UNC
1911–36	—	—	£50	£65
1911 Proof	—	—	£55	£75

GEORGE VI (1936–52)

	F	VF	EF	UNC
1937–52	—	—	£55	£75
1937 Proof	—	—	£40	£60

ELIZABETH II (1952–)

	F	VF	EF	UNC
1953	—	—	£200	£250
1954–85	—	—	£45	£75
1986–2007	—	—	£60	£85
2002 in Gold Proof	—	—	£500	£775
2008	—	—	—	£190
2009	—	—	—	£180
2010	—	—	—	£160
2011	—	—	—	£145
2012	—	—	—	£160
2013	—	—	—	£165
2014	—	—	—	£170
2015	—	—	—	£165
2016	—	—	—	£170
2017	—	—	—	£200
2018	—	—	—	£210
2019	—	—	—	£210

Elizabeth II

THREEPENCE

CHARLES II (1660–85)

	F	VF	EF	UNC
Undated	£65	£110	£195	—
1670	£75	£120	£185	—
1671	£65	£120	£175	—
1671 GRVTIA	£75	£140	£245	—
1672	£80	£130	£195	—
1673	£60	£95	£160	—
1674	£70	£110	£175	—
1675	£70	£110	£180	—
1676	£70	£115	£210	—
1676 6 over 5	£75	£120	£215	—
1676 ERA for FRA	£90	£140	£230	—
1677	£65	£90	£165	—
1678	£50	£80	£135	—
1679	£50	£80	£135	—
1679 O/A in CAROLVS	£110	£160	£250	—
1680	£60	£100	£175	—
1681	£70	£110	£190	—
1682	£60	£100	£170	—
1683	£60	£105	£170	—
1684	£60	£105	£175	—
1684/3	£70	£110	£180	—

Charles II

JAMES II (1685–88)

	F	VF	EF	UNC
1685	£70	£110	£190	—
1685 Struck on fourpence flan	£130	£185	£290	—
1686	£70	£95	£175	—
1687	£65	£90	£170	—
1687 7 over 6	£70	£95	£175	—
1688	£70	£125	£195	—
1688 8 over 7	£75	£135	£215	—

James II

WILLIAM & MARY (1688–94)

	F	VF	EF	UNC
1689	£60	£105	£190	—
1689 No stop on reverse	£70	£115	£200	—
1689 LMV over MVS (obverse)	£100	£145	£240	—

William & Mary

DATE	F	VF	EF	UNC
1690	£75	£120	£195	—
1690 9 over 6	£90	£140	£215	—
1690 6 over 5	£85	£135	£210	—
1691 First bust	£390	£590	£850	—
1691 Second bust	£250	£375	£525	—
1692	£100	£155	£265	—
1692 G below bust	£90	£165	£270	—
1692 GV below bust	£90	£160	£270	—
1692 GVL below bust	£90	£155	£275	—
1693	£135	£215	£300	—
1693 3 over 2	£145	£240	£310	—
1694	£80	£115	£200	—
1694 MARIΛ	£130	£170	£265	—
1694 GV below bust	£95	£120	£210	—

WILLIAM III (1694–1702)

	F	VF	EF	UNC
1698	£80	£130	£210	—
1699	£60	£110	£180	—
1700	£75	£135	£210	—
1701 Small lettering	£75	£130	£195	—
1701 GBA instead of GRA	£85	£150	£215	—
1701 Large lettering	£75	£130	£200	—

William III

ANNE (1702–14)

	F	VF	EF	UNC
1703	£70	£110	£195	—
1703 7 of date above crown	£85	£140	£220	—
1704	£60	£90	£160	—
1705	£80	£130	£200	—
1706	£65	£100	£170	—
1707	£55	£100	£155	—
1708	£60	£115	£180	—
1708 8 over 7	£65	£110	£190	—
1709	£70	£140	£195	—
1710	£50	£95	£145	—
1713	£65	£130	£180	—

Queen Anne

GEORGE I (1714–27)

	F	VF	EF	UNC
1717	£60	£100	£160	—
1721	£60	£100	£165	—
1723	£75	£130	£200	—
1727	£70	£125	£195	—

GEORGE II (1727–60)

	F	VF	EF	UNC
1729	£60	£95	£145	—
1731	£55	£95	£150	—
1731 Small lettering	£70	£115	£170	—
1732	£55	£95	£145	—
1732 Stop over head	£65	£110	£165	—
1735	£70	£110	£175	—
1737	£60	£95	£165	—
1739	£65	£100	£175	—
1740	£55	£90	£145	—
1743 Small and large lettering	£65	£95	£155	—
1743 Stop over head	£65	£95	£160	—
1746	£45	£80	£135	—
1746 6 over 3	£50	£85	£150	—
1760	£60	£90	£155	—

George I

GEORGE III (1760–1820)

	F	VF	EF	UNC
1762	£30	£50	£70	—
1763	£30	£50	£75	—
1763 Proof	—	—	Extremely rare	
1765	£360	£515	£800	—
1766	£70	£110	£180	—
1770	£75	£115	£190	—
1772	£55	£85	£120	—

George II

DATE	F	VF	EF	UNC
1780	£55	£85	£120	—
1784	£80	£115	£190	—
1786	£80	£110	£180	—
1792	£105	£150	£230	£335
1795	—	£40	£80	£120
1800	—	£45	£85	£130
1817	—	£50	£90	£155
1818	—	£50	£90	£155
1820	—	£45	£90	£155

GEORGE IV (1820–30)

DATE	F	VF	EF	UNC
1822	—	—	£85	£165
1823	—	—	£75	£155
1824	—	—	£75	£160
1825–30	—	—	£75	£155

WILLIAM IV (1830–37)

DATE	F	VF	EF	UNC
1831 Proof	—	—	£350	£650
1831	—	—	£110	£175
1832	—	—	£120	£215
1833–1836	—	—	£80	£170
1837	—	—	£105	£190

VICTORIA (1837–1901)

DATE	F	VF	EF	UNC
1838	—	—	£115	£225
1838 Proof	—	—	—	£1750
1839	—	—	£215	£400
1839 Proof	—	—	—	£625
1840	—	—	£160	£275
1841	—	—	£300	£525
1842	—	—	£275	£450
1843	—	—	£125	£225
1844	—	—	£200	£350
1845	—	—	£85	£165
1846	—	—	£400	£700
1847	—	—	£425	£800
1848	—	—	£400	£750
1849	—	—	£215	£350
1850	—	—	£115	£225
1851	—	—	£175	£300
1852	—	—	£450	£775
1853	—	—	£475	£825
1853 Proof	—	—	—	£900
1854	—	—	£155	£275
1855	—	—	£180	£360
1856	—	—	£100	£220
1857	—	—	£150	£275
1858	—	—	£120	£225
1859	—	—	£100	£195
1860	—	—	£135	£240
1861	—	—	£130	£235
1862	—	—	£135	£255
1863	—	—	£180	£300
1864	—	—	£125	£235
1865	—	—	£130	£250
1866	—	—	£120	£240
1867	—	—	£125	£235
1868	—	—	£115	£215
1869	—	—	£155	£275
1870	—	—	£105	£195
1871	—	—	£100	£185
1872	—	—	£95	£180
1873	—	—	£90	£170
1874	—	—	£90	£175
1875	—	—	£85	£165
1876	—	—	£85	£165
1877	—	—	£80	£160
1878	—	—	£85	£165

George III

George IV

William IV

Victoria

DATE	F	VF	EF	UNC
1879	—	—	£85	£160
1880	—	—	£80	£150
1881	—	—	£80	£150
1882	—	—	£135	£225
1883	—	—	£75	£145
1884	—	—	£75	£145
1885	—	—	£70	£130
1886	—	—	£70	£125
1887	—	—	£80	£170
1888–1892 (Jubilee Head)	—	—	£50	£110
1893–1901 (Old Head)	—	—	£40	£65

EDWARD VII (1901–10)

	F	VF	EF	UNC
1902	—	—	£30	£50
1902 Proof	—	—	—	£55
1903	—	—	£40	£85
1904	—	—	£55	£105
1905	—	—	£55	£95
1906	—	—	£45	£90
1907	—	—	£45	£90
1908	—	—	£40	£80
1909	—	—	£70	£125
1910	—	—	£80	£150

Edward VII

GEORGE V (1910–36)

	F	VF	EF	UNC
1911–34	—	—	£55	£85
1911 Proof	—	—	—	£105
1935	—	—	£65	£100
1936	—	—	£75	£135

George V

GEORGE VI (1936–52)

	F	VF	EF	UNC
1937–52	—	—	£55	£90
1937 Proof	—	—	—	£70

ELIZABETH II (1952–   )

	F	VF	EF	UNC
1953	—	—	£190	£295
1954–85	—	—	£45	£80
1986–2007	—	—	£55	£85
2002 In gold (proof)	—	—	—	£615
2008	—	—	—	£155
2009	—	—	—	£145
2010	—	—	—	£150
2011	—	—	—	£130
2012	—	—	—	£140
2013	—	—	—	£140
2014	—	—	—	£165
2015	—	—	—	£155
2016	—	—	—	£150
2017	—	—	—	£170
2018	—	—	—	£180
2019	—	—	—	£190

Elizabeth

TWOPENCE

CHARLES II (1660–85)

	F	VF	EF	UNC
Undated	£60	£90	£155	—
1668	£65	£100	£170	—
1670	£50	£80	£150	—
1671	£50	£85	£150	—
1672	£50	£85	£150	—
1672/1	£65	£100	£160	—
1673	£50	£85	£155	—
1674	£55	£95	£150	—
1675	£50	£90	£140	—
1676	£55	£95	£155	—
1677	£45	£85	£135	—
1678	£35	£75	£130	—
1679	£40	£70	£125	—
1679 HIB over FRA	£45	£75	£130	—

Charles II

DATE	F	VF	EF	UNC
1680...............................	£50	£85	£135	—
1680 over 79...........................	£45	£70	£120	—
1681...............................	£55	£80	£135	—
1682...............................	£65	£90	£165	—
1682/1 ERA for FRA	£75	£115	£215	—
1683...............................	£60	£100	£160	—
1683 over 2...........................	£60	£100	£170	—
1684...............................	£55	£95	£155	—

JAMES II (1685–88)

1686...............................	£60	£95	£160	—
1686 reads IACOBVS............	£80	£125	£215	—
1687...............................	£65	£95	£165	—
1687 ERA for FRA	£75	£130	£215	—
1688...............................	£50	£85	£150	—
1688/7	£65	£90	£170	—

James II

WILLIAM & MARY (1688–94)

1689...............................	£60	£100	£175	—
1691.......................................	£55	£85	£140	—
1692.......................................	£75	£130	£200	—
1693.......................................	£70	£115	£185	—
1693 GV below bust..............	£75	£115	£185	—
1693/2	£65	£100	£170	—
1694.......................................	£50	£85	£140	—
1694 MARLA error.................	£80	£130	£250	—
1694 HI for HIB......................	£75	£120	£210	—
1694 GVLI under bust	£60	£100	£185	—
1694 GVL under bust	£55	£95	£185	—

William & Mary

WILLIAM III (1694–1702)

1698.......................................	£65	£115	£175	—
1699.......................................	£50	£90	£145	—
1700.......................................	£65	£115	£185	—
1701.......................................	£65	£110	£170	—

William III

ANNE (1702–14)

1703.......................................	£65	£105	£180	—
1704.......................................	£50	£80	£135	—
1704 No stops on obverse	£60	£90	£170	—
1705.......................................	£60	£100	£160	—
1706.......................................	£80	£125	£195	—
1707.......................................	£50	£85	£150	—
1708.......................................	£70	£100	£175	—
1709.......................................	£85	£140	£225	—
1710.......................................	£45	£80	£115	—
1713.......................................	£70	£115	£195	—

Queen Anne

GEORGE I (1714–27)

1717.......................................	£45	£80	£130	—
1721.......................................	£50	£85	£125	—
1723.......................................	£65	£100	£160	—
1726.......................................	£55	£85	£135	—
1727.......................................	£60	£90	£150	—

GEORGE II (1727–60)

1729.......................................	£40	£85	£125	—
1731.......................................	£40	£80	£125	—
1732.......................................	£40	£80	£115	—
1735.......................................	£45	£75	£110	—
1737.......................................	£40	£85	£115	—
1739.......................................	£45	£80	£120	—
1740.......................................	£40	£70	£115	—
1743.......................................	£35	£65	£105	—
1743/0	£45	£80	£115	—
1746.......................................	£35	£70	£95	—

George II

DATE	F	VF	EF	UNC
1756....................................	£35	£65	£95	—
1759....................................	£35	£70	£95	—
1760....................................	£50	£75	£100	—

GEORGE III (1760–1820)

1763....................................	£40	£70	£95	—
1763 Proof.............................			Extremely rare	
1765....................................	£375	£500	£700	—
1766....................................	£45	£75	£95	—
1772....................................	£35	£70	£90	—
1772 second 7 over 6.............	—	£70	£95	—
1780....................................	£35	£70	£90	—
1784....................................	£40	£70	£90	—
1786....................................	£50	£80	£95	—
1792....................................	—	£90	£135	£200
1795....................................	—	£30	£60	£85
1800....................................	—	£30	£70	£85
1817....................................	—	£35	£70	£90
1818....................................	—	£35	£70	£90
1820....................................	—	£45	£80	£100

George III

GEORGE IV (1820–30)

1822–30................................	—	—	£40	£70
1825 TRITANNIAR	—	—	£60	£115

George IV

WILLIAM IV (1830–37)

1831–37................................	—	—	£45	£80
1831 Proof.............................	—	—	£125	£270

VICTORIA (1837–1901)

1838–87 (Young Head)..........	—	—	£30	£60
1859 BEITANNIAR.................	—	—	£75	£135
1861 6 over 1........................	—	—	£40	£80
1888–92 (Jubilee Head).........	—	—	£30	£55
1893–1901 (Old Head............	—	—	£25	£50
1838 Proof.............................	—	—	—	£475
1839 Proof.............................	—	—	—	£300
1853 Proof.............................	—	—	—	£325

William IV

EDWARD VII (1901–10)

1902–08................................	—	—	£25	£35
1902 Proof.............................	—	—	£30	£50
1909....................................	—	—	£45	£80
1910....................................	—	—	£50	£90

GEORGE V (1910–36)

1911–34................................	—	—	£35	£65
1911 Proof.............................	—	—	£40	£70
1935....................................	—	—	£40	£65
1936....................................	—	—	£50	£75

Victoria

GEORGE VI (1936–52)

1937–47................................	—	—	£40	£60
1937 Proof.............................	—	—	£35	£60
1948–52................................	—	—	£45	£70

ELIZABETH II (1952–   )

1953....................................	—	—	£140	£215
1954–85................................	—	—	£40	£65
1986–2007............................	—	—	£40	£70
2002 Gold Proof	—	—	—	£450
2008....................................	—	—	—	£125
2009....................................	—	—	—	£115

Elizabeth

DATE	F	VF	EF	UNC
2010	—	—	—	£110
2011	—	—	—	£85
2012	—	—	—	£115
2013	—	—	—	£120
2014	—	—	—	£130
2015	—	—	—	£115
2016	—	—	—	£135
2017	—	—	—	£170
2018	—	—	—	£170
2019	—	—	—	£175

PENNY
CHARLES II (1660–85)

	F	VF	EF	UNC
Undated	£75	£120	£200	—
1670	£70	£115	£175	—
1671	£70	£115	£170	—
1672/1	£70	£115	£175	—
1673	£65	£115	£170	—
1674	£70	£115	£175	—
1674 Gratia (error)	£105	£160	£250	—
1675	£70	£115	£170	—
1675 Gratia (error)	£105	£165	£260	—
1676	£80	£120	£185	—
1676 Gratia (error)	£115	£170	£275	—
1677	£60	£100	£165	—
1677 Gratia (error)	£95	£135	£230	—
1678	£150	£265	£380	—
1678 Gratia (error)	£180	£280	£400	—
1679	£85	£125	£210	—
1680	£80	£115	£200	—
1680 on 2d flan	£130	£250	£300	—
1681	£110	£155	£230	—
1682	£75	£125	£195	—
1682 ERA for FRA	£90	£150	£245	—
1683	£85	£120	£195	—
1683/1	£85	£150	£225	—
1684	£150	£240	£300	—
1684/3	£160	£250	£315	—

Charles II

JAMES II (1685–88)

	F	VF	EF	UNC
1685	£65	£105	£165	—
1686	£80	£110	£175	—
1687	£80	£120	£180	—
1687 7 over 6	£90	£135	£195	—
1687/8	£85	£130	£190	—
1688	£65	£100	£165	—
1688/7	£70	£110	£185	—

James II

WILLIAM & MARY (1688–94)

	F	VF	EF	UNC
1689	£450	£675	£900	—
1689 MΛRIΛ	£470	£685	£900	—
1689 GVIELMVS (Error)	£450	£700	£925	—
1690	£80	£145	£230	—
1691	£80	£150	£225	—
1691/0	£80	£160	£250	—
1692	£240	£340	£550	—
1692/1	£250	£355	£570	—
1693	£110	£180	£265	—
1694	£75	£130	£230	—
1694 HI for HIB	£120	£170	£275	—
1694 No stops on obverse	£90	£150	£240	—

William & Mary

DATE	F	VF	EF	UNC
WILLIAM III (1694–1702)				
1698	£85	£140	£200	—
1698 HI. BREX (Error)	£110	£165	£270	—
1698 IRA for FRA	£95	£150	£210	—
1699	£270	£400	£600	—
1700	£95	£150	£225	—
1701	£85	£135	£210	—

William III

	F	VF	EF	UNC
ANNE (1702–14)				
1703	£80	£125	£195	—
1705	£70	£110	£180	—
1706	£70	£95	£165	—
1708	£450	£575	£825	—
1709	£60	£95	£150	—
1710	£135	£205	£325	—
1713/0	£85	£125	£190	—

Anne

	F	VF	EF	UNC
GEORGE I (1714–27)				
1716	£45	£90	£115	—
1718	£45	£90	£115	—
1720	£50	£95	£125	—
1720 HIPEX (Error)	£75	£120	£205	—
1723	£70	£125	£180	—
1725	£50	£85	£130	—
1726	£50	£85	£125	—
1727	£65	£120	£170	—

George I

	F	VF	EF	UNC
GEORGE II (1727–60)				
1729	£45	£85	£120	—
1731	£50	£85	£125	—
1732	£50	£80	£120	—
1735	£40	£70	£100	—
1737	£40	£70	£105	—
1739	£40	£70	£100	—
1740	£45	£70	£100	—
1743	£35	£70	£95	—
1746	£45	£80	£115	—
1746/3	£50	£80	£120	—
1750	£30	£55	£85	—
1752	£30	£55	£85	—
1752/0	£35	£60	£90	—
1753	£30	£55	£85	—
1754	£30	£55	£85	—
1755	£30	£55	£85	—
1756	£30	£55	£80	—
1757	£30	£55	£80	—
1757 No colon after Gratia	£50	£80	£100	—
1758	£30	£60	£85	—
1759	£35	£60	£80	—
1760	£40	£75	£95	—

	F	VF	EF	UNC
GEORGE III (1760–1820)				
1763	£50	£75	£100	—
1763 Proof	—	—	Extremely rare	
1766	£40	£70	£90	—
1770	£55	£85	£110	—
1772	£40	£70	£85	—
1780	£100	£150	£210	—
1781	£35	£60	£85	—
1784	£45	£65	£90	—
1786	£35	£60	£90	—
1792	£40	£65	£100	£140
1795	—	£25	£50	£70

George III

DATE	F	VF	EF	UNC
1800	—	£25	£50	£70
1817	—	£25	£50	£70
1818	—	£25	£50	£70
1820	—	£30	£55	£75

GEORGE IV (1820–30)

1822–30	—		£35	£60

WILLIAM IV (1830–37)

1831–37	—	—	£45	£70
1831 Proof	—	—	£150	£270

VICTORIA (1837–1901)

1838–87 (Young Head)	—	—	£30	£55
1888–92 (Jubilee Head)	—	—	£30	£45
1893–1901 (Old Head)	—	—	£25	£35
1838 Proof	—	—	—	£265
1839 Proof	—	—	—	£185
1853 Proof	—	—	—	£215

EDWARD VII (1901–10)

1902–08	—	—	£20	£35
1902 Proof	—	—	£25	£40
1909	—	—	£40	£80
1910	—	—	£55	£100

GEORGE V (1910–36)

1911–14	—	—	£45	£80
1911 Proof	—	—	£45	£90
1915	—	—	£50	£85
1916–19	—	—	£45	£80
1920	—	—	£45	£80
1921–28	—	—	£45	£75
1929	—	—	£45	£80
1930–34	—	—	£40	£75
1935	—	—	£45	£80
1936	—	—	£55	£85

GEORGE VI (1936–52)

1937–40	—	—	£50	£80
1937 Proof	—	—	£45	£80
1941	—	—	£55	£90
1942–47	—	—	£50	£85
1948–52	—	—	£60	£95

ELIZABETH II (1952–   )

1953	—	—	£285	£400
1965–85	—	—	£45	£80
1986–2007	—	—	£45	£85
2002 Proof in gold	—	—	—	£485
2008	—	—	—	£145
2009	—	—	—	£140
2010	—	—	—	£120
2011	—	—	—	£105
2012	—	—	—	£130
2013	—	—	—	£125
2014	—	—	—	£120
2015	—	—	—	£110
2016	—	—	—	£135
2017	—	—	—	£150
2018	—	—	—	£155
2019	—	—	—	£160

George IV

William IV

Victoria

Edward VII

George V

Elizabeth II

DR KERRY RODGERS

THE COINS OF
Her Majesty's
Tiaras

Her Majesty Queen Elizabeth II is something of a collector. For her it is all about tiaras. She has acquired quite a number. Some she inherited from her mother, grandmother and great grandmother. Others were gifts. Yet others she has had made to order. Just four from her extensive collection have appeared on coins of Britain and the British Commonwealth in the course of her reign. Three of these are being worn by the Queen herself. These are "Girls of Great Britain and Ireland Tiara", "George IV State Diadem" and "Kokoshnik Tiara". Her mother wore the fourth, the "Greville Tiara". There may also be a fifth: that sported by Queen Victoria on a coin in 2001. Each holds a piece of royal history. Each has its own story. Together coins on which they occur make a small but exclusive thematic collection.

Laurel Wreath

Queen Elizabeth was 15 years into her reign before any British coins showed her wearing a tiara. On her first issues sculptor Mary Gillick chose to portray a simple laureated bust of the new monarch. In this respect Her Majesty's coin portrait echoed those of George I through George IV. In contrast her father, grandfather and great-grandfather had been shown bare-headed on Britain's coins.

Gillick's effigy would be the sole portrait of Her Majesty used for Great Britain's pre-decimal coinage from 1953-on as it would for the pre-decimal coins of Australia, Canada, New Zealand, South Africa, and Rhodesia and Nyasaland.

Girls of Great Britain and Ireland

When a new decimal coinage was introduced in Britain in 1968 a new effigy was called for. That chosen was by Arnold Machin. The young Queen is indisputably regal and wears "The Girls of Great Britain and Ireland Tiara". This same portrait had already accompanied decimalization of the coinage of Australia in 1966 and New Zealand in 1967.

This tiara is the Queen's favourite. It came into the Royal Family in 1893 as a wedding gift to Princess Victoria Mary of Teck (later Queen Mary) when she married the future King George V. It was presented to Mary by a committee of women, "The Girls of Great Britain and Ireland". They had raised some £5,000 for its purchase it from the jewellery firm of Garrard who had commissioned it from E. Wolfe & Co.

In her turn Queen Mary gave it to her granddaughter, the then Princess Elizabeth when she married Prince Philip in 1947. Since then Elizabeth has referred to it fondly as "Granny's tiara".

The tiara is extremely versatile and lightweight consisting of diamonds set in silver and gold. It consists of a narrow basal bandeau containing both round and lozenge diamonds. Above is a smaller coronet decorated with diamond-set scrolls and spikes and, originally, large oriental pearls. In 1914 Mary had the pearls removed and replaced with 13 brilliant-cut diamonds taken from the County of Surrey Fringe Tiara.

The base and coronet can be separated with the former worn as a head band and the latter worn by itself or as a necklace.

The Queen was unaware that the two pieces belonged together until after Queen Mary's death in 1953. In a later interview Her Majesty commented, "I only discovered after I had succeeded and got into her safe that I realised she'd taken the base off it". In 1969 Elizabeth had it reassembled.

This is the diadem the Queen is seen wearing most often presumably as it is both light and comfortable. It is possibly this tiara that gave rise to the observation of Princess Margaret, "The Queen is the only person who can put on a tiara with one hand, while walking down stairs."

It has appeared on at least four other coin effigies. That of Machin shows the Queen wearing it without its bandeau base. In Ian Rank Broadley's portrait used on British coins from 1998 to 2014 the base and coronet are one.

RAM designer Vladimir Gottwald also used this tiara complete with its base for an intended one-

Her Majesty wears the coronet from her favourite "Girls of Great Britain and Ireland Tiara" in this supremely regal portrait by Arnold Machin that appeared on Britain's circulating and commemorative coins from 1968 to 1984 (image courtesy & © The Royal Mint).

"a 70-year old woman with poise and bearing" is shown with the "Girls of Great Britain and Ireland" tiara complete in Ian Rank-Broadley's 1998 effigy of Her Majesty (image courtesy & © The Royal Mint).

Vladimir Gottwald of The Royal Australian Mint chose to show the Queen in her "Girls of Great Britain and Ireland Tiara" for his Australian 50 cents in 2000 (KM-437). Her Majesty wears it complete but with the spiky bits somewhat overdone (image courtesy Royal Australian Mint).

A "regal and ageless" Queen selected the historic George IV State Diadem for Rafael Maklouf's effigy of her in 1985 (image courtesy & © The Royal Mint).

Variations on the Rafael Maklouf's effigy of Her Majesty. Right Falkland Islands; left Gibraltar (images courtesy & © www. ha.com).

The effigy of the Queen by Dora de Pédery-Hunt in which she wears the George IV Diadem (image courtesy & © www.ha.com).

Jody Clark's effigy complete with George IV Diadem struck-up on 2015 bimetallic two pounds (image courtesy & © Royal Mint).

James Butler's effigy of Her Majesty used on a special issue of sovereigns struck in 2016 to mark her 90th birthday. It too uses the George IV Diadem (image courtesy & © Royal Mint).

James Berry's effigy of Queen Elizabeth sporting her Kokoshnik Tiara as used on New Zealand dollars from 1979-1982 (image courtesy & © Noble Numismatics).

The Queen wears her much loved "Girls of Great Britain and Ireland Tiara" for this conjoined portrait with Prince Philip by Philip Nathan used on the £5 coin struck to mark their Golden Wedding in 1997 (KM-997) (image courtesy & © www.ha.com).

Queen Elizabeth, the Queen Mother, sports her reworked version of the Greville Tiara on the reverse of this GB gold £5 of 2000 (KM-1007b) struck to mark her 100th birthday (image courtesy & © www.ha).

off Australian Royal Visit 50 cents in 2000 (KM-437). However, he did somewhat overdo the finials (spiky bits) on the coronet. This same effigy was used in 2010 on a Coat of Arms 50 cents included in a gold year set struck to mark its 10th anniversary.

Her Majesty sports this same tiara in a conjoined portrait with Prince Philip by Philip Nathan used for their British Golden Wedding £5 in 1997 (KM-997).

George IV State Diadem

In 1982 the Royal Mint invited 17 artists to submit portrait models to replace the Machin effigy on the nation's coins. The image accepted by the Queen for use on Britain's circulating coinage from January 1, 1985, was by Raphael Maklouf. It shows Her Majesty wearing the George IV State Diadem. This is a profoundly symbolic piece that Elizabeth reserves solely for state occasions such as the State Opening of Parliament and official portraits. As the name suggests it dates back to the reign of George IV and hence is one of the older pieces in the Queen's collection.

King George IV was more than somewhat flamboyant. He had waited a long time to become king and was determined his coronation would be the most fashionable and extravagant ever. If nothing else it had to outdo Napoleon's coronation as Emperor of France. To this end George insisted on numerous changes to the traditional British ceremony. Among other things he proposed replacing the fleurs-de-lys on the royal crown with a new patriotic device celebrating the creation of the United Kingdom: England's rose with Scotland's thistle and Ireland's shamrock. His reasoning was that his father, George III, had given up any claim to the non-existent French throne in 1800 with the Act of Union. The College of Arms put paid to this notion. It pointed out that the use of fleurs-de-lys on English coats-of-arms predates any claims to the French throne.

George was not one to let history get in the way of a show of patriotism. In 1820 he had commissioned a special tiara from Rundell, Bridge & Rundell to wear

The details of the George IV Diadem and its finials are apparent in this latest effigy of Her Majesty Queen Elizabeth II by the Royal Mint's Jody Clark as introduced on British coins from the first quarter of 2015. Image courtesy & © Royal Mint.

to his coronation. He now asked that designer Philip Liebart incorporate his new patriotic device in the diadem.

The result is what we see today: four crosses pattée alternating with four nosegays consisting of roses, thistles and shamrocks. These motifs are set on a band of diamond scrollwork between two rows of pearls. The detail is most readily seen in the current Royal Mint Engraver's portrait of Queen Elizabeth. At his coronation in 1821 George wore the completed diadem over a plumed velvet hat.

All told the piece features 1,333 diamonds with a 4 carat yellow diamond set in the front cross. Officially it is known as the "Diamond Diadem". At the time its diamonds were simply hired for the coronation. There is no record of their ever having been purchased by the monarchy and it is generally assumed that some sort of deal was done to retain the diadem intact afterwards.

Since George's day the diadem has invariably been worn by Britain's queens, be they Queen Consort or Queen Regnant. Queen Victoria was a big fan as were both Queen Alexandra and Queen Mary. Queen Elizabeth is the first to reserve its use solely for state occasions.

Apart from the Maklouf's coin portrait, in all its various manifestations, the George IV State Diadem has appeared in the effigies of Hungarian-born sculptor Dora de Pédery-Hunt used for Canadian coins from 1990 to 2002 and, most recently, on the Jody Clark effigy used on Great Britain's coins since 2015.

Her Majesty is also shown wearing this diadem in the distinctive obverse effigy by James Butler used for a special proof issue of her nation's sovereigns struck in 2016 to mark her 90th birthday.

Kokoshnik Tiara

In the late 1970s New Zealander James Berry chose to use Queen Elizabeth's spectacular Kokoshnik Tiara for an effigy of Her Majesty that was subsequently used on several New Zealand commemorative dollars.

This tiara is one of several from the Queen's collection with Russian connections. It was a present to the then Princess of Wales, the future Queen Alexandra, in 1888. At the time she and her Prince, the future King Edward VII, were celebrating their silver wedding anniversary.

The 365 peeresses of the realm, aka "The Ladies of Society", asked her Royal Highness what she might like by way of a tiara. Her request was for something in the Russian kokoshnik style. Not only was this type very fashionable at the time but Alexandra's sister, Marie Feodorovna, Empress Consort of All the Russias, commonly wore an absolute stunner.

Alexandra's version was made by Garrard. The rounded sections are modelled after a traditional Russian headdress, a kokoshnik. This is commonly made in embroidered fabric but the ladies of the Russian imperial court had decreed bejewelled forms were the preferred fashion statement.

Given its Russian antecedent's, Garrard appropriately included 61 platinum bars in Mary's Kokoshnik. These carried 488 diamonds of which two weigh 3.25 carats apiece.

After Alexandra's death her Kokoshnik was added to Queen Mary's vast hoard of jewels where it remained until inherited by the present Queen in 1953.

The four New Zealand dollars this tiara has appeared on are those of: 1979 (Arms; KM-48), 1980 (Fantail; KM-49), 1981 (Royal Visit; KM-50) and 1982 (Takahe; KM-51).

Greville tiara

The Greville Tiara aka Boucheron or Honeycomb Tiara has been seen on a number of commemorative British coins in recent years. It is not worn by the Queen but by her mother.

It was originally made for Margaret Greville a prominent society hostess and extremely wealthy brewery heiress. In 1901 she needed a new tiara for the coronation of King Edward VII. It had to be something special particularly as she was to be seated next to her best friend Alice Keppel, the King's favourite mistress. She commissioned a new diadem from the French jeweller Boucheron. It consisted of a complete circlet of tall lotus flower spikes studded with Grenville's own diamonds of which she had many. In 1921 she had this piece reworked into something akin to a Kokoshnik style. It was in this form that Queen Elizabeth, the future Queen Mother, received it in 1942 when Margaret Greville died having bequeathed all her jewels to Her Majesty.

It was inappropriate to wear any item from the collection during wartime and it was not until the late 1940s that Elizabeth appeared in public wearing the Greville circlet. In 1953 she had it reworked by Cartier adding more diamonds in the process. Subsequently it became her most worn tiara.

It was passed-on to Queen Elizabeth II in 2002 upon her mother's death. Today it is often seen on the head of the Duchess of Cornwall who has it on semi-permanent, short term loan from Her Majesty.

Among British coins it has appeared on are the Queen Mother's 80th birthday 25p (1980), the Queen Mother commemorative £5 (2000; KM1007), and the Queen Mother's memorial £5 (2002; KM-1035) plus several Commonwealth coins.

Queen Victoria's whatnot

In 2001 the Royal Mint issued a £5 coin to mark the 100th anniversary of the death of Queen Victoria (KM-1015). The reverse showed a classic portrait of young Victoria by William Wyon. The mint used this on various commemorative medals such as that marking the Queen's visit to the City of London in 1837. Subsequently it was employed for the Penny Black stamp.

Victoria is shown wearing a coronet that has from time to time been identified as the George IV Diadem. If this is indeed the case, then Wyon took several liberties with reality. Wyon would surely have been aware of what the Diadem looked like. In 1839 he showed Victoria wearing it on the reverse of the gold £5 (KM-742; S-3851).

A comparison of the 1837 and 1839 effigies makes clear that the 1837 coronet differs in a number of ways. For example it sits lower on the Queen's head. The size of the crosses pattée and nosegays are smaller and differ markedly in their arrangement if not number. And the finials on the 1837 do not appear to extend around the full extent circlet. In short, the two tiaras are quite different.

This article originally appeared in COIN NEWS magazine, June 2018.

DECIMAL COINAGE

Since the introduction of the Decimal system in the UK, many coins have been issued for circulation purposes in vast quantities. In addition, from 1982 sets of coins to non-proof standard, and including examples of each denomination found in circulation, have been issued each year. For 1982 and 1983 they were to "circulation" standard and described as "Uncirculated". Individual coins from these sets are annotated "Unc" on the lists that follow. From 1984 to the present day they were described as "Brilliant Uncirculated" (BU on the lists), and from around 1986 these coins are generally distinguishable from coins intended for circulation. They were from then produced by the Proof Coin Division of the Royal Mint (rather than by the Coin Production Room which produces circulation-standard coins). For completeness however, we have included the annotations Unc and BU back to 1982, the start year for these sets.

It is emphasised that the abbreviations Unc and BU in the left-hand columns adjacent to the date refer to an advertising description or to an engineering production standard, not the preservation condition or grade of the coin concerned. Where no such annotation appears adjacent to the date, the coin is circulation-standard for issue as such.

We have included the "mintage" figures for circulation coins down to Half Penny. The figure given for the 1997 Two Pounds, is considerably less than the actual quantity struck, because many were scrapped before issue due to failing an electrical conductivity test. Where a coin is available in uncirculated grade at, or just above, face value no price has been quoted.

Base metal Proof issues of circulation coinage (£2 or £1 to one or half penny) of the decimal series were only issued, as with Unc or BU, as part of Year Sets, but many of these sets have been broken down into individual coins, hence the appearance of the latter on the market.

The lists do not attempt to give details of die varieties, except where there was an obvious intention to change the appearance of a coin, e.g. 1992 20p.

2008 saw new reverses and modified obverses for all circulation denominations from the One Pound to the One Penny. All seven denominations were put into circulation dated 2008, all with both the old and the new reverses.

The circulation standard mintage figures have mainly been kindly supplied by courtesy of the Head of Historical Services and the Department of UK Circulation Coin Sales, both at the Royal Mint.

KILO COINS
(gold and silver)

The UK's first-ever Kilo coins were struck to commemorate the 2012 Olympic Games in 0.999 fine gold and 0.999 fine silver. These and subsequent issues are listed in detail below, and all were struck to proof standard and to similar metallic standards.

DATE	FACE VALUE	AUTHORISED ISSUE QTY.	NO. ISSUED	ISSUE PRICE
2012 Olympic Gold;				
obverse: 1998 Ian Rank-Broadley's Royal Portrait				
reverse: Sir Anthony Caro's "Individual Endeavour" £1,000	60	20	£100,000
2012 Olympic Silver;				
obverse: 1998 Rank-Broadley Royal Portrait				
reverse: Tom Phillip's "Team Endeavour".. £500	2,912	910	£3,000
2012 Diamond Jubilee Gold;				
obverse: Queen in Garter Robes (Rank-Broadley)				
reverse: Royal Arms (Buckingham Palace Gates) £1,000	21	21	£60,000
2012 Diamond Jubilee Silver;				
obverse: Queen in Garter Robes (Rank-Broadley)				
reverse: Royal Arms (Buckingham Palace Gates) £500	1,250	206	£2,600
2013 Coronation Anniversary Gold;				
obverse: 1998 Rank-Broadley Royal Portrait				
reverse: John Bergdahl's Coronation Regalia £1,000	27	13	£50,000
2013 Coronation Anniversary Silver;				
obverse: 1998 Rank-Broadley Royal Portrait				
reverse: John Bergdahl's Coronation Regalia £500	400	301	£2,600
2013 Royal Christening Gold;				
obverse: 1998 Rank-Broadley Royal Portrait				
reverse: John Bergdahl's Lily Font £1,000	22	19	£48,000
2013 Royal Christening Silver;				
obverse: 1998 Rank-Broadley Royal Portrait				
reverse: John Bergdahl's Lily Font £500	500	194	£2,600
2014 First World War Outbreak Gold;				
obverse: 1998 Rank-Broadley Royal Portrait				
reverse: Sandle's Hostile Environment.. £1,000	25	10	£45,000
2014 First World War Outbreak Silver;				
obverse: 1998 Rank-Broadley Royal Portrait				
reverse: Sandle's Hostile Environment... £500	430	165	£2,000
2015 50th Anniversary of Death of Sir Winston Churchill Gold;				
obverse: 1998 Rank-Broadley Royal Portrait				
reverse: Millner's image of Churchill.. £1,000	15	9	£45,000
2015 50th Anniversary of Death of Sir Winston Churchill Silver;				
obverse: 1998 Rank-Broadley Royal Portrait				
reverse: Milner's image of Churchill £500	170	117	£2,000
2015 The Longest Reign Gold;				
obverse: Butler Royal Portrait				
reverse: Stephen Taylor Queen's Portraits £1,000	15	15	£42,500
2016 The Longest Reign Silver;				
obverse: Butler Royal Portrait				
reverse: Stephen Taylor Queen's Portraits £500	320	278	£2,000
2016 Year of the Monkey Gold;				
obverse: Clark Royal Portrait				
reverse: Wuon-Gean Ho's Rhesus monkey £1,000	8	—	£42,500
2016 Year of the Monkey Silver;				
obverse: Butler Royal Portrait				
everse: Wuon-Gean Ho's Rhesus monkey....................................... £500	88	—	£2,000
2016 Queen's 90th Birthday Gold;				
obverse: Clark Royal Portrait				
reverse: Christopher Hobbs Floral design.................................... £1,000	25	15	—
2016 Queen's 90th Birthday Silver;				
obverse: Clark Royal Portrait				
reverse: Christopher Hobbs Floral design....................................... £500	450	447	£2,000

2018
Britannia
Silver

2018
Anniversary
of the
Armistice
Gold

2018
Lunar Year
of the Dog
Silver

2018
Sapphire
Coronation
Jubilee
Gold

DATE	FACE VALUE	AUTHORISED ISSUE QTY.	NO. ISSUED	ISSUE PRICE
2017 The Queen's Sapphire Accession Jubilee Silver; obverse: Clark Royal Portrait reverse: Gregory Cameron's design of Crowned Coat of Arms	£500	300	—	£2,050
2017 Lunar Year of the Rooster Gold; obverse: Clark Royal Portrait reverse: Wuon-Gean Ho's Rooster	£1,000	8	—	£42,500
2017 Lunar Year of the Rooster Silver; obverse: Clark Royal Portrait reverse: Wuon-Gean Ho's Rooster	£500	68	—	£2,050
2017 Platinum Wedding Gold; obverse: Etienne Millner Double Royal Portrait reverse: Heraldic shields by John Bergdahl	£1,000	31	—	£49,950
2017 Platinum Wedding Silver; obverse: Etienne Millner Double Royal Portrait reverse: Heraldic shields by John Bergdahl	£500	550	—	£2,025
2018 Anniversary of the Armistice Gold; obverse: Jody Clark Royal Portrait reverse: Kneeling soldier by Paul Day	£1,000	10	—	£49,995
2018 Anniversary of the Armistice Silver; obverse: Jody Clark Royal Portrait reverse: Kneeling soldier by Paul Day	£500	100	—	£2,025
2018 Lunar Year of the Dog Gold; obverse: Clark Royal Portrait reverse: Wuon-Gean Ho's Dog	£1,000	8	—	£42,500
2018 Lunar Year of the Dog Silver; obverse: Clark Royal Portrait reverse: Wuon-Gean Ho's Dog	£500	108	—	£2,025
2018 Britannia Silver; obverse: Jody Clark Royal Portrait reverse: Stylised bust of Britannia by David Lawrence	£500	250	—	£2,025
2018 Sapphire Coronation Jubilee Gold; obverse: Jody Clark Royal Portrait reverse: The Queen in the Royal Coach by Dominique Evans	£1,000	15	—	£49,950
2018 Sapphire Coronation Jubilee Silver; obverse: Jody Clark Royal Portrait reverse: The Queen in the Royal Coach by Dominique Evans	£500	250	—	£2,025

See also under "The Queen's Beasts" series

Illustrations on this page are not shown to scale.

243

DATE	FACE VALUE	AUTHORISED ISSUE QTY.	NO. ISSUED	ISSUE PRICE
2019 Britannia Silver;				
obverse: Jody Clark Royal Portrait				
reverse: David Lawrence's vivid portrait of Britannia beside a lion .. £500		115	—	£2,025
2019 Queen Victoria Silver;				
obverse: Jody Clark Royal Portrait				
reverse: William Wyon's classic portrait of Queen Victoria and Prince Albert				
.... £500		125	—	£2,025
2019 Lunar Year of the Pig Gold;				
obverse: Jody Clark Royal Portrait				
reverse: Harry Brockway's Pig..................................... £1000		8	—	—
2019 Lunar Year of the Pig Silver;				
obverse: Jody Clark Royal Portrait				
reverse: Harry Brockway's Pig..................................... £500		38	—	£2,025
2019 The Falcon of the Plantagenets Gold;				
obverse: Jody Clark Royal Portrait				
reverse: Jody Clark's Falcon £1000		13	—	—
2019 The Falcon of the Plantagenets Silver;				
obverse: Jody Clark Royal Portrait				
reverse: Jody Clark's Falcon £500		125	—	£2,025
2019 The Yale of Beaufort Gold;				
obverse: Jody Clark Royal Portrait				
reverse: Jody Clark's regal statue of this mythical beast £1000		13	—	—
2019 The Yale of Beaufort Silver;				
obverse: Jody Clark Royal Portrait				
reverse: Jody Clark's regal statue of this mythical beast £500		120	—	£2,025

2019 Queen Victoria

2019 Britannia

2019 Lunar Year of the Pig

2019 The Falcon of the Plantagenets

Illustrations on this page are not shown to scale.

FIVE-OUNCE COINS
(gold and silver, including Britannia Coins)

Also appearing for the first time in 2012 were Five-Ounce coins, minted in the same metals and standards as the Kilo Coins. Included here also are Five-Ounce Britannia coins, both gold (50mm) and silver (65mm) proofs, which appeared first in 2013. It should be noted that the reverses of the Britannia coins, in common with other denominations of Britannias, have a different design from those minted to BU ("bullion") standard.

DATE	FACE VALUE	AUTHORISED ISSUE QTY.	NO ISSUED	ISSUE. PRICE
2012 Olympic Gold; obverse: 1998 Rank-Broadley Royal Portrait reverse: Pegasus (C. Le Brun) £10		500	193	£11,500
2012 Olympic Silver; obverse: 1998 Rank-Broadley Royal Portrait reverse: Pegasus (C. Le Brun) £10		7,500	5,056	£525
2012 Diamond Jubilee Gold; obverse: Queen in Garter Robes (Rank-Broadley) reverse: Queen seated (facing).......................£10		250	140	£9,500
2012 Diamond Jubilee Silver; obverse: Queen in Garter Robes (Rank-Broadley) reverse: Queen seated (facing).......................£10		1,952	1,933	£450
2013 Coronation Anniversary Gold; obverse: 1998 Rank-Broadley Royal Portrait reverse: Regalia in Westminster Abbey (J. Olliffe) £10		129	74	£9,500
2013 Coronation Anniversary Silver; obverse: 1998 Rank-Broadley Royal Portrait reverse: Regalia in Westminster Abbey (J. Olliffe) £10		1,953	1,604	£450
2013 Britannia Gold; obverse: 1998 Rank-Broadley Royal Portrait reverse: Britannia seated with owl (R. Hunt)...........................£500		125	61	£8,200
2013 Britannia Silver; obverse: 1998 Rank-Broadley Royal Portrait reverse: Britannia seated with owl (R. Hunt)...........................£10		4,655	4,054	£450
2013 Royal Christening Gold; obverse: 1998 Rank-Broadley Royal Portrait reverse: Bergdahl's Lily Font £10		150	48	£8,200

DATE	FACE VALUE	AUTHORISED ISSUE QTY.	NO ISSUED	ISSUE PRICE
2013 Royal Christening Silver; obverse: 1998 Rank-Broadley Royal Portrait reverse: Bergdahl's Lily Font £10		1,660	912	£450
2014 Britannia Gold; obverse: 1998 Rank-Broadley Royal Portrait reverse: Clark's portrayal of Britannia £500		75	75	£7,500
2014 Britannia Silver; obverse: 1998 Rank-Broadley Royal Portrait reverse: Clark's portrayal of Britannia £10		1,350	1348	£395
2014 First World War Outbreak Gold; obverse: 1998 Rank-Broadley Royal Portrait reverse: Bergdahl's Britannia.......................................£10		110	36	£7,500
2014 First World War Outbreak Silver; obverse: 1998 Rank-Broadley Royal Portrait reverse: Bergdahl's Britannia.......................................£10		1,300	606	£395
2014 Lunar Year of the Horse Gold; obverse: 1998 Rank-Broadley Royal Portrait reverse: Wuon-Gean Ho's Horse................................£500		—	—	£7,500
2014 Lunar Year of the Horse Silver; obverse: 1998 Rank-Broadley Royal Portrait reverse: Wuon-Gean Ho's Horse................................£10		799	799	£395
2015 Year of the Sheep Gold; obverse: 1998 Rank-Broadley Royal Portrait reverse: Wuon-Gean Ho's Swaledale Sheep £500		38	26	£7,500
2015 Year of the Sheep Silver; obverse: 1998 Rank-Broadley Royal Portrait reverse: Wuon-Gean Ho's Swaledale Sheep £10		1,088	331	£395
2015 Britannia Gold; obverse: Clark Royal Portrait reverse: Dufort's Britannia...£500		50	60 (?)	£7,500
2015 Britannia Silver; obverse: Clark Royal Portrait reverse: Dufort's Britannia...£10		1,150	995	£395
2015 50th Anniversary of Death of Sir Winston Churchill Gold; obverse: Clark Royal Portrait reverse: Millner's image of Churchill.............................£10		60	58	£7,500
2015 50th Anniversary of Death of Sir Winston Churchill Silver; obverse: Clark Royal Portrait reverse: Millner's image of Churchill.............................£10		500	855 (?)	£450
2015 First World War Gold; obverse: Clark Royal Portrait reverse: James Butler Devastation of War £500		50	17	£6,950
2015 First World War Silver; obverse: Clark Royal Portrait reverse: James Butler Devastation of War £10		500	355	£395
2015 The Longest Reign Gold; obverse: Butler Royal Portrait reverse: Stephen Taylor Queen's Portrait...................£500		180	180	£6,950
2015 The Longest Reign Silver; obverse: Butler Royal Portrait reverse: Stephen Taylor Queen's Portrait...................£10		1,500	1499	£395
2016 Year of the Monkey Gold; obverse: Clark Royal Portrait reverse: Wuon-Gean Ho's Rhesus monkey £500		38	—	£7,500
2016 Year of the Monkey Silver; obverse: Butler Royal Portrait reverse: Wuon-Gean Ho's Rhesus monkey £10		588	—	£395
2016 Queen's 90th Birthday Gold; obverse: Clark Royal Portrait reverse: Christopher Hobbs Floral design...................£500		170	170	£7,500

DATE	FACE VALUE	AUTHORISED ISSUE QTY.	NO ISSUED	ISSUE PRICE
2016 Queen's 90th Birthday Silver; obverse: Clark Royal Portrait reverse: Christopher Hobbs Floral design.....................£10		1,750	1727	£395
2016 Britannia Gold; obverse: Clark Royal Portrait; reverse: Suzie Zamit Britannia...................................£500		75	64	£7,500
2016 Britannia Silver; obverse: Clark Royal Portrait; reverse: Suzie Zamit Britannia...................................£10		800	783	£395
2016 Shakespeare Gold; obverse: Clark Royal Portrait; reverse: Tom Phillips Shakespeare Portrait...............£500		—	50	—
2016 Shakespeare Silver; obverse: Clark Royal Portrait; reverse: Tom Phillips Shakespeare Portrait...............£10		750	343	£395
2017 Lunar Year of the Rooster Gold; obverse: Clark Royal Portrait reverse: Wuon-Gean Ho's Rooster.............................£500		38	—	£8,250
2017 The Queen's Sapphire Jubilee Gold; obverse: Clark Royal Portrait reverse: Gregory Cameron's design of Crowned Coat of Arms.£500		110	—	£8,250
2017 The Queen's Sapphire Jubilee Silver; obverse: Clark Royal Portrait reverse: Gregory Cameron's design of Crowned Coat of Arms...£10		1,500	—	£415
2017 Britannia Gold; obverse: Clark Royal Portrait reverse: Modern interpretation of Britannia by Louis Tamlyn.....£500		125	—	£8,250
2017 Britannia Silver; obverse: Clark Royal Portrait reverse: Modern interpretation of Britannia by Louis Tamlyn.......£10		1,500	—	£415
2017 The 100th Anniversary of the First World War Gold; obverse: Clark Royal Portrait reverse: Soldier design by sculptor Philip Jackson...................£500		50	—	£8,250
2017 The 100th Anniversary of the First World War Silver; obverse: Clark Royal Portrait reverse: Soldier design by sculptor Philip Jackson.....................£10		450	—	£415
2017 Royal Platinum Wedding Gold; obverse: Royal Portraits by Etienne Millner reverse: Heraldic design by John Bergdahl...............................£500		450	—	£415
2018 Lunar Year of the Dog Gold; obverse: Clark Royal Portrait reverse: Wuon-Gean Ho's Dog.................................£500		58	—	£8,565
2018 Britannia Gold; obverse: Clark Royal Portrait reverse: Stylised Britannia by David Lawrence £500		125	—	£8,565
2018 Britannia Silver; obverse: Clark Royal Portrait reverse: Stylised Britannia by David Lawrence £10		1,500	—	£420
2018 Four Generations of Royalty Gold; obverse: Clark Royal Portrait reverse: Initials of the Royal succession by Timothy Noad........£500		100	—	£8,565
2018 Four Generations of Royalty Silver; obverse: Clark Royal Portrait reverse: Initials of the Royal succession by Timothy Noad..........£10		1,000	—	£420
2018 Sapphire Coronation Gold; obverse: Clark Royal Portrait reverse: Queen in the Coronation Coach by Dominique Evans £500		85	—	£8,565
2018 Sapphire Coronation Silver; obverse: Clark Royal Portrait reverse: Queen in the Coronation Coach by Dominique Evans ...£10		1,050	—	£420
2018 Anniversary of the Armistice Gold; obverse: Clark Royal Portrait reverse: Lone Soldier by Paul Day £500		50	—	£8,565
2018 Anniversary of the Armistice Silver; obverse: Clark Royal Portrait reverse: Lone Soldier by Paul Day £10		525	—	£420

DATE	FACE VALUE	AUTHORISED ISSUE QTY.	NO ISSUED	ISSUE PRICE
2019 Britannia Gold; obverse: Jody Clark Royal Portrait reverse: David Lawrence vividly portraits Britannia beside a lion £500		70	—	£8,645
2019 Britannia Silver; obverse: Jody Clark Royal Portrait reverse: David Lawrence vividly portraits Britannia beside a lion £10		400	—	£420
2019 Queen Victoria Gold; obverse: Jody Clark Royal Portrait reverse: William Wyon's classic portrait of Queen Victoria and Prince Albert £10		70	—	£8,645
2019 Queen Victoria Silver; obverse: Jody Clark Royal Portrait reverse: William Wyon's classic portrait of Queen Victoria and Prince Albert £10		800	—	£420
2019 The Yeoman Warders Gold; obverse: Jody Clark Royal Portrait reverse: Glyn Davis............. £10		45	—	£8,645
2019 The Yeoman Warders Silver; obverse: Jody Clark Royal Portrait reverse: Glyn Davis............. £10		585	—	£420
2019 The Ceremony of the Keys Gold; obverse: Jody Clark Royal Portrait reverse: Glyn Davis............. £10		45	—	£8,645
2019 The Ceremony of the Keys Silver; obverse: Jody Clark Royal Portrait reverse: Glyn Davis............. £10		585	—	£420
2019 The Falcon of the Plantagenets Gold; obverse: Jody Clark Royal Portrait reverse: Jody Clark's Falcon £500		85	—	£8,645
2019 The Falcon of the Plantagenets Silver; obverse: Jody Clark Royal Portrait reverse: Jody Clark's Falcon £10		550	—	£420
2019 The Tower of London Crown Jewels Gold; obverse: Jody Clark Royal Portrait reverse: Glyn Davis............. £10		45	—	£8,645
2019 The Tower of London Crown Jewels Silver; obverse: Jody Clark Royal Portrait reverse: Glyn Davis............. £10		585	—	£420
2019 Lunar Year of the Pig Gold; obverse: Jody Clark Royal Portrait reverse: Harry Brockway's Pig.......... £500		38	—	£8,645
2019 Lunar Year of the Pig Silver; obverse: Jody Clark Royal Portrait reverse: Harry Brockway's Pig.......... £10		288	—	£420
2019 Legend of the Ravens Gold; obverse: Jody Clark Royal Portrait reverse: Glyn Davies............. £10		45	—	£8,645
2019 Legend of the Ravens Silver; obverse: Jody Clark Royal Portrait reverse: Glyn Davies............. £10		585	—	£420
2019 The Yale of Beaufort Gold; obverse: Jody Clark Royal Portrait reverse: Jody Clark's regal statue of this mythical beast £500		70	—	£8,645
2019 The Yale of Beaufort Silver; obverse: Jody Clark Royal Portrait reverse: Jody Clark's regal statue of this mythical beast £10		335	—	£420

FIVE POUNDS (Sovereign series)

This series is all minted in gold, and, except where stated, have the Pistrucci St George and Dragon reverse. BU coins up to 2001 bear a U in a circle. From 2009 the initials B.P. in the exergue are replaced by PISTRUCCI in small letters on the left. From 2014 the denomination is called the "Five-Sovereign" piece by the Royal Mint in their marketing publications.

DATE	Mintage	UNC
1980 Proof	10,000	£1500
1981 Proof	5,400	£1500
1982 Proof	2,500	£1500
1984 BU	15,104	£1250
1984 Proof	8,000	£1500
1985 New portrait BU	13,626	£1250
1985 — Proof	6,130	£1500
1986 BU	7,723	£1100
1987 Uncouped portrait BU	5,694	£1250
1988 BU	3,315	£1250
1989 500th Anniversary of the Sovereign. Enthroned portrayal obverse and		
Crowned shield reverse BU	2,937	£1400
1989 — Proof	5,000	£1500
1990 Reverts to couped portrait BU	1,226	£1250
1990 Proof	1,721	£1500
1991 BU	976	£1250
1991 Proof	1,336	£1500
1992 BU	797	£1250
1992 Proof	1,165	£1500
1993 BU	906	£1250
1993 Proof	1,078	£1500
1994 BU	1,000	£1250
1994 Proof	918	£1500
1995 BU	1,000	£1250
1995 Proof	1,250	£1500
1996 BU	901	£1250
1996 Proof	742	£1500
1997 BU	802	£1250
1997 Proof	860	£1500
1998 New portrait BU	825	£1250
1998 Proof	789	£1500
1999 BU	991	£1250
1999 Proof	1,000	£1500
2000 ("Bullion")	10,000	£1250
2000 BU	994	£1250
2000 Proof	3,000	£1500
2001 BU	1,000	£1250
2001 Proof	3,500	£1500
2002 Shield rev. ("Bullion")	—	£1250
2002 BU	—	£1250
2002 Proof	3,000	£1500
2003 BU	812	£1250
2003 Proof	—	£1500
2004 BU	1,000	£1250
2004 Proof	—	£1500
2005 Noad's heraldic St George and Dragon BU	936	£1500
2005 — Proof	—	£1600
2006 BU	731	£1250
2006 Proof	—	£1500
2007 BU	768	£1250
2007 Proof	—	£1500
2008 BU	750	£1250
2008 Proof	—	£1500
2009 BU	1,000	£1250
2009 Proof	—	£1500
2010 BU	1,000	£1250
2010 Proof	—	£1250

NOTE: The prices quoted in this guide are set at September 2019 with the price of gold at £1,220 per ounce and silver £14.50 per ounce—market fluctuations will have a marked effect on the values of modern precious metal coins.

Pistrucci's famous rendering of St George and the Dragon which appears on all except special commemorative five pound coins.

The obverse of the 1989 500th Anniversary of the original Sovereign coin portrays HM the Queen enthroned.

DATE	Mintage	UNC
2011 BU	657	£1250
2011 Proof...	—	£1500
2012 Day's St George and Dragon BU	496	£1250
2012 — Proof	—	£1450
2013 BU	262	£1250
2013 Proof...	—	£1500
2014 BU	—	£1250
2014 Proof...	—	£1500
2015 Proof...	—	£1500
2015 New Portrait BU	609	£1650
2015 — Proof	—	£1750
2016 BU	498	£1250
2016 Butler Portrait Proof......................................	—	£1650
2017 200th Anniversary of the Sovereign	—	£1650
2018 BU	10,500	£1500
2019 BU Matt finish...	505	£1,995

2017 200th Anniversary reverse design as the original issue.

FIVE POUNDS (Crown series)

This series commenced in 1990 when the "Crown" was declared legal tender at £5, instead of 25p as all previous issues continued to be. Mintage is in cupro-nickel unless otherwise stated. BU includes those in individual presentation folders, and those in sets sold with stamp covers and/or banknotes.

DATE	Mintage	UNC
1990 Queen Mother's 90th Birthday.	2,761,431	£6
1990 — BU	48,477	£10
1990 — Silver Proof	56,800	£40
1990 — Gold Proof..	2,500	£1500
1993 Coronation 40th Anniversary	1,834,655	£6
1993 — BU...	—	£10
1993 — Proof	—	£15
1993 — Silver Proof	58,877	£45
1993 — Gold Proof..	2,500	£1500
1996 HM the Queen's 70th Birthday	2,396,100	£6
1996 — BU...	—	£10
1996 — Proof	—	£15
1996 — Silver Proof	39,336	£45
1996 — Gold Proof..	2,127	£1500
1997 Royal Golden Wedding	1,733,000	£8
1997 — BU...	—	£10
1997 — — with £5 note...	5,000	£75
1997 — Proof	—	£20
1997 — Silver Proof	33,689	£45
1997 — Gold Proof..	2,750	£1500
1998 Prince of Wales 50th Birthday	1,407,300	£9
1998 — BU...	—	£12
1998 — Proof	—	£20
1998 — Silver Proof	13,379	£50
1998 — Gold Proof..	—	£1500
1999 Princess of Wales Memorial.	1,600,000	£10
1999 — BU...	—	£14
1999 — Proof	—	£20
1999 — Silver Proof	49,545	£60
1999 — Gold Proof..	7,500	£3000
1999 Millennium	3,796,300	£8
1999 — BU...	—	£12
1999 — Proof	—	£20
1999 — Silver Proof	49,057	£45
1999 — Gold Proof..	2,500	£1500
2000	3,147,092*	£12
2000 — BU	—	£20
2000 — — with special Millennium Dome mintmark	—	£30
2000 — Proof	—	£25
2000 — Silver Proof with gold highlight.................	14,255	£50
2000 — Gold Proof..	2,500	£1500

DATE	Mintage	UNC
2000 Queen Mother's 100th Birthday	—	£8
2000 — BU	—	£12
2000 — Silver Proof	31,316	£45
2000 — — Piedfort	14,850	£60
2000 — Gold Proof	3,000	£1500
2001 Victorian Era	851,491	£10
2001 — BU	—	£12
2001 — Proof	—	£20
2001 — Silver Proof	19,216	£50
2001 — — with frosted relief	596	£150
2001 — Gold Proof	3,000	£1500
2001 — — with frosted relief	733	£1750
2002 Golden Jubilee	3,469,243*	£9
2002 — BU	—	£12
2002 — Proof	—	£20
2002 — Silver Proof	54,012	£45
2002 — Gold Proof	5,502	£1500
2002 Queen Mother Memorial	incl. above*	£9
2002 — BU	—	£12
2002 — Silver Proof	16,117	£45
2002 — Gold Proof	3,000	£1500
2003 Coronation Jubilee	1,307,147	£10
2003 — BU	100,481	£13
2003 — Proof	—	£20
2003 — Silver Proof	28,758	£45
2003 — Gold Proof	1,896	£1500
2004 Entente Cordiale Centenary	1,205,594	£10
2004 — Proof Reverse Frosting	6,065	£15
2004 — Silver Proof	11,295	£50
2004 — — Piedfort	2,500	£125
2004 — Gold Proof	926	£1500
2004 — Platinum Proof Piedfort	501	£4000
2005 Trafalgar Bicentenary	1,075 516*	£12
2005 — BU	—	£14
2005 — Proof	—	£25
2005 — Silver Proof	21,448	£50
2005 — — Piedfort	2,818	£75
2005 — Gold Proof	1,805	£1550
2005 Bicentenary of the Death of Nelson	incl. above*	£12
2005 — BU	—	£14
2005 — Proof	—	£25
2005 — Silver Proof	12,852	£50
2005 — — Piedfort	2,818	£75
2005 — Gold Proof	1,760	£1500
2005 — Platinum Proof Piedfort	200	£4000
2006 Queen's 80th Birthday	52,267	£10
2006 — BU	—	£14
2006 — Proof	—	£20
2006 — Silver Proof	20,790	£50
2006 — — — Piedfort, selective gold plating on reverse	5,000	£75
2006 — Gold Proof	2,750	£1500
2006 — Platinum Proof Piedfort	250	£4000
2007 Queen's Diamond Wedding	30,561	£10
2007 — BU	—	£15
2007 — Proof	—	£20
2007 — Silver Proof	15,186	£50
2007 — — Piedfort	2,000	£80
2007 — Gold Proof	2,380	£1500
2007 — Platinum Proof Piedfort	250	£4000
2008 Prince of Wales 60th Birthday	14,088	£12
2008 — BU	54,746	£15
2008 — Proof	—	£20
2008 — Silver Proof	6,264	£55
2008 — — Piedfort	1,088	£90
2008 — Gold Proof	867	£1500
2008 Elizabeth I 450th Anniversary of Accession	20,047	£12
2008 — BU	26,700	£15
2008 — Proof	—	£20
2008 — Silver Proof	9,216	£50

DATE	Mintage	UNC
2008 — — — Piedfort	1,602	£90
2008 — Gold Proof	1,500	£1500
2008 — Platinum Proof Piedfort	125	£4000
2009 500th Anniversary of Henry VIII Accession	30,000	£12
2009 — BU	69,119	£15
2009 — Proof	—	£25
2009 — Silver Proof	10,419	£50
2009 — — — Piedfort	3,580	£90
2009 — Gold Proof	1,130	£1500
2009 — Platinum Proof Piedfort	100	£4250
2009 Olympic Countdown (3 years) BU	184,921	£12
2009 — Silver Proof	26,645	£55
2009 — — — Piedfort	4,874	£90
2009 — Gold Proof	1,860	£1500
2009 Olympic Celebration of Britain "The Mind" series (incl. green logo):		
Stonehenge Silver Proof	—	£60
Palace of Westminster/Big Ben Silver Proof	—	£60
— Cu Ni Proof	—	£20
Angel of the North Silver Proof	—	£60
Flying Scotsman Silver Proof	—	£60
Globe Theatre Silver Proof	—	£60
Sir Isaac Newton Silver Proof	—	£60
2010 350th Anniversary of the Restoration of the Monarchy	15,000	£12
2010 — BU	30,247	£15
2010 — Proof	—	£25
2010 — Silver Proof	6,518	£50
2010 — — — Piedfort	4,435	£100
2010 — Gold Proof	1,182	£1500
2010 — Platinum Proof Piedfort	—	£4000
2010 Olympic Countdown (2 years) BU	153,080	£12
2010 — Silver Proof	20,159	£55
2010 — — — Piedfort	2,197	£150
2010 — Gold Proof	1,562	£1500
2010 Olympic Celebration of Britain, "The Body" series (incl. red logo):		
Coastline of Britain (Rhossili Bay) Silver Proof	—	£65
Giants Causeway Silver Proof	—	£65
River Thames Silver Proof	—	£65
British Fauna (Barn Owl) Silver Proof	—	£65
British Flora (Oak Leaves and Acorn) Silver Proof	—	£65
Weather Vane Silver Proof	—	£65
2010 Olympic Celebration of Britain "The Spirit" series (incl. blue logo):		
Churchill Silver Proof	—	£75
— CuNi Proof	—	£20
Spirit of London (Kind Hearts etc.) Silver Proof	—	£75
— CuNi Proof	—	£20
Humour Silver Proof	—	£75
Unity (Floral emblems of Britain) Silver Proof	—	£75
Music Silver Proof	—	£75
Anti-slavery Silver Proof	—	£75
2011 90th Birthday of the Duke of Edinburgh BU	18,730	£12
2011 — Silver Proof	4,599	£75
2011 — — — Piedfort	2,659	£115
2011 — Gold Proof	636	£1500
2011 — Platinum Proof Piedfort	—	£6000
2011 Royal Wedding of Prince William and Catherine Middleton BU	250,000	£15
2011 — Silver Proof	26,069	£60
2011 — Gold-plated Silver Proof	7,451	£80
2011 — Silver Proof Piedfort	2,991	£95
2011 — Gold Proof	2,066	£1500
2011 — Platinum Proof Piedfort	—	£5500
2011 Olympic Countdown (1 year) BU	163,235	£12
2011 — Silver Proof	25,877	£55
2011 — — — Piedfort	4,000	£100
2011 — Gold Proof	1,300	£1500
2012 Diamond Jubilee BU	484,775	£15
2012 — Proof	16,370	£25

DATE	Mintage	UNC
2012 — Silver Proof	—	£65
2012 — Gold-plated silver proof	12,112	£85
2012 — Silver Piedfort Proof	3,187	£100
2012 — Gold proof	1,025	£1550
2012 — Platinum Piedfort Proof	20	£5500
2012 Olympic Countdown (Games Time) BU	52,261	£13
2012 — Silver Proof	12,670	£65
2012 — Silver Piedfort Proof	2,324	£120
2012 — Gold proof	1,007	£1550
2012 Official Olympic BU	315,983	£15
2012 — Silver Proof	20,810	£70
2012 — Gold Plated Silver Proof	2,180	£90
2012 — Silver Piedfort Proof	5,946	£125
2012 — Gold proof	1,045	£1550
2012 Official Paralympic BU	—	£15
2012 — Silver Proof	—	£70
2012 — Silver Piedfort Proof	—	£125
2012 — Gold proof	—	£1750
2013 60th Anniversary of the Queen's Coronation BU	57,262	£15
2013 — Proof	—	£35
2013 — Silver Proof	4,050	£80
2013 — Silver Piedfort Proof	2,626	£125
2013 — Gold-plated silver proof	2,547	£100
2013 — Gold proof	418	£1750
2013 — Platinum Piedfort Proof	106	£6000
2013 Queen's Portraits, 4 coins each with one of the four portraits, paired with James Butler's Royal Arms. Issued only as sets of 4 in precious metals (see under Proof and Specimen Set section)	—	£300
2013 Royal Birth of Prince George (St George & Dragon), Silver Proof	7,460	£150
2013 Christening of Prince George BU	56,014	£15
2013 — Silver Proof	7,264	£80
2013 — — Piedfort	2,251	£160
2013 — Gold Proof	486	£1750
2013 — Platinum Proof Piedfort	38	£6000
2014 300th Anniversary of the death of Queen Anne BU	12,181	£15
2014 — Proof	—	£35
2014 — Silver Proof	2,212	£80
2014 — — Piedfort	636	£160
2014 — Gold-plated Silver Proof	627	£100
2014 — Gold Proof	253	£1800
2014 First Birthday of Prince George Silver Proof	7,451	£80
2014 100th Anniversary of the First World War Outbreak, issued only as set of 6 coins (see under Proof and Specimen Sets)	—	—
2014 Portrait of Britain, issued only as set of 4 coins, with trichromatic colour-printing (see under Proof and Specimen Sets section)	—	—
2015 50th Anniversary of death of Sir Winston Churchill BU	—	£15
2015 — Silver Proof	4,238	£80
2015 — — Piedfort	1,800	£160
2015 — Gold Proof	325	£1800
2015 — Platinum Proof Piedfort	90	£5000
2015 200th Anniversary of the Battle of Waterloo, BU	24,554	£15
2015 — Silver Proof	2,523	£80
2015 — — Piedfort	896	£160
2015 — Gold Proof	273	£1650
2015 First World War 100th Anniversary, continued, issued only as set of 6 coins	807	—
New Portrait		
2015 2nd Birthday of Prince George, Silver Proof	4,009	£80
2015 Birth of Princess Charlotte, BU	—	£15
2015 — Silver Proof	—	£80
2015 — Gold Proof	500	£1800
2015 Christening of Princess Charlotte, Silver Proof	4,842	£1800
2015 — Gold Proof	350	£80
2015 The Longest Reign, BU	48,848	£15
2015 — Silver Proof	10,249	£80
2015 — — Piedfort	3,171	£160

DATE	Mintage	UNC
2015 — Gold Proof..	899	£1650
2015 — Platinum Proof Piedfort............................	88	£5000
2016 Queen's 90th Birthday, BU..............................	74,195	£15
2016 — Proof	—	£25
2016 — Silver Proof	8,947	£80
2016 — — Piedfort..	3,099	£160
2016 — Gold Proof..	906	£1800
2016 — Platinum Proof Piedfort............................	81	£4500
2016 Portraits of Britain, issued only as set of 4 coins, with trichromatic colour-printing (see under Proof and Specimen Sets section)	1,098	£350
2016 First World War Centenary, continued, issued only as a set of 6 Silver Proof coins.....................................	1,916	£450
2016 Battle of the Somme, Silver Proof	3,678	£85
2017 Portraits of Britain, issued only as set of 4 coins, with trichromatic colour-printing (see under Proof and Specimen Sets section)	1,500	£350
2017 1000th Anniversary of the Coronation of King Canute, BU	—	£15
2017 — Proof	—	£30
2017 — Silver Proof	3,000	£85
2017 — — Piedfort..	1,500	£175
2017 — Gold Proof..	150	£2000
2017 Prince Philip, Celebrating a Life of Service, BU	—	£15
2017 — Proof	—	£30
2017 — Silver Proof	3,000	£85
2017 — — Piedfort..	1,250	£155
2017 — Gold Proof..	300	£2000
2017 Remembrance Day Poppy	—	£15
2017 — Silver Proof	5,000	£100
2017 — — Piedfort..	1,500	£200
2017 First World War Centenary, continued, issued only as set of 6 Silver Proof coins.....................................	1,917	£500
2017 House of Windsor Centenary, BU..................	—	£15
2017 —— in pack for Engagement of Prince Harry..................	5,000	£20
2017 — Proof	—	£30
2017 — Silver Proof	13,000	£85
2017 — Piedfort..	5,500	£175
2017 — Gold Proof..	884	£2000
2017 Her Majesty's Sapphire Jubilee, BU..............	—	£15
2017 — Proof	—	£30
2017 — Silver Proof	8,600	£85
2017 — — Piedfort..	3,000	£155
2017 — Gold Proof..	650	£2000
2018 Prince George's 5th Birthday	—	£12
2018 — Proof	—	£18
2018 — Silver Proof	—	£85
2018 — — Piedfort..	—	£165
2018 — Gold Proof..	650	£2000
2018 Four generations of the Royal Family.............	—	£15
2018 — Proof	—	£20
2018 — Silver Proof	5,000	£100
2018 — — Piedfort..	2,000	£175
2018 — Gold Proof..	500	£2000
2018 250 years of the Royal Academy	—	£15
2018 — Proof	—	£20
2018 — Silver Proof	2,750	£100
2018 — — Piedfort..	—	£175
2018 — Gold Proof..	500	£2000
2018 Royal Wedding of Prince Harry	12,000	£20
2018 — Proof	—	£25
2018 — Silver Proof	15,000	£100
2018 — — Piedfort..	2,220	£175
2018 — Gold Proof..	500	£2000
2018 Portraits of Britain, issued only as set of 4 coins, with trichromatic colour-printing (see under Proof and Specimen Sets section)	2,016	£350

2017 Portrait of Britain, issued only as set of 4 coins, with trichromatic colour-printing.

2018 Britannia by David Lawrence
	Mintage	
2018 Stories of War Proof set of six coins. Silver Proof	1,918	£465
— — Gold Proof	25	£11,000
2019 The Ceremony of the Keys BU	—	£13
2019 — Silver Proof	4,000	£82.50
2019 — — Piedfort	1,160	£155
2019 — Gold	385	£1,995
2019 The Tower of London Four Coin set BU	—	£57
2019 — Silver Proof	4,000	£330
2019 — — Piedfort	1,160	£620
2019 — Gold	385	£7,980
2019 200th Anniversary of the Birth of Queen Victoria BU	unlimited	£13
2019 —Silver Proof	7,500	£82.50
2019 — — Piedfort	2,750	£155
2019 — Gold Proof	725	£1,995
2019 Pride of England BU	—	£13

DOUBLE SOVEREIGN

As with the Sovereign series Five Pound coins, those listed under this heading bear the Pistrucci St George and Dragon reverse, except where otherwise stated, and are minted in gold. They are, and always have been, legal tender at £2, and have a diameter indentical to that of the base metal Two Pound coins listed further below under a different heading. The denomination does not appear on Double Sovereigns. Most were originally issued as part of Royal Mint sets.

DATE	Mintage	UNC
1980 Proof	10,000	£600
1982 Proof	2,500	£600
1983 Proof	12,500	£600
1985 New Portrait Proof	5,849	£600
1987 Proof	14,301	£600
1988 Proof	12,743	£600
1989 500th Anniversary of the Sovereign. Enthroned portrayal obverse and Crowned shield reverse Proof	2,000	£900
1990 Proof	4,374	£600
1991 Proof	3,108	£600
1992 Proof	2,608	£600
1993 Proof	2,155	£600
1996 Proof	3,167	£600
1998 New Portrait Proof	4,500	£600
2000 Proof	2,250	£600
2002 Shield reverse Proof	8,000	£600
2003 Proof	2,250	£600
2004 Proof	2,500	£600
2005 Noad's heraldic St George and Dragon reverse Proof	—	£700
2006 Proof	—	£600
2007 Proof	—	£600
2008 Proof	—	£600
2009 Proof	—	£600
2010 Proof	2,750	£600
2011 Proof	2,950	£600
2012 Day's stylised St George and Dragon reverse, BU	60	£650
2012 — Proof	1,945	£800
2013 BU	—	£700
2013 Proof	1,895	£700
2014 BU	—	£600
2014 Proof	—	£700
2015 Proof	1,100	£700
2015 New Portrait by Jody Clark Proof	1,100	£800
2016 Butler Portrait Proof	925	£800
2017 200th Anniv. of the Sovereign design as 1817 issue	1,200	£900

Standard reverse

Reverse by Timothy Noad

Reverse by Paul Day

TWO POUNDS

This series commenced in 1986 with nickel-brass commemorative coins, with their associated base metal and precious metal BU and proof coins. From 1997 (actually issued in 1998) a thinner bi-metal version commenced with a reverse theme of the advance of technology, and from this date the coin was specifically intended to circulate. This is true also for the parallel issues of anniversary and commemorative Two Pound issues in 1999 and onwards. All have their BU and proof versions, as listed below.

In the case of Gold Proofs, a few have Certificates of Authenticity and/or green boxes of issue describing the coin as a Double Sovereign. All Gold Proofs since 1997 are of bi-metallic gold except for 2001 (red gold with the inner circle coated in yellow gold) and 2002 (Technology issue, uncoated red gold). After 2008 all RM boxes were black for all denominations.

A new definitive design was introduced during 2015 incorporating the Jody Clark portrait and Britannia by Antony Dufort but to date the mintage each year has been relatively low.

NOTE: The counterfeiting of circulation £2 coins has been around for several years but 2015 saw several proof-like base metal designs. Five types are known at present: 2011 (Mary Rose) and 2015 (all four designs).

First bi-metal standard reverse

DATE	Mintage	UNC
1986 Commonwealth Games	8,212,184	£5
1986 — BU	—	£8
1986 — Proof	59,779	£15
1986 — Silver BU	—	£25
1986 — — Proof	—	£35
1986 — Gold Proof	—	£525
1989 Tercentenary of Bill of Rights.	4,392,825	£10
1989 — BU (issued in folder with Claim of Right)	—	£25
1989 — BU folder	—	£8
1989 — Proof	—	£15
1989 — Silver Proof	—	£35
1989 — — Piedfort	—	£50
1989 Tercentenary of Claim of Right (issued in Scotland)	381,400	£25
1989 — BU (see above)	—	£30
1989 — Proof	—	£35
1989 — Silver Proof	—	£45
1989 — — Piedfort	—	£55
1994 Tercentenary of the Bank of England	1,443,116	£10
1994 — BU	—	£25
1994 — Proof	—	£30
1994 — Silver Proof	27,957	£35
1994 — — Piedfort	9,569	£60
1994 — Gold Proof	—	£550
1994 — — — with Double Sovereign obverse (no denomination)	—	£900
1995 50th Anniversary of End of WWII.	4,394,566	£8
1995 — BU	—	£10
1995 — Proof	—	£12
1995 — Silver Proof	35,751	£35
1995 — — Piedfort	—	£60
1995 — Gold Proof	—	£525
1995 50th Anniversary of The United Nations	1,668,575	£8
1995 — BU	—	£10
1995 — Proof	—	£12
1995 — Silver Proof	—	£40
1995 — — Piedfort	—	£60
1995 — Gold Proof	—	£525
1996 European Football Championships.	5,195,350	£8
1996 — BU	—	£10
1996 — Proof	—	£12
1996 — Silver Proof	25,163	£40
1996 — — Piedfort	7,634	£60
1996 — Gold Proof	—	£525
1997 Technology Standard rev. First Bi-metallic issue	13,734,625	£5
1997 — BU	—	£8
1997 — Proof	—	£12
1997 — Silver Proof	29,910	£35
1997 — — Piedfort	16,000	£60
1997 — Gold Proof (red (outer) and yellow (inner) 22ct)	—	£525

DATE	Mintage	UNC
1998 **New Portrait by Ian Rank-Broadley**	—	£4
1998 BU	91,110,375	£8
1998 Proof	—	£12
1998 Silver Proof	19,978	£35
1998 — — Piedfort...	7,646	£60
1999 Technology Standard rev....................................	33,719,000	£4
1999 Rugby World Cup	4,933,000	£6
1999 — BU	—	£10
1999 — Silver Proof (gold plated ring)	9,665	£45
1999 — — — Piedfort (Hologram)	10,000	£85
1999 — Gold Proof...	—	£525
2000 Technology Standard rev....................................	25,770,000	£4
2000 — BU	—	£6
2000 — Proof	—	£10
2000 — Silver Proof	—	£40
2001 Technology Standard rev....................................	34,984,750	£4
2001 — BU...	—	£5
2001 — Proof	—	£10
2001 Marconi...	4,558,000	£5
2001 — BU...	—	£8
2001 — Proof	—	£10
2001 — Silver Proof (gold plated ring)	11,488	£40
2001 — — — Reverse Frosting (issued in set with Canada $5)...........................	—	£65
2001 — — — Piedfort..	6,759	£60
2001 — Gold Proof...	—	£525
2002 Technology Standard rev....................................	13,024,750	£4
2002 — BU...	—	£6
2002 — Proof	—	£10
2002 — Gold Proof (red 22ct)	—	£525
2002 Commonwealth Games, Scotland	771,750	£15
2002 — Wales	558,500	£15
2002 — Northern Ireland..	485,500	£30
2002 — England...	650,500	£15
2002 — BU (issued in set of 4)...................................	—	£60
2002 — Proof (issued in set of 4)	—	£75
2002 — Silver Proof (issued in set of 4)	—	£200
2002 — — — Piedfort (painted) (issued in set of 4)....	—	£275
2002 — Gold Proof (issued in set of 4)	—	£2300
2003 Technology Standard rev....................................	17,531,250	£4
2003 — BU...	—	£8
2003 — Proof	—	£12
2003 DNA Double Helix..	4,299,000	£5
2003 — BU...	41,568	£8
2003 — Proof	—	£10
2003 — Silver Proof (Gold-plated ring)	11,204	£40
2003 — — — Piedfort..	8,728	£60
2003 — Gold Proof...	3,237	£525
2004 Technology Standard rev....................................	11,981,500	£4
2004 — BU...	—	£6
2004 — Proof	—	£12
2004 Trevithick Steam Locomotive	5,004,500	£5
2004 — BU...	56,871	£8
2004 — Proof	—	£10
2004 — Silver BU	1,923	£25
2004 — — Proof (Gold-plated ring)............................	10,233	£45
2004 — — — Piedfort..	5,303	£60
2004 — Gold Proof...	1,500	£525
2005 Technology Standard rev....................................	3,837,250	£4
2005 — BU...	—	£6
2005 — Proof	—	£8
2005 Gunpowder Plot	5,140,500	£5
2005 — BU...	—	£8
2005 — Proof	—	£10
2005 — Silver Proof	4,394	£40
2005 — — — Piedfort..	4,585	£65
2005 — Gold Proof...	914	£525

DATE	Mintage	UNC
2005 End of World War II..	10,191,000	£5
2005 — BU...	—	£8
2005 — Silver Proof	21,734	£40
2005 — — — Piedfort...	4,798	£65
2005 — Gold Proof..	2,924	£525
2006 Technology Standard rev.	16,715,000	£4
2006 — Proof	—	£6
2006 Brunel, The Man (Portrait)	7,928,250	£5
2006 — BU...	—	£6
2006 — Proof	—	£10
2006 — Silver Proof	7,251	£40
2006 — — — Piedfort...	3,199	£65
2006 —Gold Proof...	1,071	£525
2006 Brunel, His Achievements (Paddington Station)	7,452,250	£5
2006 — BU...	—	£6
2006 — Proof	—	£10
2006 — Silver Proof	5,375	£40
2006 — — — Piedfort...	3,018	£65
2006 —Gold Proof..	746	£525
2007 Technology Standard rev.	10,270,000	£4
2007 — Proof	—	£8
2007 Tercentenary of the Act of Union.......................	7,545,000	£5
2007 BU	—	£6
2007 — Proof	—	£8
2007 — Silver Proof	8,310	£45
2007 — — — Piedfort...	4,000	£65
2007 — Gold Proof..	750	£525
2007 Bicentenary of the Abolition of the Slave Trade .	8,445,000	£6
2007 — BU...	—	£8
2007 — Proof	—	£10
2007 — Silver Proof	7,095	£45
2007 — — — Piedfort...	3,990	£65
2007 — Gold Proof..	1,000	£500
2008 Technology Standard rev.	15,346,000	£4
2008 — BU...	—	£6
2008 — Proof	—	£12
2008 Centenary of 4th Olympiad, London	910,000	£6
2008 — BU...	—	£8
2008 — Proof	—	£12
2008 — Silver Proof	6,841	£45
2008 — — — Piedfort...	1,619	£70
2008 — Gold Proof..	1,908	£500
2008 Olympic Games Handover Ceremony.................	853,000	£6
2008 — BU...	47,765	£8
2008 — Silver Proof	30,000	£45
2008 — — — Piedfort...	3,000	£75
2008 — Gold Proof..	3,250	£500
2009 Technology Standard rev.	8,775,000	£4
2009 — BU...	—	£5
2009 — Proof	—	£10
2009 — Silver Proof	—	£45
2009 250th Anniversary of birth of Robert Burns........	3,253,000	£5
2009 — BU...	120,223	£8
2009 — Proof	—	£12
2009 — Silver Proof	9,188	£45
2009 — — — Piedfort...	3,500	£70
2009 — Gold Proof..	1,000	£500
2009 200th Anniversary of birth of Charles Darwin.....	3,903,000	£5
2009 — BU...	119,713	£8
2009 — Proof	—	£12
2009 — Silver Proof	9,357	£45
2009 — — — Piedfort...	3,282	£70
2009 — Gold Proof..	1,000	£500
2010 Technology Standard rev.	6,890,000	£4
2010 — BU...	—	£8
2010 — Proof	—	£12

DATE	Mintage	UNC
2010 — Silver Proof	—	£40
2010 Florence Nightingale 150 Years of Nursing	6,175,000	£4
2010 — BU	73,160	£10
2010 — Proof	—	£12
2010 — Silver Proof	5,117	£45
2010 — — Piedfort	2,770	£70
2010 — Gold Proof	472	£500
2011 Technology Standard rev.	24,375,000	£4
2011 — BU	—	£5
2011 — Proof	—	£12
2011 — Silver Proof	—	£35
2011 500th Anniversary of the Mary Rose	1,040,000	£9
2011 — BU	53,013	£10
2011 — Proof	—	£12
2011 — Silver Proof	6,618	£45
2011 — — — Piedfort	2,680	£75
2011 — Gold Proof	692	£500
2011 400th Anniversary of the King James Bible	975,000	£9
2011 — BU	56,268	£10
2011 — Proof	—	£15
2011 — Silver Proof	4,494	£45
2011 — — — Piedfort	2,394	£75
2011 — Gold Proof	355	£500
2012 Technology Standard rev.	3,900,000	£4
2012 — BU	—	£6
2012 — Proof	—	£12
2012 — Silver Proof	—	£30
2012 — Gold Proof	—	£550
2012 200th Anniversary of birth of Charles Dickens	8,190,000	£4
2012 — BU	15,035	£9
2012 — Proof	—	£12
2012 — Silver Proof	2,631	£45
2012 — — — Piedfort	1,279	£75
2012 — Gold Proof	202	£500
2012 Olympic Handover to Rio	845,000	£8
2012 — BU	28,356	£20
2012 Proof	—	£25
2012 — Silver Proof	3,781	£85
2012 — — — Piedfort	2,000	£120
2012 — Gold Proof	771	£550
2013 Technology Standard rev.	15,860,250	£4
2013 — BU	—	£6
2013 — Proof	—	£12
2013 — Silver Proof	—	£65
2013 — Gold Proof	—	£550
2013 150th Anniversary of the London Underground, Roundel design	1,560,000	£6
2013 — BU	11,647	£12
2013 — Proof	—	£18
2013 — Silver Proof	3,389	£50
2013 — — — Piedfort	162	£100
2013 — Gold Proof	132	£550
2013 150th Anniversary of the London Underground, Train design	1,690,000	£6
2013 — BU	11,647	£12
2013 — Proof	—	£18
2013 — Silver Proof	4,246	£50
2013 — — — Piedfort	186	£100
2013 — Gold Proof	140	£550
2013 350th Anniversary of the Guinea	2,990,000	£5
2013 — BU	10,340	£12
2013 — Proof	—	£18
2013 — Silver Proof	1,640	£50
2013 — — — Piedfort	969	£100
2013 — Gold Proof	284	£600
2014 Technology Standard rev.	18,200,000	£4

DATE	Mintage	UNC
2014 — BU..	—	£10
2014 — Proof	—	£25
2014 — Silver Proof	—	£55
2014 100th Anniversary of First World War Outbreak.	5,720,000	£4
2014 — BU..	—	£10
2014 — Proof	—	£20
2014 — Silver Proof	4,983	£50
2014 — — — Piedfort..	2,496	£100
2014 — Gold Proof..	—	£750
2014 500th Anniversary of Trinity House....................	3,705,000	£4
2014 — BU..	10,521	£10
2014 — Proof	—	£20
2014 — Silver Proof	1,285	£50
2014 — — — Piedfort..	652	£100
2014 — Gold Proof..	204	£750
2015 Technology Standard rev.	35,360,058	£3
2015 — BU..	39,009	£10
2015 — Proof	3,930	£20
2015 — Silver Proof	1,512	£50
2015 — Gold Proof..	406	£750
2015 Anniversary of First World War—Royal Navy	650,000	£9
2015 — BU..	39,009	£10
2015 — Proof	—	£20
2015 — Silver Proof	3,030	£50
2015 — — Piedfort..	1,512	£100
2015 — Gold Proof..	406	£750
2015 800th Anniversary of Magna Carta....................	1,495,000	£10
2015 — BU..	32,818	£15
2015 — Proof	—	£20
2015 — Silver Proof	2,995	£50
2015 — — Piedfort..	1,988	£100
2015 — Gold Proof..	399	£695

New Portrait by Jody Clark

2015 — Silver Proof	—	£50
2015 — — — Piedfort..	—	£100
2015 — Gold Proof..	—	£695
2015 Britannia—the new standard reverse design	650,000	£6
2015 — BU..	—	£10
2015 — Proof	—	£20
2015 — Silver Proof	—	£50
2015 — Gold Proof..	—	£750
2015 — Platinum Proof	—	£900
2016 Britannia Standard rev.	2,925,000	£5
2016 — BU..	—	£10
2016 — Proof	—	£20
2016 — Silver Proof	—	£50
2016 400th Anniversary, Shakespeare's death, Comedies	4,355,000	£4
2016 — — BU...	—	£10
2016 — — Proof...	—	£20
2016 — — Silver Proof..	951	£50
2016 — — — Piedfort..	533	£125
2016 — — Gold Proof..	152	£750
2016 — Tragedies	5,695,000	£4
2016 — — BU...	—	£10
2016 — — Proof...	—	£20
2016 — — Silver Proof..	1,004	£50
2016 — — — — Piedfort..	679	£125
2016 — — Gold Proof..	209	£750
2016 — Histories..	4,615,000	£4
2016 — — BU...	—	£10
2016 — — Proof...	—	£20
2016 — — Silver Proof..	965	£50
2016 — — — Piedfort..	624	£125

Britanni standar reverse

DATE	Mintage	UNC
2016 — — Gold Proof	156	£750
2016 350th Anniversary of Great Fire of London	5,135,000	£4
2016 — BU	23,215	£10
2016 — Proof	—	£20
2016 — Silver Proof	1,649	£50
2016 — — Piedfort	1,356	£125
2016 — Gold Proof...	259	£750
2016 Anniversary of First World War—Army	9,550,000	£4
2016 — BU	19,066	£10
2016 — Proof	—	£20
2016 — Silver Proof	1,703	£50
2016 — — Piedfort	931	£125
2016 — Gold Proof...	279	£750
2017 Britannia Standard rev.	—	£5
2017 — BU	—	£10
2017 — Proof	—	£20
2017 — Silver Proof	—	£50
2017 — Gold Proof...	—	£750
2017 Anniversary of First World War—Aviation...........	—	£10
2017 — BU	—	£12
2017 — Proof	—	£20
2017 — Silver Proof	7,000	£75
2017 — — Piedfort	3,500	£125
2017 — Gold Proof...	634	£750
2017 Jane Austen	—	£10
2017 — BU	—	£12
2017 — Proof	—	£20
2017 — Silver Proof	8,000	£75
2017 — — Piedfort	4,000	£125
2017 — Gold Proof...	884	£850
2018 Britannia Standard rev.	—	£3
2018 — BU	—	£10
2018 — Proof	—	£20
2018 — Silver Proof	—	£50
2018 — Gold Proof...	—	£750
2018 Bicentenary of Mary Shelley's "Frankenstein" ..	—	£12
2018 — BU	—	£15
2018 — Proof	—	£25
2018 — Silver Proof	—	£50
2018 — Gold Proof...	—	£750
2018 Journey to Armistice	—	—
2018 — BU	—	£12
2018 — Proof	—	£20
2018 — Silver Proof	5,000	£50
2017 — — Piedfort	2,500	£125
2018 — Gold Proof...	750	£750
2018 Centenary of the RAF	—	£10
2018 — BU	—	£15
2018 — Proof	—	£25
2018 — Silver Proof	7,500	£50
2017 — — Piedfort	3,000	£125
2018 — Gold Proof...	1,000	£750
2018 250th Anniversary of Captain Cook's "Voyage of Discovery"	—	£10
2018 — BU	—	£15
2018 — Proof	—	£25
2018 — Silver Proof	4,795	£50
2017 — — Piedfort	4,000	£125
2018 —Gold Proof..	340	£750

Note: The silver editions are silver centres with silver outers plated with gold.
The gold issues are 22ct yellow gold centres with 22ct red gold outers.

DATE	Mintage	UNC
2019 D-Day: 75th Anniversary BU	unlimited	£10
2019 — Silver Proof	8,750	£67.50
2019 — — Piedfort	3,010	£110
2019 — Gold	750	£845
2019 Captain Cook BU	unlimited	£10
2019 — Silver Proof	5,000	£67.50
2019 — Gold	350	£845
2019 Samuel Pepys BU	unlimited	£10
2019 — Silver Proof	3,500	£67.50
2019 — — Piedfort	2,019	£110
2019 — Gold	350	£845
2019 Wedgwood BU	—	£10
2019 — Silver Proof	4,500	£67.50
2019 — — Piedfort	2,250	£110
2019 — Gold	350	£845

2019 75th Anniversary of
D-Day

2019 250th Anniversary of
Samuel Pepys' Last Diary
entry

2019
260th Anniversary of
Wedgwood

2019 250th Anniversary of
Captain Cook's "Voyage of
Discovery"—II

SOVEREIGN

All are minted in gold, bear the Pistrucci St George and Dragon reverse except where stated, and are legal tender at one pound. From 2009 there is no streamer behind St George's Helmet in the Pistrucci design.

DATE	Mintage	UNC
1974	5,002,566	£300
1976	4,150,000	£300
1976 Brilliant Proof	—	£10,000
1978	6,550,000	£300
1979	9,100,000	£300
1979 Proof	50,000	£300
1980	5,100,000	£300
1980 Proof	91,200	£350
1981	5,000,000	£300
1981 Proof	32,960	£350
1982	2,950,000	£300
1982 Proof	22,500	£350
1983 Proof	21,250	£350
1984 Proof	19,975	£350
1985 **New portrait** Proof	17,242	£400
1986 Proof	17,579	£350
1987 Proof	22,479	£350
1988 Proof	18,862	£350
1989 500th Anniversary of the Sovereign—details as Five Pounds (Sov. Series). Proof	23,471	£1000
1990 Proof	8,425	£400
1991 Proof	7,201	£400
1992 Proof	6,854	£400
1993 Proof	6,090	£400
1994 Proof	7,165	£400
1995 Proof	9,500	£400
1996 Proof	9,110	£400
1997 Proof	9,177	£400
1998 **New Portrait** Proof	11,349	£450
1999 Proof	11,903	£400
2000 (first Unc issue since 1982)	129,069	£350
2000 Proof	12,159	£475
2001	49,462	£300
2001 Proof	10,000	£450
2002 Golden Jubilee Shield Rev. ("bullion")	74,263	£375
2002 Proof	20,500	£600
2003 ("bullion")	43,208	£325
2003 Proof	12,433	£450
2004 ("bullion")	30,688	£300
2004 Proof	10,175	£400
2005 Noad heraldic St George and Dragon	75,542	£475
2005 — Proof	12,500	£600
2006 ("bullion")	—	£375
2006 Proof	9,195	£475

Standard reverse

500th Anniversary reverse

Golden Jubilee Shield reverse

Noad modern reverse

IMPORTANT NOTE:
The prices quoted in this guide are set at September 2019 with the price of gold at £1,220 per ounce and silver £14.50 per ounce—market fluctuations can have a marked effect on the values of modern precious metal coins.

DATE	Mintage	UNC
2007 ("bullion")	75,000	£300
2007 Proof	8,199	£450
2008 ("bullion")	35,000	£325
2008 Proof	12,500	£425
2009 ("bullion")	75,000	£325
2009 Proof	9,770	£425
2010 ("bullion")	243,986	£300
2010 Proof	8,828	£475
2011 ("bullion")	250,000	£300
2011 Proof	15,000	£375
2012 Day's St George and Dragon BU "bullion"	250,000	£400
2012 — Proof	5,501	£750
2013 BU ("bullion"	2,695	£300
2013 Proof)	8,243	£425
2013 With "I" mintmark, minted by MMTC-PAMP, Haryana, India, under Licence from, and the supervision of, the Royal Mint	—	£400
2014 BU ("bullion"	15,000	£325
2014 Proof)	9,725	£475
2014 BU ("bullion") with "I" mintmark	—	£400
2015 BU ("bullion")	10,000	£375
2015 Proof	9,800	£475
2015 **New Portrait** by Jody Clark BU	10,000	£350
2015— Proof	8,800	£475
2016 BU ("bullion")	1,500	£325
2016 90th Birthday, Butler portrait Proof	9,675	£525
2017 200th Anniversary of the Sovereign. Original 1817 "garter" design. Proof-like	1,817	£525
2017 — Piedfort	3,750	£1000
2017 BU with 200 Privy mark	—	£700
2018 BU ("bullion")	—	£325
2018 Proof	10,500	£475
2018 — Piedfort	2,675	£1000
2019 BU Matt finish	25,000	£365

Day's stylised reverse

200th Anniversary reverse

HALF SOVEREIGN

Legal Tender at 50 pence, otherwise the notes for the Sovereign apply. From 2009 the exergue in the Pistrucci design is larger in area, and the initials B.P. are absent. From 2011, however, the initials were restored.

DATE	Mintage	UNC
1980 Proof only	86,700	£200
1982	2,500,000	£175
1982 Proof	21,590	£200
1983 Proof	19,710	£200
1984 Proof	19,505	£200
1985 New portrait Proof	15,800	£200
1986 Proof	17,075	£200
1987 Proof	20,687	£200
1988 Proof	18,266	£200
1989 500th Anniversary of the Sovereign—details as Five Pounds (Sov. Series) Proof	21,824	£550
1990 Proof	7,889	£250
1991 Proof	6,076	£250
1992 Proof	5,915	£250
1993 Proof	4,651	£250
1994 Proof	7,167	£250
1995 Proof	7,500	£250
1996 New Portrait Proof	7,340	£250
1997 Proof	9,177	£250
1998 Proof	7,496	£250
1999 Proof	9,403	£250
2000	146,822	£175
2000 Proof	9,708	£200

Standard reverse

500th Anniversary reverse

Noad Heraldic reverse

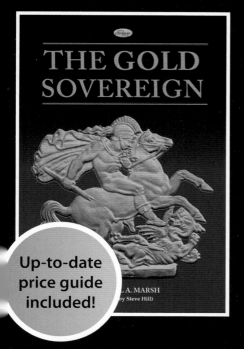

DATE	Mintage	UNC
2001	98,763	£175
2001 Proof	7,500	£200
2002 Golden Jubilee Shield reverse ("bullion")	61,347	£200
2002 Proof	—	£225
2003 ("bullion")	47,805	£175
2003 Proof	—	£200
2004 ("bullion")	32,479	£175
2004 Proof	—	£225
2005 Noad heraldic St George and Dragon	—	£275
2005 — Proof	—	£300
2006 ("bullion")	—	£175
2006 Proof	—	£225
2006 ("bullion")	—	£175
2007 Proof	—	£200
2008 ("bullion")	—	£175
2008 Proof	—	£200
2009 ("bullion")	—	£175
2009 Proof	—	£200
2010 ("bullion")	16,485	£175
2010 Proof	—	£200
2011 ("bullion")	—	£175
2011 Proof	—	£200
2012 Diamond Jubilee "bullion" or BU	—	£200
2012 — Proof	—	£250
2013 BU "bullion"	—	£175
2013 Proof	—	£200
2014 BU "bullion"	—	£175
2014 Proof	—	£250
2014 BU "bullion" with "I" mintmark	—	£200
2015 BU "bullion"	500	£175
2015 Proof	1,704	£275
2015 New Jody Clark portrait Proof	—	£275
2016 BU "bullion"	472	£175
2016 90th Birthday, Butler portrait Proof	1,995	£275
2017 200th Anniversary of the Sovereign. Original 1817 "garter" design. Proof-like	1,817	£325
2017 With 200 Privy mark	—	£475
2018 BU "bullion"	—	£175
2018 Proof	2,500	£225
2019 BU Matt finish	4,620	£240

Golden Jubilee Shield reverse

Diamond Jubilee reverse

200th Anniversary reverse

QUARTER SOVEREIGN

Minted in 22ct gold, this denomination was introduced in 2009 in the same style as the rest of the sovereign series.

DATE	Mintage	UNC
2009 ("bullion")	50,000	£115
2009 Proof	13,495	£135
2010 ("bullion")	250,000	£115
2010 Proof	6,007	£140
2011 ("bullion")	50,000	£115
2011 Proof	7,764	£140
2012 Diamond Jubilee "bullion"	250,000	£165
2012 — Proof	7,579	£225
2013 ("bullion")	—	£115
2013 Proof	1,729	£115
2014 ("bullion")	—	£115
2014 Proof	1,696	£140
2015 ("bullion")	4,600	£115
2015 Proof	1,808	£100
2015 Jody Clark portrait Proof	550	£140
2016 Butler portrait Proof	1,727	£195
2017 200th Anniversary Proof	5,100	£195
2018 ("bullion")	—	£115
2018 Proof	—	£175
2019 BU Matt finish	1,750	£150

ONE POUND

Introduced into circulation in 1983 to replace the £1 note, the original, £1 coins are minted in nickel-brass unless otherwise stated. The reverse changed yearly until 2008, and until 2008 the Royal Arms was the "definitive" version. 2008 also saw the introduction of the Matthew Dent Uncrowned Shield of the Royal Arms, a new "definitive", and this reverse appeared in 2008 and every year until 2017. A Capital Cities Series of two coins each year for two years commenced in 2010. From 2013 a further 4-coin series over two years was issued, portraying two floral emblems associated with each of the four countries making up the United Kingdom. Collectors and others should be aware of the many different counterfeit £1 coin versions that circulated up until 2017, a high proportion of which do not have matching obverses and reverses although many do. These original £1 coins have now been withdrawn from circulation. A 12-sided bi-metallic coin replaced the round £1 coin in 2017 which incorporates several security features to help defeat the counterfeiters.

DATE	Mintage	UNC

1983, 1993, 1998, 2003
*EDGE: **DECUS ET TUTAMEN***

DATE	Mintage	UNC
1983 Royal Arms	443,053,510	£3
1983 — BU	1,134,000	£5
1983 — Proof	107,800	£8
1983 — Silver Proof	50,000	£32
1983 — — — Piedfort	10,000	£85
1984 Scottish Thistle	146,256,501	£3
1984 — BU	199,430	£6
1984 — Proof	106,520	£8
1984 — Silver Proof	44,855	£35
1984 — — Piedfort	15,000	£50
1985 **New portrait.** Welsh Leek	228,430,749	£3
1985 — BU	213,679	£5
1985 — Proof	102,015	£6
1985 — Silver Proof	50,000	£35
1985 — — Piedfort	15,000	£50
1986 Northern Ireland Flax	10,409,501	£3
1986 — BU	—	£6
1986 — Proof	—	£7
1986 — Silver Proof	37,958	£35
1986 — — Piedfort	15,000	£50
1987 English Oak	39,298,502	£3
1987 — BU	—	£5
1987 — Proof	—	£8
1987 — Silver Proof	50,000	£35
1987 — — Piedfort	15,000	£50
1988 Crowned Shield Of The Royal Arms	7,118,825	£4
1988 — BU	—	£7
1988 — Proof	—	£8
1988 — Silver Proof	50,000	£35
1988 — — Piedfort	10,000	£60
1989 Scottish Thistle	70,580,501	£4
1989 — BU	—	£6
1989 — Proof	—	£9
1989 — Silver Proof	22,275	£35
1989 — — Piedfort	10,000	£50
1990 Welsh Leek	—	£4
1990 — BU	97,269,302	£6
1990 — Proof	—	£7
1990 — Silver Proof	23,277	£35
1991 Northern Ireland Flax	38,443,575	£3
1991 — BU	—	£6
1991 — Proof	—	£9
1991 — Silver Proof	22,922	£35
1992 English Oak	36,320,487	£2
1992 — BU	—	£6
1992 — Proof	—	£7
1992 — Silver Proof	13,065	£35
1993 Royal Arms	114,744,500	£3
1993 — BU	—	£6

1984, 1989
NEMO ME IMPUNE LACESSIT

1985, 1990
PLEIDIOL WYF I'M GWLAD

1986, 1991
DECUS ET TUTAMEN

1987, 1992
DECUS ET TUTAMEN

DATE	Mintage	UNC
1993 — Proof	—	£7
1993 — Silver Proof	16,526	£35
1993 — — — Piedfort	12,500	£55
1994 Scottish Lion	29,752,525	£4
1994 — BU..	—	£6
1994 — Proof	—	£8
1994 — Silver Proof	25,000	£35
1994 — — — Piedfort	11,722	£55
1995 Welsh Dragon	34,503,501	£3
1995 — BU..	—	£6
1995 — — (Welsh)	—	£7
1995 — Proof	—	£10
1995 — Silver Proof	27,445	£35
1995 — — — Piedfort	8,458	£65
1996 Northern Ireland Celtic Cross	89,886,000	£4
1996 — BU..	—	£6
1996 — Proof	—	£7
1996 — Silver Proof	25,000	£35
1996 — — Piedfort	10,000	£55
1997 English Lions	57,117,450	£4
1997 — BU..	—	£6
1997 — Proof	—	£7
1997 — Silver Proof	20,137	£35
1997 — — — Piedfort	10,000	£55
1998 *New portrait.* Royal Arms. BU.......	—	£15
1998 — Proof	—	£20
1998 — Silver Proof	13,863	£35
1998 — — — Piedfort	7,894	£50
1999 Scottish Lion. BU	—	£15
1999 — Proof	—	£20
1999 — Silver Proof	16,328	£35
1999 — — — Reverse Frosting..................	—	£45
1999 — — — Piedfort	9,975	£60
2000 Welsh Dragon	109,496,500	£3
2000 — BU..	—	£6
2000 — Proof	—	£8
2000 — Silver Proof	15,913	£35
2000 — — — Reverse Frosting..................	—	£45
2000 — — — Piedfort	9,994	£55
2001 Northern Ireland Celtic Cross.	63,968,065	£3
2001 — BU..	58,093,731	£6
2001 — Proof	—	£8
2001 — Silver Proof	11,697	£35
2001 — — — Reverse Frosting..................	—	£45
2001 — — — Piedfort	8,464	£50
2002 English Lions	77,818,000	£3
2002 — BU..	—	£5
2002 — Proof	—	£8
2002 — Silver Proof	17,693	£35
2002 — — — Reverse Frosting..................	—	£45
2002 — — — Piedfort	6,599	£50
2002 — Gold Proof....................................	—	£425
2003 Royal Arms	61,596,500	£4
2003 — BU..	23,760	£6
2003 — Proof	—	£10
2003 — Silver Proof	15,830	£35
2003 — — — Piedfort	9,871	£50
2004 Forth Railway Bridge........................	39,162,000	£4
2004 — BU..	24,014	£6
2004 — Proof	—	£10
2004 — Silver Proof	11,470	£35
2004 — — — Piedfort	7,013	£50
2004 — Gold Proof....................................	—	£425
2005 Menai Bridge	99,429,500	£4
2005 — BU..	—	£6
2005 — Proof	—	£10
2005 — Silver Proof	8,371	£35

1988
DECUS ET TUTAMEN

1994, 1999
NEMO ME IMPUNE LACESSIT

1995, 2000
PLEIDIOL WYF I'M GWLAD

1996, 2001
DECUS ET TUTAMEN

1997, 2002
DECUS ET TUTAMEN

2004
PATTERNED EDGE

DATE	Mintage	UNC
2005 — — — Piedfort	6,007	£50
2005 — Gold Proof	—	£425
2006 Egyptian Arch	38,938,000	£4
2006 — BU	—	£6
2006 — Proof	—	£10
2006 — Silver Proof	14,765	£35
2006 — — — Piedfort	5,129	£50
2006 — Gold Proof	—	£425
2007 Gateshead Millennium Bridge	26,180,160	£4
2007 — BU	—	£6
2007 — Proof	—	£10
2007 — Silver Proof	10,110	£40
2007 — — — Piedfort	5,739	£50
2007 — Gold Proof	—	£425
2008 Royal Arms	3,910,000	£3
2008 — BU	18,336	£6
2008 — Proof	—	£8
2008 — Silver Proof	8,441	£35
2008 — Gold Proof	674	£425
2008 — Platinum Proof	—	£500
2008 A series of 14 different reverses, the 25th Anniversary of the modern £1 coin, Silver Proof with selected gold highlighting on the reverses. the latter being all those used since 1983, the coins being with appropriate edge lettering	—	£400
2008 The same as above, Gold Proof (the 2008 Royal Arms being already listed above)	150	£5800
2008 **New Rev.,** Shield of the Royal Arms, no border beads on Obv.	29,518,000	£3
2008 BU	—	£5
2008 Proof	—	£6
2008 Silver Proof	5,000	£35
2008 Silver Proof Piedfort	2,456	£55
2008 Gold Proof	860	£450
2008 Platinum Proof	—	£575
2009	7,820,000	£2
2009 BU	130,644	£5
2009 Proof	—	£6
2009 Silver Proof	8,508	£35
2009 Gold Proof	540	£595
2010	38,505,000	£2
2010 BU	—	£5
2010 Proof	—	£6
2010 Silver BU	—	£30
2010 — Proof	—	£40
2010 City Series (London)	2,635,000	£3
2010 — BU	66,313	£7
2010 — Proof	—	£9
2010 — Silver Proof	7,693	£40
2010 — — — Piedfort	3,682	£55
2010 — Gold Proof	950	£450
2010 City Series (Belfast)	6,205,000	£2
2010 — BU	64,461	£7
2010 — Proof	—	£9
2010 — Silver Proof	5,805	£40
2010 — — — Piedfort	3,503	£55
2010 — Gold Proof	585	£500
2011	25,415,000	£3
2011 BU	—	£4
2011 Proof	—	£8
2011 Silver BU (in 21st and 18th Birthday cards)	—	£45
2011 — Proof	—	£55
2011 City Series (Cardiff)	1,615,000	£5

2005
PATTERNED EDGE

2006
PATTERNED EDGE

2007
PATTERNED EDGE

2008 (proof sets — silver and gold)
DECUS ET TUTAMEN

2008, 2009, 2010, 2011
DECUS ET TUTAMEN

2011
**Y DDRAIG GOCH
DDYRY CYCHWYN**

DATE	Mintage	UNC
2011 — BU	47,933	£7
2011 — Proof	—	£9
2011 — Silver Proof	5,553	£40
2011 — — — Piedfort	1,615	£60
2011 — Gold Proof	524	£500
2011 City Series (Edinburgh)	935,000	£6
2011 — BU	47,896	£7
2011 — Proof	—	£9
2011 — Silver Proof	4,973	£45
2011 — — — Piedfort	2,696	£60
2011 — Gold Proof	499	£500
2012	35,700,030	£3
2012 BU	—	£5
2012 Proof	—	£8
2012 Silver BU (in Silver Baby Gift)	—	£75
2012 Silver Proof	—	£50
2012 — with selective gold plating	—	£35
2012 Gold Proof	—	£450
2013	13,090,500	£3
2013 BU	—	£6
2013 Proof	—	£8
2013 Silver BU	—	£60
2013 Silver Proof	—	£45
2013 Gold Proof	—	£450
2013 Floral Series (England)	5,270,000	£2
2013 — BU	6112	£6
2013 — Proof	—	£10
2013 — Silver Proof	3,334	£45
2013 — — — Piedfort	1,071	£60
2013 — Gold Proof	284	£500
2013 Floral Series (Wales)	5,270,000	£2
2013 — BU	6112	£6
2013 — Proof	—	£10
2013 — Silver Proof	3,094	£45
2013 — — — Piedfort	860	£60
2013 — Gold Proof	274	£500
2013 Royal Coat of Arms (Sewell), Gold Proof	—	£500
2013 Crowned Royal Arms (Gorringe), Gold Proof	—	£500

(The above two coins are part of a set of three, along with the 2013 gold proof, with definitive reverse with Uncrowned Royal Arms (Dent)).

2014	79,305,200	£3
2014 BU	—	£6
2014 Proof	—	£10
2014 Silver BU	—	£50
2014 Silver Proof	—	£55
2014 Floral Series (Scotland)	5,185,000	£2
2014 — BU	3,832	£6
2014 — Proof	—	£10
2014 — Silver Proof	1,540	£45
2014 — — Piedfort	—	£60
2014 — Gold Proof	154	£850
2014 Floral Series (Northern Ireland)	5,780,000	£2
2014 — BU	—	£6
2014 — Proof	—	£10
2014 — Silver Proof	1,502	£45
2014 — — — Piedfort	788	£60
2014 — Gold Proof	166	£850
2015	29,580,200	£3
2015 BU	—	£6
2015 Proof	—	£10
2015 Silver Proof	—	£50
2015 Gold Proof	—	£450
2015 Platinum Proof	—	—

2011
NISI DOMINUS FRUSTRA

2013 Wales £1 Floral gold proof.

Most £1 coins are also available in precious metals.

2014 Scotland £1 Floral gold proof.

2015

DATE	Mintage	UNC
2015 *New Portrait* BU	62,495,640	£3
2015 Proof	—	£10
2015 Silver Proof	—	£50
2015 Gold Proof	—	£450
2015 Platinum Proof	—	£650
2015 Heraldic Royal Arms	—	£3
2015 — BU	—	£6
2015 — Silver Proof	—	£50
2015 — — — Piedfort	—	£100
2015 — Gold Proof	—	£450
2016	—	£15
2016 BU	—	£20
2016 Proof	—	£25
2016 Silver Proof	—	£50
2016 The Last Round Pound		
2016 — BU	96,089	£15
2016 — Proof	—	£20
2016 — Silver Proof	7,491	£55
2016 — — — Piedfort	2,943	£150
2016 — Gold Proof	499	£650
2016 **12-sided coin Nations of the Crown design**		
2016	648,936,536	£3
2016 BU	—	£15
2017	749,616,200	£3
2017 BU	—	£12
2017 Silver Proof	26,000	£150
2017 Silver Proof Piedfort	4,500	£250
2017 Gold Proof	2,951	£650
2017 Platinum Proof	250	£750

2016 The last round pound

12-sided issue with Jody Clark portrait obverse and reverse by 15-year-old David Pearce

FIFTY PENCE

Introduced as legal tender for 10 shillings to replace the banknote of that value prior to decimalisation, coins of the original size are no longer legal tender. Unless otherwise stated, i.e. for commemoratives, the reverse design is of Britannia. The reverse legend of NEW PENCE became FIFTY PENCE from 1982.

The description of "Unc" has been used against some 50 pence pieces dated 2009 and 2011 (for Olympic and Paralympic sports) to distinguish them from coins minted to circulation standard and BU standard, being a standard between the latter two. The uncirculated standard coins have a more even rim than the circulation standard examples, particularly observable on the obverse.

Since the surge of interest in collecting 50p coins prices have increased. The following values are for uncirculated coins. Any found in change will of course have been circulated and will not command such a high premium but the rarer ones will still be worth more than face value.

DATE	Mintage	UNC
1969	188,400,000	£2
1970	19,461,500	£3
1971 Proof	—	£8
1972 Proof	—	£7
1973 Accession to EEC	89,775,000	£3
1973 — Proof	—	£8
1973 — Silver Proof Piedfort	About 24	£3000
1974 Proof	—	£7
1975 Proof	—	£8
1976	43,746,500	£2
1976 Proof	—	£7
1977	49,536,000	£2
1977 Proof	—	£6
1978	72,005,000	£2
1978 Proof	—	£6

Accession to the EEC 1973.

DATE	Mintage	UNC
1979	58,680,000	£2
1979 Proof	—	£6
1980	89,086,000	£2
1980 Proof	—	£6
1981	74,002,000	£2
1981 Proof	—	£8
1982	51,312,000	£3
1982 Unc	—	£6
1982 Proof	—	£8
1983	62,824,000	£2
1983 Unc	—	£6
1983 Proof	—	£8
1984 BU (only issued in Year Sets)	158,820	£5
1984 Proof	—	£12
1985 *New portrait*	682,103	£2
1985 BU (only issued in Year Sets)	—	£5
1985 Proof	—	£6
1986 BU (only issued in Year Sets)	—	£5
1986 Proof	—	£12
1987 BU (only issued in Year Sets)	—	£4
1987 Proof	—	£12
1988 BU (only issued in Year Sets)	—	£4
1988 Proof	—	£12
1989 BU (only issued in Year Sets)	—	£4
1989 Proof	—	£12
1990 BU (only issued in Year Sets)	—	£4
1990 Proof	—	£12
1991 BU (only issued in Year Sets)	—	£5
1991 Proof	—	£12
1992 BU (only issued in Year Sets)	—	£7
1992 Proof	—	£12
1992 Presidency of EC Council and EC accession 20th anniversary (includes 1993 date)	109,000	£60
1992 — BU	—	£75
1992 — Proof	—	£85
1992 — Silver Proof	26,890	£100
1992 — — Piedfort	10,993	£120
1992 — Gold Proof	—	£550
1993 BU (only issued in Year Sets)	—	£5
1993 Proof	—	£12
1994 50th Anniversary of the Normandy Landings	6,705,520	£3
1994 — BU (also in presentation folder)	—	£8
1994 — Proof	—	£15
1994 — Silver Proof	40,000	£35
1994 — — Piedfort	10,000	£60
1994 — Gold Proof	—	£500
1995 BU (only issued in Year Sets)	—	£8
1995 Proof	—	£12
1996 BU (only issued in Year Sets)	—	£8
1996 Proof	—	£12
1996 Silver Proof	—	£25
1997 BU	—	£8
1997 Proof	—	£10
1997 Silver Proof	—	£25
1997 *New reduced size*	456,364,100	£2
1997 BU	—	£5
1997 Proof	—	£6
1997 Silver Proof	—	£25
1997 — — Piedfort	—	£35
1998 *New portrait*	64,306,500	£2
1998 BU	—	£5
1998 Proof	—	£8
1998 Presidency and 25th anniversary of EU entry	5,043,000	£3
1998 — BU	—	£5
1998 — Proof	—	£8
1998 — Silver Proof	8,859	£30
1998 — — Piedfort	8,440	£45
1998 — Gold Proof	—	£450

Presidency of the EC Council 1992.

1994

1998 EU Presidency

1998 NHS

2000 Public Libraries

DATE	Mintage	UNC
1998 50th Anniversary of the National Health Service	5,001,000	£3
1998 — BU	—	£5
1998 — Silver Proof	9,032	£30
1998 — — — Piedfort	5,117	£45
1998 — Gold Proof	—	£450
1999	24,905,000	£2
1999 BU	—	£5
1999 Proof	—	£10
2000	27,915,500	£2
2000 BU	—	£5
2000 Proof	—	£7
2000 150th Anniversary of Public Libraries	11,263,000	£2
2000 — BU	—	£6
2000 — Proof	—	£9
2000 — Silver Proof	7,634	£30
2000 — — — Piedfort	5,721	£45
2000 — Gold proof	—	£400
2001	84,998,500	£2
2001 BU	—	£5
2001 Proof	—	£7
2002	23,907,500	£2
2002 BU	—	£5
2002 Proof	—	£7
2002 Gold Proof	—	£375
2003	23,583,000	£2
2003 BU	—	£5
2003 Proof	—	£6
2003 Suffragette	3,124,030	£4
2003 — BU	9582	£7
2003 — Proof	—	£9
2003 — Silver Proof	6,267	£30
2003 — — — Piedfort	6,795	£45
2003 — Gold Proof	942	£350
2004	35,315,500	£2
2004 BU	—	£5
2004 Proof	—	£8
2004 Roger Bannister	9,032,500	£3
2004 — BU	10,371	£6
2004 — Proof	—	£8
2004 — Silver Proof	4,924	£30
2004 — — — Piedfort	4,054	£45
2004 — Gold Proof	644	£350
2005	25,363,500	£2
2005 BU	—	£6
2005 Proof	—	£8
2005 Samuel Johnson	17,649,000	£3
2005 — BU	—	£5
2005 — Proof	—	£8
2005 — Silver Proof	4,029	£30
2005 — — — Piedfort	3,808	£45
2005 — Gold Proof	—	£350
2006	24,567,000	£2
2006 Proof	—	£8
2006 Silver Proof	—	£30
2006 Victoria Cross, The Award	12,087,000	£3
2006 — BU	—	£5
2006 — Proof	—	£8
2006 — Silver Proof	6,310	£30
2006 — — — Piedfort	3,532	£50
2006 — Gold Proof	866	£350
2006 Victoria Cross, Heroic Acts	10,000,500	£3
2006 — BU	—	£5
2006 — Proof	—	£8
2006 — Silver Proof	6,872	£30
2006 — — — Piedfort	3,415	£50
2006 — Gold Proof	804	£350
2007	11,200,000	£2
2007 BU	—	£6
2007 Proof	—	£8

2003 Suffragettes

2004 Roger Bannister

2005 Samuel Johnson

2006 Victoria Cross—the Award

2006 Victoria Cross—Heroic Acts

273

DATE	Mintage	UNC
2007 Centenary of Scout Movement	7,710,750	£3
2007 — BU...	—	£8
2007 — Proof..	—	£12
2007 — Silver Proof	10,895	£30
2007 — — — Piedfort...	1,555	£65
2007 — Gold Proof...	1,250	£400
2008	3,500,000	£2
2008 — BU..	—	£5
2008 — Proof..	—	£6
2008 — Silver Proof	—	£25
2008 — Gold Proof...	—	£400
2008 — Platinum Proof	—	£1550
2008 **New Shield Rev.** Obv. rotated by approx. 26⁰...	22,747,000	£5
2008 BU...	—	£6
2008 Proof...	—	£8
2008 Silver Proof...	—	£25
2008 Silver Proof Piedfort	—	£45
2008 Gold Proof...	—	£400
2008 Platinum Proof...	—	£1550
2009 BU...	—	£10
2009 Proof...	—	£15
2009 Silver Proof...	—	£25
2009 250th Anniversary of Kew Gardens...................	210,000	£85
2009 — BU..	128,364	£100
2009 — Proof..	—	£125
2009 — Silver Proof	7,575	£175
2009 — — — Piedfort...	2,967	£250
2009 — Gold Proof...	629	£550
2009 Olympic and Paralympic Sports		
(Track & Field Athletics) Unc (Blue Peter Pack)	19,751	£100
2009 16 different reverses from the past marking the		
40th Anniversary of the 50p coin. Proof	1,039	£300
2009 — Silver Proof	1,163	£650
2009 — Gold Proof...	70	£8000
2009 — — — Piedfort...	40	£20,950
2010 BU...	—	£12
2010 Proof...	—	£25
2010 Silver Proof...	—	£35
2010 100 years of Girl Guiding UK............................	7,410,090	£3
2010 — BU..	99,075	£7
2010 — Proof..	—	£20
2010 — Silver Proof	5,271	£35
2010 — — — Piedfort...	2,879	£55
2010 — Gold Proof...	355	£575
2011 BU...	—	£10
2011 Proof...	—	£20
2011 Silver Proof...	—	£50
2011 50th Anniversary of the WWF...........................	3,400,000	£4
2011 — BU..	67,299	£6
2011 — Proof..	—	£25
2011 — Silver Proof	24,870	£45
2011 — — — Piedfort...	2,244	£65
2011 — Gold Proof...	243	£675

2007 Centenary of Scouting

2008 Shield design

2009 Kew Gardens

2010 100 years of Guiding

DATE	Mintage	UNC
2011 Olympic & Paralympic Sports Issues:		
Aquatics Unc, head clear of lines (as illustrated)	2,179,000	£4
— Head with lines BU....................	—	£850
— Head clear of lines. BU	—	£5
— Silver BU	30,000	£25
Archery Unc...	3,345,000	£3
— BU	—	£4
— Silver BU	30,000	£25
Athletics Unc	2,224,000	£3
— BU	—	£4
— Silver BU	30,000	£25
Badminton Unc...	2,133,000	£3
— BU	—	£4
— Silver BU	30,000	£25
Basketball Unc	1,748,000	£3
— BU	—	£4
— Silver BU	30,000	£25
Boccia Unc	2,166,000	£3
— BU	—	£4
— Silver BU	30,000	£25
Boxing Unc	2,148,000	£3
— BU	—	£4
— Silver BU	30,000	£25
Canoeing Unc..	2,166,000	£3
— BU	—	£4
— Silver BU	30,000	£25
Cycling Unc	2,090,000	£3
— BU	—	£4
— Silver BU	30,000	£25
Equestrian Unc..	2,142,000	£3
— BU	—	£4
— Silver BU	30,000	£25
Fencing Unc	2,115,000	£3
— BU	—	£4
— Silver BU	30,000	£25
Football Unc	1,125,000	£10
— BU	—	£15
— Silver BU	30,000	£35
Goalball Unc	1,615,000	£8
— BU	—	£10
— Silver BU	30,000	£25
Gymnastics Unc	1,720,000	£3
— BU	—	£4
— Silver BU	30,000	£25
Handball Unc...	1,676,000	£8
— BU	—	£10
— Silver BU	30,000	£30
Hockey Unc	1,773,000	£3
— BU	—	£4
— Silver BU	30,000	£25
Judo Unc	1,161,000	£10
— BU	—	£5
— Silver BU	30,000	£35
Modern Pentathlon Unc	1,689,000	£3
— BU	—	£4
— Silver BU	30,000	£25
Rowing Unc	1,717,000	£3
— BU	—	£4
— Silver BU	30,000	£25
Sailing Unc..	1,749,000	£3
— BU	—	£4
— Silver BU	30,000	£25
Shooting Unc...	1,656,000	£3
— BU	—	£4
— Silver BU	30,000	£25
Table Tennis Unc...	1,737,000	£3
— BU	—	£4
— Silver BU	30,000	£25

Aquatics
by Jonathan Olliffe

Archery
by Piotr Powaga

Athletics
by Florence Jackson

Badminton
by Emma Kelly

Basketball
by Sarah Payne

275

*Boccia
by Justin Chung*

*Boxing
by Shane Abery*

*Canoeing
by Timothy Lees*

*Cycling
by Theo Crutchley-Mack*

*Equestrian
by Thomas Babbage*

*Fencing
by Ruth Summerfield*

*Football
by Neil Wolfson*

*Goalball
by Jonathan Wren*

*Gymnastics
by Jonathan Olliffe*

*Handball
by Natasha Ratcliffe*

*Hockey
by Robert Evans*

*Judo
by David Cornell*

*Modern Pentathlon
by Daniel Brittain*

*Rowing
by Davey Podmore*

*Sailing
by Bruce Rushin*

*Shooting
by Pravin Dewdhory*

*Table Tennis
by Alan Linsdell*

*Taekwando
by David Gibbons*

*Tennis
by Tracy Baines*

*Triathlon
by Sarah Harvey*

DATE	Mintage	UNC
Taekwondo Unc	1,664,000	£3
— BU	—	£4
— Silver BU	30,000	£25
Tennis Unc	1,454,000	£8
— BU	—	£10
— Silver BU	30,000	£25
Triathlon Unc	1,163,000	£10
— BU	—	£15
— Silver BU	30,000	£30
Volleyball Unc	2,133,000	£3
— BU	—	£4
— Silver BU	30,000	£25
Weightlifting Unc	1,879,000	£3
— BU	—	£4
— Silver BU	30,000	£25
Wheelchair Rugby Unc	1,765,000	£3
— BU	—	£4
— Silver BU	30,000	£25
Wrestling Unc	1,129,000	£10
— BU	—	£15
— Silver BU	30,000	£35

Volleyball
by Daniela Boothman

Weight Lifting
by Rob Shakespeare

Note—*Each of the artists of the 29 Olympic sports above was presented with a gold proof coin with their own design. The Track & Field Athletics design coin was dated 2009, the Cycling was dated 2010, and the remaining 2011.*

	Mintage	UNC
2012	32,300,030	£2
2012 BU	—	£5
2012 Proof	—	£10
2012 Silver Proof with selective gold plating	—	£50
2012 Gold Proof	—	£500
2012 Gold Proof Piedfort. *The 11 Olympic sports in which the United Kingdom Team GB achieved a Gold Medal was celebrated with an issue limit of only 27 Piedfort coins for each sport, some in sets, some as individual coins (see under Proof and Specimen sets)*	27	
2013	10,301,000	£2
2013 BU	—	£5
2013 Proof	—	£10
2013 Silver Proof	2,013	£55
2013 Gold Proof	198	£550
2013 100th anniversary of Birth of Christopher Ironside	7,000,000	£8
2013 — BU	4,403	£10
2013 — Proof	—	£15
2013 — Silver Proof	1,823	£50
2013 — — Piedfort	816	£90
2013 — Gold Proof	198	£450
2013 Centenary of the Birth of Benjamin Britten	5,300,000	£8
2013 — BU	—	£10
2013 — Silver Proof	717	£55
2013 — — Piedfort	515	£90
2013 — Gold Proof	70	£450
2014	49,001,000	£2
2014 BU	—	£5
2014 Proof	—	£12
2014 Silver Proof	—	£55
2014 XX Commonwealth Games	6,502,918	£8
2014 — BU	—	£10
2014 — Proof	—	£15
2014 — Silver Proof	—	£45
2014 — — Piedfort	—	£100
2014 — Gold Proof	—	£450
2015	20,101,000	£2
2015 BU	—	£5
2015 Proof	—	£10
2015 Silver Proof	—	£30
2015 Gold Proof	—	£350
2015 Platinum Proof	—	—
2015 Battle of Britain 75th Anniversary BU (no denomination)	35,199	£4

Wheelchair Rugby
by Natasha Ratcliffe

Wrestling
by Roderick Enriquez

2013 Christopher Ironside

DATE	Mintage	UNC
2015 — Proof	—	£12
2015 — Silver Proof	2,839	£30
2015 — — — Piedfort	1,422	£80
2015 — Gold Proof	389	£350

New Portrait by Jody Clark

	Mintage	UNC
2015 Battle of Britain 75th Anniversary (with denomination) UNC	5,900,000	£3
2015 Standard Shield rev.	—	£2
2015 BU	—	£5
2015 Proof	—	£12
2015 Silver Proof	—	£30
2015 Gold Proof	—	£350
2015 Platinum Proof	—	—
2016 BU	—	£4
2016 Proof	—	£12
2016 Silver Proof	—	£35
2016 Battle of Hastings 950th Anniversary	6,700,000	£3
2016 — BU	21,718	£5
2016 — Proof	—	£10
2016 — Silver Proof	2,338	£35
2016 — — — Piedfort	1,469	£150
2016 — Gold Proof	237	£350
2016 Beatrix Potter 150th Anniversary	6,900,000	£4
2016 — BU	61,658	£5
2016 — Proof	—	£10
2016 — Silver Proof	7,471	£35
2016 — — — Piedfort	2,486	£250
2016 — Gold Proof	—	£550
2016 Beatrix Potter: Peter Rabbit	9,600,000	£4
2016 — BU	93,851	£15
2016 — Silver Proof with coloured highlights	15,245	£50
2016 Beatrix Potter: Jemima Puddle-Duck	2,100,000	£6
2016 — BU	54,929	£12
2016 — Silver Proof with coloured highlights	15,171	£75
2016 Beatrix Potter: Mrs. Tiggy-Winkle	8,800,000	£4
2016 — BU	47,597	£10
2016 — Silver Proof with coloured highlights	15,243	£50
2016 Beatrix Potter: Squirrel Nutkin	5,000,000	£4
2016 — BU	45,884	£10
2016 — Silver Proof with coloured highlights	15,143	£50
2016 Team GB for Olympics	6,400,000	£3
2016 — BU	34,162	£10
2016 — Silver Proof	4,456	£25
2016 — — — Piedfort	1,246	£150
2016 — Gold Proof	302	£400
2017 375th anniversary of Sir Isaac Newton's birth	1,800,000	£5
2017 — BU	—	£10
2017 — Proof	—	£15
2017 — Silver Proof	7,000	£50
2017 — — — Piedfort	4,500	£95
2017 — Gold Proof	634	£760
2017 Beatrix Potter: Peter Rabbit	19,900,000	£4
2017 — BU	—	£12
2017 — — Silver Proof with coloured highlights	40,000	£50
2017 — — Gold Proof	450	£1000
2017 Beatrix Potter: Mr. Jeremy Fisher	9,900,000	£4
2017 — BU	—	£8
2017 — Silver Proof with coloured highlights	40,000	£50
2017 Beatrix Potter: Tom Kitten	9,500,000	£4
2017 — BU	—	£8
2017 — Silver Proof with coloured highlights	40,000	£50
2017 Beatrix Potter: Benjamin Bunny	25,000,000	£4
2017 — BU	—	£8
2017 — Silver Proof with coloured highlights	—	£50
2018 375th anniversary of Sir Isaac Newton's birth (see above: 2018 only available from the Royal Mint Experience)		£75

2015 Battle of Britain

2016 Beatrix Potter

2016 Peter Rabbit

2016 Team GB

2017 Isaac Newton

DATE	Mintage	UNC
2018 Anniversary of the Representation of the People Act	—	£3
2018 Beatrix Potter: Peter Rabbit	—	£5
2018 — BU	—	£5
2018 — Silver Proof with coloured highlights	—	£50
2018 — Gold Proof	450	£1000
2018 Beatrix Potter: Flopsy Bunny	—	£4
2018 — BU	—	£5
2018 — Silver Proof with coloured highlights	—	£50
2018 Beatrix Potter: The Tailor of Gloucester	—	£5
2018 — BU	—	£6
2018 — Silver Proof with coloured highlights	—	£50
2018 Beatrix Potter: Mrs Tittlemouse	—	£5
2018 — BU	—	£6
2018 — Silver Proof with coloured highlights	—	£50
2018 Paddington Bear at Paddington Station	—	£5
2018 — BU	—	£10
2018 — Silver Proof with coloured highlights	75,000	£60
2018 — Gold Proof	1,250	£780
2018 Paddington Bear at Buckingham Palace	—	£5
2018 — BU	—	£10
2018 — Silver Proof with coloured highlights	75,000	£60
2018 — Gold Proof	1,250	£780
2018 The Snowman BU	—	£10
2018 — Silver Proof	15,000	£60
2018 — Gold Proof	400	£775
2019 Stephen Hawking BU	—	£10
2019 — Silver Proof	7,000	£55
2019 — — Piedfort	2,500	£95
2019 — Gold Proof	400	£795
2019 Sherlock Holmes BU	unlimited	£10
2019 — Silver Proof	7,500	£55
2019 — — Piedfort	3,500	£95
2019 — Gold Proof	600	£795
2019 The Gruffalo BU	—	£10
2019 — Silver Proof	30,000	£65
2019 — Gold Proof	600	£795
2019 Peter Rabbit BU	—	£10
2019 — Silver Proof	30,000	£65
2019 — Gold Proof	500	£795
2019 Paddington Bear at the Tower of London	—	£3
2019 — BU	—	£10
2019 — Silver Proof with coloured highlights	25,000	£65
2019 — Gold Proof	600	£980
2019 Paddington Bear at St. Paul's	—	£3
2019 — BU	—	£10
2019 — Silver Proof with coloured highlights	25,000	£65
2019 — Gold Proof	600	£980

2018
Flopsy Bunny

2018
The Snowman

Stephen Hawking

Sherlock Holmes

The four 2017 Beatrix Potter 50p commemoratives in silver with colour

Paddington at the Tower of London

279

TWENTY-FIVE PENCE (CROWN)

This series is a continuation of the pre-decimal series, there having been four crowns to the pound. The coins below have a legal tender face value of 25p to this day, and are minted in cupro-nickel except where stated otherwise.

DATE	Mintage	UNC
1972 Royal Silver Wedding	7,452,100	£2
1972 — Proof	150,000	£8
1972 — Silver Proof	100,000	£35
1977 Silver Jubilee	37,061,160	£2
1977 — in Presentation folder	Incl. above	£3
1977 — Proof	193,000	£8
1977 — Silver Proof	377,000	£30
1980 Queen Mother 80th Birthday	9,306,000	£2
1980 — in Presentation folder	Incl. above	£3
1980 — Silver Proof	83,670	£30
1981 Royal Wedding	26,773,600	£2
1981 — in Presentation folder	Incl. above	£3
1981 — Silver Proof	218,140	£30

TWENTY PENCE

The series commenced in 1982, some 11 years after the introduction of decimal coinage. Its presence from introduction date meant that there was no requirement for ten pence circulation-standard coins until the latter's size was reduced in 1992. Its alloy is uniquely 84% copper and 16% nickel, unlike the 75/25 of the fifty pence.

DATE	Mintage	UNC
1982	740,815,000	£2
1982 Unc	—	£3
1982 Proof	—	£7
1982 Silver Proof Piedfort	—	£25
1983	158,463,000	£1
1983 Unc	—	£3
1983 Proof	—	£6
1984	65,350,000	£1
1984 BU	—	£3
1984 Proof	—	£6
1985 *New portrait*	74,273,699	£2
1985 BU	—	£4
1985 Proof	—	£6
1986 BU	—	£5
1986 Proof	—	£8
1987	137,450,000	£1
1987 BU	—	£3
1987 Proof	—	£5
1988	38,038,344	£1
1988 BU	—	£3
1988 Proof	—	£5
1989	132,013,890	£1
1989 BU	—	£3
1989 Proof	—	£5
1990	88,097,500	£1
1990 BU	—	£3
1990 Proof	—	£6
1991	35,901,250	£1
1991 BU	—	£3
1991 Proof	—	£6
1992	Est. approx. 1,500,000	£4
1992 BU	—	£5
1992 *Enhanced effigy*	Est. approx. 29,705,000	£4
1992 — BU	—	£5
1992 — Proof	—	£8
1993	123,123,750	£1
1993 BU	—	£3
1993 Proof	—	£5
1994	67,131,250	£1
1994 BU	—	£3
1994 Proof	—	£5
1995	102,005,000	£1
1995 BU	—	£3
1995 Proof	—	£5
1996	83,163,750	£2
1996 BU	—	£3
1996 Proof	—	£5
1996 Silver Proof	—	£25
1997	89,518,750	£2
1997 BU	—	£3
1997 Proof	—	£5
1998 *New portrait*	76,965,000	£2
1998 BU	—	£4
1998 Proof	—	£5
1999	73,478,750	£2
1999 BU	—	£3
1999 Proof	—	£5
2000	136,428,750	£2
2000 BU	—	£3
2000 Proof	—	£5
2000 Silver Proof	—	£25
2001	148,122,500	£2
2001 BU	—	£3
2001 Proof	—	£5
2002	93,360,000	£2
2002 BU	—	£3
2002 Proof	—	£5

DATE	Mintage	UNC
2002 Gold Proof	—	£275
2003	153,383,750	£2
2003 BU	—	£4
2003 Proof	—	£6
2004	120,212,500	£2
2004 BU	—	£4
2004 Proof	—	£6
2005	124,488,750	£2
2005 BU	—	£4
2005 Proof	—	£6
2006	114,800,000	£2
2006 BU	—	£6
2006 Proof	—	£7
2006 Silver Proof	—	£25
2007	117,075,000	£2
2007 BU	—	£4
2007 Proof	—	£6
2008	11,900,000	£2
2008 BU	—	£4
2008 Proof	—	£7
2008 Silver Proof	—	£25
2008 Gold Proof	—	£300
2008 Platinum Proof	—	£750
2008 **New Rev.,** date on Obv.	115,022,000	£2
2008 — paired with old Obv. (thus no date).. Est. approx. 120,000 (?) .		£65
2008 BU	—	£3
2008 Proof	—	£6
2008 Silver Proof	—	£25
2008 — — Piedfort	—	£30
2008 Gold Proof	—	£300
2008 Platinum Proof	—	£750
2009	121,625,300	£2
2009 BU	—	£5
2009 Proof	—	£7
2009 Silver Proof	—	£25
2010	112,875,500	£2
2010 BU	—	£5
2010 Proof	—	£7
2010 Silver Proof	—	£25
2011	191,625,000	£2
2011 BU	—	£5

DATE	Mintage	UNC
2011 Proof	—	£8
2011 Silver Proof	—	£25
2012	69,650,030	£2
2012 BU	—	£5
2012 Proof	—	£8
2012 Silver Proof (issued in set with Victorian 4 Shilling piece)	—	£25
2012 — — with selective gold plating	—	£35
2012 Gold Proof	—	£300
2013	66,325,000	£2
2013 BU	—	£5
2013 Proof	—	£10
2013 Silver Proof	—	£20
2013 Gold Proof	—	£300
2014	173,775,000	£2
2014 BU	—	£5
2014 Proof	—	£10
2014 Silver Proof	—	£25
2015	63,175,000	£3
2015 BU	—	£5
2015 Proof	—	£10
2015 Silver Proof	—	£25
2015 Gold Proof	—	£350
2015 Platinum Proof	—	—
2015 **New Portrait**	131,250,000	£3
2015 — BU	—	£5
2015 — Proof	—	£5
2015 — Silver Proof	—	£30
2015 — Gold Proof	—	£300
2015 — Platinum Proof	—	—
2016	161,000,000	£3
2016 BU	—	£5
2016 Proof	—	£10
2016 Silver Proof	—	£25
2017	—	—
2017 BU	—	£5
2017 Proof	—	£10
2017 Silver Proof	—	£25
2018	—	£2
2018 BU	—	£5
2018 Proof	—	£10
2018 Silver Proof	—	£25

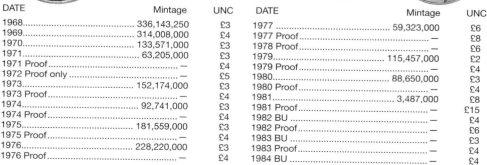

TEN PENCE

The series commenced before decimalisation with the legend NEW PENCE, this changed to TEN PENCE from 1982. These "florin-sized" coins up to 1992 are no longer legal tender. Cupro-nickel was replaced by nickel-plated steel from 2011.

DATE	Mintage	UNC
1968	336,143,250	£3
1969	314,008,000	£4
1970	133,571,000	£3
1971	63,205,000	£3
1971 Proof	—	£4
1972 Proof only	—	£5
1973	152,174,000	£3
1973 Proof	—	£4
1974	92,741,000	£3
1974 Proof	—	£4
1975	181,559,000	£3
1975 Proof	—	£4
1976	228,220,000	£3
1976 Proof	—	£4

DATE	Mintage	UNC
1977	59,323,000	£6
1977 Proof	—	£8
1978 Proof	—	£6
1979	115,457,000	£2
1979 Proof	—	£4
1980	88,650,000	£3
1980 Proof	—	£4
1981	3,487,000	£8
1981 Proof	—	£15
1982 BU	—	£4
1982 Proof	—	£6
1983 BU	—	£3
1983 Proof	—	£4
1984 BU	—	£4

281

Angel of the North	James Bond	Cricket	Double-decker bus	English breakfast
Fish and chips	Greenwich Mean Time	Houses of Parliament	Ice cream	Jubilee
King Arthur	Loch Ness	Mackintosh	NHS	Oak tree
Pillar box	Queueing	Robin	Stonehenge	Tea
Union Flag	Village	World Wide Web	X marks the spot	Yeoman warder

Zebra crossing

In 2018 a new series was introduced for the 10p denomination. There are 26 coins each depicting a letter of the alphabet as shown above.

DATE	Mintage	UNC
1984 Proof	—	£6
1985 *New portrait* BU	—	£5
1985 Proof	—	£7
1986 BU	—	£4
1986 Proof	—	£6
1987 BU	—	£4
1987 Proof	—	£7
1988 BU	—	£5
1988 Proof	—	£7
1989 BU	—	£6
1989 Proof	—	£9
1990 BU	—	£6
1990 Proof	—	£9
1991 BU	—	£6
1991 Proof	—	£9
1992 BU	—	£5
1992 Proof	—	£7
1992 Silver Proof	—	£12
1992 *Size reduced (24.5mm)*	1,413,455,170	£3
1992 BU	—	£4
1992 Proof	—	£5
1992 Silver Proof	—	£12
1992 — — Piedfort	—	£35
1993 BU	—	£2
1993 Proof	—	£7
1994 BU	—	£2
1994 Proof	—	£7
1995	43,259,000	£1
1995 BU	—	£5
1995 Proof	—	£7
1996	118,738,000	£2
1996 BU	—	£4
1996 Proof	—	£7
1996 Silver Proof	—	£25
1997	99,196,000	£2
1997 BU	—	£4
1997 Proof	—	£4
1998 *New portrait* BU	—	£8
1998 Proof	—	£10
1999 BU	—	£4
1999 Proof	—	£11
2000	134,733,000	£1
2000 BU	—	£4
2000 Proof	—	£7
2000 Silver Proof	—	£15
2001	129,281,000	£1
2001 BU	—	£3
2001 Proof	—	£4
2002	80,934,000	£2
2002 BU	—	£3
2002 Proof	—	£5
2002 Gold Proof	—	£250
2003	88,118,000	£2
2003 BU	—	£3
2003 Proof	—	£5
2004	99,602,000	£1
2004 BU	—	£3
2004 Proof	—	£5
2005	69,604,000	£1
2005 BU	—	£2
2005 Proof	—	£4
2006	118,803,000	£1
2006 BU	—	£3
2006 Proof	—	£7
2006 Silver Proof	—	£25
2007	72,720,000	£1

DATE	Mintage	UNC
2007 BU	—	£4
2007 Proof	—	£7
2008	9,720,000	£1
2008 BU	—	£4
2008 Proof	—	£5
2008 Silver Proof	—	£25
2008 Gold Proof	—	£250
2008 Platinum Proof	—	£450
2008 *New Rev.*, no border beads on Obv.	71,447,000	£1
2008 BU	—	£4
2008 Proof	—	£5
2008 Silver Proof	—	£25
2008 — — Piedfort	—	£45
2008 Gold Proof	—	£250
2008 Platinum Proof	—	£450
2009	84,360,000	£1
2009 BU	—	£3
2009 Proof	—	£5
2009 Silver Proof	—	£25
2010	96,600,500	£1
2010 BU	—	£5
2010 Proof	—	£7
2010 Silver Proof	—	£25
2011 Nickel-plated steel	59,603,850	£1
2011 — BU	—	£5
2011 — Proof	—	£10
2011 Silver Proof	—	£25
2012	11,600,030	£1
2012 BU	—	£5
2012 Proof	—	£10
2012 Silver proof with selective gold plating	—	£30
2012 Gold Proof	—	£250
2013	320,200,750	£1
2013 BU	—	£5
2013 Proof	—	£10
2013 Silver Proof	—	£25
2013 Gold Proof	—	£250
2014	490,202,020	£1
2014 BU	—	£5
2014 Proof	—	£12
2014 Silver Proof	—	£25
2015	119,000,000	£1
2015 BU	—	£4
2015 Proof	—	£5
2015 Silver Proof	—	£25
2015 Gold Proof	—	£250
2015 Platinum Proof	—	—
2015 *New portrait*	91,900,000	£1
2015 — BU	—	£5
2015 — Proof	—	£6
2015 — Silver Proof	—	£25
2015 — Gold Proof	—	£250
2015 — Platinum Proof	—	—
2016	135,200,000	£1
2016 BU	—	£4
2016 Proof	—	£6
2016 Silver Proof	—	£25
2017	32,300,000	£1
2017 BU	—	£4
2017 Proof	—	£5
2017 Silver Proof	—	£25
2018	—	£1
2018 Proof	—	£4
2018 Alphabet series (26 different letters)	—	£1
2019 Alphabet series (26 different letters)	—	£1

SIX PENCE

This new denomination has been struck, dated 2016, as part of the Royal Mint's gifting range. They are of Sterling silver to BU standard, and of diameter 19.41mm. Being similar in size to the pre-decimal 6d (or latterly 2 1/2p) they have also been marketed as part of a 3-coin set along with two old sixpences (£50), the 2016 6p being £30 on its own. A 2018 single sixpence costs £15.

FIVE PENCE

This series commenced simultaneously with the Ten Pence (qv). They were the same size and weight as their predecessor, the shilling, and such coins up to 1990 are no longer legal tender. As with the Ten Pence, cupro-nickel was replaced by nickel-plated steel from 2011.

DATE	Mintage	UNC	DATE	Mintage	UNC
1968	98,868,250	£3	1990 Silver Proof	—	£20
1969	120,270,000	£3	1990 — Piedfort	—	£25
1970	225,948,525	£3	1991	724,979000	£1
1971	81,783,475	£3	1991 BU	—	£3
1971 Proof	—	£3	1991 Proof	—	£5
1972 Proof	—	£7	1992	453,173,500	£1
1973 Proof	—	£8	1992 BU	—	£3
1974 Proof	—	£8	1992 Proof	—	£7
1975	141,539,000	£3	1993 BU	—	£3
1975 Proof	—	£6	1993 Proof	—	£5
1976 Proof	—	£7	1994	93,602,000	£1
1977	24,308,000	£8	1994 BU	—	£5
1977 Proof	—	£9	1994 Proof	—	£7
1978	61,094,000	£4	1995	183,384,000	£1
1978 Proof	—	£4	1995 BU	—	£5
1979	155,456,000	£4	1995 Proof	—	£7
1979 Proof	—	£4	1996	302,902,000	£1
1980	220,566,000	£3	1996 BU	—	£4
1980 Proof	—	£4	1996 Proof	—	£7
1981 Proof	—	£7	1996 Silver proof	—	£25
1982 BU	—	£7	1997	236,596,000	£1
1982 Proof	—	£9	1997 BU	—	£4
1983 BU	—	£5	1997 Proof	—	£7
1983 Proof	—	£6	1998 *New portrait*	217,376,000	£1
1984 BU	—	£4	1998 BU	—	£4
1984 Proof	—	£6	1998 Proof	—	£7
1985 *New Portrait*. BU	—	£2	1999	195,490,000	£1
1985 Proof	—	£7	1999 BU	—	£4
1986 BU	—	£2	1999 Proof	—	£7
1986 Proof	—	£7	2000	388,512,000	£1
1987	48,220,000	£1	2000 BU	—	£4
1987 BU	—	£3	2000 Proof	—	£7
1987 Proof	—	£5	2000 Silver Proof	—	£25
1988	120,744,610	£1	2001	337,930,000	£1
1988 BU	—	£3	2001 BU	—	£3
1988 Proof		£5	2001 Proof	—	£5
1989	101,406,000	£1	2002	219,258,000	£1
1989 BU	—	£4	2002 BU	—	£3
1989 Proof	—	£5	2002 Proof	—	£5
1990 BU	—	£2	2002 Gold Proof	—	£175
1990 Proof	—	£5	2003	333,230,000	£1
1990 Silver Proof	—	£15	2003 BU	—	£3
1990 *Size reduced (18mm)*	1,634,976,005	£2	2003 Proof	—	£5
1990 BU	—	£3	2004	271,810,000	£1
1990 Proof	—	£4	2004 BU	—	£3

DATE	Mintage	UNC
2004 Proof	—	£5
2005	236,212,000	£1
2005 BU	—	£3
2005 Proof	—	£5
2006	317,697,000	£1
2006 BU	—	£3
2006 Proof	—	£7
2006 Silver Proof	—	£25
2007	246,720,000	£1
2007 BU	—	£5
2007 Proof	—	£7
2008	92,880,000	£1
2008 BU	—	£3
2008 Proof	—	£5
2008 Silver Proof	—	£25
2008 Gold Proof	—	£175
2008 Platinum Proof	—	£250
2008 **New Rev.,** no border beads on Obv	155,172,000	£1
2008 BU	—	£4
2008 Proof	—	£5
2008 Silver Proof	—	£20
2008 — — Piedfort	—	£35
2008 Gold Proof	—	£175
2008 Platinum Proof	—	£250
2009	132,960,300	£1
2009 BU	—	£6
2009 Proof	—	£7
2009 Silver Proof	—	£15
2010	296,245,500	£1
2010 BU	—	£4
2010 Proof	—	£5
2010 Silver Proof	—	£15
2011 Nickel-plated steel	50,400,000	£1
2011 — BU	—	£4

DATE	Mintage	UNC
2011 — Proof	—	£6
2011 Silver Proof	—	£15
2012	339,802,350	£1
2012 BU	—	£5
2012 Proof	—	£8
2012 Silver Proof with selective gold plating	—	£15
2012 Gold Proof	—	£175
2013	318,800,750	£1
2013 BU	—	£5
2013 Proof	—	£8
2013 Silver Proof	—	£25
2013 Gold Proof	—	£225
2014	885,004,520	£1
2014 BU	—	£5
2014 Proof	—	£8
2014 Silver Proof	—	£20
2015 **New Portrait**	536,600,000	£2
2015 BU	—	£4
2015 Proof	—	£6
2015 Silver Proof	—	£20
2015 Gold Proof	—	£250
2015 Platinum Proof	—	—
2016	308,200,000	£2
2016 BU	—	£4
2016 Proof	—	£6
2016 Silver Proof	—	£20
2017	220,515,000	—
2017 BU	—	—
2017 Proof	—	—
2017 Silver Proof	—	£25
2017 Gold Proof	—	£250
2018	—	—
2018 BU	—	—
2018 Proof	—	—
2018 Silver Proof	—	£25

TWO PENCE

Dated from 1971, and legal tender from Decimal Day that year, early examples are found in the blue Specimen decimal set wallets of 1968. They were minted in bronze up to 1991, and mainly in copper-plated steel from 1992. However details of where this rule does not totally apply (1992, 1996, 1998–2000 and 2002, 2006, 2008 and 2009) are given below. As with other denominations, "NEW" was replaced by "TWO" from 1982. Note that some years the 2p is only issued in the Year Sets

DATE	Mintage	UNC
1971	1,454,856,250	£2
1971 Proof	—	£3
1972 Proof	—	£6
1973 Proof	—	£8
1974 Proof	—	£8
1975	Est. approx. 273,145,000	£2
1975 Proof	—	£4
1976	Est. approx. 53,779,000	£2
1976 Proof	—	£4
1977	109,281,000	£2
1977 Proof	—	£4
1978	189,658,000	£3
1978 Proof	—	£4

DATE	Mintage	UNC
1979	260,200,000	£2
1979 Proof	—	£4
1980	408,527,000	£1
1980 Proof	—	£2
1981	353,191,000	£4
1981 Proof	—	£4
1982 Legend changed to TWO PENCE	205,000	£4
1982 Proof	—	£5
1983	631,000	£2
1983 Error NEW instead of TWO	—	£1000
1983 Proof	—	£4
1984	158,820	£2
1984 Proof	—	£4

DATE	Mintage	UNC
1985 *New portrait*	107,113,000	£2
1985 BU	—	£2
1985 Proof	—	£4
1986	168,967,500	£1
1986 BU	—	£2
1986 Proof	—	£4
1987	218,100,750	£1
1987 BU	—	£2
1987 Proof	—	£4
1988	419,889,000	£1
1988 BU	—	£2
1988 Proof	—	£4
1989	359,226,000	£1
1989 BU	—	£2
1989 Proof	—	£4
1990	204,499,700	£1
1990 BU	—	£2
1990 Proof	—	£3
1991	86,625,250	£1
1991 BU	—	£2
1991 Proof	—	£5
1992 Copper plated steel	102,247,000	£1
1992 Bronze BU	—	£2
1992 — Proof	—	£5
1993	235,674,000	£1
1993 BU	—	£2
1993 Proof	—	£3
1994	531,628,000	£1
1994 BU	—	£2
1994 Proof	—	£5
1995	124,482,000	£1
1995 BU	—	£2
1995 Proof	—	£5
1996	296,278,000	£1
1996 BU	—	£2
1996 Proof	—	£5
1996 Silver Proof	—	£25
1997	496,116,000	£1
1997 BU	—	£2
1997 Proof	—	£5
1998 *New Portrait*	Est. approx. 120,243,000	£1
1998 BU	—	£2
1998 Proof	—	£4
1998 Bronze	Est. approx. 93,587,000	£1
1999	353,816,000	£1
1999 Bronze BU	—	£2
1999 — Proof	—	£4
2000	536,659,000	£1
2000 BU	—	£3
2000 Proof	—	£5
2000 Silver Proof	—	£22
2001	551,880,000	£1
2001 BU	—	£2
2001 Proof	—	£4
2002	168,556,000	£1
2002 BU	—	£3
2002 Proof	—	£4
2002 Gold Proof	—	£275
2003	260,225,000	£1
2003 BU	—	£2
2003 Proof	—	£4
2004	356,396,000	£1
2004 BU	—	£2
2004 Proof	—	£4
2005	280,396,000	£1
2005 BU	—	£2
2005 Proof	—	£3

DATE	Mintage	UNC
2006	170,637,000	£1
2006 BU	—	£3
2006 Proof	—	£4
2006 Silver Proof	—	£15
2007	254,500,000	£2
2007 BU	—	£3
2007 Proof	—	£5
2008	10,600,000	£2
2008 BU	—	£3
2008 Proof	—	£5
2008 Silver Proof	—	£25
2008 Gold Proof	—	£275
2008 Platinum Proof	—	£450
2008 *New Rev.*, no border beads on Obv	241,679,000	£2
2008 — BU	—	£3
2008 — Proof	—	£5
2008 — Silver Proof	—	£20
2008 — Silver Proof Piedfort	—	£45
2008 — Gold Proof	—	£300
2008 — Platinum Proof	—	£500
2009	150,500,500	£2
2009 BU	—	£3
2009 Proof	—	£5
2009 Silver Proof	—	£25
2010	99,600,000	£2
2010 BU	—	£3
2010 Proof	—	£6
2010 Silver Proof	—	£25
2011	144,300,000	£2
2011 BU	—	£3
2011 Proof	—	£6
2011 Silver Proof	—	£25
2012	67,800,000	£2
2012 BU	—	£3
2012 Proof	—	£8
2012 Silver Proof with selective gold plating	—	£45
2012 Gold Proof	—	£275
2013	40,600,000	£2
2013 BU	—	£3
2013 Proof	—	£8
2013 Silver Proof	—	£25
2013 Gold Proof	—	£275
2014	247,600,020	£2
2014 BU	—	£3
2014 Proof	—	£8
2014 Silver Proof	—	£45
2015 *New Portrait*	139,200,000	£2
2015 BU	—	£3
2015 Proof	—	£5
2015 Silver Proof	—	£25
2015 Gold Proof	—	£275
2015 Platinum Proof	—	£300
2016	185,200,000	£2
2016 BU	—	£3
2016 Proof	—	£5
2016 Silver Proof	—	£25
2017	16,600,000	£2
2017 BU	—	£3
2017 Proof	—	£5
2017 Silver Proof	—	£25
2018 BU (only issued in year sets)	—	£5
2018 Proof	—	£8
2018 Silver Proof	—	£30
2019 BU (only issued in year sets)	—	£5
2019 Proof	—	£8
2019 Silver Proof	—	£25

ONE PENNY

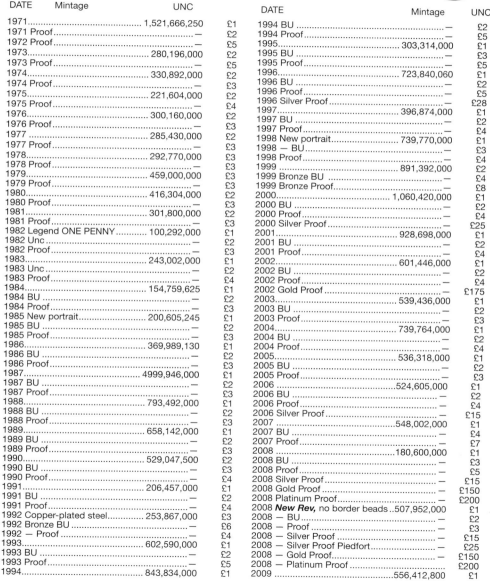

The history of this coin is very similar to that of the Two Pence coin (qv) except that all 1998 examples were of copper-plated steel.

DATE	Mintage	UNC
1971	1,521,666,250	£1
1971 Proof	—	£2
1972 Proof	—	£5
1973	280,196,000	£2
1973 Proof	—	£5
1974	330,892,000	£2
1974 Proof	—	£3
1975	221,604,000	£2
1975 Proof	—	£4
1976	300,160,000	£2
1976 Proof	—	£3
1977	285,430,000	£2
1977 Proof	—	£3
1978	292,770,000	£3
1978 Proof	—	£3
1979	459,000,000	£3
1979 Proof	—	£3
1980	416,304,000	£2
1980 Proof	—	£3
1981	301,800,000	£2
1981 Proof	—	£3
1982 Legend ONE PENNY	100,292,000	£1
1982 Unc	—	£2
1982 Proof	—	£3
1983	243,002,000	£1
1983 Unc	—	£2
1983 Proof	—	£4
1984	154,759,625	£1
1984 BU	—	£2
1984 Proof	—	£3
1985 New portrait	200,605,245	£1
1985 BU	—	£2
1985 Proof	—	£3
1986	369,989,130	£1
1986 BU	—	£2
1986 Proof	—	£3
1987	4999,946,000	£1
1987 BU	—	£2
1987 Proof	—	£3
1988	793,492,000	£1
1988 BU	—	£2
1988 Proof	—	£3
1989	658,142,000	£1
1989 BU	—	£2
1989 Proof	—	£3
1990	529,047,500	£2
1990 BU	—	£3
1990 Proof	—	£4
1991	206,457,000	£1
1991 BU	—	£2
1991 Proof	—	£4
1992 Copper-plated steel	253,867,000	£3
1992 Bronze BU	—	£6
1992 — Proof	—	£4
1993	602,590,000	£1
1993 BU	—	£2
1993 Proof	—	£5
1994	843,834,000	£1

DATE	Mintage	UNC
1994 BU	—	£2
1994 Proof	—	£5
1995	303,314,000	£1
1995 BU	—	£3
1995 Proof	—	£5
1996	723,840,060	£1
1996 BU	—	£2
1996 Proof	—	£5
1996 Silver Proof	—	£28
1997	396,874,000	£1
1997 BU	—	£2
1997 Proof	—	£4
1998 New portrait	739,770,000	£1
1998 — BU	—	£3
1998 Proof	—	£4
1999	891,392,000	£2
1999 Bronze BU	—	£4
1999 Bronze Proof	—	£8
2000	1,060,420,000	£1
2000 BU	—	£2
2000 Proof	—	£4
2000 Silver Proof	—	£25
2001	928,698,000	£1
2001 BU	—	£2
2001 Proof	—	£4
2002	601,446,000	£1
2002 BU	—	£2
2002 Proof	—	£4
2002 Gold Proof	—	£175
2003	539,436,000	£1
2003 BU	—	£2
2003 Proof	—	£3
2004	739,764,000	£1
2004 BU	—	£2
2004 Proof	—	£4
2005	536,318,000	£1
2005 BU	—	£2
2005 Proof	—	£3
2006	524,605,000	£1
2006 BU	—	£2
2006 Proof	—	£4
2006 Silver Proof	—	£15
2007	548,002,000	£1
2007 BU	—	£4
2007 Proof	—	£7
2008	180,600,000	£1
2008 BU	—	£3
2008 Proof	—	£5
2008 Silver Proof	—	£15
2008 Gold Proof	—	£150
2008 Platinum Proof	—	£200
2008 **New Rev,** no border beads	507,952,000	£1
2008 — BU	—	£2
2008 — Proof	—	£3
2008 — Silver Proof	—	£15
2008 — Silver Proof Piedfort	—	£25
2008 — Gold Proof	—	£150
2008 — Platinum Proof	—	£200
2009	556,412,800	£1

DATE	Mintage	UNC
2009 BU	—	£3
2009 Proof	—	£4
2009 Silver BU, in "Lucky Baby Gift Pack"	—	£15
2009 — Proof	—	£15
2010	609,603,000	£1
2010 BU	—	£3
2010 Proof	—	£4
2010 Silver BU, in "Lucky Baby Gift Card"	9,701	£15
2010 — Proof	—	£15
2011	431,004,000	£1
2011 BU	—	£2
2011 Proof	—	£3
2011 Silver BU in "Lucky Baby Pack"	—	£18
2011 – Proof	—	£15
2012	227,201,000	£1
2012 BU	—	£2
2012 Proof	—	£4
2012 Silver BU (three different packagings)	—	£15
2012 Silver Proof with selective gold plating	—	£18
2012 Gold Proof	—	£175
2013	260,900,000	£1
2013 BU	—	£2
2013 Proof	—	£5
2013 Silver BU	—	£25
2013 — Proof	—	£30
2013 Gold Proof	—	£175
2014	464,801,520	£1
2014 BU	—	£2
2014 Proof	—	£5
2014 Silver BU	—	£20
2014 Silver Proof	—	£25

DATE	Mintage	UNC
2015	154,600,000	£1
2015 BU	—	£2
2015 Proof	—	£5
2015 Silver BU	—	£20
2015 — Proof	—	£25
2015 Gold Proof	—	£200
2015 Platinum Proof	—	—
2015 *New Portrait*	418,201,016	£2
2015 — BU	—	£3
2015 — Proof	—	£6
2015 — Silver Proof	—	£25
2015 — Gold Proof	—	£200
2015 — Platinum Proof	—	—
2016	371,002,000	£1
2016 BU	—	£2
2016 Proof	—	£5
2016 Silver BU	2,842	£20
2016 Silver Proof	—	£25
2017	240,999,600	£1
2017 BU	—	£2
2017 Proof	—	£5
2017 Silver BU	—	£20
2017 Silver Proof	—	£25
2018 BU (only issued in year sets)	—	£2
2018 Proof	—	£5
2018 Silver BU	—	£20
2018 Silver Proof	—	£25
2019 BU (only issued in year sets)	—	£5
2019 Proof	—	£8
2019 Silver BU	—	£20
2018 Silver Proof	—	£25

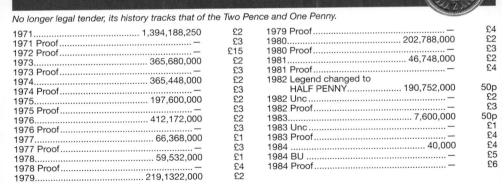

HALF PENNY

No longer legal tender, its history tracks that of the Two Pence and One Penny.

	Mintage	UNC
1971	1,394,188,250	£2
1971 Proof	—	£3
1972 Proof	—	£15
1973	365,680,000	£2
1973 Proof	—	£3
1974	365,448,000	£2
1974 Proof	—	£3
1975	197,600,000	£2
1975 Proof	—	£3
1976	412,172,000	£2
1976 Proof	—	£3
1977	66,368,000	£1
1977 Proof	—	£3
1978	59,532,000	£1
1978 Proof	—	£4
1979	219,1322,000	£2

	Mintage	UNC
1979 Proof	—	£4
1980	202,788,000	£2
1980 Proof	—	£3
1981	46,748,000	£2
1981 Proof	—	£4
1982 Legend changed to		
HALF PENNY	190,752,000	50p
1982 Unc	—	£2
1982 Proof	—	£3
1983	7,600,000	50p
1983 Unc	—	£1
1983 Proof	—	£4
1984	40,000	£4
1984 BU	—	£5
1984 Proof	—	£6

THE BRITANNIA SERIES

In addition to the large Britannia coin issues already listed, the series, which started in 1997, has grown to include many denominations and strikes in silver, gold and platinum. The coins are essentially bullion pieces and their values are usually related to the current price of precious metals, therefore no attempt has been made in this publication to give values for the series. To ascertain the value of a piece it is necessary to check with the prevailing price of precious metals. These issues are not listed in this publication for reasons of space but full information will be available on the Royal Mint's website, www.royalmint.com. It is also anticipated that the full list of issues will be included in this publication in due course.

SILVER

The silver Britannia series commenced in 1997, and, as with the Gold Britannia series, sets of the coins are listed in the "Proof and Specimen Sets" section. Coins contain one Troy ounce of fine silver (£2) alloyed to Britannia standard, i.e. 95.8 per cent fine silver, or fractions of one ounce as follows: half ounce (£1), quarter ounce (50 pence) and one tenth of an ounce (20 pence). Reverses change anually, all four coins of any particular date being of the same design. The reverses by Philip Nathan appear as follows: 1997 Chariot, 1998 Standing Britannia, 1999 Chariot, 2000 Standing Britannia, 2001 Una and the Lion, 2002 Standing Britannia, 2003 Britannia's Helmeted Head, 2004 Standing Britannia, 2005 Britannia Seated, 2006 Standing Britannia, 2009 Chariot.

The 2007 design is by Christopher Le Brun, and features a seated Britannia with Lion at her feet. The 2008 is by John Bergdahl, and features a standing Britannia facing left.

Two pounds Britannia coins to BU or "bullion" standard have been issued as individual coins for each year from 1998 onwards. 2010 features Suzie Zamit's Britannia with a portrait with a Corinthian style helmet.

The 2011 coins feature a seated Britannia and Union Flag, as described in the Britannia gold series above.

2012 saw the 15th anniversary of the Silver Series, but the reverse chosen was that of the Standing Britannia by Philip Nathan, which also marked the 25th Gold series. In addition, there is a 9-coin proof set of Half-Ounce silver coins dated 2012 featuring each of the Reverses used in the past, a 25th Anniversary collection. The story of the 2013 silver Britannia coins closely parallels that of the gold coins. The silver one-twentieth of an ounce has the logical face value of 10 pence.

The 2014 Silver Britannias closely follow the pattern of the three designs of 2014 Gold. This included the introduction of the silver one-fortieth of an ounce, with a face value of 5 pence. The Nathan Britannia has crenellated borders on both the obverse and the reverse, while the Year of the Horse has plain borders on both. Examples exist, however, of both One ounce silver bullion coins having the Other's obverse, thus producing two error coins, or "mules". 2014 also saw the SS *Gairsoppa* Quarter-ounce silver Britannia bullion coin with the edge inscription SS GAIRSOPPA. These coins have the Nathan Britannia reverse, and are struck from metal recovered from the vessel which was sunk by enemy action in 1941.

Both 2013 and 2014 one-ounce BU bullion Nathan Britannia coins exist with snakes or horses (respectively) on a plain edge. These were the result of a contract between the Royal Mint and the bullion dealers A-mark of Santa Monica, California, and commemorate Chinese Lunar years. In 2015 Designer Jody Clark scored a first when his portrayal of Britannia was used on the £50 coin which also carried his new portrait of the Queen.

GOLD

In 1987 the gold Britannia £100 coin was introduced. It contained one Troy ounce of fine gold, alloyed to 22 carat, and this has continued to the present day. At the same time, and also continuing, gold coins of face value £50, £25 and £10 appeared, containing a half ounce, quarter ounce and one tenth of an ounce of fine gold respectively. From 1987 to 1989 the alloy was of copper (Red Gold), whereas from 1990 to the present day the alloy has been of silver and copper (yellow gold).

Proof sets of these coins are listed in the "Proof and Specimen Sets" section. In addition, non-proof coins have been minted, it is believed for each of the four coins for every year. The one ounce £100 Britannia is primarily issued as a bullion coin in the non-proof standard, originally in competition with the South African Krugerrand. Its price is quoted daily on the financial pages of some newspapers.

There were five reverse designs by Philip Nathan:- 1987-1996 Standing Britannia, 1997 Chariot, 1998-2000 Standing Britannia, 2001 Una and the Lion, 2002 Standing Britannia, 2003 Britannia's Helmeted Head, 2004 Standing Britannia, 2005 Britannia seated, 2006 Standing Britannia. For 2007 the design is a Seated Britannia with lion at her feet, by Christopher Le Brun. The 2008 design is of Britannia standing and facing left, by John Bergdahl. The 2009 reverse is similar to that of 1997, Britannia on a chariot, while 2010 has Suzie Zamit's Britannia potrait with a Corinthian style helmet. The 2011 design is by David Mach, and portrays a seated Britannia with trident and shield, replicating the design on a 1937 penny, superimposed on a Union Flag. The rotation of the coin from left to right, or vice-versa, creates an illusion of Britannia moving with the ripple of the flag.

In general the proof coins have reverse features frosted, The proofs with Standing Britannia and Una and the Lion reverses include P NATHAN on the reverse, whereas the equivalent bullion coins include NATHAN. The other three reverses have PN on both proofs and bullion coins.

2012 was the 25th anniversary of the Gold Britannia coin series, and the reverse design chosen was that of the 1987 coins, standing Britannia, by Philip Nathan. This was repeated in 2013, but only for Brilliant Uncirculated "Bullion" coins. A separate new series was introduced for Proof coins, a seated Britannia with an owl was featured, the artist being Robert Hunt. The range of Britannia Proofs was increased from 4 to 6, with the addition of a Five-ounce coin (qv) and a one-twentieth of an ounce, curiously denominated at One Pound and with a diameter of 12mm, just larger than a Maundy One Penny. All 2013 Gold Britannias are minted in 0.999 Au alloy.

2014 and 2015 each saw three Reverse designs. The Nathan outstretched arm of Britannia continued as the bullion coin. The series by new artists were of a standing Britannia facing left with lion (2014) by Jody Clark, and a "head and shoulders" Britannia holding the trident on her right shoulder, by Antony Dufont, the latter coin included the Clark portrayal of the Queen on the obverse.

The 2016 series Reverse was designed by Suzie Zamit and depicts Britannia as the Warrior Queen. The 2017 series celebrating the 30th anniversary of the gold Britannia used a design by Louis Tamlin which depicts a helmeted outline of Britain .

A further new denomination appeared in 2014, the gold one-fortieth of an ounce, diameter 8mm and face value 50 pence.

In 2018 David Lawrence chose to portray a beautiful head and shoulders of Britannia wearing a Corinthian helmet, returning to her classical roots. However, for 2019 David once again had her standing in a warlike pose with a lion at her feet and pointing her trident towards the sun. As David Lawrence himself explained: "My initial thoughts were influenced by the great engravers of the past. Their work has classical grace and gravitas I was keen to recreate . . . The end result is an Anglicised version of ancient Rome."

PRECIOUS METAL BULLION AND COLLECTOR COINS (SERIES)

The Shengxiào Collection

The Shengxiào Collection of Lunar Coins by designer Wuon-Gean Ho was begun for the Year of the Horse in 2014 bringing the Royal Mint in line with most other major mints of the world. As the series is growing we are listing them separately here, however, the larger denominatiions have also been listed under their respective headings.

Date	Weight Face value/	Auth. issue qty	No. Issued	Issue price
2014 YEAR OF THE HORSE				
Silver bullion.............................	1 ounce /£2	—	—	BV
Silver Proof	1 ounce/£2	8,888	—	£85
Silver Proof 5	ounces/£10	1,488	—	£450
Gold BU .... One-tenth	ounce/£10	2,888	1,779	£225
Gold bullion.............................	1 ounce/£100	—	—	BV
Gold Proof.............................	1 ounce/£100	888	811	£1,950
2015 YEAR OF THE SHEEP				
Silver bullion.............................	1 ounce /£2	—	—	BV
Silver Proof	1 ounce/£2	9,888	4,463	£85
Silver Proof with gold plating......	1 ounce/£2	4,888	1,358	£120
Silver Proof 5	ounces/£10	1,088	—	£395
Gold BU .... One-tenth	ounce/£10	2,888	922	£225
Gold bullion.............................	1 ounce/£100	—	—	BV
Gold Proof.............................	1 ounce/£100	888	548	£1,950
Gold Proof...........................5	ounces/£500	38	—	£7,500
2016 YEAR OF THE MONKEY				
Silver bullion.............................	1 ounce /£2	—	—	BV
Silver Proof	1 ounce/£2	8,888	—	£85
Silver Proof 5	ounces/£10	588	—	£395
Silver Proof 1	kilo/£500	88	—	£2,000
Gold BU .... One-tenth	ounce/£10	1,888	—	£175
Gold bullion.............................	1 ounce/£100	—	—	BV
Gold Proof.............................	1 ounce/£100	888	—	£1,495
Gold Proof...........................5	ounces/£500	38	—	£7,500
Gold Proof...........................1	kilo/£1,000	8	—	£42,500
2017 YEAR OF THE ROOSTER				
Silver bullion.............................	1 ounce /£2	—	—	BV
Silver Proof	1 ounce/£2	3,888	—	£85
Silver Proof 5	ounces/£10	388	—	£415
Silver Proof 1	kilo/£500	88	—	£2,050
Gold BU .... One-tenth	ounce/£10	2,088	—	£205
Gold bullion.............................	1 ounce/£100	—	—	BV
Gold Proof.............................	1 ounce/£100	688	—	£1,780
Gold Proof...........................5	ounces/£500	38	—	£8,250
Gold Proof.............................	1 kilo/£1,000	8	—	£49,995
2018 YEAR OF THE DOG				
Silver bullion.............................	1 ounce /£2	—	BV	
Silver Proof	1 ounce/£2	5,088	£85	
Silver Proof 5	ounces/£10	388	£415	
Silver Proof 1	kilo/£500	108	£2,050	
Gold BU .... One-tenth	ounce/£10	1,088	£175	
Gold bullion.............................	1 ounce/£100	—	BV	
Gold Proof.............................	1 ounce/£100	888	£1,795	

Date	Weight/ Face value	Auth. issue qty	No. Issued	Issue price
2019 LUNAR YEAR OF THE PIG				
Silver bullion	1 ounce /£2	—	—	BV
Silver Proof	1 ounce/£2	3,888	—	£85
Silver Proof	5 ounces/£10	288	—	£420
Silver Proof	1 kilo/£500	38	—	£2,025
Gold BU	One-tenth ounce/£10	1,088	—	£210
Gold bullion	1 ounce/£100	—	—	BV
Gold Proof	1 ounce/£100	888	—	£1,880
Gold Proof	5 ounces/£500	38	—	£8,645
Gold Proof	1 kilo/£1,000	8	—	—

The Queen's Beasts

In 2016 a new series of coins was introduced by the Royal Mint entitled "The Queen's Beasts". These are intended as a homage to Her Majesty becoming Britain's longest reigning monarch and each coin in the series represents one of the heraldic animals sculpted by James Woodford, RA, for the Coronation ceremony held in Westminster Abbey in 1953. The 6-foot tall sculptures each symbolised the various strands of royal ancestry and were inspired by the King's Beasts of Henry VIII that still line the bridge at Hampton Court .So far six beasts have been chosen as the subjects of the reverse designs of the series: the Lion (bullion and collector), the Griffin (bullion only), the Dragon (bullion and collector), the Unicorn (bullion and collector), the Bull (bullion and collector) and the Falcon (collector coin only). The coins all carry the effigy of Her Majesty the Queen by Jody Clark on the obverse with the heraldic beasts, by the same designer, appearing on the reverse. The coins have been struck in a variety of metals and in different sizes with the bullion issues and the collector coins actually bearing slightly different designs, even though the "beast" is the same". To make it simple for collectors to follow the series we list them below, showing the issue price, rather than under their various denominations.

Date	Weight Face value/	Auth. issue qty	Issue price
THE LION OF ENGLAND			
2016 Silver bullion	2 ounces/£5	—	BV
2016 Gold bullion	1 ounce/£100	—	BV
2017 Cu-Ni BU	£5	—	£13
2017 Silver Proof	1 ounce/£2	8,500	£85
2017 Silver Proof	5 ounces/£10	2,500	£415
2017 Silver bullion	10 ounces/£10	—	BV
2017 Silver Proof	1 kilo/£500	350	£2,050
2017 Gold Proof	Quarter ounce/£25	2,500	£475
2017 Gold Proof	1 ounce/£100	1,000	£1,780
2017 Gold Proof	5 ounces/£500	125	£8,25
2017 Gold proof	1 kilo/£1,000	—	£49,995
2017 Platinum bullion	1 ounce/£100	—	BV
THE GRIFFIN OF EDWARD III			
2017 Silver bullion	2 ounces/£5	—	BV
2017 Gold bullion	Quarter ounce/£25	—	BV
2017 Gold bullion	1 ounce/£100	—	BV
THE RED DRAGON OF WALES			
2017 Silver bullion	2 ounces/£5	—	BV
2017 Gold bullion	Quarter ounce/£25	—	BV
2017 Gold bullion	1 ounce/£100	—	BV
2018 Gold Proof	1 kilo/£1000	—	£49,995
2018 Silver Proof	1 kilo/£500	—	£2025
THE UNICORN OF SCOTLAND			
2017 Cu-Ni BU	£5	—	£13
2017 Silver Proof	1 ounce/£2	6,250	£85
2017 Silver Proof	5 ounces/£10	750	£415
2017 Silver Proof	10 ounces/£10	850	£795
2017 Silver Proof	1 kilo/£500	225	£2,050
2017 Gold Proof	Quarter ounce/£25	1,500	£475

Date	Weight Face value/	Auth. issue qty	Issue price
THE BLACK BULL OF CLARENCE			
2018 Cu-Ni BU £5		—	£13
2018 Silver Proof .... 1 ounce/£2		6,000	£85
2018 Silver Proof .... 5 ounces/£10		700	£420
2018 Silver Proof .... 10 ounces/£10		600	£795
2018 Silver Proof ....1 kilo/£500		150	£2,025
2018 Gold Proof .... 1 ounce/£100		500	£1,850
2018 Gold Proof .... 5 ounces/£500		85	£8,565
THE YALE OF BEAUFORT			
2019 Cu-Ni BU £5		—	£13
2019 Silver Proof .... 1 ounce/£2		—	BV
2019 Silver Proof .... 10 ounces/£10		240	£795
2019 Silver Proof ....1 kilo/£500		120	£2,025
2019 Gold Proof .... 1/4 ounce/£25		—	BV
2019 Gold Proof .... 1 ounce/£100		—	BV
2019 Gold Proof .... 5 ounces/£500		70	£8,645
2019 Gold Proof ....1 kilo/£1000		13	—

The Valiant

The Valiant series of silver bullion-related coins portraying St George slaying the Dragon by artist Etienne Millner was introduced in 2018 with an attractive 10 ounce silver piece with the weight shown in the field. In 2019 the design has been modified to give the weight in the legend around the circumference of the reverse. The obverse carries the effigy of Her Majesty the Queen by Jody Clark.

Date	Weight Face value/	Auth. issue qty	Issue price
2018 silver ....10 ounces		—	£191.58
2019 silver .... 1 ounce		100,000	£19.76
2019 silver ....10 ounces		—	£198.60

The Royal Arms

Another bullion coin aimed at the investor, The Royal Arms series in gold and silver was introduced in 2019. The coins carry the Royal Arms as depicted by Eric Sewell in 1983 but reinterpreted in this design by Timothy Noad.

Date	Weight Face value/	Auth. issue qty	Issue price
2019 silver .... 1 ounce/£2		—	£19.86
2019 gold .... 1 ounce/£100		—	£1,287.71

This information is correct at the time of going to press (September 2019) but, as the reader can see, there are numerous possibilities for other coins in each series to achieve uniformity. To keep up to date on the new releases visit www.royalmint. com and www.royalmintbullion.com or check in COIN NEWS magazine every month.

With an interesting programme of issues intended to promote coin collecting, the Royal Mint produced a series of coins which were offered to the public at face value. The first issue was made in 2013 and was a £20 coin. The series was extended in 2015 to include a £100. In the same year the £50 silver coin in the Britannia series was offered as part of this programme. The issues are listed below.

HUNDRED POUNDS

Following on from the late 2013 introduction of the Twenty Pounds (see below) a "Hundred Pounds for £100" appeared, again a 0.999 Fine Silver coin, of two ounces weight, in early 2015.

DATE	Auth. issue qty	No. Issued	UNC
2015 Big Ben, BU	50,000	49,147	£100
2015 Buckingham Palace, BU	50,000	47,851	£100
2016 Trafalgar Square	—	14,878	£100

FIFTY POUNDS

A new denomination introduced in 2015, with the slogan "Fifty Pounds for £50". A double first for Jody Clark, minted in 99.99 silver, diameter 34mm.

DATE	Auth. issue qty	No. Issued	UNC
2015 Britannia BU	100,000	78,644	£50
2016 Shakespeare BU	—	14,948	£60

TWENTY POUNDS

Another new denomination was added in late 2013. Marketed by the Royal Mint under the slogan "Twenty Pounds for £20", it is a 27mm diameter 0.999 Fine silver coin.

DATE	Auth. issue qty	No. Issued	UNC
2013 Pistrucci St George & Dragon BU	250,000		£24
2014 Centenary of the outbreak of the WWI	—	141,751	£24
2015 Sir Winston Churchill	—	132,142	£20
2015 The Longest Reigning Monarch, New Portrait	—	149,408	£20
2016 The 90th Birthday of Her Majesty the Queen	—	116,354	£20
2016 The Welsh Dragon	—	—	£25
2016 Christmas Nativity	—	29,929	£30
2017 Platinum Wedding Anniversary	70,000	—	£25

PROOF AND SPECIMEN SETS

NOTE: The prices quoted in this guide were set at September 2019 with the price of gold around £1,220 per ounce and silver £14.50 per ounce—market fluctuations will have a marked effect on the values of modern precious metal coins. However, the prices quoted here for the *recently issued* sets are the original Royal Mint retail prices.

The following listings are an attempt to include all officially marketed products from the Royal Mint of two coins or more, but excluding those which included non-UK coins. It is appreciated that not all have been advertised as new to the public, but it is assumed that at some time they have been, or will be, available. In a few cases, therefore, the prices may be conjectural but are, nevertheless, attempts at listing realistic values, in some instances based on an original retail price. In the case of Elizabeth II sets, if no metal is stated in the listing, the coins in the sets are of the same metal as the circulation coin equivalent. In addition to the above we have excluded historical gold coin sets, such as sets of sovereigns from different mints, where the dates of the coins vary from one set to another.

DATE	FDC

GEORGE IV
1826 £5–farthing (11 coins) .... From £45,000

WILLIAM IV
1831 Coronation £2–farthing (14 coins) .... From £35,000

VICTORIA
1839 "Una and the Lion" £5–farthing (15 coins) .... From £100,000
1853 Sovereign–quarter farthing, including "Gothic"crown (16 coins) .... From £75,000
1887 Golden Jubilee £5–3d (11 coins) .... From £30,000
1887 Golden Jubilee Crown–3d (7 coins) .... From £5500
1893 £5–3d (10 coins) .... From £30,000
1893 Crown–3d (6 coins) .... From £5000

EDWARD VII
1902 Coronation £5–Maundy penny, matt proofs (13 coins) .... From £6500
1902 Coronation Sovereign–Maundy penny, matt proofs (11 coins) .... From £3500

GEORGE V
1911 Coronation £5–Maundy penny (12 coins) £8000
1911 Sovereign–Maundy penny (10 coins) £3500
1911 Coronation Halfcrown–Maundy penny (8 coins) £1500
1927 New types Crown–3d (6 coins) £850

GEORGE VI
1937 Coronation £5–half sovereign (4 coins) £6500
1937 Coronation Crown–farthing including Maundy money (15 coins) £550
1950 Mid-century Halfcrown–farthing (9 coins) £200
1951 Festival of Britain, Crown–farthing (10 coins) £250

ELIZABETH II
1953 Proof Coronation Crown–farthing (10 coins) £125
1953 Currency (plastic) set halfcrown–farthing (9 coins) £15
1968 Specimen decimal set 10p, 5p and 1971-dated bronze in blue wallet (5 coins) £3
1970 Proof Last £sd coins (issued from 1972) Halfcrown–halfpenny (8 coins) £20
1971 Proof (issued 1973) 50p–half penny (6 coins) £18
1972 Proof (issued 1976) 50p–half penny (7 coins including Silver Wedding crown) £24
1973 Proof (issued 1976) 50p–half penny (6 coins) £16
1974 Proof (issued 1976) 50p–half penny (6 coins) £18
1975 Proof (issued 1976) 50p–half penny (6 coins) £18

DATE	FDC
1976 Proof 50p–half penny (6 coins)	£18
1977 Proof 50p–half penny (7 coins including Silver Jubilee crown)	£22
1978 Proof 50p–half penny (6 coins)	£16
1979 Proof 50p–half penny (6 coins)	£18
1980 Proof gold sovereign series (4 coins)	£2500
1980 — 50p–half penny (6 coins)	£16
1981 Proof £5, sovereign, Royal Wedding Silver crown, 50p–half penny (9 coins)	£800
1981 — 50p–half penny (6 coins)	£18
1982 Proof gold sovereign series (4 coins)	£2500
1982 — 50p–half penny (7 coins)	£20
1982 Uncirculated 50p–half penny (7 coins)	£15
1983 Proof gold double-sovereign to half sovereign (3 coins)	£1250
1983 — £1–half penny (8 coins) (includes H. J. Heinz sets)	£25
1983 Uncirculated £1–half penny (8 coins) (includes Benson & Hedges and Martini sets)	£30
1983 — — (8 coins) (only Benson & Hedges and Martini sets) with "2 NEW PENCE" legend	£1250
1983 — 50p–half penny (7 coins) (H. J. Heinz sets)	£16
1983 — — (7 coins) (H. J. Heinz set) with "2 NEW PENCE" legend	£1250
1984 Proof gold five pounds, sovereign and half-sovereigns (3 coins)	£1250
1984 — £1 (Scottish rev.)–half penny (8 coins)	£20
1984 BU £1 (Scottish rev.)–half penny (8 coins)	£16
1985 New portrait proof gold sovereign series (4 coins)	£1250
1985 Proof £1–1p in de luxe case (7 coins)	£25
1985 — in standard case	£20
1985 BU £1–1p (7 coins) in folder	£15
1986 Proof gold Commonwealth Games £2, sovereign and half sovereign (3 coins)	£1250
1986 — Commonwealth Games £2–1p, de luxe case (8 coins)	£30
1986 — — in standard case (8 coins)	£25
1986 BU £2–1p in folder (8 coins)	£20
1987 Proof gold Britannia set (4 coins)	£2250
1987 — — — £25 and £10 (2 coins)	£450
1987 — — double- to half sovereign (3 coins)	£1250
1987 — £1–1p in de luxe case (7 coins)	£35
1987 — £1–1p in standard case (7 coins)	£25
1987 BU £1–1p in folder (7 coins)	£20
1988 Proof gold Britannia set (4 coins)	£2250
1988 — — — £25 and £10 (2 coins)	£450
1988 — — double- to half sovereign (3 coins)	£1250
1988 — £1–1p in de luxe case (7 coins)	£35
1988 — £1–1p in standard case (7 coins)	£30
1988 BU £1–1p in folder (7 coins) (includes Bradford & Bingley sets)	£18
1989 Proof gold Britannia set (4 coins)	£2250
1989 — — — £25 and £10 (2 coins)	£450
1989 — — 500th anniversary of the sovereign series set (4 coins)	£4000
1989 — — — double- to half sovereign (3 coins)	£2250
1989 — Silver Bill of Rights £2, Claim of Right £2 (2 coins)	£65
1989 — — Piedfort as above (2 coins)	£100
1989 BU £2 in folder (2 coins)	£25
1989 Proof £2 (both)–1p in de luxe case (9 coins)	£35
1989 — in standard case (9 coins)	£30
1989 BU £1–1p in folder (7 coins)	£25
1990 Proof gold Britannia set (4 coins)	£2250
1990 — — sovereign series set (4 coins)	£2250
1990— — double- to half sovereign (3 coins)	£1250
1990 — silver 5p, 2 sizes (2 coins)	£28
1990 — £1–1p in de luxe case (8 coins)	£35
1990 — £1–1p standard case (8 coins)	£30
1990 BU £1–1p in folder (8 coins)	£20
1991 Proof gold Britannia set (4 coins)	£2250
1991 — — sovereign series set (4 coins)	£2250
1991 — — double- to half sovereign (3 coins)	£1250
1991 — £1–1p in de luxe case (7 coins)	£35
1991 — £1–1p in standard case (7 coins)	£28
1991 BU £1–1p in folder (7 coins)	£18

DATE	FDC
1992 Proof gold Britannia set (4 coins)	£2250
1992 — — sovereign series set (4 coins)	£2250
1992 — — double- to half sovereign (3 coins)	£1250
1992 — £1–1p including two each 50p and 10p de luxe case (9 coins)	£38
1992 — £1–1p as above in standard case (9 coins)	£32
1992 BU £1–1p as above in folder (9 coins)	£16
1992 — with Enhanced Effigy on obverse of 20p	£25
1992 Proof silver 10p, two sizes (2 coins)	£25
1993 Proof gold Britannia set (4 coins)	£2250
1993 — — sovereign series set (4 coins plus silver Pistrucci medal)	£2250
1993 — — double- to half sovereign (3 coins)	£1250
1993 — Coronation anniversary £5–1p in de luxe case (8 coins)	£38
1993 — — in standard case (8 coins)	£35
1993 BU £1–1p including 1992 EU 50p (8 coins)	£15
1994 Proof gold Britannia set (4 coins)	£2250
1994 — — sovereign series set (4 coins)	£2250
1994 — — £2 to half sovereign (3 coins)	£1250
1994 — Bank of England Tercentenary £2–1p in de luxe case (8 coins)	£38
1994 — — in standard case (8 coins)	£35
1994 BU £1–1p in folder (7 coins)	£18
1994 Proof gold 1992 and 1994 50p (2 coins)	£350
1994 — "Family silver" set £2–50p (3 coins)	£65
1995 Proof gold Britannia set (4 coins)	£2250
1995 — — sovereign series (4 coins)	£2250
1995 — — £2 to half sovereign (3 coins)	£850
1995 — 50th Anniversary of WWII £2–1p in de luxe case (8 coins)	£40
1995 — — as above in standard case (8 coins)	£35
1995 BU as above in folder (8 coins)	£16
1995 Proof "Family Silver" set £2 (two) and £1 (3 coins)	£90
1996 Proof gold Britannia set (4 coins)	£2250
1996 — — sovereign series set (4 coins)	£2250
1996 — — double- to half sovereign (3 coins)	£1250
1996 — Royal 70th Birthday £5–1p in de luxe case (9 coins)	£50
1996 — — as above in standard case (9 coins)	£45
1996 BU Football £2–1p in folder (8 coins)	£20
1996 Proof gold Britannia £10 and half-sovereign (2 coins)	£550
1996 — sovereign and silver £1 (2 coins)	£250
1996 — — "Family silver" set £5–£1 (3 coins)	£85
1996 — silver 25th Anniversary of Decimal currency £1–1p (7 coins)	£150
1996 Circulation and BU 25th Anniversary of Decimalisation 2s 6d–halfpenny (misc.) and £1–1p in folder (14 coins)	£25
1997 Proof gold Britannia set (4 coins)	£2250
1997 — — sovereign series set (4 coins)	£2250
1997 — — — £2 to half sovereign (3 coins)	£1250
1997 — Silver Britannia set (4 coins)	£150
1997 — Golden Wedding £5–1p in red leather case	£45
1997 — — as above in standard case (10 coins)	£35
1997 BU £2 to 1p in folder (9 coins)	£25
1997 Proof silver 50p set, two sizes (2 coins)	£45
1997/1998 Proof silver £2 set, both dates (2 coins)	£70
1998 Proof gold Britannia set (4 coins)	£2250
1998 — — sovereign series set (4 coins)	£2250
1998 — — double- to half sovereign (3 coins)	£1250
1998 Proof silver Britannia set (4 coins)	£185
1998 Prince of Wales £5–1p (10 coins) in red leather case	£45
1998 — as above in standard case (10 coins)	£38
1998 BU £2–1p in folder (9 coins)	£16
1998 Proof silver European/NHS 50p set (2 coins)	£60
1998 BU Britannia/EU 50p set (2 coins)	£8
1999 Proof gold Britannia set (4 coins)	£2250
1999 — — Sovereign series set (4 coins)	£2250
1999 — — £2 to half sovereign (3 coins)	£1250
1999 Princess Diana £5–1p in red leather case (9 coins)	£65
1999 — as above in standard case (9 coins)	£45

DATE	FDC
1999 BU £2–1p (8 coins) in folder	£20
1999 Proof "Family Silver" set. Both £5, £2 and £1 (4 coins)	£150
1999 Britannia Millennium set. Bullion £2 and BU £5 (2 coins)	£30
1999/2000 Reverse frosted proof set, two x £1 (2 coins)	£75
2000 Proof gold Britannia set (4 coins)	£2250
2000 — — Sovereign series set (4 coins)	£2250
2000 — — — double- to half sovereign (3 coins)	£1250
2000 Millennium £5–1p in de luxe case (10 coins)	£50
2000 — — as above in standard case (10 coins)	£45
2000 — Silver set Millennium £5 to 1p plus Maundy (13 coins)	£225
2000 BU £2–1p set in folder (9 coins)	£20
2000 Millennium "Time Capsule" BU £5 to 1p (9 coins)	£30
2001 Proof gold Britannia set (4 coins)	£2250
2001 — Sovereign series set (4 coins)	£2250
2001 — — — £2–half sovereign (3 coins)	£1250
2001 — Silver Britannia set (4 coins)	£150
2001 — Victoria £5–1p in Executive case (10 coins)	£100
2001 — — as above in red leather case (10 coins)	£75
2001 — — as above in "Gift" case (10 coins)	£48
2001 — — as above in standard case (10 coins)	£40
2001 BU £2–1p in folder (9 coins)	£18
2002 Proof gold Britannia set (4 coins)	£2250
2002 — — Sovereign series set, all Shield rev. (4 coins)	£2250
2002 — — — double- to half sovereign (3 coins)	£1250
2002 — — Golden Jubilee set £5–1p plus Maundy (13 coins)	£4500
2002 — Golden Jubilee £5–1p in Executive case (9 coins)	£75
2002 — — as above in red leather de luxe case (9 coins)	£50
2002 — — as above in "Gift" case (9 coins)	£42
2002 — — as above in standard case (9 coins)	£40
2002 BU £2–1p (8 coins) in folder	£16
2002 Proof Gold Commonwealth Games £2 set (4 coins)	£2250
2002 — Silver Piedfort Commonwealth Games £2 set (4 coins)	£250
2002 — — Commonwealth Games £2 set (4 coins)	£125
2002 — Commonwealth Games £2 set (4 coins)	£30
2002 BU Commonwealth Games £2 set (4 coins) in folder	£25
2003 Proof gold Britannia set (4 coins)	£2250
2003 — — — £50–£10 (3 coins)	£1250
2003 — — — type set, one of each £100 reverse (4 coins)	£2500
2003 — — Sovereign series set (4 coins)	£2250
2003 — — — series £2–half sovereign (3 coins)	£1250
2003 — Silver Britannia set (4 coins)	£45
2003 — — — type set (one of each £2 reverse) (4 coins)	£85
2003 — £5 to 1p, two of each £2 and 50p in Executive case (11 coins)	£80
2003 — — as above in red leather case (11 coins)	£55
2003 — — as above in standard case (11 coins)	£48
2003 BU £2 (two)–1p in folder (10 coins)	£22
2003 Proof silver Piedfort set. DNA £2, £1 and Suffragette 50p (3 coins)	£150
2003 Proof "Family Silver" set £5, Britannia and DNA £2, £1 and Suffragette 50p (5 coins)	£175
2003 Circ & BU "God Save the Queen" Coronation anniversary set 5s/0d to farthing (1953) and £5 to 1p (2003) in folder (19 coins)	£55
2003 Circulation or bullion "Royal Sovereign" collection, example of each Elizabeth II date (21 coins)	£3500
2004 Proof gold Britannia set (4 coins)	£2250
2004 — — — £50 to £10 (3 coins)	£1250
2004 — — — Sovereign series set (4 coins)	£2250
2004 — — — Series £2–half sovereign (3 coins)	£1250
2004 (Issue date) Royal Portrait gold sovereign set, all proof except the first: Gillick, Machin, Maklouf and Rank-Broadley sovereigns, and the 2nd, 3rd and 4th of above half-sovereigns, various dates (7 coins)	£2250
2004 Proof silver Britannia set (4 coins)	£150
2004 — "Family Silver" set £5, Britannia and Trevithick £2, £1 and Bannister 50p (5 coins)	£165
2004 — Silver Piedfort set, Trevithick £2, £1 and Bannister 50p (3 coins)	£175
2004 — £2 to 1p, two each of £2 and 50p in Executive case (10 coins)	£75

DATE   FDC

2004 — — as above in red leather case (10 coins)..£45
2004 — — as above in standard case (10 coins)...£40
2004 BU £2 to 1p in folder (10 coins)...£22
2004 — "New Coinage" set, Trevithick £2, £1 and Bannister 50p (3 coins)...................................£10
2004 BU "Season's Greetings" £2 to 1p and Royal Mint Christmas medal in folder (8 coins) £18
2005 Proof Gold Britannia set (4 coins)...£2250
2005 — — £50 to £10 (3 coins)..£1250
2005 — — Sovereign series set (4 coins)...£2250
2005 — — — series, double to half sovereign (3 coins)..£1250
2005 — Silver Britannia (4 coins)..£135
2005 — Gold Trafalgar and Nelson £5 crowns (2 coins)...£2250
2005 — Silver, as above (2 coins)..£85
2005 — — Piedfort, as above (2 coins)..£135
2005 — Silver Piedfort set, Gunpowder Plot and World War II £2, £1 and Johnson 50p (4 coins)....£200
2005 — £5 to 1p, two of each of £5, £2 and 50p in Executive case (12 coins).................................£80
2005 — — as above in red leather case (12 coins)...£60
2005 — — as above in standard case (12 coins) £45
2005 BU Trafalgar and Nelson £5 crowns in pack (2 coins)..£25
2005 — £2 (two) to 1p in folder (10 coins)...£25
2005 — "New Coinage" set, Gunpowder Plot £2, £1 and Johnson 50p (3 coins)..............................£10
2005 — "Merry Xmas" £2 to 1p and Royal Mint Christmas medal in folder (8 coins) £20
2006 Proof Gold Britannia set (4 coins)...£2250
2006 — — Sovereign Series set (4 coins)...£2250
2006 — — — series, double to half sovereign (3 coins) £1250
2006 — Silver Britannia (4 coins)..£145
2006 — Silver Brunel £2 coin set (2 coins)..£75
2006 — — Piedfort Brunel £2 coin set (2 coins)..£125
2006 — Gold Brunel £2 coin set (2 coins)..£950
2006 — Silver VC 50p coin set (2 coins)..£58
2006 — Silver Piedfort VC 50p coin set (2 coins)...£115
2006 — Gold VC 50p coin set (2 coins)..£675
2006 — Silver proof set, £5 to 1p plus Maundy coins (13 coins)...£325
2006 — — Piedfort collection £5, with trumpets enhanced with 23 carat gold, both Brunel £2, £1,
       both VC 50p (6 coins) £350
2006 — — Britannia £2 "Golden Silhouette" collection, five different reverses, all dated 2006 (5 coins) £350
2006 — Britannia £25 Gold "Portrait" collection, five different reverses, all dated 2006 (5 coins) £1550
2006 — £5 to 1p, three of each £2 and 50p in Executive case (13 coins)..£80
2006 — as above in red leather case (13 coins)..£55
2006 — as above in standard case (13 coins) £45
2006 BU £2 (two), £1, 50p (two) and to 1p in folder (10 coins)...£18
2006 Proof Brunel £2 in folder (2 coins)..£15
2006 — VC 50p in folder (2 coins)..£15
2006 — Gold Half-Sovereign set dated 2005 Noad and 2006 Pistrucci St George and the Dragon (2 coins)........£250
2007 — Gold Britannia set (4 coins)...£2500
2007 — — Sovereign Series set (4 coins)...£2250
2007 — — — series, double to half sovereign (3 coins)..£1250
2007 — — Sovereign and half-sovereign (2 coins) £375
2007 — "Family Silver" set, Britannia, £5 crown, Union and Slavery £2, Gateshead £1
       and Scouting 50p (6 coins) £225
2007 Proof Silver Piedfort Collection, as "Family Silver" above but excluding a Britannia (5 coins).........£300
2007 — Silver £1 Bridge series coins, dated 2004 to 2007 (4 coins)...£135
2007 — Silver Proof Piedfort £1 Bridge Series, dated 2004 to 2007 (4 coins) £275
2007 — Gold £1 Bridge series coins, dated as above (4 coins)..£2250
2007 — £5 to 1p, three £2 and two 50p in Executive case (12 coins) £85
2007 — as above, Deluxe in red leather case (12 coins) £65
2007 — as above, in standard case (12 coins) £50
2007 BU £2 (two) to 1p (9 coins)..£18
2007 Proof Silver Britannia (four coins)..£145
2007 — Platinum Britannia (4 coins)..£5000
2007 Satin Proof Silver Britannia, 20th Anniversary Collection, six different reverses, all dated 2007 (6 coins) £300
2007 50th Anniversary Sovereign set, 1957 circulation standard and 2007 Proof (2 coins)..............£450
2008 Proof Gold Britannia set (4 coins)...£2250
2008 — Platinum Britannia set (4 coins) £5000

DATE	FDC
2008 — Silver Britannia set (4 coins)	£150
2008 — Gold Sovereign series set (4 coins)	£2250
2008 — — double to half-sovereign (3 coins)	£1250
2008 — — Sovereign and half-sovereign (2 coins)	£500
2008 — "Family silver" set, 2x £5, Britannia £2, Olympiad £2 and Royal Arms £1 (5 coins)	£200
2008 — Silver Piedfort Collection, 2x £5, Olympiad £2 and Shield of Royal Arms £1 (4 coins)	£285
2008 — 2 x £5, 2 x £2, £1 to 1p in Executive case (11 coins)	£85
2008 — as above, Deluxe in black leather case (11 coins)	£55
2008 — as above, in standard back case (11 coins)	£60
2008 BU 2 x £2, Royal Arms £1 to 1p (9 coins)	£20
2008 — "Emblems of Britain" ("old" Revs) Royal Arms £1 to 1p (7 coins)	£15
2008 — "Royal Shield of Arms" ("new" Revs) Shield of Royal Arms £1 to 1p (7 coins)	£15
2008 — Above two sets housed in one sleeve	£28
2008 Proof Base Metal "Royal Shield of Arms" set, £1 to 1p (7 coins)	£40
2008 — Silver "Emblems of Britain" set, £1 to 1p (7 coins)	£160
2008 — — "Royal Shield of Arms" set, £1 to 1p (7 coins)	£160
2008 — — Above two sets in one black case	£325
2008 — Gold "Emblems of Britain" set, £1 to 1p (7 coins)	£3500
2008 — — "Royal Shield of Arms" set, £1 to 1p (7 coins)	£3500
2008 — — Above two sets in one oak-veneer case	£6750
2008 — Platinum "Emblems of Britain" set, £1 to 1p (7 coins)	£8500
2008 — — "Royal Shield of Arms" set, £1 to 1p (7 coins)	£8500
2008 — — Above two sets in one walnut veneer case	£15,750
2008 — Silver Piedfort "Royal Shield of Arms" set, £1 to 1p (7 coins)	£325
2008 — Gold set of 14 £1 coins, one of each Rev used since 1983, all dated 2008 (25th anniversary) (14 coins)	£9500
2008 — Silver with gold Rev highlighting as above (14 coins)	£500
2008 — 2 x £2, Royal Arms £1 to 1p (9 coins) Christmas Coin Sets, two different outer sleeves, Father Christmas or Three Wise men	£20
2009 Proof Gold Britannia set (4 coins)	£2200
2009 — Platinum Britannia set (4 coins)	£4000
2009 — Silver Britannia set (4 coins)	£150
2009 — Gold Sovereign series set (5 coins)	£2700
2009 — — — double to half-sovereign (3 coins)	£1250
2009 — — sovereign and half-sovereign (2 coins)	£450
2009 — "Family Silver" set, Henry VIII £5, Britannia £2, Darwin and Burns £2, £1 and Kew 50p (6 coins)	£225
2009 — Silver Piedfort collection, Henry VIII £5, Darwin and Burns £2 and Kew Gardens 50p (4 coins)	£275
2009 — Silver Set, £5 to 1p (12 coins)	£275
2009 — Base metal Executive set, £5 to 1p (12 coins)	£80
2009 — — — Deluxe set, £5 to 1p (12 coins)	£55
2009 — — — Standard set, £5 to 1p (12 coins)	£45
2009 BU Base metal set, £2 to 1p (11 coins)	£22
2009 — — —, £1 to 1p "Royal Shield of Arms" set (7 coins)	£12
2009 — — —, £2 to 1p (8 coins)	£15
2009 Proof set of 50p coins as detailed in FIFTY PENCE section, CuNi (16 coins)	£195
2009 — Silver (16 coins)	£425
2009 — Gold (16 coins)	£8500
2009 — Gold Piedfort (16 coins)	£20,000
2009 "Mind" set of £5 coins, silver (6 coins)	£350
2010 Gold Britannia set (4 coins)	£2750
2010 — — —, £50 to £10 (3 coins)	£1500
2010 — Silver Britannia set (4 coins)	£140
2010 — Gold Olympic Series "Faster", £100 and £25 (2), (3 coins)	£2250
2010 — Sovereign series set (5 coins)	£2750
2010 — — — double to half (3 coins)	£1250
2010 — — — sovereign to quarter (3 coins)	£550
2010 — "Silver Celebration" set, Restoration £5, Nightingale £2, London and Belfast £1 and Girlguiding 50p (5 coins)	£185
2010 Silver Piedfort set, coins as in "Silver Celebration" set (5 coins)	£300
2010 — Silver Collection, £5 to 1p (13 coins)	£300
2010 — Base Metal Executive Set, £5 to 1p (13 coins)	£80

DATE		FDC
2010 — — Deluxe set		£50
2010 — — Standard set		£40
2010 BU — Capital Cities £1 (2 coins)		£15
2010 — — Set, £2 to 1p (12 coins)		£35
2010 — — Definitive pack, £2 to 1p (8 coins)		£20
2010 Proof "Body" Collection of £5 coins, silver (6 coins)		£300
2010 Proof "Spirit" Collection of £5 coins, silver (6 coins)		£300
2011 Proof Gold Britannia set (4 coins)		£2750
2011 — — Premium set (3 coins)		£1500
2011 — Sovereign set (5 coins)		£3000
2011 — — double to half (3 coins)		£1200
2011 — — sovereign to quarter (3 coins)		£650
2011 — Silver Britannia set (4 coins)		£180
2011 — Olympic gold "Higher" set (3 coins)		£2650
2011 — — — "Faster" (2010) and "Higher" set (6 coins) in 9-coin case		£5300
2011 — Silver Collection, £5 to 1p (14 coins)		£400
2011 — — Celebration set, Duke of Edinburgh £5, Mary Rose and King James bible Cardiff and Edinburgh £1 and WWF 50p (6 coins)		£250
2011 — — — Piedfort, as above (6 coins)		£395
2011 Executive Proof Base metal set (14 coins)		£85
2011 De-luxe Proof Base metal set (14 coins)		£50
2011 Standard Proof Base metal set (14 coins)		£40
2011 BU set including £2, £1 and 50p commemoratives (13 coins)		£26
2011 BU set of Definitives (8 coins)		£25
2012 Proof Gold Britannia Set (4 coins)		£3600
2012 — — — £50 down (3 coins)		£1900
2012 — — — Half-ounce anniversary(9coins)		£9500
2012 — Sovereign set (5 coins)		£4000
2012 — — Double to Half (3 coins)		£1650
2012 — — Sovereign to Quarter (3 coins)		£825
2012 — Silver Britannia set (4 coins)		£195
2012 — Silver Britannia Half-Ounce Anniversary (9 coins)		£500
2012 BU Sovereign set Double to Half (3 coins)		£1550
2012 Proof Olympic gold Stronger set (3 coins)		£3500
2012 — — — 2x £25 (2 coins)		£1200
2010, 2011, 2012 Proof Olympic gold complete set (9 coins)		£10,500
2009, 2010, 2011, 2012 Complete Countdown sets:		
Gold Proof (4 coins)		£11,500
Silver Proof Piedport (4 coins)		£850
Silver Proof (4 coins)		£325
CuNi BU (4 coins)		£45
2012 Proof Gold set, Diamond Jubilee £5, Dickens & Technology £2, £1 to 1p (10 coins)		£8500
2012 — Silver set, as above with Selective Gold plating on £1 to 1p coins (10 coins)		£490
2012 — set (Premium) (10 coins)		£100
2012 — set (Collector) (10 coins)		£55
2012 BU set, include Diamond Jubilee £5 (10 coins)		£40
2012 — set, Technology £2 to 1p (8 coins)		£21
2012 Proof Gold, Diamond Jubilee £5 and Double Sovereign (2 coins)		£3200
2012 — Olympic and Paralympic £5 (2 coins)		£5500
2012 — Gold Piedfort 50p set, one each of the coins of Olympic sports in which Team GB gained gold medals (11 coins)		£25,000
2013 Proof Gold Britannia set, £100 to £1 (5 coins)		£3100
2013 — — — £50 to £10 (3 coins)		£1375
2013 — — —.£25 to £1 (3 coins)		£675
2013 — Silver Britannia set, £2 to 10p (5 coins)		£195
2013 — — — 20p and 10p (2 coins)		£39
2013 — Sovereign set (5 coins)		£4000
2013 — — Double to Half (3 coins)		£1650
2013 — — One to Quarter (3 coins)		£825
2013 — Gold £5 Portraits set (4 coins)		£9500
2013 — Silver Portraits set (4 coins)	1,465	£400
2013 — Silver Piedfort Portraits set (4 coins)	697	£800
2013 — Gold set, £5 Coronation anniversary to 1p (15 coins)		£12,500

DATE	FDC
2013 — Gold set of both London Underground £2 (2 coins)	£2000
2013 — Silver Piedfort set, as above (2 coins)	£200
2013 — Silver set, as above (2 coins)	£100
2013 BU set, as above (2 coins)	£20
2013 — Gold set, 30th anniversary of the One Pound coin, reverses from 1983 (Sewell), 1988 (Gorringe) and 2013 (Dent). (3 coins)	£3600
2013 — Silver, as above (3 coins)	£150
2013 BU Sovereign set, Double to Half (3 coins), struck June 2, 2013	£1550
2013 Proof Silver annual set, £5 Coronation anniv to 1p (15 coins)	£600
2013 — — Piedfort commemorative set (7 coins)	£650
2013 — "Premium" set (15 coins plus a "Latent Image" item)	£150
2013 — "Collector" set (15 coins)	£110
2013 — Commemorative set (7 coins)	£65
2013 BU annual set (15 coins)	£50
2013 — Definitive Set (8 coins)	£25
2014 Proof Gold Britannia (Clark) set £100 to 50p (6 coins)	£2600
2014 — — £50 to £10 (3 coins)	£1175
2014 — — £25 to £1 (3 coins)	£595
2014 — Silver Britannia (Clark) set £2 to 5p (6 coins)	£200
2014 — — 20p to 5p (3 coins)	£45
2014 — Sovereign set (5 coins)	£3300
2014 — — Double to half (3 coins)	£1300
2014 — — One to quarter (3 coins)	£625
2014 — Gold Commemorative set, £5 Queen Anne, 2 x £2, 2 x £1, 50p (6 coins)	£5500
2014 — Silver Piedfort set, as above (6 coins)	£570
2014 — — set as above (6 coins)	£295
2014 — — all major coins of 2014 (14 coins)	£560
2014 — Premium set (14 coins and a premium medal)	£155
2014 — Collector set (14 coins)	£110
2014 — Commemorative set (6 coins)	£65
2014 BU annual set (14 coins)	£50
2014 — definitive set (8 coins)	£25
2014 — Floral £1 set, Scotland and Northern Ireland (2 coins)	£18
2014 Proof Silver Outbreak of First World War set of £5 (6 coins)	£450
2014 — Gold set as above (6 coins)	—
2014 — Silver Portrait of Britain £5 Silver collection (4 coins)	£36
2015 Proof Gold Britannia (Dufort) set £100 to 50p, Clark portrait (6 coins)	£2,600
2015 — — — £50 to £10 (3 coins)	£1,175
2015 — — — £10 to 50p (3 coins)	£350
2015 — Silver Britannia (Dufort) set £2 to 5p, Clark portrait (6 coins)	£200
2015 — Sovereign set, Rank-Broadley portrait (5 coins)	£2700
2015 — — Double to half, Rank-Broadley portrait (3 coins)	£1300
2015 — — One to quarter, Rank-Broadley portrait (3 coins)	£625
2015 — Gold Commemorative set, 2 x £5, 2 x £2, 2 x £1, 50p, Rank-Broadley portrait (5 coins)	£5500
2015 — Silver Piedfort set, as above (5 coins)	£570
2015 — — set as above (5 coins)	£295
2015 — Base metal set as above (5 coins)	£65
2015 — Platinum definitive set £2 to 1p, Rank-Broadley portrait plus £2 to 1p Clark portrait (16 coins)	£12,500
2015 — Gold ditto	£7,600
2015 — Silver ditto	£480
2015 — Base metal ditto	£120
2015 BU definitive set as per Platinum set above (16 coins)	£50

The above four entries are also available as 8-coin sets with either the Rank-Broadley ("Final Edition") or the Clark ("First Edition" portrait. These are issued at half the prices quoted above.

2015 Proof Silver set of definitive and commemorative coins, Rank-Broadley portrait (13 coins)	£560
2015 — Premium set as above (13 coins and a Premium medal)	£155
2015 BU Collector set as above (13 coins and medal)	£110
2015 Proof Double to half sovereign, Clark portrait (3 coins)	£1,200
2015 — Silver commemorative set, Anniversary of First World War (6 coins)	£450
2015 Portrait of Britain Silver Proof Collection (4x£5 with colour)	£310
2016 Proof Gold Britannia (Zamit) set (6 coins)	£2,895
2016 — — — £50 to £10 (3 coins)	£1,350
2016 Proof Silver Britannia (Zamit) set (6 coins)	£200

DATE	FDC
2016 — Sovereign set, Butler Portrait (5 coins)	£2,700
2016 — — Double to half, Butler Portrait (3 coins)	£1,200
2016 — — One to quarter, Butler Portrait (3 coins)	£625
2016 — Gold Commemorative set, £5, 5x £2, £1, 50p (8 coins)	£6,100
2016 — Silver Piedfort set, as above (8 coins)	£595
2016 — — set as above (8 coins)	£395
2016 — Base metal set as above (8 coins)	£95
2016 — silver set, commemoratives and definitives (16 coins)	£595
2016 — Base metal set as above, Premium plus Medal (16 coins)	£195
2016 — — Collector set (16 coins)	£145
2016 Portrait of Britain Silver Proof Collection (4x£5 with colour)	£310
2016 BU Annual set including commemoratives (16 coins)	£55
2016 — Definitive set (8 coins)	£30
2016 Proof Silver set of £5 coins, Anniversary of First World War (6 coins)	£450
2016 Beatrix Potter 150th Anniversary 50p coin set (5 coins)	£55
2017 "Premium" set (13 coins & premium medal)	£195
2017 "Collector" Proof set (13 coins & medal)	£145
2017 Commemorative Proof (5 coins), 2x£5, 2x£2, 50p	£95
2017 Silver Piedfort Commemorative set (coins as above)	£595
2017 Silver Commemorative set (coins as above)	£350
2017 Silver set (13 coins £5–1p)	£625
2017 Portrait of Britain Silver Proof Collection (4x£5 with colour)	£310
2017 Proof Silver Outbreak of First World War set of £5 (6 coins)	£450
2017 Silver Proof Britannia (6 coins £20–5p) by Louis Tamlin	£215
2017 Gold Britannia set (3 coins £50–£10) by Louis Tamlin	£1,425
2017 Gold Britannia set (6 coins £100–50p) by Louis Tamlin	£3,295
2017 BU Annual set (13 coins as above)	£55
2017 Definitive set (8 coins)	£30
2018 BU Annual set (13 coins)	£55
2018 Annual Proof set (13 coins)	£155
2018 Definitive set (8 coins)	£30
2018 "Premium" set (13 coins & premium medal)	£210
2018 Portrait of Britain Silver Proof Collection (4x£5 with colour)	£310
2018 Centenary of World War I Silver Proof set of £5 (6 coins)	£465
2018 — Gold (6 coins)	£11,100
2018 Silver Britannia (6 coins £20–5p)	£215
2018 Gold Britannia set (3 coins £50–£10)	£1,430
2018 Gold Britannia set (6 coins £100–50p)	£3,300
2018 Silver Piedfort set (5 coins)	£555
2018 Silver set (5 commemorative and 8 circulating coins)	£610
2018 Commemorative coin set (5 coins)	£95
2019 BU Annual set (13 coins)	£55
2019 Annual Proof set with Medal (13 coins)	£210
2019 Definitive set (8 coins)	£30
2019 Proof set in Silver (13 coins in silver £5–1p)	£610
2019 Gold Proof commemorative set (5 coins £5–50p)	£6,300
2019 Silver Proof Piedfort commemorative set (5 coins)	£550
2019 Sovereign Proof set (5 coins)	£4,200
2019 "Premium" Sovereign Proof set (3 coins)	£1,695
2019 Sovereign Proof set (3 coins)	£890
2019 Paddington Bear Silver Proof set (2 coins)	£65
2019 Paddington Bear BU set (2 coins)	£10
2019 Silver Britannia "Premium" Proof set (6 coins £2–5p)	£215
2019 Gold Britannia Proof set (3 coins £50–£10)	£1,730
2019 Gold Britannia "Premium" Proof set (6 coins, £100–50p)	£3,895

2019 Celebrating 50 Years of the 50 Pence sets (3 types:

i. *British Military and Culture Set* (10 coins): New 50 Pence, Girl Guides, Kew Gardens, Roger Bannister, Scouting, Battle of Hastings, Battle of Britain, D-Day, Victoria Cross 150th Anniversary, Victoria Cross Heroic Acts, BU	£76.50
ii. *British Military Set* (5 coins): Battle of Hastings, Battle of Britain, D-Day, Victoria Cross 150th Anniversary, Victoria Cross Heroic Acts, BU	£45
2019 — — Proof (3,500)	£90
2019 — — Silver Proof (1,969)	£225
2019 — — Gold (75)	£3,825

ii. *British Culture Set* (5 coins): New 50 Pence, Girl Guides, Kew Gardens, Roger Bannister, Scouting, BU £45
2019 — — Proof (3,500)...£90
2019 — — Silver Proof (1,969) £225
2019 — — Gold (75)..£3,825

In addition to the above the Royal Mint produce the BU sets detailed above in Wedding and in Baby gift packs each year. Also the following patterns have been made available:

1999 (dated 1994) Bi-metal £2, plus three unprocessed or part-processed elements.. —
2003 Set of patterns of £1 coins with bridges designs, in gold, hall-marked on edges (4 coins) .... —
2003 — silver £1 as above (4 coins)..£150
2004 — gold £1 featuring heraldic animal heads, hall-marked on edge (4 coins)..£1000
2004 — silver £1 featuring heraldic animal heads, hall-marked on edge (4 coins)..£350

IMPORTANT NOTE:

In this section the prices quoted were set at September 2019 with the price of gold at around £1,220 per ounce and silver £14.50 per ounce. As the market for precious metals is notoriously volatile and unpredictable any price fluctuations have a marked effect on the values of modern precious metal coins, therefore it is important to seek professional advice when requiring a valuation for any of the precious metal sets listed. *The prices quoted here are for guidance only whereas the prices quoted for the recently issued sets are the original Royal Mint retail prices.*

ABBREVIATIONS COMMONLY USED TO DENOTE METALLIC COMPOSITION

Cu	Copper
Cu/Steel	Copper plated Steel
Ag/Cu	Silver plated copper
Ae	Bronze
Cu-Ni	Cupro-Nickel
Ni-Ag	Nickel Silver (note: does not contain silver)
Brass/Cu-Ni	Brass outer, Cupro-Nickel inner
Ni-Brass	Nickel-Brass
Ag	Silver
Au/Ag	Gold plated silver
Au	Gold
Pl	Platinum

SCOTLAND

The coins illustrated are pennies representative of the reign, unless otherwise stated.

	F	VF

DAVID I (1124–53)
Berwick, Carlisle, Edinburgh and Roxburgh Mints

	F	VF
Penny in the name of David	£1250	£4500
Cut Halfpenny	Extremely rare	
Penny in name of Stephen	£1000	£4000

David I

HENRY (1136–52)
Bamborough, Carlisle and Corbridge Mints for the Earl of Huntingdon and Northumberland

	F	VF
Penny	£1500	£6250
Cut Halfpenny	Extremely rare	

MALCOLM IV (1153–65)
Berwick and Roxburgh Mints

Penny (5 different types)	Extremely rare	

Henry

WILLIAM THE LION (1165–1214)
Berwick, Edinburgh, Dun (Dunbar?), Perth and Roxburgh Mints

	F	VF
Penny - cross pattee early issue ..... from	£1500	£4000
Penny – pellet & crescent ..... from	£175	£500
Penny – short cross & stars – mint & moneyer ..... from	£140	£400
Penny – short cross & stars HVE WALTER & var ..... from	£100	£295

ALEXANDER II (1214–49)
Berwick and Roxburgh Mints

	F	VF
Penny – in the name of William the Lion ..... from	£400	£1200
Penny – in own name ..... from	£600	£1750

William the Lion

ALEXANDER III (1249–86)
FIRST COINAGE (1250–80)
Pennies struck at the Mints at

	F	VF
Aberdeen ..... from	£140	£325
Ayr ..... from	£200	£550
Berwick ..... from	£75	£175
Dun (Dumfries / Dunfermline? / Dundee?) ..... from	£160	£400
Edinburgh ..... from	£140	£325
Forfar ..... from	£325	£900
Fres (Dumfries) ..... from	£275	£650
Glasgow ..... from	£275	£650
Inverness ..... from	£260	£580
Kinghorn ..... from	£325	£900
Lanark ..... from	£245	£625
Montrose ..... from	£530	£1100
Perth ..... from	£100	£265
Roxburgh ..... from	£110	£285
St Andrews ..... from	£260	£575
Stirling ..... from	£190	£525

Alexander II

SECOND COINAGE (1280–86)

	F	VF
Penny	£65	£145
Halfpenny	£90	£325
Farthing	£250	£750

Alexander III First Coinage

Alexander III Second Coinage

	F	VF

JOHN BALIOL (1292–1306)

FIRST COINAGE (Rough Surface issue)

		F	VF
Penny	from	£125	£275
Halfpenny	from	£400	Ex. rare
Penny – St. Andrews	from	£175	£475
Halfpenny – St. Andrews	from	£800	Ex. rare

SECOND COINAGE (Smooth Surface issue)

		F	VF
Penny	from	£200	£475
Halfpenny	from	£150	£425
Farthing		Extremely rare	
Penny – St. Andrews	from	£350	£950
Halfpenny – St. Andrews		Extremely rare	

John Baliol

ROBERT BRUCE (1306–29)

Berwick Mint

		F	VF
Penny	from	£750	£2000
Halfpenny	from	£500	£12500
Farthing	from	£950	£2950

Robert Bruce

DAVID II (1329–71)

Aberdeen and Edinburgh Mints

		F	VF
Noble		Extremely Rare	
Groat (Edinburgh)	from	£125	£325
Groat (Aberdeen)	from	£750	£1750
Halfgroat (Edinburgh)	from	£105	£275
Halfgroat (Aberdeen)	from	£525	£1250
Penny 1st Coinage 2nd Issue	from	£65	£195
Penny 2nd Coinage (Edinburgh)	from	£100	£275
Penny 2nd Coinage (Aberdeen)	from	£450	£1100
Halfpenny	from	£250	£725
Farthing	from	£350	£950

David II

ROBERT II (1371–90)

Dundee, Edinburgh and Perth Mints

		F	VF
Groat	from	£110	£325
Halfgroat	from	£135	£395
Penny	from	£85	£215
Halfpenny	from	£95	£275

Robert II

ROBERT III (1390–1406)

Aberdeen, Dumbarton, Edinburgh, Perth Mints

		F	VF
Lion or crown	from	£2000	£5750
Demy lion or halfcrown	from	£1250	£4500
Groat	from	£100	£275
Halfgroat	from	£175	£350
Penny	from	£250	£725
Halfpenny	from	£275	£850

JAMES I (1406–37)

Aberdeen, Edinburgh, Inverness, Linlithgow, Perth, Stirling Mints

		F	VF
Demy	from	£950	£2750
Half demy	from	£750	£2250
Groat Edinburgh	from	£175	£395
Groat Other Mints	from	£375	£1000
Penny	from	£250	£650
Halfpenny		Extremely rare	

Robert III Lion

F   VF

JAMES II (1437–60)

Aberdeen, Edinburgh, Linlithgow, Perth, Roxburgh, Stirling Mints

	F	VF
Demy .... from	£1050	£2950
Lion.. from	£1250	£4500
Half lion	Extremely rare	
Early groats (fleur-de-lis) Edinburgh .... from	£195	£550
Early groats (fleur-de-lis) Other Mints....................................	Extremely rare	
Later groats (crown) Edinburgh .... from	£325	£950
Later groats (crown) Other Mints.. from	£450	£1250
Later Halfgroats (crown) Edinburgh..................................... from	£600	£1650
Later Halfgroats (crown) Other Mints	Extremely rare	
Penny (billon) .... from	£250	£650

JAMES III (1460–88)

Aberdeen, Berwick and Edinburgh Mints

	F	VF
Rider..	£1750	£4500
Half rider	£1750	£4500
Quarter rider..	£2500	£7000
Unicorn	£2750	£7500
Groat (facing bust) Edinburgh .... from	£175	£500
Groat (facing bust) Berwick... from	£500	£1450
Groat (thistle & mullet) Edinburgh...................................... from	£250	£650
Groat (threequarter bust) Edinburgh.................................. from	£450	£1250
Groat (threequarter bust) Aberdeen .... from	£550	£1650
Halfgroat .... from	£450	£1250
Penny (silver) .... from	£325	£950
Plack (billon) .... from	£175	£450
Half plack) .... from	£195	£525
Penny (billon) .... from	£150	£425
Farthing (copper)	£200	£650
Penny – ecclesiastical issue.. from	£70	£185
Farthing – ecclesiastical issue... from	£125	£350

James III Groat, Berwick Mint

JAMES IV (1488–1513)

Edinburgh Mint

	F	VF
Unicorn...	£1500	£4250
Half unicorn	£1500	£4250
Lion or crown	Extremely rare	
Half lion	Extremely rare	
Groat... from	£400	£1375
Halfgroat... from	£700	£2000
Penny (silver) .... from	£150	£400
Plack .... from	£40	£100
Half plack	Extremely rare	
Penny (billon) .... from	£40	£120

James IV Unicorn

JAMES V (1513–42)

Edinburgh Mint

	F	VF
Unicorn	£2050	£5125
Half Unicorn	Extremely rare	
Crown	£1350	£4250
Ducat or Bonnet piece .... from	£1250	£5000
Two-thirds ducat..	£2500	£6500
One-third ducat	£3500	£9500
Groat... from	£225	£625
One-third groat .... from	£275	£775
Plack .... from	£50	£125
Bawbee .... from	£60	£165
Half bawbee .... from	£140	£325
Quarter bawbee...	Extremely rare	

James V Ducat or Bonnet Piece

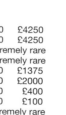

	F	VF

MARY (1542–67)

Mary Lion or Forty-Four Shillings

Edinburgh and Stirling Mints

FIRST PERIOD (1542–58)

	F	VF
Crown...	£1500	£4250
Twenty shillings	Extremely rare	
Lion (Forty-four shillings)	£1500	£5000
Half lion (Twenty-two shillings)	£1750	£5750
Ryals (Three pounds....................................	£4000	£11500
Half ryal	£4500	£12500
Portrait testoon..	£5000	£14500
Non-portrait testoon......................... from	£275	£825
Half testoon .... from	£250	£750
Bawbee .... from	£65	£180
Half bawbee .... from	£125	£325
Bawbee - Stirling..	£125	£400
Penny (facing bust)........................... from	£325	£900
Penny (no bust) .... from	£225	£650
Lion.. from	£50	£145
Plack.. from	£70	£195

SECOND PERIOD (Francis and Mary, 1558–60)

	F	VF
Ducat (Sixty shillings)	Extremely rare	
Non-portrait testoon......................... from	£325	£975
Half testoon .... from	£375	£1000
12 penny groat .... from	£80	£225
Lion.. from	£55	£135

THIRD PERIOD (Widowhood, 1560–65)

	F	VF
Portrait testoon..	£3250	£9500
Half testoon.	£3000	£8500

FOURTH PERIOD (Henry and Mary, 1565–67)

	F	VF
Portrait ryal.	£45000	£125000
Non-portrait ryal .... from	£750	£1750
Two-third ryal.................................... from	£650	£1550
One-third ryal.................................... from	£850	£2550

FIFTH PERIOD (Second widowhood, 1567)

	F	VF
Non-portrait ryal .... from	£750	£1750
Two thirds ryal .... from	£475	£1350
One-third ryal.................................... from	£650	£1550

JAMES VI (1567–1603)

(Before accession to the English throne)

James VI Fourth coinage
Ten Shillings

FIRST COINAGE (1567–71)

	F	VF
Ryal.. from	£400	£1100
Two-thirds ryal .... from	£300	£750
One-third ryal.................................... from	£350	£900

SECOND COINAGE (1571–80)

	F	VF
Twenty pounds	£25,000	£75,000
Noble (or half merk)........................... from	£115	£275
Half noble (or quarter merk)............... from	£125	£300
Two merks or Thistle dollar................. from	£1500	£3750
Merk .... from	£2500	£7250

THIRD COINAGE (1580–81)

	F	VF
Ducat..	£5000	£14500
Sixteen shillings..	£2500	£7250

	F	VF
Eight shillings	£1950	£5750
Four shillings	£4000	£9500
Two shillings	Extremely rare	

FOURTH COINAGE (1582–88)
Lion noble	£5500	£15000
Two-third lion noble	£4750	£13500
One-third lion noble	Extremely rare	
Forty shillings	£5000	£14500
Thirty shillings	£650	£1850
Twenty shillings	£425	£1250
Ten shillings	£425	£1250

FIFTH COINAGE (1588)
Thistle noble	£1700	£5250

SIXTH COINAGE (1591–93)
"Hat" piece	£4000	£10000
"Balance" half merk ...... from	£300	£895
"Balance" quarter merk	£725	£2000

James VI Seventh Coinage Rider

SEVENTH COINAGE (1594–1601)
Rider	£1250	£3500
Half rider	£1000	£3500
Ten shillings ...... from	£160	£450
Five shillings ...... from	£125	£375
Thirty pence ...... from	£225	£625
Twelve pence ...... from	£130	£375

EIGHTH COINAGE (1601–04)
Sword and sceptre piece ...... from	£550	£1650
Half sword and sceptre piece ...... from	£425	£1250
Thistle-merk ...... from	£110	£350
Half thistle-merk ...... from	£65	£175
Quarter thistle-merk ...... from	£55	£135
Eighth thistle-merk ...... from	£50	£110

BILLON AND COPPER ISSUES
Eightpenny groat ...... from	£45	£125
Fourpenny groat ...... from	£350	£1000
Twopenny plack ...... from	£130	£375
Hardhead ...... from	£35	£95
Twopence ...... from	£80	£230
Penny plack ...... from	£160	£750
Penny ...... from	£500	£1250

*James VI Seventh Coinage
10 Shillings*

JAMES VI (1603–25)
(After accession to the English throne)

Unit ...... from	£950	£2350
Double crown ...... from	£1100	£3250
British crown ...... from	£750	£1750
Halfcrown ...... from	£550	£1550
Thistle crown ...... from	£650	£2050
Sixty shillings ...... from	£350	£1000
Thirty shillings ...... from	£175	£450
Twelve shillings ...... from	£175	£575
Six shillings ...... from	£500	Ex. rare
Two shillings ...... from	£35	£100
One shilling ...... from	£125	£350
Copper twopence ...... from	£25	£70
Copper penny ...... from	£85	£250

*James VI after accession thirty
shillings*

	F	VF

CHARLES I (1625–49)

FIRST COINAGE (1625–36)

		F	VF
Unit		£1250	£3500
Double crown		£1000	£3150
British crown		Extremely rare	
Sixty shillings		£850	£2750
Thirty shillings		£175	£500
Twelve shillings		£150	£425
Six shillings	from	£350	£1000
Two shillings		£45	£110
One shilling		£150	£495

SECOND COINAGE (1636)

	F	VF
Half merk	£120	£300
Forty penny piece	£75	£210
Twenty penny piece	£70	£200

*Charles I Third Coinage
Sixty Shillings*

THIRD COINAGE (1637–42)

		F	VF
Unit	from	£1250	£4250
Half unit	from	£950	£2950
British crown	from	£600	£1750
British half crown	from	£525	£1500
Sixty shillings		£775	£1850
Thirty shillings	from	£175	£550
Twelve shillings	from	£120	£375
Six shillings	from	£80	£225
Half merk	from	£120	£395
Forty pence	from	£40	£110
Twenty pence	from	£25	£70

FOURTH COINAGE (1642)

	F	VF
Three shillings thistle	£60	£150
Two shillings large II	£40	£110
Two shillings small II	£60	£155
Two shillings no value	£80	£225

*Charles I Fourth Coinage
Two Shillings*

COPPER ISSUES

(1629 Issue)

	F	VF
Twopence (triple thistle	£25	£70
Penny	£175	£500

(1632-39 Issue)

		F	VF
Twopence (Stirling turner	from	£25	£70

(1642-50 ISSUE)

	F	VF
Twopence (CR crowned	£20	£55

CHARLES II (1660–85)

FIRST COINAGE

Four merks

		F	VF
1664 Thistle above bust		£1250	£4000
1664 Thistle below bust		£2500	£7250
1665		£5000	Extremely rare
1670	varieties from	£1250	£3250
1673		£1250	£3250
1674 F below bust	varieties from	£1000	£3000
1675		£850	£2250

Two merks

		F	VF
1664 Thistle above bust		£1000	£2500

Charles II two merks

	F	VF
1664 Thistle below bust	£2500	£7250
1670	£1200	£3000
1673	£750	£1950
1673 F below bust	£1200	£3000
1674	£950	£2750
1674 F below bust	£950	£2750
1675	£650	£1550

Merk

	F	VF
1664 .... varieties from	£250	£715
1665	£275	£780
1666	£325	£850
1668	£325	Ex. rare
1669 .... varieties from	£100	£275
1670	£145	£375
1671	£110	£300
1672 .... varieties from	£100	£275
1673 .... varieties from	£110	£300
1674	£250	£715
1674 F below bust	£225	£650
1675 F below bust	£200	£550
1675	£210	£585

Charles II Dollar

Half merk

	F	VF
1664	£275	£725
1665 .... varieties from	£325	£600
1666 .... varieties from	£300	£750
1667	£325	£600
1668	£150	£400
1669 .... varieties from	£105	£285
1670 .... varieties from	£150	£400
1671 .... varieties from	£105	£285
1672	£150	£400
1673	£175	£475
1675 F below bust	£175	£475
1675	£195	£550

SECOND COINAGE
Dollar

	F	VF
1676	£750	£2000
1679	£650	£1650
1680	£750	£1650
1681	£550	£1325
1682	£475	£1250

Charles II Sixteenth Dollar

Half Dollar

	F	VF
1675	£650	£1500
1676	£750	£1950
1681	£400	£1100

Quarter Dollar

	F	VF
1675	£195	£550
1676 .... varieties from	£90	£225
1677 .... varieties from	£145	£400
1678	£165	£450
1679	£185	£500
1680	£135	£325
1681	£105	£275
1682 .... varieties from	£145	£400

Eighth Dollar

	F	VF
1676 .... varieties from	£85	£210

Charles II Bawbee

	F	VF
1677	£125	£300
1678/7	£195	£495
1679	£300	Ext. rare
1680 .... varieties from	£150	£345
1682 .... varieties from	£225	£495

Sixteenth Dollar

1677	£85	£210
1678/7 .... varieties from	£120	£320
1679/7	£135	£360
1680 .... varieties from	£135	£360
1681	£75	£175

Copper Issues

Twopence CR crowned .... varieties from	£25	£70
Bawbees 1677-79 .... varieties from	£65	£195
Turners 1677-79 .... varieties from	£45	£125

JAMES VII (1685–89)

Sixty shillings

1688 proof only .... varieties from	—	£3250

Forty shillings

1687 .... varieties from	£400	£950
1688 .... varieties from	£400	£950

Ten shillings

1687	£165	£525
1688 .... varieties from	£250	£700

James VII ten shillings

WILLIAM & MARY (1689–94)

Sixty shillings

1691	£295	£1100
1692	£475	£1750

Forty shillings

1689 .... varieties from	£295	£850
1690 .... varieties from	£185	£525
1691 .... varieties from	£195	£550
1692 .... varieties from	£225	£600
1693 .... varieties from	£195	£550
1694 .... varieties from	£225	£775

Twenty shillings

1693	£450	£1500
1694	Extremely rare	

Ten shillings

1689	Extremely rare	
1690 .... varieties from	£295	£750
1691 .... varieties from	£195	£600
1692 .... varieties from	£195	£600
1694 .... varieties from	£250	£700

Five shillings

1691	£200	£575
1694 .... varieties from	£120	£350

Copper Issues

Bawbees 1691–94 .... varieties from	£100	£275
Bodle (Turners) 1691–94 .... varieties from	£55	£180

William & Mary ten shillings

	F	VF

WILLIAM II (1694–1702)

	F	VF
Pistole	£3000	£7500
Half pistole	£3750	£8500

Forty shillings

	F	VF
1695 .... varieties from	£175	£550
1696	£200	£525
1697	£250	£550
1698	£200	£495
1699	£325	£650
1700	Extremely rare	

Twenty shillings

	F	VF
1695	£200	£625
1696	£200	£625
1697 .... varieties from	£250	£700
1698 .... varieties from	£175	£650
1699	£225	£625

William II ten shillings

Ten shillings

	F	VF
1695	£175	£500
1696	£175	£500
1697 .... varieties from	£175	£500
1698 .... varieties from	£175	£500
1699	£325	£850

Five shillings

	F	VF
1695	£70	£195
1696	£65	£180
1697 .... varieties from	£75	£225
1699	£95	£275
1700	£85	£230
1701	£125	£350
1702	£225	£625

Copper Issues

	F	VF
Bawbee 1695–97 .... varieties from	£85	£325
Bodle (Turners) 1695–97 .... varieties from	£50	£150

Anne five shillings

ANNE (1702–14)

Pre-Union 1702–7
Ten shillings

	F	VF
1705	£175	£450
1706 .... varieties from	£225	£650

Five shillings

	F	VF
1705 .... varieties from	£85	£225
1706	£85	£225

POST-UNION 1707–14
See listing in English section.

JAMES VIII (The Old Pretender) (1688–1766)

A number of Guineas and Crowns in various metals were struck in 1828 using original dies prepared by Norbert Roettiers, all bearing the date 1716. These coins are extremely rare and are keenly sought after.

Crown

1716 .... Generally EF+	£2500	

Our grateful thanks go to David Stuart of ABC Coins & Tokens
who has spent many hours updating the Scottish section.

ISLE OF MAN

DATE	F	VF	EF	UNC

PENNY (Copper except where stated)

	F	VF	EF	UNC
1709 Cast	£55	£185	£350	—
1709 Silver cast Proof	—	—	—	£2000
1709 Brass	£50	£175	£350	—
1733 "Quocunque"	£40	£75	£275	£450
1733 "Ouocunoue"	£45	£85	£300	£750
1733 Bath metal "Quocunque"	£30	£75	£300	—
1733 Silver Proof	—	—	—	£850
1733 Bronze Proof	—	—	—	£500
1733 Proof	—	—	—	£675
1733 Cap frosted	£35	£75	£300	£500
1733 Brass, cap frosted	£40	£75	£325	£650
1733 Silver Proof cap frosted	—	—	—	£650
1733 Bronze annulets instead of pellets	£50	£100	£400	£500
1758	£30	£50	£250	£450
1758 Proof	—	—	—	£650
1758 Silver Proof	—	—	—	£1000
1786 Engrailed edge	£35	£65	£275	£450
1786 Engrailed edge Proof	—	—	—	£600
1786 Plain edge Proof	—	—	—	£1000
1786 Pellet below bust	£35	£65	£275	£550
1798	£35	£65	£250	£500
1798 Proof	—	—	—	£450
1798 Bronze Proof	—	—	—	£450
1798 Copper-gilt Proof	—	—	—	£2000
1798 Silver Proof	—	—	—	£2500
1813	£40	£75	£300	£500
1813 Proof	—	—	—	£650
1813 Bronze Proof	—	—	—	£650
1813 Copper-gilt Proof	—	—	—	£2500
1839	£35	£75	£200	£450
1839 Proof	—	—	—	£500

HALF PENCE (Copper except where stated)

	F	VF	EF	UNC
1709 Cast	£50	£125	£250	—
1709 Brass	£55	£185	£500	—
1723 Silver	£725	£1250	£3500	—
1723 Copper	£300	£600	£1750	£2500
1733 Copper	£35	£55	£225	£450
1733 Bronze	£35	£55	£225	£450
1733 Silver Proof plain cap	—	—	—	£700
1733 Silver Proof frosted cap	—	—	—	—
1733 Bronze Proof	—	—	—	£500
1733 Bath metal plain cap	£40	£50	£215	—
1733 Bath metal frosted cap	£40	£50	£215	—
1758	£40	£50	£215	£450
1758 Proof	—	—	—	£800
1786 Engrailed edge	£30	£45	£120	£350
1786 Proof engrailed edge	—	—	—	£450
1786 Plain edge	£40	£65	£250	£350
1786 Proof plain edge	—	—	—	£650
1786 Bronze Proof	—	—	—	£450
1798	£35	£45	£150	£350
1798 Proof	—	—	—	£450
1798 Bronze Proof	—	—	—	£400

DATE	F	VF	EF	UNC
1798 Copper-gilt Proof	—	—	—	£1500
1798 Silver Proof	—	—	—	£1500
1813	£30	£45	£150	£300
1813 Proof	—	—	—	£375
1813 Bronze Proof	—	—	—	£350
1813 Copper-gilt Proof	—	—	—	£1250
1839	£30	£45	£150	£300
1839 Bronze Proof	—	—	—	£450

FARTHING

	F	VF	EF	UNC
1839 Copper	£30	£45	£150	£300
1839 Bronze Proof	—	—	—	£450
1839 Copper-gilt Proof	—	—	—	£2500

The last issue of coins made in the Isle of Man had been in 1839 but in 1970 Spink & Son Ltd was commissioned to produce a modern coinage for the Isle of Man Government which was struck at the Royal Mint. From 1973 onwards the Pobjoy Mint took over the contract and became a very prolific producer of definitive and commemorative issues. It is not proposed to give a complete listing of all these coins but the Crown and 25p, which from the collector's point of view are the most interesting in the series, are listed below. However, as the prices for these items vary dramatically according to the source it has been decided not to price them. Additionally a special 50p coin was issued to celebrate Christmas each year. In 2017 the contract to produce the coinage was awarded to the Tower Mint and their initial new designs appear later in the book.

The listings that follow are of the ordinary uncirculated cupro-nickel crown-size coins. Many of these coins were also produced in other metals, including silver, gold and platinum in non proof and proof form and in 1984 some were also issued in silver clad cupro-nickel in proof form.

DATE

1970 Manx Cat
1972 Royal Silver Wedding
1974 Centenary of Churchill's birth£15
1975 Manx Cat
1976 Bi-Centenary of American Independence
1976 Centenary of the Horse Drawn Tram
1977 Silver Jubilee
1977 Silver Jubilee Appeal
1978 25th Anniversary of the Coronation
1979 300th Anniversary of Manx Coinage
1979 Millennium of Tynwald (5 coins)
1980 22nd Olympics (3 coins)
1980 80th Birthday of Queen Mother
1980 Derby Bicentennial
1980 Winter Olympics
1981 Duke of Edinburgh Award Scheme (4 coins)
1981 Prince of Wales' Wedding (2 coins)
1981 Year of Disabled (4 coins)
1982 12th World Cup—Spain (4 coins)
1982 Maritime Heritage (4 coins)
1983 Manned Flight (4 coins)
1984 23rd Olympics (4 coins)
1984 Commonwealth Parliamentary Conference (4 coins)
1984 Quincentenary of College of Arms (4 coins)
1985 Queen Mother (6 coins)
1986 13th World Cup—Mexico (6 coins)
1986 Prince Andrew Wedding (2 coins)
1987 200th Anniversary of the United States Constitution
1987 America's Cup Races (5 coins)
1988 Australia Bicentennial (6 coins)

DATE

1988 Bicentenary of Steam Navigation (6 coins)
1988 Manx Cat
1989 Queen Elizabeth II & Prince Philip Royal Visit
1989 Bicentenary of the Mutiny on the Bounty (4 coins)
1989 Bicentenary of Washington's Inauguration (4 coins)
1989 Persian Cat
1989 Royal Visit
1990 150th Anniversary of the Penny Black
1990 25th Anniversary of Churchill's Death (2 coins)
1990 Alley Cat
1990 Queen Mother's 90th Birthday
1990 World Cup—Italy (4 coins)
1991 1992 America's Cup
1991 Centenary of the American Numismatic Association
1991 Norwegian Forest Cat
1991 10th Anniversary of Prince of Wales' Wedding (2 coins)
1992 1992 America's Cup
1992 Discovery of America (4 coins)
1992 F.1 World Champion Nigel Mansell
1992 Siamese Cat
1993 Maine Coon Cat
1993 Preserve Planet Earth—Dinosaurs (2 coins)
1994 Indycar World Series Champion Nigel Mansell
1994 Japanese Bobtail Cat
1994 Normandy Landings (8 coins)
1994 Preserve Planet Earth—Endangered Animals (3 coins)
1994 Preserve Planet Earth—Mammoth
1994 World Football Cup (6 coins)
1994 Year of the Dog
1995 Aircraft of World War II (19 coins)
1995 America's Cup
1995 Famous World Inventions—Series i (12 coins)
1995 Man in Flight—Series i (8 coins)
1995 Man in Flight—Series ii (8 coins)
1995 Preserve Planet Earth—Egret and Otter
1995 Queen Mother's 95th Birthday
1995 Turkish Cat
1995 Year of the Pig
1996 70th Birthday of HM the Queen
1996 Burmese Cat
1996 European Football Championships (8 coins)
1996 Explorers (2 coins)
1996 Famous World Inventions—Series ii (6 coins)
1996 Football Championships Winner
1996 King Arthur & the Knights of the Round Table (5 coins)
1996 Olympic Games (6 coins)
1996 Preserve Planet Earth—Killer Whale and Razorbill
1996 Robert Burns (4 coins)
1996 The Flower Fairies—Series i (4 coins)
1996 Year of the Rat
1997 10th Anniversary of the "Cats on Coins" series (silver only)
1997 90th Anniversary of the TT Races (4 coins)
1997 Explorers—Eriksson and Nansen (2 coins)
1997 Long-haired Smoke Cat
1997 Royal Golden Wedding (2 coins)
1997 The Flower Fairies—Series ii (4 coins)
1997 Year of the Ox
1998 125th Anniversary of Steam Railway (8 coins)
1998 18th Winter Olympics, Nagano (4 coins)
1998 Birman Cat
1998 Explorers—Vasco da Gama and Marco Polo (2 coins)
1998 FIFA World Cup (4 coins)
1998 International Year of the Oceans (4 coins)
1998 The Flower Fairies—Series iii (4 coins)
1998 The Millennium (16 coins issued over 3 years)
1998 Year of the Tiger
1999 175th Anniversary of the RNLI

DATE

1999 27th Olympics in Sydney (5 coins)
1999 50th Birthday of HRH the Prince of Wales
1999 Queen Mother's 100th Birthday (4 coins)
1999 Rugby World Cup (6 coins)
1999 The Millennium (4 coins)
1999 Titanium Millennium crown
1999 Wedding of HRH Prince Edward and Sophie Rhys-Jones
1999 Year of the Rabbit
2000 18th Birthday of HRH Prince William
2000 60th Anniversary of the Battle of Britain
2000 BT Global Challenge
2000 Explorers, Francisco Piarro and Wilem Brents (2 coins)
2000 Life and times of the Queen Mother (4 coins)
2000 Millennium—own a piece of time
2000 Queen Mother's 100th Birthday
2000 Scottish Fold cat
2000 Year of the Dragon
2001 75th Birthday of HM the Queen
2001 Explorers, Martin Frobisher and Roald Amundsen (2 coins)
2001 Harry Potter (6 coins)
2001 Joey Dunlop
2001 Life and times of the Queen Mother (2 coins)
2001 The Somali cat
2001 Year of the Snake
2002 A Tribute to Diana Princess of Wales—5 years on
2002 Introduction of the Euro
2002 The Bengal Cat
2002 The Queen's Golden Jubilee—i (1 coin)
2002 The Queen's Golden Jubilee—ii (4 coins)
2002 The XIX Winter Olympiad, Salt Lake City (2 coins)
2002 World Cup 2002 in Japan/Korea (4 coins)
2002 Year of the Horse
2003 Anniversary of the "Star of India"
2003 Lord of the Rings (5 coins)
2003 The Balinese Cat
2003 Year of the Goat
2004 100 Years of Powered Flight (2 coins)
2004 Olympics (4 coins)
2005 200th Anniversary of the Battle of Trafalgar
2005 400th Anniversary of the Gun Powder Plot (2 coins)
2005 60th Anniversary of D-Day (6 coins)
2005 60th Anniversary of Victory in Europe
2005 Bicentenary of the Battle of Trafalgar (6 coins)
2005 Harry Potter and the Goblet of Fire (4 coins)
2005 Italy and the Isle of Man TT races (2 coins)
2005 Lord of the Rings: The Return of the King
2005 Manx Hero Lt. John Quilliam and the Battle of Trafalgar (2 coins)
2005 The Himalayan Cat with kittens
2005 Bicentenary of the Battle of Trafalgar and Death of Nelson
2006 100 Years of Norwegian Independence
2006 150th Anniversary of the Victoria Cross (2 coins)
2006 30th Anniversary of the first Translantic Flight
2006 80th Birthday of Her Majesty the Queen (4 coins)
2006 The Battles that Changed the World—Part II (6 coins)
2007 Fairy Tales—Sleeping Beauty, The Three Little Pigs (2 coins)
2007 The Centenary of the Scouting
2007 The Centenary of the TT races
2007 The Graceful Swan
2007 The Ragdoll Cat
2007 The Royal Diamond Wedding Anniversary
2008 50th Anniversary of Paddington Bear
2008 Burmilla Cat
2008 Centenary of the Olympics
2008 Prince Charles 60th Birthday
2008 The Adorable Snowman
2008 The Olympic Collection—The Olympics coming to London

DATE

2008 The Return of Tutankhamun
2008 UEFA European Football Championships
2008 Year of Planet Earth
2009 40th Anniversary of the 1st Concorde Test Flight
2009 50 Years of Championship Racing
2009 Fifa World Cup South Africa 2010
2009 The Chinchilla Cat
2009 Winter Olympics (2 coins)
2010 25th Anniversary of the Gold Angel coin
2010 50 Years of racing by the Suzuki Racing Team
2010 Abyssinian Cat and her Kitten
2010 Celebrating 15 Years of the Gold Noble
2011 A Lifetime of Service—Queen Elizabeth II and Prince Philip
2011 Buckingham Palace
2011 Donatello's famous Chellini Madonna
2011 Engagement of HRH Prince William to Catherine Middleton
2011 Royal Wedding of HRH Prince William and Catherine Middleton
2011 The Turkish Angora Cat
2011 TT Races
2011 Year of the Rabbit coloured coin
2012 Centenary of RMS Titanic
2012 European Football Championships (4 coins)
2012 Juno Moneta Coin
2012 Manx Cat Coin
2012 Olympics (6 coins).
2012 Petra Coin
2012 River Thames Diamond Jubilee Pageant
2013 Anniversary of Queen Victoria and Queen Elizabeth II Coronations
2013 Kermode Bear
2013 Lifetime of Service—Queen Elizabeth II and Prince Philip
2013 Siberian Cat
2013 St. Patrick Commemorative
2013 Winter Olympic (4 coins)
2014 200th Anniversary of Matthew Flinders
2014 70th Anniversary of D-Day (poppies picked out in red)
2014 Centenary of WWI
2014 Snowman and Snow Dog Crown (£5)
2014 Snowshoe Cat
2014 The Snowman & Snowdog Christmas crown (+ coloured issue)
2014 Winter Olympic Games (4 Coin Collection)
2015 175th Anniversary of the Penny Black Stamp (issued in a pack)
2015 200th Anniversary of the Battle of Waterloo—Napoleon
2015 200th Anniversary of the Battle of Waterloo—Wellington
2015 75th Anniversary of the Battle of Britain (search lights in yellow)
2015 Her Majesty the Queen Elizabeth II Longest reigning Monarch
2015 Paddington Bear
2015 Penny Black (Crown)
2015 Selkirk Rex Cat
2015 Sir Winston Churchill
2016 90th Birthday Queen Elizabeth II
2016 Tobacco Brown Cat

TOWER MINT ISSUES:
2017 70 Years of Service Prince Philip
2017 Christmas Dove £5
2017 Platinum Wedding Anniversary
2017 Battle of Stiklestad (Crown)
2017 100 years of the House of Windsor
2017 Battle of Hafrsfjord
2017 Harald Fairhair
2017 Saint Olav
2017 Thor
2018 65th Coronation Anniversary
2018 Birth of Prince Louis (£5)
2018 Isle of Man TT 110 Years (Reissued)
2018 Armistice Centenary

ISLE OF MAN DECIMAL COINAGE—TOWER MINT ISSUES

FIVE POUNDS—Triskele symbol ("Alpaca" metal)
TWO POUNDS—Tower of Refuge (Cupro-nickel/Nickel-brass)
ONE POUNDS—Raven and Falcon (Nickel-brass)
FIFTY PENCE —Manx Loughtan Sheep (Cupro-nickel)
TWENTY PENCE—Viking Longship (Cupro-nickel)
TEN PENCE—The Manx Cat(Nickel plated steel)
FIVE PENCE—Manx Shearwater bird (Nickel plated steel)

The above designs, introduced in 2017 for the island's own coinage which circulates alongside our UK coins, replace the previous series which appeared in numerous styles from 1971 onwards. Since taking over the contract to produce the island's coinage in 2017 the Tower Mint have also struck a number of commemorative pieces including a superb pair of bi-metallic £2 coins depicting scenes from the island's famous TT Race which takes place each year. The coins portray the legendary Steve Hislop setting the lap record in 1989. In addition an attractive set of six 50p coins celebrating the stories of Peter Pan were issued in various collector versions. It is anticipated that these and the other Tower Mint strikes will be fully listed in forthcoming editions of the YEARBOOK.

DATE	F	VF	EF	UNC
TEN SHILLINGS				
1966	—	£5	£10	£15
1966 Proof	—	—	—	£30
THREEPENCE				
1956	£1	£4	£8	£10
1956 Proof	—	—	—	£15
1959	£1	£4	£8	£15
1966 Proof	—	—	—	£15
EIGHT DOUBLES				
1834	£10	£15	£50	£200
1858 5 berries	£6	£10	£50	£150
1858 4 berries	£6	£10	£50	£160
1864 1 stalk	£6	£10	£40	£70
1864 3 stalks	£6	£10	£30	£75
1868	£6	£10	£30	£75
1874	£4	£6	£20	£55
1885H	£4	£6	£20	£50
1889H	£3	£4	£20	£45
1893H small date	£3	£4	£20	£45
1893H large date	£3	£4	£20	£45
1902H	£3	£4	£20	£45
1903H	£3	£4	£20	£45
1910	£3	£4	£20	£45
1911H	£3	£4	£20	£50
1914H	£1	£3	£10	£35
1918H	£1	£3	£8	£25
1920H	£1	£3	£8	£25
1934H	£1	£3	£10	£35
1934H Proof	—	—	—	£250
1938H	£1	£3	£10	£25
1945H	£1	£2	£8	£15
1947H	£1	£2	£8	£15
1949H	—	£2	£9	£15
1956	—	£1	£7	£15
1956	—	£1	£5	£15
1959	—	£1	£5	£15
1966 Proof	—	—	—	£35
FOUR DOUBLES				
1830	£4	£9	£50	£150
1830 Mule with obv. St Helena 1/2d	—	£850	—	—
1858	£6	£12	£50	£150
1864 Single stalk	£2	£6	£20	£60
1864 3 stalks	£2	£6	£25	£65
1868	£3	£7	£22	£75
1874	£2	£6	£22	£75
1885H	£2	£6	£20	£45
1889H	£2	£3	£15	£35
1893H	£2	£3	£15	£35
1902H	£2	£3	£10	£30
1903H	£2	£3	£13	£30
1906H	£2	£3	£10	£25
1908H	£2	£3	£10	£25
1910H	£2	£3	£10	£25
1911H	£2	£3	£8	£25
1914H	£2	£3	£15	£50
1918H	£2	£3	£12	£35
1920H	£2	£3	£10	£35
1945H	£2	£3	£10	£35
1949H	£2	£3	£12	£35
1956	£1	£2	£8	£15
1966 Proof	—	—	—	£20

DATE	F	VF	EF	UNC
TWO DOUBLES				
1858..	£6	£10	£50	£200
1868 Single stick	£6	£12	£55	£200
1868 3 stalks	£7	£15	£85	£225
1874..	£4	£10	£50	£150
1885H...	£3	£6	£20	£35
1889H...	£3	£5	£20	£35
1899H...	£3	£5	£25	£50
1902H...	£3	£5	£20	£35
1903H...	£3	£5	£20	£35
1906H...	£3	£5	£20	£35
1908H...	£3	£5	£20	£35
1911H...	£3	£5	£25	£45
1914H...	£3	£5	£25	£45
1917H...	£7	£20	£85	£225
1918H...	£3	£5	£15	£30
1920H...	£3	£5	£15	£30
1929H...	£2	£3	£12	£20
ONE DOUBLE				
1830..	£3	£4	£22	£50
1868..	£4	£10	£50	£135
1868/30..	£5	£7	£27	£85
1885H...	£2	£3	£10	£25
1889H...	£1	£2	£8	£20
1893H...	£1	£2	£8	£20
1899H...	£1	£2	£8	£20
1902..	£1	£2	£8	£20
1903H...	£1	£2	£8	£20
1911H...	£1	£2	£10	£25
1911 (new shield)	£1	£2	£8	£20
1914H...	£1	£2	£10	£20
1929H...	£1	£2	£6	£20
1933H...	£1	£2	£6	£20
1938H...	£1	£2	£6	£20

DECIMAL COINAGE

Ordinary circulating coinage from 1986 onwards is usually available in uncirculated condition at a small premium above face value thus it is not listed here. The coins listed are cupro-nickel unless otherwise stated.

	UNC
ONE HUNDRED POUNDS	
1994 50th Anniversary of Normandy Landings. Gold proof....................	£1500
1995 Anniversary of the Liberation. Gold proof	£1500
FIFTY POUNDS	
1994 50th Anniversary of Normandy Landings. Gold proof....................	£1000
1995 Anniversary of the Liberation. Gold proof	£1000
1998 Queen Elizabeth and Queen Mother Gold proof...........................	£1000
1999 Queen Elizabeth and Queen Mother Gold	£1000
2004 Anniversary of D-Day. Gold	£1100
2013 70th Anniversary of the Dambuster Raid. Silver proof 10oz	£600
2015 Magna Carta 800 anniversary. Silver proof 10oz	£500
TWENTY-FIVE POUNDS	
1994 50th Anniversary of Normandy Landings. Gold	£550
1994 — Gold proof..	£650
1995 Anniversary of the Liberation. Gold proof	£550
1995 Queen Mothers 95th Birthday. Gold...	£550
1996 European Football Championships. Gold proof.............................	£650
1997 Royal Golden Wedding. Gold proof	£650
1998 Royal Air Force. Gold proof..	£650
2000 Queen Mother 100th Birthday. Gold proof	£650
2001 Queen Victoria centennial Gold proof	£650
2001 Queen Victoria Gold proof..	£650
2001 HM the Queen's 75th Birthday. Gold proof	£600
2002 Princess Diana memorial. Gold proof...	£ 600

Since the introduction of decimal coinage a number of companies have been involved in marketing the coins of the Channel Islands. As a consequence many special limited edition commemorative coins have been issued in a wide variety of sizes, metals and finishes. These are very numerous with some issues being produced in very small numbers and many are omitted from our listings. These issues are generally outside of the scope of this catalogue.

DATE	UNC
2002 Duke of Wellington. Gold proof	£550
2002 Golden Jubilee. Gold proof	£550
2002 Queen Mother. Gold proof	£550
2003 Golden Jubilee. Gold proof	£550
2003 Golden Hind. Gold proof	£550
2004 Anniversary of D-Day. Gold proof	£550
2004 Age of Steam—Truro. Gold proof	£550
2004 Age of Steam—Mallard. Gold proof	£550
2004 HMS Invincible. Gold proof	£550
2005 HMS Ark Royal. Gold proof	£550
2006 FIFA World Cup. Gold proof	£550

TEN POUNDS

1994 50th Anniversary of Normandy Landings. Gold proof	£250
1995 Anniversary of the Liberation. Gold proof	£275
1997 Royal Golden wedding. 5oz Silver proof	£200
2000 Century of Monarchy. 5oz Silver proof	£150
2000 Guernsey Gold proof "Nugget"	£275
2001 19th Century Monarchy. Silver proof	£150
2002 18th Century Monarchy. Silver proof	£150
2003 1700 Years of Monarchy. Silver proof	£150
2004 16th Century Monarchy. Silver proof	£150
2004 Anniversary of D-Day. Silver proof	£150
2004 150th anniversary of the Crimean War. Gold proof	£6000
2005 Return of the Islanders. Silver proof	£50
2005 — Gold proof	£6000
2005 Anniversary of Trafalgar. Gold proof	£5000
2005 End of World War II. Silver proof	£25
2005 — Gold proof	£6000
2005 — Platinum proof	£6250
2009 Anniversary of Moon Landing. Silver proof	£75
2009 — Gold proof	£5000
2012 Diamond Jubilee. 5oz Silver proof	£250
2013 Coronation Jubilee. 5oz Silver proof	£250
2017 Sapphire Jubilee. 5oz Silver proof	£450
2017 The House of Windsor. 5oz Silver proof	£450
2018 RAF Centenary 5oz Silver proof	£450
2019 200th Anniversary of Queen Victoria birth. 5oz Silver Proof, Gold detail	£495

FIVE POUNDS

1995 Queen Mother's 95th birthday	£25
1995 — Silver proof	£55
1995 — Small size Gold	£250
1996 HM the Queen's 70th birthday	£18
1996 — Silver proof	£55
1996 European Football Championships	£15
1996 — Silver proof	£25
1997 Royal Golden Wedding	£15
1997 — Silver proof	£25
1997 — Small size Gold. BU	£250
1997 Castles of the British Isles—Castle Cornet, Guernsey	£15
1997 — Silver proof	£25
1997 Castles of the British Isles—Caernarfon Castle. Silver proof	£30
1997 Castles of the British Isles—Leeds Castle. Silver proof	£30
1998 Royal Air Force.	£15
1998 Royal Air Force. Silver proof	£30
1999 Millennium. Brass	£15
1999 — Silver proof	£25
1999 Wedding of HRH Prince Edward and Sophie Rhys-Jones	£15
1999 — Silver proof	£25
1999 Queen Mother	£25
1999 — Silver proof	£80
1999 Winston Churchill	£15
1999 — Large size Gold	£1000
2000 Queen Mother's 100th Birthday	£10
2000 — Silver proof	£85
2000 — Small size Gold proof	£250
2000 Centuries of the British Monarchy	£45

DATE	UNC
2000 — Silver proof	£85
2000 — Small size Gold proof	£250
2001 The Reign of Queen Victoria	£20
2001 — Gold proof	£360
2001 — proof	£60
2001 — Silver proof	£60
2001 HM the Queen's 75th Birthday	£15
2001 — Silver proof	£25
2001 — Small size Gold proof	£250
2001 19th Century Monarchy	£20
2001 — Silver proof	£25
2001 — Small size Gold proof	£250
2002 Golden Jubilee (two types)	£15
2002 — Silver proof	£25
2002 Princess Diana Memorial	£15
2002 — proof	£25
2002 — Gold proof	£1000
2002 Century of Monarchy	£15
2002 — Silver proof	£25
2002 — Small size Gold proof	£250
2002 Queen Mother Memoriam	£15
2002 — proof	£20
2002 — Silver proof	£25
2002 — Small size Gold proof	£250
2002 — Large size Gold proof	£1000
2003 Duke of Wellington	£15
2003 — Silver proof	£25
2003 — Small size Gold proof	£250
2003 — Large size Gold proof	£1000
2003 Prince William	£20
2003 — Silver proof	£35
2003 — Gold proof	£1000
2003 Golden Hind	£20
2003 17th Century Monarchy	£20
2003 History of the Royal Navy, Nelson	£20
2003 — Nelson with coloured flag proof	£25
2004 — Invincible. Silver proof	£30
2004 16th Century monarchs	£15
2004 History of the Railways, Mallard	£12
2004 — City of Truro	£15
2004 — The Boat Train	£12
2004 — The Train Spotter	£15
2004 History of the Royal Navy, Henry VIII	£15
2004 — Invincible	£15
2004 Anniversary of D-Day	£12
2004 — Silver proof	£25
2004 — Gold proof	£1000
2004 Anniversary of the Crimean War. Plain	£12
2004 — with colour	£15
2004 — Silver proof	£25
2004 — Gold proof with colour	£1250
2005 200th Anniversary of the Battle of Trafalgar	£20
2005 60th Anniversary of the Liberation of the Channel Islands	£20
2005 End of World War II. Silver proof	£25
2005 — Gold proof	£1250
2005 Anniversary of Liberation. Gold proof	£1250
2006 Royal 80th Birthday. Silver proof	£25
2006 FIFA World Cup. Silver proof	£25
2006 Great Britons—Sir Winston Churchill Silver. Issued as part of set.	£60
2006 80th Birthday of Her Majesty the Queen	£20
2007 History of the Royal Navy—Henry VIII, The Golden Hind (2 coins)	£65
2007 Royal Diamond Wedding	£20
2008 90th Anniversary of the RAF (10 different designs in silver proof) ea.	£35
2009 British warships (6 different designs in silver proof) .... ea.	£35
2009 Anniversary of Apollo Moon landings. Cu-ni	£5
2009 — Silver proof	£35
2010 Charles II Unite. Gold proof	£1500

DATE	UNC
2010 Florence Nightingale. Gold proof	£1500
2010 Battle of Britain 70th anniversary. Silver and coloured	£55
2011 350th Anniversary of the Crown Jewels. Silver proof	£95
2011 90th Anniversary of the British Legion (Gold-plated copper)	£45
2011 — Silver proof	£95
2011 40th Anniversary of decimalisation proof	£20
2011 Anniversary of the sinking of the *Titanic*	£20
2011 — Silver proof	£55
2011 30th Birthday of Duke of Cambridge	£20
2011 — Silver proof	£55
2011 Wedding of Prince William and Kate Middleton	£25
2011 — Silver proof	£55
2011 400th Anniversary of the King James Bible	£25
2012 Diamond Jubilee £5	£25
2012 — Gold proof	£1500
2012 The Tribute to the British Army. Gold proof	£2000
2013 70th Anniversary of the Dambuster Raid.	£20
2013 — Silver proof	£65
2013 — Gold proof	£2000
2013 Coronation Jubilee	£25
2013 — Silver proof	£55
2013 — Gold proof	£2000
2013 200th Guinea Anniversary	£25
2013 — Silver proof	£55
2013 — Gold proof	£2000
2014 Centenary of the First World War. Silver proof	£85
2014 — 5oz Silver proof	£450
2014 — Gold proof	£2500
2015 VE Day 70th Anniversary	£15
2015 Magna Carta 800th anniversary	£15
2016 90th Birthday of HM the Queen BU	£15
2016 — Silver Proof	£75
2016 Battle of the Somme	£12
2016 Battle of Hastings Anniversary	£15
2017 Sapphire Jubilee. Silver plated	£10
2017 Prince Philip Years of Service (only available in 3-coin set)	£20
2017 70th Royal Wedding Anniversary Silver proof	£75
2018 Centenary of WWI	£15
2018 — Silver proof	£75
2018 Prince Harry Royal Wedding Silver proof	£75
2018 65th Coronation Jubilee Silver proof	£75
2019 The King's Speech Outbreak of WWII 80th anniversary Silver proof	£85
2019 — Silver Proof 5oz	£495
2019 75th Anniversary of D-Day. Cu-Ni with Gold ink	£25
2019 Remembrance poppy	£5

TWO POUNDS

1985 40th anniversary of Liberation	£10
1985 — proof	£30
1985 — Silver proof	£55
1986 Commonwealth Games, in plastic case	£12
1986 — in special folder	£12
1986 — .500 Silver	£45
1986 — .925 Silver proof	£55
1987 900th Anniv. of death of William the Conqueror, in folder	£15
1987 — Silver proof	£55
1987 — Gold proof	£1300
1988 William II, in presentation folder	£15
1988 — Silver proof	£55
1989 Henry I, in presentation folder	£15
1989 — Silver proof	£55
1989 Royal Visit	£15
1989 — Silver proof	£55
1990 Queen Mother's 90th birthday	£15
1990 — Silver proof	£55
1991 Henry II, in presentation folder	£15
1991 — Silver proof	£55

DATE	UNC

1993 40th Anniversary of the Coronation... £15
1993 — Silver proof.. £60
1994 Anniversary of the Normandy Landings £15
1994 — Silver proof.. £55
1995 50th Anniversary of Liberation £154
1995 — Silver proof.. £55
1995 — Silver Piedfort proof.. £100
1997 Conserving Nature i... £12
1997 — Silver proof.. £55
1997 Bimetallic Latent image £8
1997 — proof £10
1998 Conserving Nature ii.. £10
1998 Bimetallic Latent image £6
2003 — £6
2006 — £8
2011 Prince Philip's 90th Birthday (conjoined portraits) £6
2011 — Silver proof.. £50
2011 40th Anniversary of Decimalisation....................................... £12
2012 Diamond Jubilee Proof... £20
2012 "8 Doubles" modern variant... —

ONE POUND

1981 .... £10
1981 Gold proof £300
1981 Gold piedfort £500
1983 New specification, new reverse.. £10
1985 New design (in folder) £10
1995 Queen Mother's 95th Birthday. Silver proof £50
1996 Queen's 70th Birthday. Silver proof...................................... £55
1997 Royal Golden Wedding. Silver BU.. £20
1997 — Silver proof.. £55
1997 Castles of the British Isles—Tower of London. Silver proof only ... £35
1998 Royal Air Force. Silver proof... £45
1999 Wedding of Prince Edward. Silver proof £55
1999 Queen Mother. Silver proof.. £55
1999 Winston Churchill. Silver proof £55
2000 Millennium. Silver proof (Gold plated) £65
2000 Queen Mother's 100th Birthday. Silver proof £45
2001 .... £2
2001 HM the Queen's 75th Birthday. Silver proof.......................... £45
2002 William of Normandy. Silver £20
2003 .... £2
2006.. £2
2015 Magna Carta 800th anniversary. Gold proof £500
2018 HRH Prince Charles 70th Birthday. Gold proof £500
2018 RAF Centenary £15

FIFTY PENCE (initially 7-sided, later issues round)

1969 Ducal cap reverse... £4
1970.. £6
1971 proof £9
1981.. £4
1982.. £4
1985 New flower design... £4
2000 60th Anniversary of the Battle of Britain. £4
2000 — Silver proof... £55
2000 — Silver piedfort... £55
2000 — Gold proof... £365
2003.. £2
2003 Coronation Jubilee (four types) £2
2003 — Proof £4
2006.. £2
2008.. £2
2012 The Diamond Jubilee (coloured portrait)............................. £10
2012 — Cu-Ni Fine Gold-Plated £5
2013 60th Anniversary of Coronation (two different designs: Queen in

DATE	UNC
State Coach and Queen in White Dress), Gold clad steel	£5 ea.
2013 The RAF 617 Squadron Gold-plated copper	£15
2013 The RAF No. 1 Squadron Gold-plated copper.............................	£15
2013 The Red Arrows. Gold-plated copper	£15
2013 Battle of Britain Memorial Flight. Gold-plated copper	£15
2013 50th Anniversary of the Flying Scotsman's retirement in 1963......	£25
2014 New Queen Elizabeth II	£45
2015 Queen Elizabeth II—Reflections of a Reign, Cu-Ni	£5
2016 90th Birthday of Queen Elizabeth II (two round crown-size	
coloured coins)	£5 ea.
2016 Churchill Tank. Gold-plated copper	£10
2016 Centenary of the WWI Tank. Gold-plated copper	£10
2017 The Spitfire. Silver-plated copper..	£12
2017 Sapphire Jubilee, Cu-Ni	£10
2017 Prince George's Birthday. Gold-plated	£25
2018 RAF Centenary. Gold-plated	£25
2019 Concorde 50th Anniversary	£6
2019 Concorde 50th Anniversary set (3 designs: Runway, Take Off, Flight)	£25
2019 Concorde 50th anniversary (paired with a Jersey 50p).................	£12
2019 — SIlver Proof	£125

TWENTY-FIVE PENCE

1972 Royal Silver Wedding	£12
1972 — Silver proof..	£45
1977 Royal Silver Jubilee	£10
1977 — Silver proof..	£45
1978 Royal Visit	£10
1978 — Silver proof..	£45
1980 Queen Mother's 80th birthday	£10
1980 — Silver proof..	£45
1981 Royal Wedding	£10
1981 — Silver proof..	£45

**Ordinary circulating coinage from 1986 onwards is usually available in
uncirculated condition at a small premium above face value thus it is not
listed here. The coins listed are cupro-nickel unless otherwise stated.**

JERSEY

DATE	F	VF	EF	UNC
FIVE SHILLINGS				
1966	—	£3	£7	£15
1966 Proof	—	£3	£9	£25
ONE QUARTER OF A SHILLING				
1957	—	£2	£5	£10
1960 Proof	—	—	£5	£15
1964	—	—	£4	£10
1966	—	—	£4	£10
ONE TWELFTH OF A SHILLING				
1877H	£2	£3	£20	£65
1877H Proof in nickel	—	—	—	£1275
1877 Proof only	—	—	—	£500
1877 Proof in nickel	—	—	—	£1275
1881	£3	£3	£15	£60
1888	£2	£3	£15	£50
1894	£2	£3	£20	£50
1909	£2	£3	£15	£35
1911	£2	£3	£10	£30
1913	£2	£3	£10	£30
1923 Spade shield	£2	£3	£12	£35
1923 Square shield	£2	£3	£10	£30
1926	£2	£3	£12	£45
1931	£2	£3	£8	£15
1933	£2	£3	£8	£15
1935	£2	£3	£8	£15
1937	£2	£3	£8	£15
1946	£2	£3	£8	£15
1947	—	£3	£8	£15
"1945" GVI	—	—	£2	£10
"1945" QE2	—	—	£2	£8
1957	—	—	£2	£7
1960 1660–1960 300th anniversary	—	—	£2	£7
1960 Mule	—	—	—	£175
1964	—	£2	£3	£10
1966 "1066–1966"	—	—	£1	£8
ONE THIRTEENTH OF A SHILLING				
1841	£4	£8	£40	£200
1844	£4	£9	£40	£200
1851	£5	£12	£60	£250
1858	£4	£9	£45	£200
1861	£5	£13	£60	£175
1865 Proof only	—	—	—	£750
1866 with LCW	£2	£5	£95	£150
1866 without LCW Proof only	—	—	—	£400
1870	£4	£8	£40	£125
1871	£4	£8	£42	£125
ONE TWENTY-FOURTH OF A SHILLING				
1877H	£3	£4	£15	£60
1877 Proof only	—	—	—	£300
1888	£3	£4	£15	£45
1894	£3	£4	£15	£45
1909	£3	£4	£15	£45
1911	£2	£3	£10	£45

DATE	F	VF	EF	UNC
1913	£2	£3	£10	£45
1923 Spade shield	£2	£3	£10	£35
1923 Square shield	£2	£3	£8	£35
1926	£2	£3	£10	£25
1931	£2	£3	£10	£25
1933	£2	£3	£10	£25
1935	£2	£3	£10	£25
1937	£1	£2	£6	£20
1946	£1	£2	£6	£20
1947	£1	£2	£6	£20

ONE TWENTY-SIXTH OF A SHILLING

	F	VF	EF	UNC
1841	£4	£7	£30	£100
1844	£4	£7	£25	£100
1851	£3	£6	£25	£100
1858	£4	£11	£50	£200
1861	£3	£6	£25	£65
1866	£3	£6	£30	£85
1870	£3	£6	£20	£55
1871	£3	£6	£20	£55

ONE FORTY-EIGHTH OF A SHILLING

	F	VF	EF	UNC
1877H	£6	£12	£60	£150
1877 Proof only	—	—	—	£450

ONE FIFTY-SECOND OF A SHILLING

	F	VF	EF	UNC
1841	£9	£25	£60	£200
1861 Proof only	—	—	—	£650

DECIMAL COINAGE

Ordinary circulating coinage from 1986 onwards is usually available in uncirculated condition at a small premium above face value thus it is not listed here.

ONE HUNDRED POUNDS

1990 50th Anniversary of the Battle of Britain. Gold Proof. £1000
1995 50th Anniversary of Liberation. Gold proof £1000

FIFTY POUNDS

1972 Silver Wedding. Gold proof £850
1990 50th Anniversary of the Battle of Britain. Gold proof £850
1995 50th Anniversary of Liberation. Gold proof £850
2003 Golden Jubilee. Silver Proof (100mm) £650
2013 RMS Titanic Centenary. 10oz Silver proof £600

TWENTY-FIVE POUNDS

1972 25th Royal Wedding anniversary. Gold £350
1972 — Gold proof £400
1990 50th Anniversary of Battle of Britain. Gold proof £350
1995 50th Anniversary of Liberation. Gold proof £350
2002 Princess Diana memorial. Gold proof £350
2002 Queen Mother. Gold proof £350
2002 Golden Jubilee. Gold proof £350
2002 Duke of Wellington. Gold proof £350
2003 Golden Jubilee. Gold proof £350
2003 History of the Royal Navy. Naval Commanders £350
2003 — Francis Drake £350
2003 — Sovereign of the Seas £350
2004 60th Anniversary of D-Day. Gold proof £350
2004 Charge of the Light Brigade. Gold proof £350
2004 HMS Victory. Gold proof £350
2004 John Fisher 1841–1920 Gold proof £350
2004 The Coronation Scot. Gold proof £350
2004 The Flying Scotsman. Gold proof £350
2004 Golden Arrow. Gold proof £350

Since the introduction of decimal coinage a number of companies have been involved in marketing the coins of the Channel Islands. As a consequence many special limited edition commemorative coins have been issued in a wide variety of sizes, metals and finishes. These are very numerous with some issues being produced in very small numbers and many are omitted from our listings. These issues are generally outside of the scope of this catalogue.

DATE	UNC
2004 Rocket and Evening Star. Gold proof	£350
2005 Andrew Cunningham. Gold proof	£350
2005 HMS Conqueror. Gold Proof	£350
2005 200th Anniversary of Nelson. Gold proof	£350
2009 500th Anniversary of Accession. Gold proof	£350

TWENTY POUNDS
1972 Royal Wedding. The Ormer. Gold	£350
1972 — Gold proof	£450

TEN POUNDS
1972 25th Royal Wedding anniversary. Gold	£175
1972 — Gold proof	£200
1990 50th Anniversary of the Battle of Britain. Gold proof	£180
1995 50th Anniversary of Liberation. Gold proof	£140
2003 Coronation Anniversary. Gold/silver proof	£50
2004 150th anniversary of the Crimean War. Gold proof	£6000
2005 Trafalgar. Gold proof	£5000
2005 End of World War II. Silver proof	£25
2007 Diamond Wedding. Platinum proof	£280
2008 History of RAF. Silver proof	£25
2011 Royal Wedding of HRH Prince William & Catherine Middleton, silver (65mm)	£395
2012 Poppy. 5oz Silver Proof	£350
2013 Flying Scotsman. 5oz Silver proof	£350
2014 First World War Centenary 5oz Silver proof	£450
2017 Masterpiece Poppy. 5oz Silver proof	£400
2017 Battle of Britain Memorial Flight. 5oz Silver proof	£400
2018 Prince George's 5th Birthday 5oz Silver proof	£400
2018 Coronation Anniversary. 5oz Silver proof	£400
2018 Prince George's 5th birthday 5oz Silver proof	£425
2019 Remembrance Poppy. Gold proof 5oz (20 struck)	£12,000

(Enlarged)

(Reduced)

FIVE POUNDS
1972 Gold proof	£65
1990 50th Anniversary of the Battle of Britain. Silver Proof (5 ounces)	£180
1997 Royal Golden Wedding	£10
1997 — Silver proof	£25
2000 Millennium. Silver proof	£35
2002 Princess Diana memorial	£12
2002 — Silver proof	£30
2002 — Gold proof	£800
2002 Royal Golden Jubilee	£25
2003 Golden Jubilee	£20
2003 — Silver proof	£55
2003 — Gold proof	£1000
2003 Prince William 21st Birthday	£15
2003 — Silver Proof	£55
2003 — Gold proof	£1000
2003 Naval Commanders	£15
2003 — Silver proof	£55
2003 — Gold proof	£1000
2003 Francis Drake	£15
2003 — Silver proof	£55
2003 — Gold proof	£1000
2003 Sovereign of the Seas	£15
2003 — Silver proof	£55
2003 — Gold proof	£1000
2004 60th Anniversary of 'D' Day	£15
2004 — Silver proof	£55
2004 — Gold proof	£1000
2004 Charge of the Light Brigade	£15
2004 — Silver proof	£50
2004 — Gold proof	£1000
2004 HMS Victory	£15

(Enlarged)

DATE	UNC
2004 — Silver proof	£55
2004 — Gold proof	£1000
2004 John Fisher 1841–1920	£15
2004 — Silver proof	£55
2004 —Gold proof	£1000
2004 The Coronation Scot	£15
2004 — Silver proof	£55
2004 — Gold proof	£1000
2004 The Flying Scotsman	£15
2004 — Silver proof	£55
2004 — Silver/Gold proof	£500
2004 — Gold proof	£1000
2004 Golden Arrow	£15
2004 — Silver proof	£55
2004 — Gold proof	£1000
2005 Driver and Fireman	£15
2005 — Silver proof	£45
2005 — Gold proof	£1000
2005 Box Tunnel and King Loco	£15
2005 — Silver Proof	£45
2005 — Gold Proof	£1000
2005 Rocket and Evening Star	£15
2005 — Silver proof	£45
2005 — Silver/Gold proof	£500
2005 — Gold proof	£1000
2005 200th Anniversary of the Battle of Trafalgar	£30
2005 Andrew Cunningham	£20
2005 — Silver proof	£65
2005 — Gold proof	£1000
2005 HMS Conqueror	£15
2005 — Silver proof	£20
2005 — Gold proof	£1000
2005 Battle of Trafalgar	£15
2005 — Silver proof	£45
2005 — Gold proof (9mm)	£500
2005 — Gold proof (38.6mm)	£1000
2005 Returning Evacuees	£15
2005 — Silver proof	£45
2005 — Gold proof	£1000
2005 Searchlights and Big Ben	£15
2005 — Silver proof	£45
2005 — Gold proof	£1000
2006 60th Anniversary of the Liberation of the Channel Islands	£30
2006 80th Birthday of Her Majesty the Queen (3-coin set)	—
2006 Sir Winston Churchill	£15
2006 — Silver proof	£45
2006 — Gold proof	£1000
2006 Charles Darwin	£15
2006 — Silver proof	£45
2006 — Gold proof	£1000
2006 Bobby Moore	£20
2006 — Silver Proof	£55
2006 — Gold Proof	£1150
2006 Florence Nightingale	£20
2006 — Silver proof	£55
2006 — Gold proof	£1000
2006 Queen Mother	£20
2006 — Silver proof	£55
2006 — Gold proof	£1000
2006 Henry VIII	£15
2006 — Silver proof	£55
2006 — Gold proof	£1000
2006 Princess Diana	£20
2006 — Silver Proof	£60
2006 — Gold Proof	£1250
2006 Sir Christopher Wren	£15
2006 — Silver proof	£55

DATE	UNC
2006 — Gold proof	£1000
2006 HM the Queen's 80th Birthday—Streamers	£15
2006 — Silver proof	£60
2006 — Gold proof	£1000
2006 HM the Queen's 80th Birthday—Trooping colour	£25
2006 — Proof	£60
2006 — Silver proof	£1000
2006 — Silver/Gold proof	£650
2006 — Gold proof	£1150
2006 HM the Queen's 80th Birthday—Wembley Stadium	£20
2006 — Silver proof	£55
2006 — Gold proof	£1150
2006 Guy Gibson	£15
2006 — Silver proof	£55
2006 — Gold proof	£1150
2006 Eric James Nicholson	£15
2006 — Silver proof	£55
2006 — Gold proof	£1150
2006 Hook, Chard and Bromhead	£15
2006 — Silver proof	£55
2006 — Gold proof	£1150
2006 1st Lancs Fusiliers	£15
2006 — Silver proof	£55
2006 — Gold proof	£1150
2006 Noel Chavasse	£15
2006 — Silver proof	£55
2006 — Gold proof	£1150
2006 David Mackay	£15
2006 — Silver proof	£55
2006 — Gold proof	£1150
2006 Coronation Scot. Silver proof	£60
2006 Flying Scotsman. Silver proof	£60
2006 Fireman and Driver. Silver proof	£60
2006 Box Tunnel. Silver proof	£60
2007 Diamond Wedding balcony scene waving	£15
2007 — Silver proof	£60
2007 Diamond Wedding cake	£15
2007 — Silver proof	£60
2007 Diamond Wedding balcony scene waving	£15
2007 —Silver proof	£60
2007 Diamond Wedding HM the Queen and Prince Philip	£20
2007 — Silver proof	£60
2007 Diamond Wedding arrival at Abbey	£20
2007 — Silver proof	£55
2007 — Gold proof	£1150
2008 George & Dragon	£20
2008 Dambusters, Wallis, Chadwick, Gibson	£15
2008 — Silver/Copper proof	£30
2008 — Silver proof	£55
2008 Frank Whittle	£15
2008 — Silver proof	£55
2008 — Gold proof	£1150
2008 R. J. Mitchell	£15
2008 — Silver proof	£55
2008 — Gold proof	£1150
2008 Maj. Gen. Sir Hugh Trenchard	£15
2008 — Silver proof	£55
2008 — Gold proof	£1150
2008 Bomber Command	£15
2008 — Silver proof	£55
2008 — Gold proof	£1150
2008 Coastal Command	£20
2008 — Silver proof	£60
2008 — Gold proof	£1200
2008 Fighter Command	£20
2008 — Silver proof	£60

DATE UNC

2008 — Gold proof	£1200
2008 Battle of Britain	£20
2008 — Silver proof	£60
2008 — Gold proof	£1200
2008 RBL Poppy	£20
2008 — Silver proof	£60
2008 — Gold proof	£1200
2008 Flying Legends	£15
2008 — Silver proof	£55
2008 — Gold proof	£1150
2009 George & Dragon. Silver proof	£50
2009 Great Battles Series (8 coins). Silver proof. each.	£25
2009 Capt. Cook and *Endeavour*. Silver proof	£55
2009 500th Anniversary of Accession of Henry VIII. Silver proof	£55
2010 Battle of Britain heroes (3 coins available). Silver proof. each.	£50
2011 Landmark birthdays of HM the Queen & Prince Philip	£15
2011 90th Anniversary of the British Legion (poppy-shaped)	£40
2011 — Silver proof	£95
2011 — 5oz silver	£500
2011 — Gold proof	£2500
2011 30th Birthday of the Duke of Cambridge. Silver proof	£50
2011 Wedding of Prince William and Kate Middleton. Silver proof	£50
2011 —Gold proof	£1500
2011 Spirit of the Nation (4 coins). Silver proof, each	£50
2012 HM the Queen's Diamond Jubilee. Gold proof	£2000
2012 Poppy. Silver Proof	£65
2012 — Gold Proof	£2000
2012 RMS *Titanic* Centenary. Cu-Ni Gold plated	£15
2012 — Silver Proof	£65
2013 Coronation Jubilee. Silver proof	£65
2013 — Gold Proof	£2000
2013 The Flying Scotsman. Silver proof	£65
2013 350th Guinea Anniversary. Silver proof	£55
2013 — Gold Proof	£2000
2013 Poppy Coin. Silver proof	£95
2014 70th Anniversary of D-Day. Silver proof	£85
2014 — Gold Proof	£2500
2014 Remembrance Day (two designs), Cu-Ni	£10
2014 — Silver	£50
2014 The Red Arrows 50th Display Season. Silver proof	£95
2014 William Shakespeare—450th Birthday. Silver proof	£80
2015 Remembrance day "Lest we forget", Cu-Ni	£10
2015 50th Anniversary of Winston Churchill's death, Cu-Ni	£10
2015 The Longest Reign, Cu-Ni	£10
2015 200th Anniversary of the Battle of Waterloo, Cu-Ni	£10
2015 Red Arrows, Cu-Ni	£10
2016 90th Birthday of Queen Elizabeth II	£10
2016 Remembrance Day, Cu-Ni	£10
2017 Royal 70th Wedding Anniversary. Cu-Ni	£10
2017 Prince Philip 70 Years of Service. Cu-Ni	£12
2017 — Silver proof	£75
2017 Remembrance Day. Cu-Ni	£12
2017 — Cu-Ni Gold plated	£25
2017 — Silver proof	£85
2018 Prince George's 5th Birthday. Silver proof	£75
2018 Coronation 65th Anniversary. Cu-Ni	£10
2018 — Silver proof	£75
2018 Remembrance Day. Cu-Ni	£12
2018 — Cu-Ni Gold plated	£20
2018 — Silver proof	£75
2018 Dove of Peace. Cu-Ni	£12
2018 RAF 100. Cu-Ni	£15
2018 — Silver proof	£85
2019 Remembrance Poppy Gold Proof	£2,950
2019 — Silver Proof	£90
2019 —Cu-Ni	£5

DATE	UNC
2019 Concorde's first supersonic flight comm. Silver Proof.....................	£85
2019 50th Anniversary of Moon Landing. Silver with Black Proof finish....	£125

TWO POUNDS FIFTY PENCE

1972 Royal Silver Wedding	£25
1972 — Silver proof...	£35

TWO POUNDS

(note all modern Proof coins have frosted relief)

1972 Royal Silver Wedding. Silver..	£25
1972 — Silver proof...	£35
1981 Royal Wedding, nickel silver (crown size)..	£5
1981 — in presentation pack..	£8
1981 — Silver proof...	£20
1981 — Gold proof...	£450
1985 40th Anniversary of Liberation (crown size).......................................	£5
1985 — in presentation pack..	£12
1985 — Silver proof...	£20
1985 — Gold proof...	£1150
1986 Commonwealth Games..	£6
1986 — in presentation case..	£8
1986 — .500 silver...	£12
1986 — .925 silver proof	£20
1987 World Wildlife Fund 25th Anniversary	£80
1987 — Silver proof...	£25
1989 Royal Visit	£15
1989 — Silver proof...	£25
1990 Queen Mother's 90th Birthday	£15
1990 — Silver proof...	£25
1990 — Gold proof...	£600
1990 50th Anniversary of the Battle of Britain, silver proof.........................	£30
1993 40th Anniversary of the Coronation..	£15
1993 — Silver proof...	£20
1993 — Gold proof...	£600

1995 50th Anniversary of Liberation...	£15
1995 — Silver Proof	£25
1995 — — Piedfort...	£75
1996 HM the Queen's 70th Birthday	£15
1996 — Silver proof...	£25
1997 Bi-metal	£5
1997 — Silver proof...	£50
1997 — new portrait..	£5
1998 —	£5
2003 —	£5
2005 —	£5
2006 —	£5
2007 —	£5
2011 Prince Philip's 90th Birthday	£12
2012 HM the Queen's Diamond Jubilee. Gold proof	£1000
2019 Red Arrows..	£10

ONE POUND

1972 Royal Silver Wedding	£15
1972 — Silver proof...	£20
1981...	£15
1981 Silver proof	£15
1981 Gold proof	£350
1983 New designs and specifications on presentation card (St Helier).....	£5
1983 — Silver proof...	£20
1983 — Gold proof...	£350
1984 Presentation wallet (St Saviour)..	£20
1984 — Silver proof...	£45
1984 — Gold proof...	£450

DATE	UNC
1984 Presentation wallet (St Brelade)	£20
1984 — Silver proof	£45
1984 — Gold proof	£500
1985 Presentation wallet (St Clement)	£25
1985 — Silver proof	£45
1985 — Gold proof	£500
1985 Presentation wallet (St Lawrence)	£25
1985 — Silver proof	£40
1985 — Gold proof	£490
1986 Presentation wallet (St Peter)	£15
1986 — Silver proof	£35
1986 — Gold proof	£500
1986 Presentation wallet (Grouville)	£20
1986 — Silver proof	£40
1986 — Gold proof	£500
1987 Presentation wallet (St Martin)	£20
1987 — Silver proof	£40
1987 — Gold proof	£500
1987 Presentation wallet (St Ouen)	£18
1987 — Silver proof	£40
1987 — Gold proof	£500
1988 Presentation wallet (Trinity)	£20
1988 — Silver proof	£40
1988 — Gold proof	£500
1988 Presentation wallet (St John)	£15
1988 — Silver proof	£40
1988 — Gold proof	£450
1989 Presentation wallet (St Mary)	£15
1989 — Silver proof	£40
1989 — Gold proof	£450

1991 Ship Building in Jersey Series

1991 "Tickler". Nickel-brass	£5
1991 "Tickler". Silver proof	£25
1991 — Gold proof Piedfort	£500
1991 "Percy Douglas". Nickel-brass	£5
1991 "Percy Douglas". Silver proof	£25
1991 — Gold proof Piedfort	£500
1992 "The Hebe". Nickel-brass	£5
1992 "The Hebe". Silver proof	£25
1992 — Gold proof Piedfort	£500
1992 "Coat of Arms". Nickel-brass	£5
1992 "Coat of Arms". Silver proof	£25
1992 — Gold proof Piedfort	£500
1993 "The Gemini". Nickel-brass	£5
1993 "The Gemini". Silver proof	£25
1993 — Gold proof Piedfort	£500
1993 "The Century". Nickel-brass	£5
1993 "The Century". Silver proof	£25
1993 — Gold proof Piedfort	£500
1994 "Resolute". Nickel-brass	£5
1994 "Resolute". Silver proof	£25
1994 — Gold proof Piedfort	£500
1997 — Nickel-brass	£5
1998 — — Nickel-brass	£5
2003 — — Nickel-brass	£5
2005 — — Nickel-brass	£5
2006 — — Nickel-brass	£5
2007 Diana Commem. Gold proof	£450
2012 Diamond Jubilee. Gold proof	£450
2013 Coronation Jubilee. Gold proof	£500
2018 WWI Armistice. Gold Proof	£500

DATE	UNC

FIFTY PENCE

1969	£10
1972 Royal Silver Wedding. Silver..	£12
1972 — Silver proof...	£12
1980 —	£1
1980 Arms	£2
1980 — Proof	£5
1981 —	£1
1981 —	£5
1981 — Proof	£5
1983 Grosnez Castle	£10
1983 — Silver proof...	£12
1984 —	£2
1985 40th Anniversary of Liberation...	£3
1986	£5
1986	£5
1987	£5
1988	£5
1989	£5
1990	£5
1992	£5
1994	£5
1997	£5
1997 Smaller size	£4
1998 —	£3
2003	£3
2003 Coronation Anniversary (4 types)	£4
2003 — 4 types. Silver proof...	£15
2005	£4
2006..	£4
2009	£5
2011 Diamond Jubilee (full colour reverse, gold-plated)............................	£15
2013 Coronation Jubilee	£25
2014 Lord Kitchener. Gold plated steel......................................	£15
2015 Battle of Britain. Gold plated steel	£35
2016 Battle of Hastings, Halley's Comet. Silver..........................	£15
2016 Bayeux Tapestry. Silver	£15
2016 Battle of the Somme. Gold plated steel	£25
2018 RAF Centenary. Gold plated brass	£22
2019 50th Anniversary 50p (paired with Guernsey 50p). Silver proof	£125

TWENTY-FIVE PENCE

1977 Royal Jubilee..	£3
1977 — Silver proof...	£20

TWENTY PENCE

1982 Corbiere Lighthouse (cased)	£8
1982 — Silver proof piedfort	£35
1983 — Obv. with date, rev. no date on rocks	£5
1983 — — Silver proof...	£15
1984 —	£1
1986 —	£1
1987 —	£1
1989 —	£1
1992 —	£1
1994 —	£1
1996 —	£1
1997 —	£1
1998 —	£1
2002 —	£1
2003 —	£1
2005 —	£1
2006 —	£1

DATE   UNC

2007 — £1
2009 — £1

SOVEREIGN—Gold sovereign size
1999 The Millennium. King William on Throne £300
1999 — Gold proof..   £35°0

TEN PENCE
1968 Arms...   £1
1975 Arms...   £1
1979 (dated 1975 on thick flan)...   £2
1980 — £1
1980 — Proof...   £5
1981 - £1
1981 — Proof £5
1983 L'Hermitage £1
1983 — Silver proof..   £5
1984 — £1
1985 — £1
1986 — £1
1987 — £1
1988 — £1
1989 — £1
1990 — £1
1992 — £1
1997 — £1
2002 — £1
2003 — £1
2005 — £1
2006 — £1
2007 — £1

FIVE PENCE
1968 Arms...   £1
1980 — £1
1981 — £1
1981 — Proof...   £2
1983 Seymour Towers..   £1
1983 — Silver proof..   £5
1984 — £1
1985 — £1
1986 — £1
1987 — £2
1988 — £1
1990 — £1
1991 — £1
1992 — £5
1993 — £1
1997 — £4
1998 — £1
2002 — £1
2003 — £1
2005 — £5
2006 — £1
2008 — £1

Other denominations are generally available at face value or a small premium above. However, in 2017 a one penny was struck in Platinum to celebrate the 70th Wedding Anniversary of HM The Queen and Prince Philip. In 2018 a penny was struck in gold to celebrate the 65th Anniversary of the Coronation. These were available in limited quantities and retailed at £295. In 2019 a "Datestruck" 200th Anniversary Birth of Queen Victoria penny struck in gold retailed at £695. Also in 2019 a D-Day 75th Anniversary penny in gold was produced and retailed at £175.

ALDERNEY

DATE   UNC

ONE THOUSAND POUNDS
2003 Concorde. Gold proof...   —
2004 D-Day Anniversary. Gold proof................................   —
2005 Prince Harry's 21st Birthday. Gold proof..................   —
2011 Wedding of Prince William and Catherine Middleton. Gold proof.....   —

ONE HUNDRED POUNDS
1994 50th Anniversary of D-Day Landings. Gold proof £285
2003 Prince Wiliam. Gold proof (100mm) ....   —
2005 Trafalgar Anniversary. Gold proof (100mm)................   —

FIFTY POUNDS
1994 50th Anniversary of D–Day Landing. Gold proof..............   £500
2003 Anniversary of Coronation (4 types). Silver proof ea. (100mm)......... £500
2003 Prince William. Silver proof (100mm)............................   £500
2004 Anniversary of D-Day. Silver proof (100mm) £500
2005 200th Anniversary of the Battle of Trafalgar. Silver proof (100mm)...   £500

TWENTY FIVE POUNDS
1993 40th Anniversary of Coronation. Gold proof...................   £200
1994 50th Anniversary of D-Day Landings. Gold proof £200
1997 Royal Golden Wedding. Gold proof £295
1997 — Silver proof..   £40
1999 Winston Churchill. Gold proof £350
2000 Queen Mother. Gold proof..   £325
2000 60th Anniversary of the Battle of Britain. Gold proof £275
2001 Royal Birthday. Gold proof £300
2002 Golden Jubilee. Gold proof £295
2002 Princess Diana. Gold proof £295
2002 Duke of Wellington. Gold proof £300
2003 Prince William. Gold proof £300
2003 HMS Mary Rose. Gold proof...................................   £300
2004 D-Day Anniversary. Gold proof................................   £395
2004 The Rocket. Gold proof £295
2004 Merchant Navy Class Locomotive. Gold proof £295
2005 Battle of Saints Passage. Gold proof £295
2006 World Cup 2006 (4 Coins). Gold ea.............................   £350

TEN POUNDS
1994 50th Anniversary of D–Day Landing. Gold proof..............   £150
2003 Concorde. Silver proof (65mm) £280
2005 60th Anniversary of the Liberation of the Channel Islands (65mm)... £250
2007 80th Birthday of Her Majesty the Queen (65mm)............   £180
2008 Concorde. Silver proof £180
2008 90th Anniversary of the end of WWI. Silver Proof £180
2009 50th Anniversary of the Mini—Silver with colour..............   £180
2012 Prince William's 30th Birthday ....   —

FIVE POUNDS
1995 Queen Mother £15
1995 — Silver proof..   £50
1995 — Silver piedfort...   £155
1995 — Gold proof...   £900
1996 HM the Queen's 70th Birthday £20
1996 — Silver proof..   £60
1996 — Silver piedfort...   £150
1996 — Gold proof...   £1000
1999 Eclipse of the Sun £25
1999 — Silver proof with colour centre.............................   £55
1999 Winston Churchill. Gold proof £1000
2000 60th Anniversary of the Battle of Britain.....................   £25
2000 — Silver proof..   £55

DATE	UNC
2000 Queen Mother. 100th Birthday. Silver proof	£50
2000 Millennium. Silver proof	£35
2001 HM Queen's 75th Birthday.	£15
2001 — Silver proof	£45
2002 Golden Jubilee. Silver proof	£50
2002 50 Years of Reign.	£15
2002 —Silver proof	£50
2002 Diana memorial	£15
2002 — Silver proof	£45
2002 — Gold proof	£900
2002 Duke of Wellington	£20
2002 — Silver proof	£50
2002 — Gold proof	£900
2003 Prince William	£20
2003 — Silver proof	£50
2003 — Gold proof	£900
2003 Mary Rose	£20
2003 — Silver proof	£120
2003 Alfred the Great. Silver proof	£150
2003 —Gold proof	£1000
2003 Last Flight of Concorde	£25
2003 — Silver proof	£150
2003 — Gold proof	£1000
2004 Anniversary of D-Day	£20
2004 — Silver proof	£75
2004 — Gold proof	£1000
2004 Florence Nightingale	320
2004 — Silver proof	£45
2004 150th Anniversary of the Crimean War	£20
2004 — Silver proof	£45
2004 — Gold proof	£1000
2004 The Rocket	£20
2004 — Silver proof	£45
2004 — Gold proof	£900
2004 Royal Scot	£20
2004 — Silver proof	£45
2004 Merchant Navy Class Locomotive	£20
2004 — Silver proof	£45
2005 End of WWII. Silver proof	£45
2005 — Gold proof	£900
2005 200th Anniversary of the Battle of Trafalgar	£16
2005 — Silver proof	£50
2005 History of the Royal Navy. John Woodward. Silver proof	£30
2005 Anniversary of Liberation. Gold proof	£1000
2005 Anniversary of the Battle of Saints Passage	£15
2005 — Silver proof	£45
2005 HMS Revenge 1591	£15
2005 — Silver proof	£45
2005 Prince Harry's 21st Birthday. Gold proof	£1000
2006 80th Birthday of Her Majesty the Queen (3-coin set) ea	£20
2006 Gold plated portraits of Her Majesty the Queen	—
2006 80th Birthday of Her Majesty the Queen (3-coin set) ea	£16
2007 History of the Royal Navy—*Mary Rose* (2 coins) ea	£16
2007 150th Anniversary of the Victoria Cross (18 coin set). Silver proof	£250
2007 Monarchs of England (12 coin set). Gold plated	£150
2008 90th Anniversary of the end of WWI (3 coins). Gold proof	£2500
2008 Classic British Motorcars (18 coin set). Silver proof.	£250
2008 Concorde. Gold proof	£1000
2009 50th Anniversary of the Mini (4 coins). Silver proof ea.	£50
2011 Royal Engagement gold proof	£1000
2011 — Gold plated silver proof	£150
2011 — Silver proof	£55
2011 — Cupro Nickel	£15
2011 John Lennon Silver proof	£55
2011 Battle of Britain 70th Anniversary silver proof	£55
2012 RMS *Titanic*	£15
2012 Remembrance Day (Re-issued 2013)	£25

DATE	UNC
2014 70th Anniversary of D-Day	£15
2014 — Silver proof	£25
2014 — Gold proof	£1000
2014 Destiny to Dynasty. Silver proof	£25
2014 300th Anniversary of the Coronation of King George I	£20
2014 — Silver proof	£25
2014 — Gold proof	£1000
2014 Centenary of the birth of poet Dylan Thomas	£15
2014 — Silver proof	£45
2014 — Gold proof	£1000
2014 Remembrance Day "Remember the Fallen"	—
2015 Churchill Quotations (4-coin set)	£40
2015 — Silver proof (4-coin)	£250
2015 70th Anniversary of VE Day	£15
2015 — Silver proof	£45
2015 — Silver proof piedfort	£75
2015 150th Anniversary of the Salvation Army	£10
2015 — Silver proof	£45
2015 Remembrance Day	—
2015 — Silver	—
2015 — — piedfort	—
2016 The FIFA World Cup	£15
2016 — Silver proof	£45
2016 — Gold proof	£1000
2016 Remembrance Day	—
2016 — Silver Proof	—
2016 — — piedfort	—
2017 Remembrance Day	£17
2017 — Silver Proof	£90
2017 — Silver Piedfort	£170

TWO POUNDS

1989 Royal Visit	£12
1989 — Silver proof	£25
1989 — Silver piedfort	£45
1989 — Gold proof	£1000
1990 Queen Mother's 90th Birthday	£12
1990 — Silver proof	£25
1990 — Silver piedfort	£45
1990 — Gold proof	£1000
1992 40th Anniversary of Accession	£15
1992 — Silver proof	£35
1992 — Silver piedfort	£50
1992 — Gold proof	£1000
1993 40th Anniversary of Coronation	£15
1993 — Silver proof	£35
1993 — Silver piedfort	£50
1994 50th Anniversary of D-Day Landings	£15
1994 — Silver proof	£35
1994 — Silver piedfort	£50
1995 50th Anniversary of Return of Islanders	£15
1995 — Silver proof	£35
1995 — Silver piedfort	£50
1995 — Gold proof	£1000
1997 WWF Puffin	£18
1997 — Silver proof	£35
1997 Royal Golden Wedding	£20
1997 — Silver proof	£50
1999 Eclipse of the Sun. Silver	£20
1999 — Silver proof	£50
1999 — Gold proof	£1250
2000 Millennium. Silver proof	£50

ONE POUND

1993 40th Anniversary of Coronation Silver proof	£50
1995 50th Anniversary of VE Day Silver proof	£45
1995 — Gold proof	£500
2008 Concorde. Gold proof	£275
2009 50th Anniversary of the Mini. Gold proof	£375

IRELAND

As in the English hammered section (q.v.) the prices given here are for the most common coins in the series. For a more specialised listing the reader is referred to Coincraft's *Standard Catalogue of Scotland, Ireland, Channel Islands & Isle of Man*, or other specialised publications. Collectors should be aware that with most of the coins of the Irish series there are many varieties struck at different mints. The coins listed are all silver unless mentioned otherwise. Another important factor to consider when collecting early Irish coins is that few examples exist in high grades.

	F	VF

HIBERNO-NORSE ISSUES (995–1155)
Penny, imitating English silver pennies,
many various types £300   £600

JOHN, Lord of Ireland (1185–99)
Halfpenny, profile ....   Extremely rare
Halfpenny, facing £100   £450
Farthing £450   £1500

Hiberno-Norse phase II example.

JOHN de COURCY, Lord of Ulster (1177–1205)
Halfpenny ....   Extremely rare
Farthing £700   £3500

JOHN as King of England and Lord of Ireland (c. 1199–1216)
Penny £70   £400
Halfpenny £175   £5000
Farthing £650   £2500

John Lord of Ireland penny.

HENRY III (1216–72)
Penny £150   £575

EDWARD I (1272–1307)
Penny £75   £200
Halfpenny £75   £175
Farthing £150   £450

Henry III penny.

No Irish coins were struck for Edward II (1307–27).

EDWARD III (1327–77)
Halfpenny ....   Extremely rare

No Irish coins were struck for Richard II (1377–99), Henry IV (1399–1413) or Henry V (1413–22).

HENRY VI (1422–61)
Penny ....   Extremely rare

Edward I penny.

EDWARD IV (1461–83)

	F	VF
"Anonymous crown" groat	£700	£13500
— penny	£1200	—
"Titled crown" groat	£1600	—
— halfgroat		Extremely rare
— penny		Extremely rare
Cross on rose/Sun groat	£1850	
Bust/Rose on sun double groat	£2250	£7500
— groat	£2250	—
— halfgroat		Extremely rare
— penny		Extremely rare
Bust/Cross & pellets groat—First issue	£150	£575
— halfgroat	£650	£1700
— penny	£100	£375
— halfpenny		Extremely rare
— Second (light) issue	£150	£500
— halfgroat	£650	£1700
— penny	£100	
— halfpenny	£250	Extremely rare
Bust/Rose on cross groat	£570	£1500
— penny	£80	£245
Billon/Copper issues		
Small crown/Cross farthing (1460–61)	£1700	—
— half farthing ("Patrick")	£1100	—
Large crown/Cross farthing (1462)		Extremely rare
Patricius/Salvator farthing (1463–65)	£350	£2000
— half farthing		Extremely rare
Shield/Rose on sun farthing	£200	£1000

Edward IV groat. "Anonymous crown" issue.

Edward IV penny struck in Dublin.

RICHARD III (1483–85)

	F	VF
Bust/Rose on cross groat	£1100	£4000
— halfgroat		Unique
— penny		Unique
Bust/Cross and pellets penny	£100	£3200
Shield/Three-crowns groat	£650	£3000

HENRY VII (1485–1509)

	F	VF
Early issues (1483–90)		
Shield/Three crowns groat	£170	£525
— halfgroat	£250	£565
— penny	£650	£2600
— halfpenny		Extremely rare
Later issues (1488–90)		
Shield/Three crowns groat	£100	£400
— halfgroat	£200	£600
— penny	£500	£1350
Facing bust groat (1496–1505)	£150	£425
— halfgroat	£1100	—
— penny	£1000	—

Richard III bust/rose on cross groat.

LAMBERT SIMNEL
(as EDWARD VI, Pretender, 1487)

	F	VF
Shield/Three crowns groat	£1300	£4500

Henry VII groat.

	F	VF

HENRY VIII (1509–47)

"Harp" groat	£150	£4000
— halfgroat	£500	£2600

The "Harp" coins have crowned initials either side of the reverse harp,
e.g. HR (Henricus Rex), HA (Henry and Anne Boleyn), HI (Henry and Jane
Seymour), HK (Henry and Katherine Howard).

Posthumous (Portrait) issues

Sixpence	£175	£575
Threepence	£150	£575
Threehalfpence	£500	£1800
Threefarthings	£650	£2200

Henry VIII Posthumous portrait issues threepence.

EDWARD VI (1547–53)

Shilling (base silver) 1552 (MDLII)	£1100	£3600
Brass contemporary copy	£100	£400

MARY (1553–54)

Shilling 1553 (MDLIII)	£1000	£3500
Shilling 1554 (MDLIIII)		Extremely rare
Groat		Extremely rare
Halfgroat		Extremely rare
Penny		Extremely rare

PHILIP & MARY (1554–58)

Shilling	£350	£1500
Groat	£150	£475
Penny		Extremely rare

ELIZABETH I (1558–1603)

Base silver portrait coinage

Shilling	£375	£1600
Groat	£200	£800

Philip & Mary shilling

Fine silver, portrait coinage (1561)

Shilling	£300	£1200
Groat	£350	£1200

Third (base silver) shield coinage

Shilling	£250	£800
Sixpence	£200	£550

Copper

Threepence	£275	£750
Penny	£70	£220
Halfpenny	£100	£325

JAMES I (1603–25)

Shilling	£110	£425
Sixpence	£110	£275

Coins struck under Royal Licence
from 1613

"Harrington" farthing (small size)	£75	£275
"Harrington" farthing (large size)	£75	£250
"Lennox" farthing	£75	£250

Elizabeth I "fine" shilling of 1561.

CHARLES I (1625–49)

During the reign of Charles I and the Great Rebellion many coins were struck under unusual circumstances, making the series a difficult but fascinating area for study. Many of the "coins" were simply made from odd-shaped pieces of plate struck with the weight or value.

	F	VF
Coins struck under Royal Licence from 1625		
"Richmond" farthing	£60	£250
"Maltravers" farthing	£50	£250
"Rose" farthing	£50	£250
Siege money of the Irish Rebellion, 1642–49		
"Inchiquin" Money (1642)		
Crown	£2500	£6500
Halfcrown	£2000	£5500
Shilling		Extremely rare
Ninepence		Extremely rare
Sixpence		Extremely rare
Groat		Extremely rare
"Dublin" Money (1643)		
Crown	£1000	£3600
Halfcrown	£600	£2600
"Ormonde" Money (1643–44)		
Crown	£575	£1600
Halfcrown	£375	£1200
Shilling	£150	£475
Sixpence	£150	£475
Groat	£120	£400
Threepence	£120	£350
Twopence	£500	£1600
"Ormonde" gold coinage (1646)		
Double pistole. 2 known (both in museums)		Extremely rare
Pistole. 10 known (only 1 in private ownership		Extremely rare
"Ormonde" Money (1649)		
Crown		Extremely rare
Halfcrown	£1300	£4000
Dublin Money 1649		
Crown	£3000	£8000
Halfcrown	£2200	£5000

Charles I "Ormonde" crown.

Issues of the Confederated Catholics

	F	VF
Kilkenny issues (1642–43)		
Halfpenny	£310	£1000
Farthing	£410	£1200
Rebel Money (1643–44)		
Crown	£2600	£5600
Halfcrown	£3000	£5600
"Blacksmith's" Money (16??)		
Imitation of English Tower halfcrown	£750	£3200

A rare Charles I "Rebel" halfcrown.

	F	VF

Local Town issues of "Cities of Refuge"

Bandon
Farthing (copper) .... Extremely rare

Cork
	F	VF
Shilling		Extremely rare
Sixpence	£775	£1500
Halfpenny (copper)		Extremely rare
Farthing (copper)	£620	—

Kinsale
	F	VF
Farthing (copper)	£400	—

Youghal
	F	VF
Farthing (copper)	£500	£2200

CHARLES II (1660–85)

	Fair	F	VF	EF
"Armstrong" coinage				
Farthing (1660–61)	£75	£250	—	—
"St Patrick's" coinage				
Halfpenny	£235	£475	—	—
Farthing	£85	£200	£500	£1600
Legg's Regal coinage				
Halfpennies				
1680 large lettering	£35	£100	£300	—
1681 large lettering	—	£200	£695	—
1681 small lettering			Extremely rare	
1682 small lettering	—	£200	£675	—
1683 small lettering	£35	£45	£450	
1684 small lettering	£50	£125	£675	—

Halfpenny of Charles I.

JAMES II (1685–88)

REGAL COINAGE

Halfpennies
	Fair	F	VF	EF
1685	£35	£85	£320	£750
1686	£35	£65	£200	£650
1687			Extremely rare	
1688	£40	£125	£300	£1400

"St Patrick" farthing of Charles II.

Our grateful thanks to Del Parker, specialist in Irish rarities, for supplying the images for this section. An impressive and extensive range of Irish coins can be viewed and purchased at his website at www.irishcoins.com.

	Fair	F	VF	EF

EMERGENCY COINAGE

GUN MONEY
Most of these coins were struck in gun metal but a few rare specimens are also known struck in gold and in silver

Crowns

	Fair	F	VF	EF
1690 (many varieties)......................from	£45	£65	£650	—

Large halfcrowns
Dated July 1689–May 1690

	Fair	F	VF	EF
....from	£35	£65	£225	—

Small halfcrowns
Dated April–October1690

	Fair	F	VF	EF
....from	£35	£65	£250	—

Large shillings
Dated from July 1689–April 1690

	Fair	F	VF	EF
....from	£35	£75	£125	£500

Small shillings
Dated from April–September 1690

	Fair	F	VF	EF
....from	£25	£35	£125	£450

"Gun Money" crown.

Sixpences
Dated from June 1689–October 1690

	Fair	F	VF	EF
....from	£35	£60	£300	—

PEWTER MONEY (1689–90)

	Fair	F	VF	EF
Crown...	£700	£1200	£3200	—
Groat..			Extremely rare	
Penny large bust....................................	£230	£675	—	—
— small bust	£165	£485	£1400	—
Halfpenny large bust	£130	£345	£800	—
— small bust	£110	£245	£700	—

LIMERICK MONEY (1690–91)

	Fair	F	VF	EF
Halfpenny, reversed N in HIBERNIA......	£35	£75	£275	—
Farthing, reversed N in HIBERNIA.........	£35	£75	£275	—
— normal N	£45	£135	£325	—

WILLIAM & MARY (1689–94)

Halfpennies

	Fair	F	VF	EF
1692...	£15	£50	£100	£695
1693...	£15	£50	£85	£675
1694...	£25	£75	£135	£750

WILLIAM III (1694–1702)

	Fair	F	VF	EF
1696 Halfpenny draped bust................	£35	£85	£265	—
1696 — crude undraped bust	£45	£275	£900	—

William & Mary half-penny of 1693.

No Irish coins were struck during the reign of Queen Anne (1706–11).

DATE	F	VF	EF	UNC

GEORGE I (1714–27)

Farthings

1722 D.G. REX Harp to left (Pattern)..............	£650	£1600	£2400	—
1723 D.G. REX Harp to right	£120	£225	£525	—
1723 DEI GRATIA REX Harp to right	£35	£65	£265	£650
1723 — Silver Proof	—	—	—	£2500
1724 DEI GRATIA REX Harp to right	£60	£150	£365	£875

Halfpennies

1722 Holding Harp left	£55	£130	£395	£1100
1722 Holding Harp right	£45	£120	£350	£800
1723/2 Harp right	£50	£150	£350	£800
1723 Harp right	£25	£65	£200	£565
1723 Silver Proof	—	—	—	£3575
1723 Obv. Rs altered from Bs	£35	£100	£295	—
1723 No stop after date	£25	£80	£295	£550
1724 Rev. legend divided	£40	£100	£300	—
1724 Rev. legend continuous	£40	£110	£395	—

GEORGE II (1727–60)

Farthings

1737..	£35	£60	£185	£500
1737 Proof	—	—	—	£525
1737 Silver Proof	—	—	—	£1300
1738..	£35	£65	£165	£485
1744..	£35	£65	£165	£485
1760	£30	£50	£100	£385

Halfpenny of George II

Halfpennies

1736..	£25	£60	£225	£650
1736 Proof	—	—	—	£685
1736 Silver Proof	—	—	—	£1400
1737..	£25	£50	£225	—
1738..	£30	£60	£225	—
1741..	£30	£60	£225	—
1742..	£30	£60	£225	—
1743..	£30	£60	£185	—
1744/3	£30	£60	£195	—
1744..	£30	£60	£375	—
1746..	£30	£60	£250	—
1747..	£30	£60	£225	—
1748..	£30	£60	£225	—
1749..	£30	£60	£225	—
1750..	£30	£60	£225	—
1751..	£30	£60	£225	—
1752..	£30	£60	£225	—
1753..	£30	£60	£250	—
1755..	£30	£110	£350	—
*1760	£30	£75	£250	—

GEORGE III (1760–1820)

All copper unless otherwise stated

Pennies

1805..	£20	£40	£190	£500
1805 Proof	—	—	—	£600
1805 in Bronze Proof	—	—	—	£600
1805 in Copper Gilt Proof.............................	—	—	—	£600
1805 in Silver Proof (restrike).......................	—	—	—	£3500

George III proof penny 1805

DATE	F	VF	EF	UNC
Halfpennies				
1766...	£30	£55	£165	—
1769...	£30	£55	£165	—
1769 Longer bust	£40	£75	£250	£675
1774 Pattern only Proof.................................	—	—	—	£2000
1775...	£30	£55	£200	£475
1775 Proof	—	—	—	£675
1776...	£55	£140	£400	—
1781...	£45	£60	£175	£450
1782...	£45	£60	£175	£450
1805...	£18	£45	£120	£450
1805 Copper Proof...	—	—	—	£450
1805 in Bronze	—	—	—	£300
1805 in Gilt Copper	—	—	—	£475
1805 in Silver (restrike)	—	—	—	£1850
Farthings				
1806...	£20	£35	£100	£200
1806 Copper Proof...	—	—	—	£375
1806 Bronzed Copper Proof	—	—	—	£265
1806 Copper Gilt Proof	—	—	—	£350
1806 Silver Proof (restrike)	—	—	—	£1200

GEORGE IV (1820–30)

Pennies				
1822...	£20	£40	£195	£450
1822 Proof...	—	—	—	£595
1823...	£12	£25	£150	£400
1823 Proof...	—	—	—	£620

One of the scarcer dates, a 1776 George III halfpenny.

DATE	F	VF	EF	UNC
Halfpennies				
1822	£20	£40	£125	£400
1822 Proof	—	—	—	£650
1823	£20	£40	£125	£400
1823 Proof	—	—	—	£695

NB Prooflike Uncirculated Pennies and Halfpennies of 1822/23 are often mis-described as Proofs. The true Proofs are rare. Some are on heavier, thicker flans.

Farthings				
1822 (Pattern) Proof	—	—	—	£1875

TOKEN ISSUES BY THE BANK OF IRELAND

Five Pence in Silver

	F	VF	EF	UNC
1805	£30	£45	£75	£375
1806	£30	£65	£150	£400
1806/5	£60	£145	£450	£1475

Ten Pence in Silver

	F	VF	EF	UNC
1805	£20	£35	£95	£265
1806	£20	£65	£150	£295
1813	£20	£35	£95	£325
1813 Proof	—	—	—	£475

Thirty Pence in Silver

	F	VF	EF	UNC
1808	£45	£100	£250	£675

1804 six shillings.

Six Shillings

	F	VF	EF	UNC
1804 in Silver	£100	£250	£465	£1875
1804 Proof	—	—	—	£1800
1804 in Copper (restrike)	—	—	—	£800
1804 Copper Gilt	—	—	—	£1750
1804 in Gilt Silver	—	—	—	£3000

In this series fully struck specimens, with sharp hair curls, etc., are worth appreciably more than the prices quoted.

IRISH FREE STATE/EIRE

DATE	F	VF	EF	UNC
TEN SHILLINGS				
1966 Easter Rising	—	£12	£18	£25
1966 Cased Proof	—	—	—	£25
1966 special double case	—	—	—	£85
HALF CROWNS				
Silver				
1928	£7	£12	£40	£85
1928 Proof	—	—	—	£95
1930	£12	£35	£175	£575
1931	£12	£35	£175	£545
1933	£12	£25	£175	£575
1934	£12	£12	£55	£275
1937	£60	£200	£650	£1900
Modified obverse: Eire				
1938				Unique
1939	£7	£17	£30	£85
1939 Proof	—	—	—	£650
1940	£8	£18	£35	£95
1941	£7	£17	£35	£95
1942	£7	£20	£35	£90
1943	£85	£300	£995	£3450
Cupro-nickel				
1951	£2	£3	£20	£75
1951 Proof	—	—	—	£525
1954	£2	£3	£15	£95
1954 Proof	—	—	—	£525
1955	£2	£3	£15	£45
1955	—	—	—	£600
1959	£2	£3	£12	£50
1961	£2	£3	£25	£60
1961 Obv as 1928, rev. as 1951	£30	£75	£325	£775
1962	£2	£3	£6	£35
1963	£2	£3	£6	£35
1964	£2	£3	£6	£35
1966	£2	£3	£6	£35
1967	£2	£3	£6	£35
FLORINS				
Silver				
1928	£3	£6	£25	£65
1928 Proof	—	—	—	£80
1930	£5	£20	£150	£475
1930 Proof				Unique
1931	£5	£20	£175	£475
1933	£5	£18	£140	£475
1934	£15	£125	£275	£775
1934 Proof	—	—	—	£3000
1935	£5	£18	£65	£200
1937	£6	£25	£140	£425
Modified obverse: Eire				
1939	£3	£6	£35	£85
1939 Proof	—	—	—	£685
1940	£5	£6	£30	£85
1941	£5	£6	£35	£80
1941 Proof	—	—	—	£875
1942	£6	£15	£30	£85
1943	£3000	£6000	£10000	£22500

Beware of fake 1943 florins.

DATE	F	VF	EF	UNC
Cupro-nickel				
1951	60p	£2	£15	£50
1951 Proof	—	—	—	£495
1954	60p	£2	£10	£50
1954 Proof	—	—	—	£400
1955	—	£2	£6	£50
1955 Proof	—	—	—	£565
1959	40p	£2	£6	£45
1961	60p	£3	£15	£55
1962	40p	£2	£6	£30
1963	30p	£2	£6	£30
1964	30p	£2	£6	£30
1965	30p	£2	£6	£30
1966	30p	£2	£6	£30
1968	30p	£2	£6	£30

SHILLINGS
Silver

DATE	F	VF	EF	UNC
1928	£3	£10	£208	£50
1928 Proof	—	—	—	£75
1930	£6	£25	£100	£465
1930 Proof	—	—	—	£865
1931	£3	£17	£95	£475
1933	£3	£17	£95	£460
1935	£3	£13	£50	£160
1937	£10	£75	£250	£1300
1939	£3	£6	£25	£75
1939 Proof	—	—	—	£775
1940	£3	£6	£17	£60
1941	£3	£5	£17	£60
1942	£3	£5	£12	£55
Cupro-nickel				
1951	£1	£2	£6	£25
1951 Proof	—	—	—	£450
1954	£1	£2	£6	£25
1954 Proof	—	—	—	£500
1955	£1	£2	£6	£25
1959	£1	£2	£6	£35
1962	50p	£2	£3	£22
1963	50p	£2	£3	£15
1964	50p	£2	£3	£15
1966	50p	£2	£3	£15
1968	50p	£2	£3	£15

SIXPENCES
Nickel

DATE	F	VF	EF	UNC
1928	£1	£6	£20	£60
1928 Proof	—	—	—	£65
1934	£1	£3	£18	£100
1935	£1	£3	£25	£130
Modified obverse: Eire				
1939	£1	£2	£10	£65
1939 Proof	—	—	—	£675
1940	£1	£2	£6	£65
Cupro-nickel				
1942	£1	£2	£9	£65
1945	£3	£12	£35	£100
1946	£5	£10	£100	£400
1947	£2	£2	£25	£95
1948	£1	£3	£15	£75
1949	£1	£2	£10	£50
1950	£2	£3	£25	£100
1952	£1	£2	£5	£25

DATE	F	VF	EF	UNC
1953	£1	£2	£5	£35
1953 Proof	—	—	—	£125
1955	£1	£2	£4	£30
1956	£1	£2	£3	£30
1956 Proof	—	—	—	£175
1958	£2	£3	£12	£70
1958 Proof	—	—	—	£395
1959	50p	60p	£3	£25
1960	50p	60p	£2	£25
1961	—	£2	£3	£25
1962	£2	£6	£35	£80
1963	£1	£3	£6	£20
1964	£1	£2	£5	£15
1966	£1	£2	£5	£15
1967	£1	£2	£2	£12
1968	£1	£2	£2	£12
1969	£2	£3	£6	£25

THREEPENCES
Nickel

	F	VF	EF	UNC
1928	£2	£3	£10	£45
1928 Proof	—	—	—	£45
1933	£3	£13	£75	£385
1934	£1	£3	£15	£85

Modified obverse: Eire

	F	VF	EF	UNC
1935	£2	£4	£30	£235
1939	£3	£7	£60	£385
1939 Proof	—	—	—	£1200
1940	£2	£3	£13	£75

Cupro-nickel

	F	VF	EF	UNC
1942	—	£2	£6	£65
1942 Proof	—	—	—	£525
1943	£2	£3	£15	£80
1946	£2	£5	£10	£55
1946 Proof	—	—	—	£525
1948	£2	£3	£25	£85
1949	—	£2	£6	£45
1950	—	£2	£6	£35
1950 Proof	—	—	—	£555
1953	—	£2	£4	£20
1956	—	£2	£3	£15
1961	—	60p	£2	£5
1962	—	60p	£2	£10
1963	—	60p	£2	£10
1964	—	60p	£2	£5
1965	—	60p	£2	£5
1966	—	60p	£2	£5
1967	—	60p	£2	£5
1968	—	—	£2	£5

PENNIES

	F	VF	EF	UNC
1928	£2	£3	£12	£55
1928 Proof	—	—	—	£65
1931	£2	£4	£35	£125
1931 Proof	—	—	—	£1000
1933	£2	£5	£50	£275
1935	£1	£2	£25	£85
1937	£1	£2	£35	£135
1937 Proof	—	—	—	£1100

Modified obverse: Eire

	F	VF	EF	UNC
1938		Only two known		
1940	£10	£50	£175	£765
1941	£1	£2	£10	£35
1942	—	£2	£5	£25

DATE	F	VF	EF	UNC
1943	—	£2	£6	£45
1946	—	£2	£4	£20
1948	—	£2	£4	£20
1949	—	£2	£4	£20
1949 Proof	—	—	—	£500
1950	—	£2	£6	£40
1952	—	£2	£4	£15
1962	—	£2	£4	£15
1962 Proof	—	—	—	£200
1963	—	—	£2	£15
1963 Proof	—	—	—	£200
1964	—	—	£2	£10
1964 Proof	—	—	—	£500
1965	—	—	£1	£5
1966	—	—	£1	£5
1967	—	—	£1	£5
1968	—	—	£1	£5
1968 Proof	—	—	—	£300

HALFPENNIES

	F	VF	EF	UNC
1928	£2	£3	£15	£45
1928 Proof	—	—	—	£45
1933	£6	£20	£100	£520
1935	£5	£10	£50	£220
1937	£2	£5	£15	£65
Modified obverse: Eire				
1939	£5	£10	£50	£200
1939 Proof	—	—	—	£900
1940	£2	£4	£50	£195
1941	£1	£2	£6	£25
1942	£1	£2	£6	£25
1943	£1	£2	£8	£35
1946	£2	£5	£20	£100
1949	£1	£2	£6	£25
1953	—	£2	£3	£12
1953 Proof	—	—	—	£500
1964	—	—	£1	£5
1965	—	—	£1	£6
1966	—	—	£1	£4
1967	—	—	£1	£4

FARTHINGS

	F	VF	EF	UNC
1928	£3	£4	£15	£30
1928 Proof	—	—	—	£45
1930	£3	£4	£10	£32
1931	£4	£6	£15	£35
1931 Proof	—	—	—	£875
1932	£4	£6	£18	£45
1933	£3	£4	£12	£32
1935	£4	£6	£18	£35
1936	£4	£6	£18	£35
1937	£3	£4	£12	£32
Modified obverse: Eire				
1939	£3	£4	£10	£20
1939 Proof	—	—	—	£675
1940	£4	£5	£10	£25
1941	£3	£4	£6	£12
1943	£3	£4	£6	£12
1944	£3	£4	£6	£12
1946	£3	£4	£6	£12
1949	£4	£6	£8	£25
1949 Proof	—	—	—	£475
1953	£3	£4	£5	£12
1953 Proof	—	—	—	£345
1959	£3	£4	£5	£12
1966	£3	£4	£5	£12

For the 1928–50 copper issues it is worth noting that UNC means UNC with some lustre. BU examples with full lustre are extremely elusive and are worth much more than the quoted prices.

IRISH DECIMAL COINAGE

DATE	MINTAGE	BU
HALF PENCE		
1971	100,500,000	£5
1975	10,500,000	£6
1976	5,500,000	£6
1978	20,300,000	£5
1980	20,600,000	£4
1982	9,700,000	£4
1985	2,800,000	Rare
1986. Only issued in the 1986 set	19,750,000	£120

ONE PENNY

1971	100,500,000	£5
1974	10,000,000	£10
1975	10,000,000	£15
1976	38,200,000	£5
1978	25,700,000	£8
1979	21,800,000	£12
1980	86,700,000	£3
1982	54,200,000	£5
1985	19,200,000	£8
1986	36,600,000	£5
1988	56,800,000	£5
1990	65,100,000	£5
1992	25,600,000	£6
1993	10,000,000	£6
1994	45,800,000	£5
1995	70,800,000	£3
1996	190,100,000	£1
1998	40,700,000	£1
2000	Unknown	£1

TWO PENCE

1971	75,500,000	£5
1975	20,000,000	£10
1976	5400,000	£12
1978	12,000,000	£12
1979	32,400,000	£8
1980	59,800,000	£6
1982	30,400,000	£5
1985	14,500,000	£6
1986	23,900,000	£6
1988	35,900,000	£5
1990	34,300,000	£5
1992	10,200,000	£10

DATE	MINTAGE	BU
1995	55,500,000	£5
1996	69,300,000	£2
1998	33,700,000	£2
2000	Unknown	£2

FIVE PENCE

1969 Toned	5,000,000	£5
1970	10,000,000	£5
1971	8,000,000	£8
1974	7,000,000	£10
1975	10,000,000	£10
1976	20,600,000	£5
1978	28,500,000	£5
1980	22,200,000	£5
1982	24,400,000	£4
1985	4,200,000	£8
1986	15,300,000	£5
1990	7,500,000	£5
Size reduced to 18.4mm		
1992	74,500,000	£5
1993	89,100,000	£5
1994	31,100,000	£5
1995	12,000,000	£5
1996	14,700,000	£2
1998	158,500,000	£2
2000	Unknown	£1

TEN PENCE

1969	27,000,000	£12
1971	4,000,000	£12
1973	2,500,000	£16
1974	7,500,000	£12
1975	15,000,000	£12
1976	9,400,000	£12
1978	30,900,000	£10
1980	44,600,000	£8
1982	7,400,000	£8
1985	4,100,000	£10
1986. Only issued in the 1986 set	11,280	£285
Size reduced to 22mm		
1992	2 known	—
1993	80,100,000	£5
1994	58,500,000	£5

DATE	MINTAGE	BU
1995	16,100,000	£5
1996	18,400,000	£3
1997	10,000,000	£3
1998	10,000,000	£3
1999	24,500,000	£3
2000	Unknown	£3

TWENTY PENCE

DATE	MINTAGE	BU
1985. Only 600 minted and 556 melted down, only 3 known	Extremely rare	
1986	50,400,000	£8
1988	20,700,000	£6
1992	14,800,000	£5
1994	11,100,000	£5
1995	18,200,000	£5
1996	29,300,000	£5
1998	25,000,000	£3
1999	11,000,000	£3
2000	Unknown	£2

FIFTY PENCE

DATE	MINTAGE	BU
1970	9,000,000	£8
1971	650,000	£7
1974	1,000,000	£55
1975	2,000,000	£55
1976	3,000,000	£45
1977	4,800,000	£55
1978	4,500,000	£45
1979	4,000,000	£45
1981	6,000,000	£25
1982	2,000,000	£25
1983	7,000,000	£25
1986. Only issued in the 1986 set	10,000	£300
1988	7,000,000	£5
1988 Dublin Millennium	5,000,000	£5
1988 — Proof	50,000	£25
1996	6,000,000	£7
1997	6,000,000	£7
1998	13,800,000	£5
1999	7,000,000	£4
2000	Unknown	£4

ONE POUND

DATE	MINTAGE	BU
1990	42,300,000	£5
1990 Proof	50,000	£25
1994	14,900,000	£5
1995	9,200,000	£5
1995 UN silver proof in case of issue	2,850	£175
1996	9,200,000	£5
1998	22,960,000	£4
1999	10,000,000	£5
2000	4,000,000	£5

	MINTAGE	BU
2000 Millennium	5,000,000	£5
2000 – Silver Proof Piedfort	90,000	£35

OFFICIAL COIN SETS ISSUED BY THE CENTRAL BANK

1971 Specimen set in green wallet. 6 coins	£20
1975 6 coin set	£55
1978 6 coin set	£55
1978 6 coin set. Black cover, scarce	£75
1982 6 coin set. Black cover	£75
1986 Specimen set in card folder 1/2p to 50p, 7 coins. Very scarce. Most sets have glue problems	£650
1996 7 coin set	£60
1998 7 coin set	£50
2000 Millennium set. Last decimal set	£125
2000 — With 1999 instead of the 2000 £1 coin	£275

*Dublin
Millennium 50p*

OFFICIAL AND SEMI-OFFICIAL COMMEMORATIVE MEDALS

It is probably a strong love of history, rather than the strict disciplines of coin collecting that make collectors turn to commemorative medals. The link between the two is intertwined, and it is to be hoped that collectors will be encouraged to venture into the wider world of medallions, encouraged by this brief guide, originally supplied by Daniel Fearon (author of the *Catalogue of British Commemorative Medals)* and kindly updated again this year by Charles Riley.

James I Coronation, 1603

DATE	VF	EF
JAMES I		
1603 Coronation (possibly by C. Anthony), 29mm, Silver	£1200	£1950
QUEEN ANNE		
1603 Coronation, 29mm, AR	£800	£1500
CHARLES I		
1626 Coronation (by N. Briot), 30mm, Silver	£650	£1000
1633 Scottish Coronation (by N. Briot), 28mm, Silver	£450	£795
1649 Memorial (by J. Roettier). Struck after the Restoration, 50mm, Bronze	£90	£175
CROMWELL		
1653 Lord Protector (by T. Simon), 38mm, Silver	£700	£1700
— Cast examples	£350	£600
CHARLES II		
1651 Scottish Coronation, in exile (from design by Sir J. Balfour), 32mm, Silver	£2000	£4000
CHARLES II		
1661 Coronation (by T. Simon), 29mm		
— Gold	£2500	£5000
— Silver	£350	£550
1685 Death (by N. Roettier), 39mm, Bronze	£150	£325

Charles II Coronation, 1661

DATE	VF	EF

JAMES II
1685 Coronation (by J. Roettier), 34mm
— Gold £2000 £3600
— Silver £400 £700

MARY
1685 Coronation (by J. Roettier), 34mm
— Gold £2000 £4000
— Silver £400 £650

WILLIAM & MARY
1689 Coronation (by J. Roettier), 32mm
— Gold £1750 £3000
— Silver £350 £550
1689 Coronation, "Perseus" (by G. Bower),
   38mm, Gold £1750 £3000

MARY
1694 Death (by N. Roettier), 39mm, Bronze........ £95 £245

WILLIAM III
1697 "The State of Britain" (by J. Croker), 69mm,
   Silver £850 £1500

ANNE
1702 Accession, "Entirely English" (by J. Croker), 34mm
— Gold £1750 £3000
— Silver £150 £225
1702 Coronation (by J. Croker), 36mm
— Gold £2000 £3500
— Silver £225 £300
1707 Union with Scotland (by J. Croker, rev. by S. Bull), 34mm
— Gold £1750 £3000
— Silver £200 £300
1713 Peace of Utrecht (by J. Croker—issued in gold to Members
of Parliament), 34mm
— Gold £850 £1500
— Silver £150 £250

Queen Anne, 1702–1713.

GEORGE I
1714 Coronation (by J. Croker), 34mm
— Gold £1500 £2000
— Silver £250 £350
1727 Death (by J. Dassier), 31mm, Silver £150 £275

GEORGE II
1727 Coronation (by J. Croker), 34mm
— Gold £1500 £3200
— Silver £125 £225

QUEEN CAROLINE
1727 Coronation (by J. Croker), 34mm
— Gold £1750 £3000
— Silver £185 £375
1732 The Royal Family (by J. Croker), 70mm
— Silver £1500 £3000
— Bronze.. £400 £700

George I Coronation, 1714.

DATE	VF	EF

GEORGE III
1761 Coronation (by L. Natter), 34mm
— Gold £2750 £4250
— Silver £350 £550
— Bronze....................................... £150 £250

QUEEN CHARLOTTE
1761 Coronation (by L. Natter), 34mm
— Gold £1850 £3500
— Silver £375 £600
— Bronze....................................... £150 £295
1810 Golden Jubilee, "Frogmore", 48mm, Silver £130 £275
— Bronze....................................... £95 £175

GEORGE IV
1821 Coronation (by B. Pistrucci), 35mm
— Gold £1100 £1750
— Silver £200 £325
— Bronze....................................... £95 £150

WILLIAM IV
1831 Coronation (by W. Wyon; rev.shows
    Queen Adelaide), 33mm
— Gold £1250 £2500
— Silver £175 £325
— Bronze....................................... £95 £150

QUEEN VICTORIA
1838 Coronation (by B. Pistrucci), 37mm
— Gold £1200 £1850
— Silver £185 £320
— Bronze....................................... £60 £120

George III, Coronation, 1761

Queen Victoria Coronation, 1838

Queen Victoria Diamond Jubilee 1897

DATE	VF	EF

1887 Golden Jubilee (by J. E. Boehm, rev. by Lord Leighton)
— Gold, 58mm £2750 £4250
— Silver, 78mm £250 £500
— Bronze, 78mm £95 £180

1897 Diamond Jubilee (by G. de Saulles),
— Gold, 56mm £2750 £4250
— Silver, 56mm £95 £125
— Bronze, 56mm £35 £60
— Gold, 25mm £450 £600
— Silver, 25mm £20 £35

EDWARD VII
1902 Coronation (August 9) (by G. W. de Saulles)
— Gold, 56mm £3500 £4250
— Silver, 56mm £95 £150
— Bronze, 56mm £30 £55
— Gold, 31mm £550 £800
— Silver, 31mm £20 £30

Some rare examples of the official medal show the date as June 26, the original date set for the Coronation which was postponed because the King developed appendicitis.

GEORGE V
1911 Coronation (by B. Mackennal)
— Gold, 51mm £3500 £4250
— Silver, 51mm £95 £250
— Bronze, 51mm £30 £65
— Gold, 31mm £550 £800
— Silver, 31mm £20 £35

1935 Silver Jubilee (by P. Metcalfe)
— Gold, 58mm £3500 £4250
— Silver, 58mm £100 £150
— Gold, 32mm £550 £800
— Silver, 32mm £20 £30

PRINCE EDWARD
1911 Investiture as Prince of Wales (by W. Goscombe John)
— Gold, 31mm £1000 £1950
— Silver, 31mm £50 £85

EDWARD VIII
1936 Abdication (by L. E. Pinches), 35mm
— Gold £750 £1200
— Silver £45 £65
— Bronze £20 £35

GEORGE VI
1937 Coronation (by P. Metcalfe)
— Gold, 58mm £3500 £4000
— Silver, 58mm £65 £95
— Gold, 32mm £650 £750
— Silver, 32mm £25 £35
— Bronze, 32mm £12 £15

George V Silver Jubilee, 1935

Edward, Prince of Wales, 1911

Edward VIII, Abdication, 1936.

DATE	VF	EF

ELIZABETH II
1953 Coronation (by Spink & Son)—illustrated

	VF	EF
— Gold, 57mm	£3000	£3500
— Silver, 57mm	£65	£125
— Bronze, 57mm	£35	£65
— Gold, 32mm...................................	£450	£550
— Silver, 32mm	£25	£35
— Bronze, 32mm	£12	£15
1977 Silver Jubilee (by A. Machin)		
— Silver, 57mm	—	£70
— Silver, 44mm	—	£40

The gold medals are priced for 18ct—they can also be found as 22ct and 9ct, and prices should be adjusted accordingly.

PRINCE CHARLES
1969 Investiture as Prince of Wales (by M. Rizello)

— Silver, 57mm	—	£75
— Bronze gilt, 57mm...........................	—	£40
— Silver, 45mm	—	£35
— Gold, 32mm...................................	—	£450
— Silver, 32mm	—	£35
— Bronze, 32mm	—	£10

QUEEN ELIZABETH THE QUEEN MOTHER
1980 80th Birthday (by L. Durbin)

— Silver, 57mm	—	£65
— Silver, 38mm	—	£38
— Bronze, 38mm	—	£25

N.B.—Official Medals usually command a premium when still in their original case of issue.

Prince Charles, Prince of Wales 1969.

The Royal Mint Museum contains a charming group of medallic portraits of seven of the children of Queen Victoria and Prince Albert. They appear to have been made in 1850 and therefore do not include the two children who were born after that date. The skilfully-executed portraits are the work of Leonard Wyon, a member of the extremely talented family of engravers whose name is so well known to numismatists. The son of William Wyon, he was actually born in the Royal Mint in 1826. These particular portraits were not commissioned by the Mint and little is known about the circumstances in which they were prepared, but for some reason the dies have survived in the Royal Mint Museum, along with single-sided bronze impressions roughly the size of a half-crown.

Images and information courtesy of Dr Kevin Clancy, The Royal Mint.

Directory
section

O N the following pages will be found the most useful names and addresses needed by the coin collector.

At the time of going to press with this edition of the YEARBOOK the information is correct, as far as we have been able to ascertain. However, people move and establishments change, so it is always advisable to make contact with the person or organisation listed before travelling any distance, to ensure that the journey is not wasted.

Should any of the information in this section not be correct we would very much appreciate being advised in good time for the preparation of the next edition of the COIN YEARBOOK.

*(Those members with a retail premises are indicated with an *)*

Museums
and libaries

Listed below are the Museums and Libraries in the UK which have coins or items of numismatic interest on display or available to the general public.

A

• Kings Museum, University of Aberdeen, Old Aberdeen Town House, **Aberdeen**, AB9 1AS. Tel: 01224 274 330.

• Curtis Museum (1855), High Street, **Alton**, Hants, GU34 1BA. Tel: 01962 678140. *General collection of British coins.*

• Ashburton Museum, The Bullring, **Ashburton**, Devon, TQ13 7DT. Tel: 0808 1203865. *Ancient British and Roman antiquities including local coin finds.*

• Ashwell Village Museum (1930), Swan Street, **Ashwell**, Baldock, Herts, SG7 5NY. Tel: 01462 742 956 *Roman coins from local finds, local trade tokens, Anglo-Gallic coins and jetons.*

• Buckinghamshire County Museum (1862), Church Street, **Aylesbury**, Bucks, HP20 2QP. Tel: 01296 331 441. *Roman and medieval English coins found locally, 17th/18th century Buckinghamshire tokens, commemorative medals.*

B

• Banbury Museum, Castle Quay Shopping Center, Spiceball Park Road, **Banbury**, Oxon, OX16 2PQ. Tel: 01295 236165. *Wrexlin Hoard of Roman coins.*

• Museum of Barnstaple and North Devon (1931). **Closed for redevelopment until autumn 2019. Temporary Pop Up Museum on The Strand Barnstaple.** Tel: 01271 346 747. *General coin and medal collection, including local finds. Medals of the Royal Devonshire Yeomanry.*

• Roman Baths Museum, Abbey Church Yard, Stall St, **Bath**, Avon, BA1 1LZ. Tel: 01225 477 785. *Comprehensive collection of Roman coins from local finds.*

• Bagshaw Museum and Art Gallery (1911), Wilton Park, **Batley**, West Yorkshire, WF17 0AS. Tel: 01924 324 765. *Roman, Scottish, Irish, English hammered, British and foreign coins, local traders' tokens, political medalets, campaign medals and decorations.*

• The Higgins Art Gallery and Museum (1961), Castle Lane, **Bedford**, MK40 3XD. Tel: 01234 718 618. *Collections of the Bedford Library and Scientific Institute, the Beds Archaeological Society and Bedford Modern School (Pritchard Memorial) Museum.*

• Ulster Museum (1928), Botanic Gardens, **Belfast**, BT9 5AB. Tel: 028 9044 0000 *Irish, English and British coins and commemorative medals.*

• Berwick Museum and Art Gallery (1867), The Clock Block, Berwick Barracks, Parade, **Berwick**, TD15 1DQG. Tel: 01670 62445. *Roman, Scottish and medievial coins.*

• Treasure House and Art Gallery (1910), Champney Road, **Beverley**, Humberside, HU17 8HE. Tel: 01482 393939. *Beverley trade tokens, Roman, English, British and foreign coins.*

• Bignor Roman Villa (1811), **Bignor**, nr Pulborough, West Sussex, RH20 1PH. Tel: 01798 869 259. *Roman coins found locally.*

• City Museum and Art Gallery (1861), Chamberlain Square, **Birmingham**, B3 3DH. Tel: 0121 348 8000. *Coins, medals and tokens - special emphasis on the products of the Soho, Heaton, Birmingham and Watt mints.*

• Blackburn Museum, Museum Street, **Blackburn**, Lancs, BB1 7AJ. Tel: 01254 667 130. *Incorporates the Hart (5,000 Greek, Roman and early English) and Hornby (500 English coins) collections, as well as the museum's own collection of British and Commonwealth coins.*

• Bognor Regis Museum, 25 – 27 West Street, **Bognor Regis**, West Sussex, PO21 1XA. Tel: 01243 865 636 *Roman, English and British coins and trade tokens.*

• Bolton Museum and Art Gallery,(1893), Le Mans Crescent, **Bolton**, Lancashire, BL1 1SE. **Tel: 01204 332211**

• Roman Town and Museum (1949) Main Street, Aldborough, **Boroughbridge**, N. Yorks, YO51 9ES. Tel: 01423 322 768. *Roman coins.*

• The Museum (1929), South Street, **Boston**, Lincs, PE21 6HT. Tel: 01205 365 954. *Small collection of English coins.*

• Natural Science Society Museum (1903), 39 Christchurch Road, **Bournemouth**, Dorset, BH1 3NS. Tel: 01202 553 525. *Greek, Roman and English hammered coins (including the Hengistbury Hoard), local trade tokens.*

• Bolling Hall Museum (1915), Bowling Hall Road, **Bradford**, West Yorkshire, BD4 7LP. Tel: 01274 431 826. *Some 2,000 coins and tokens, mostly 18th–20th centuries.*

• Bridport Museum (1932), 25 South Street, **Bridport**, Dorset DT6 3RJ. Tel: 01308 458 703. *Roman coins, mainly from excavations at Claudian Fort.*

• Bristol Museum and Art Gallery (1820), Queen's Road, **Bristol**, BS8 1RL. Tel: 0117 922 3571. *Ancient British, Roman (mainly from local hoards), English hammered coins, especially from the Bristol mint, and several hundred local trade tokens.*

• Buxton Museum and Art Gallery (1891), Terrace Road, **Buxton**, Derbyshire, SK17 6DA. Tel: 01629 533 540. *English and British coins, tokens and commemorative medals. Numismatic library.*

C

• Segontium Fort Museum (1928), Beddgelert Road, **Caernarfon**, Gwynedd, LL55 2LN. Tel: 0300 025 6000. *Roman coins and artifacts excavated from the fort.*

• Fitzwilliam Museum (1816), Trumpington Street, **Cambridge**, CB2 1RB. Tel: 01223 332 900. *Ancient, English, medieval European, oriental coins, medals, plaques, seals and cameos.*

• National Museum & Galleries of Wales, Cathays Park, **Cardiff**, CF10 3NP. Tel: 0300 111 2 333. *Greek, Celtic, Roman and British coins and tokens with the emphasis on Welsh interest. Also military, civilian and comm. medals.*

• Guildhall Museum (1979), 31-33 Fisher Street, **Carlisle**, Cumbria, CA3 8JE. Tel: 01228 618 718. *General collection of coins and medals.*

• Tullie House (1877), Castle Street, **Carlisle**, Cumbria, CA3 8TP. Tel: 01228 618 718. *Roman, medieval and later coins from local finds, including medieval counterfeiter's coin-moulds.*

• Gough's Caves Museum (1934), The Cliffs, **Cheddar**, Somerset, BS27 3QF. Tel: 01934 742 343. *Roman coins.*

• Chelmsford Museum (1835), Oaklands Park, Moulsham Street, **Chelmsford**, Essex, CM2 9AQ. Tel: 01245 605 700. *Ancient British, Roman, medieval and later coins mainly from local finds, local medals.*

• Chepstow Museum, Bridge Street, Chepstow, (1949), **Chepstow**, Gwent, NP15 5EZ. Tel: 01291 625 981. *Local coins and trade tokens.*

• Grosvenor Museum (1886), 27 Grosvenor Street, **Chester**, CH1 2DD. Tel: 01244 972 197. *Roman coins from the fortress site, Anglo-Saxon, English medieval and post-medieval coins of the Chester and Rhuddlan mints, trade tokens, English and British milled coins.*

• Public Library (1879), New Beetwell Street, **Chesterfield**, Derbyshire, S40 1QN. Tel: 01629 533 400. *Roman coins from local finds, Derbyshire trade tokens, medals, seals and railway passes. Numismatic library and publications.*

• Red House Museum (1919), Quay Road, **Christchurch**, Dorset. Tel: 01202 482 860. *Coins of archaeological significance from Hampshire and Dorset, notably the South Hants Hoard, ancient British, Armorican, Gallo-Belgic, Celtic and Roman coins, local trade tokens and medals.*

• Corinium Museum (1856), Park Street, **Cirencester**, Glos.Tel:01285 655 611. *Roman coins.*

• Colchester and Essex Museum (1860), The Castle, **Colchester**, Essex. Tel: 01206 282 931. *Ancient British and Roman coins from local finds, medieval coins (especially the Colchester Hoard), later English coins and Essex trade tokens, commemorative medals.*

D

• Public Library, Museum and Art Gallery (1921), Crown Street, **Darlington**, Co Durham DL1 1ND. Tel: 01325 462 034. *Coins, medals and tokens.*

• Borough Museum (1908), 18 - 20 Market Street, **Dartford**, Kent, DA1 1EU. Tel: 01322 224 739. *Roman, medieval and later English hammered coins, trade tokens and commemorative medals.*

• Dartmouth Museum (1953), The Butterwalk, **Dartmouth**, Devon TQ6 9PZ. Tel: 01803 832 923. *Coins and medals of a historical and maritime nature.*

• Museum and Art Gallery (1878), The Strand, **Derby**, DE1 1BS. Tel:01332 641 901. *Roman coins, English silver and copper regal coins, Derbyshire tradesmen's tokens, British campaign medals and decorations of the Derbyshire Yeomanry and the 9/12 Royal Lancers.*

• Museum and Art Gallery (1909), Chequer Road, **Doncaster**, South Yorkshire, DN1 2AE. Tel: 01302 734 293. *General collection of English and foreign silver and bronze coins. Representative collection of Roman imperial silver and bronze coins, including a number from local hoards. English trade tokens, principally of local issues, medals.*

• Dorset County Museum (1846), High West Street, **Dorchester**, Dorset, DT1 1XA. Tel: 01305 262 735. *British, Roman, medieval and later coins of local interest.*

• Burgh Museum (1835), The Observatory, Rotchell Road, **Dumfries** Tel: 01387 253 374. *Greek, Roman, Anglo-Saxon, medieval English and Scottish coins, especially from local hoards. Numismatic library.*

• The McManus Dundee's Art Galleries and Museums (1873). Albert Square, **Dundee**, DD1 1DA. Tel:01382 307 200. *Coins and medals of local interest.*

• The Cathedral Treasury (995 AD), The College, **Durham**, DH1 3EH. Tel: 0191 338 7178. *Greek and Roman coins bequeathed by Canon Sir George Wheeler (1724), Renaissance to modern medals, medieval English coins, especially those struck at the Durham ecclesiastical mint.*

• Durham Heritage Centre, St Mary le Bow, North Bailey, **Durham**, DH1 3ET. Tel: 0191 384 5589. *Roman, medieval and later coins, mainly from local finds.*

E

• National Museum of Scotland (1781), Chambers Street, **Edinburgh**, EH1 1JF. Tel: 0300 123 6789. *Roman, Anglo-Saxon, English and Scottish coins, trade tokens, commemorative medals and communion tokens. Numismatic library. Publications.*

• Royal Albert Memorial Museum (1868), Queen Street, **Exeter**, EX4 3RX. Tel: 01392 265 858. *Roman and medieval. Coins of the Exeter Mint.*

G

• Hunterian Museum (1807), Gilbert Scott Building, University Of Glasgow, University Avenue, **Glasgow**, G12 8QQ. Tel: 0141 330 4221. *Greek, Roman, Byzantine, Scottish, English and Irish coins, Papal and other European medals, Indian and Oriental coins, trade and communion tokens.*

• Kelvingrove Art Gallery and Museum (1888), Argyle Street, **Glasgow.** Tel: 0141 276 9599. *General collection of coins, trade tokens, communion tokens, commemorative and military medals.*

• Riverside Museum (1974), 100 Pointhouse Place **Glasgow**, G3 8RS. Tel: 0141 287 2720. *Transport tokens and passes, commemorative medals, badges and insignia of railway companies and shipping lines.*

• City Museum and Art Gallery (1859), Brunswick Road, **Gloucester.** Tel: 01452 396 131. *Ancient British, Roman, Anglo-Saxon (from local finds), early medieval (from local mints), Gloucestershire trade tokens.*

• Guernsey Museum and Art Gallery, St Peter Port, **Guernsey.** Tel: 01481 726 518. *Armorican, Roman, medieval and later coins, including the coins, medals, tokens and paper money of Guernsey.*

• Guildford Museum (1898), Castle Hill, **Guildford**, Surrey, GU1 3SX. Tel: 01483 444 751. *Roman and medieval coins and later medals.*

H

• Gray Museum and Art Gallery, Church Square, Clarence Road, **Hartlepool**, Cleveland. Tel: 01429 869 706. *General collection, including coins from local finds.*

• Public Museum and Art Gallery (1890), John's Place, Bohemia Road , **Hastings**, East Sussex. Tel: 01424 451 052 *General collection of English coins, collection of Anglo-Saxon coins from Sussex mints.*

• City Museum (1874), Broad Street, **Hereford** HA4 9AU. Tel: 01432 260692

• Hertford Museum (1902), 18 Bull Plain, **Hertford.** Tel: 01992 582 686. *British, Roman, medieval and later English coins and medals.*

• Honiton and Allhallows Public Museum (1946), High Street, **Honiton**, Devon. Tel:01404 44966. *Small general collection, including coins from local finds.*

• Museum and Art Gallery (1891), 19 New Church Road, **Hove**. Tel:0300 029 0200. *English coins, Sussex trade tokens and hop tallies, campaign medals, orders and decorations, comm. medals.*

• Tolson Memorial Museum (1920), Ravensknowle Park, **Huddersfield**, West Yorkshire. Tel: 01484 223 240. *Representative collection of British coins and tokens, Roman and medieval coins, mainly from local finds.*

• Hull and East Riding Museum (1928), 36 High Street, **Hull.** Tel: 01482 300 300. *Celtic, Roman and medieval coins and artifacts from local finds. Some later coins including tradesmen's tokens.*

I

• The Manx Museum, Douglas, **Isle of Man.** Tel: 01624 648 000. *Roman, Celtic, Hiberno-Norse, Viking, medieval English and Scottish coins, mainly from local finds, Manx traders' tokens from the 17th to 19th centuries, Manx coins from 1709 to the present day.*

J

• Jersey Museum, Weighbridge, St Helier, **Jersey** Tel: 01534 633 300. *Armorican, Gallo-Belgic, Roman, medieval English and French coins, coins, paper money and tokens of Jersey.*

K

• Cliffe Castle Museum, Spring Gardens Lane, **Keighley** West Yorkshire. Tel: 01535 618 231. *Roman coins found locally.*

• Dick Institute Museum and Art Gallery (1893), Elmbank Avenue, **Kilmarnock**, Ayrshire. Tel: 01563 554 300. *General collection of coins and medals, and the Hunter-Selkirk collection of communion tokens.*

L

• City Museum (1923), Old Town Hall, Market Square, **Lancaster.** Tel: 01524 64637. *Roman, Anglo-Saxon, medieval English coins, provincial trade tokens, medals of the King's Own Royal Lancashire Regiment.*

• City Museum (1820), Millenium Square, **Leeds**, West Yorkshire. Tel: 0113 378 5001. *Greek, Roman, Anglo-Saxon, English medieval, Scottish, Irish, British, Commonwealth and foreign coins. Several Roman and Saxon hoards. The Backhouse collection of Yorkshire banknotes, the Thornton collection of Yorkshire tokens, British and foreign commemorative medals.*

• New Walk Museum (1849), 53 New Walk, **Leicester.** Tel: 0116 225 4900. *Roman, medieval and later coins, mainly from local finds, tokens, commemorative medals, campaign medals and decorations.*

• Pennington Hall Museum and Art Gallery, **Leigh**, Lancashire. *Roman and British coins and medals.*

• City Library, Art Gallery and Museum (1859), The Friary, **Lichfield**, Staffs. Email: info@lichfieldheritage. org.uk. *Roman, medieval and later English coins, Staffordshire trade tokens and commemorative medals.*

• World Museum(1851), William Brown Street, **Liverpool**, L3 8EN. Tel: 0151 478 4393. *General collection of Roman, medievaland later British coins, tokens.*

• Bank of England Museum, Bartholomew Lane, **London**. Tel: 020 3461 4878. *Exhibits relating to gold bullion, coins, tokens and medals, the design and manufacture of banknotes, and a comprehensive collection of bank notes dating from the 17th century to the present day.*

• British Museum(1752), HSBC Coin Gallery, Great Russell Street, **London**, WC1. Tel: 020 7323 8000. *Almost a million coins, medals, tokens and badges of all period from Lydia, 7th century BC to the present time. Extensive library of books and periodicals.*

• British Numismatic Society (1903), Warburg Institute, Woburn Square, **London**, WC1. *Library containing over 5,000 volumes, including sale catalogues, periodicals and pamphlets. Open to members only.*

• Gunnersbury Park Museum (1927), Acton, **London**, W3. Tel: 0203 9610280

• Horniman Museum and Library (1890), 100 London Road, Forest Hill, **London**, SE23 3PQ Tel: 020 8699 1872. *General collection, primitive currency, some tokens.*

• Imperial War Museum, Lambeth Road, **London**, SE1 6HZ. Tel: 020 7416 5000. *Emergency coinage of two world wars, occupation and invasion money, extensive collection of German Notgeld, commemorative, propaganda and military medals, badges and insignia.*

• Sir John Soane's Museum (1833), 13 Lincoln's Inn Fields, **London**, WC2. Tel: 020 7405 2107. *Napoleonic medals and medallic series of the late 18th and early 19th centuries.*

• National Maritime Museum, Romney Road, Greenwich, **London**, SE10. Tel: 020 8858 4422. *Commemorative medals with a nautical or maritime theme, naval medals and decorations.*

• Victoria and Albert Museum (1852), Cromwell Road, South Kensington, **London**, SW7 2RL. Tel: 020 7942 2000. *Byzantine gold and medieval Hispano-Mauresque coins (Department of Metalwork), large collection of Renaissance and later medals (Department of Architecture and Sculpture). Numismatic books.*

• Ludlow Museum (1833). The Assembly Rooms. Castle Square, **Ludlow.** Tel: 01584 871 970. *Roman and medieval coins from local finds.*

• Luton Museum and Art Gallery (1927), Wardown House, Old Bedford Road, **Luton**, Beds. Tel: 01582 878100. *Coins, tokens and medals.*

M

• Museum and Art Gallery (1858), St Faiths Street, **Maidstone**, Kent. Tel: 01622 602169. *Ancient British, Roman, Anglo-Saxon and medieval coins found in Kent, modern British coins, Kent trade tokens, banknotes, hop tallies and tokens, primitive currency, collections of Kent Numismatic Society.*

• The Manchester Museum (1868), The University, **Manchester**. Tel: 0161 275 2648. *Very fine collections of Greek and Roman coins, comprehensive collections of English, European and Oriental coins, over 30,000 in all.*

• Margate Museum (1923), Market Place, Margate Old Town, **Margate**, Kent. Tel: 01843 231 213. *Small collection of coins, including Roman from local finds.*

• Montrose Museum and Art Gallery (1836). Panmure Place, **Montrose**, Angus, DD10 8HF. Tel: 01674 907447. *Scottish and British coins.*

N

• Newark-on-Trent Museum (1912), 14 Appletongate, **Newark**, Notts. Tel 01636 680333 *Siege pieces, trade tokens and coins from local finds and hoards.*

• West Berkshire Museum, The Wharf, **Newbury**, Berkshire. Tel: 01635 519562. *Ancient British, Roman and medieval coins and artifacts, later coins and tokens.*

• Great North Museum, Hancock Barras Bridge, **Newcastle-upon-Tyne.** Tel: 0191 208 6765. *Ancient coins.*

O

• Heberden Coin Room, Ashmolean Museum (1683), **Oxford**. Tel: 01865 278058. *Extensive collections of all periods, notably Greek, Roman, English and Oriental coins, Renaissance portrait and later medals, tokens and paper money. Large library. Numerous publications.*

P

• Peterborough Museum (1881), Priestgate, **Peterborough**, Cambs. Tel: 01733 864 663. *Roman (mainly from local hoards and finds), Anglo-Saxon, medieval English, British and modern European coins, English and British commemorative medals and tokens.*

• City Museum and Art Gallery (1897), Drake Circus, **Plymouth**, Devon. **Closed for redevelopment until Spring 2020**

• Waterfront Museum, 4 High Street, **Poole**, BH15 1BW. Tel: 01202 262 600. *General collection of British and foreign coins, medals and tokens (view by appointment).*

• Portsmouth Museum (1972), Museum Road, Old **Portsmouth**, PO1 2LJ. Tel: 023 9283 4779. *Roman, medieval and later coins mainly from local finds and archaeological excavation, British coins, trade tokens of Hampshire, commemorative medals.*

• Harris Museum and Art Gallery (1893), Market Square, **Preston**, PR1 2PP. Tel: 01772 258 248. *English and British coins, tokens and medals.*

R

• The Museum of Reading (1883), Blagrave Street, **Reading**, RG1 1QH. Tel: 0118 937 3400. *British, Roman and medieval English coins, many from local finds, tradesmen's tokens and commemorative medals.*

• Rochdale Pioneers Museum (1905), 31 Toad Lane, **Rochdale**, OL12 ONU. Tel: 01706 524 920. *Roman and medieval coins from local finds, Rochdale trade tokens, miscellaneous British and foreign coins and medals.*

• Clifton Park Museum (1893), Clifton Park, **Rotherham**, S65 2AA. Tel: 01709 336 633. *Collection includes Roman coins from Templeborough Forts, medieval English coins from local hoards and a general collection of British coins.*

S

• Saffron Walden Museum (1832) (1939), Museum Street, **Saffron** Walden, CB10 1JL. Tel: 01799 510 333. *Ancient British, Roman, medieval and later coins, mainly from local finds and archaeological excavation, trade tokens and commemorative medals.*

• Verulamium Museum, St Michael's, **St Albans**, Herts . Tel: 01727 751 810. *Coins and artifacts excavated from the Roman town.*

• Salisbury and South Wiltshire Museum (1861), The Kings House 65 The Close, **Salisbury**, Wilts. Tel: 01722 332 151. *Collection of coins minted or found locally, including finds of Iron Age, Roman, Saxon and medieval coins, as well as 18th and 19th century tradesmen's tokens.*

• Richborough Castle Museum (1930), **Sandwich**, Kent. Tel: 0304 612013. *Roman coins of 1st–5th centuries from excavations of the Richborough site.*

• Rotunda Museum (1829), Vernon Road, **Scarborough**, YO11 2PS. Tel: 01723 353 665. *Collection of over 4,000 Roman coins, 1,500 English and 600 coins from local finds, siege pieces and trade.*

• Gold Hill Museum (1946), Gold Hill, **Shaftesbury**, Dorset, SP7 8JW. Tel: 01747 852 157. *Hoard of Saxon coins.*

• Weston Park Museum (1875), Western Bank, **Sheffield.** Tel: 0114 278 2600. *Over 5,000 coins of all periods, but mainly English and modern British. European coins, imperial Roman (including three hoards of about 500 coins each), Yorkshire trade tokens, British historical medals, campaign medals. Library.*

• Shrewsbury Museum and Art Gallery, The Music Hall, Market Street, **Shrewsbury**. Tel: 01743 258 885 *Coins minted at Shrewsbury 925-1180, Civil War coinage of 1642, Shropshire tradesmen's tokens, English coins and medals.*

• Atkinson Art Gallery (1878), Lord Street, **Southport,** Lancs. Tel: 01704 53333 *Roman coins.*

• Southwold Museum (1933), 9-11 Victoria Street, **Southwold**, IP18 6HZ. Tel: 07708 781317. *General collection of coins, specialised Suffolk trade tokens.*

• Stockport Museum (1860), 30-31 Market Place, **Stockport**, Cheshire SK1 1ES. Tel: 0161 474 4444 *Miscellaneous collection of coins, tokens and medals.*

• Museum in the Park (1899), Stratford Park, Stratford Road, **Stroud**, Glos GL5 4AF. Tel: 01453 7633 394. *Ancient British, Roman, Saxon, Norman, later medieval English, British coins and Gloucestershire trade tokens.*

• Sunderland Museum and Winter Gardens (1846), Burdon Road, **Sunderland,** Tyne & Wear SR1 1PP. Tel: 0191 553 2323. *Roman imperial, medieval and later English, including examples of the pennies minted at Durham, modern British and foreign coins, 17th-19th century tradesmen's tokens and local medallions.*

• Swansea Museum (1835), Victoria Road, **Swansea**, W. Glamorgan, SA1 1SN. Tel: 01792 653 763. *Coins and medals of local interest.*

T

• Tamworth Castle and Museum (1899), The Holloway, **Tamworth**, Staffs. Tel: 01827 709 626. *Anglo-Saxon coins, medieval English including coins of the Tamworth mint, later English and British coins, tokens, commemorative medallions and medals.*

• The Museum of Somerset, Taunton Castle, Castle Green, **Taunton**, Somerset TA1 4AA. Tel: 01823 255 088. *Celtic, Roman, Anglo-Saxon, early Medieval, tokens, medallions and banknotes. Strong emphasis on locally-found items.*

• Thurrock Museum and Heritage Srvice (1956), Second Floor, Thameside Complex, Orsett Road, Grays, Essex, RM17 5DX. Tel: 01375 413 965. *Roman coins.*

• Royal Cornwall Museum (1818), River Street, **Truro**, Cornwall TR1 2SJ. Tel: 01872 272 205. *Coins, tokens and medals pertaining principally to the county of Cornwall.*

W

• Wakefield Museum (1919), Burton Street, **Wakefield,** West Yorkshire WF1 2EB. Tel: 01924 305 376. *Roman and medieval English silver and copper coins.*

• Epping Forest District Museum, 39/41 Sun Street, **Waltham Abbey**, Essex, EN9 1EL. tEL 01992 716882 *Ancient British, Roman and medieval coins, Essex tradesmen's tokensof local interest.*

• Warrington Museum and Art Gallery (1848). Bold Street, **Warrington**, Cheshire, WA1 1DR. Tel: 01925 442399. *Coins, medals and tokens.*

• Worcester City Museum (1833), Foregate Street, **Worcester.** Tel: 01905 25371. *Roman, medieval and later coins and tokens. Coins of the Worcester mint.*

• Wells Museum (18903), 8 Cathedral Green, **Wells,** Somerset. Tel: 01749 673 477. *Ancient and modern British and world coins, local trade tokens and medals.*

• Museum of Wigan Life (1878), 41 Library Street, **Wigan**, Lancashire. *British, Commonwealth and foreign coins from about 1660 to the present. Roman coins from local sites, commemorative medals.*

• City Museum (1851), The Square, **Winchester**, Hants. Tel: 01962 863064. *Roman and medieval coins chiefly from local hoards and finds. Hampshire tradesmen's tokens and commemorative medals. Small reference library.*

• Wisbech and Fenland Museum (1835), Museum Square, **Wisbech,** Cambridgeshire. Tel: 01945 583 817, *British Roman, medieval and later coins, medals and tokens.*

Y

• York Castle Museum (1938), Eye of York, **York**, YO1 9RY. Tel: 01904 687 687. *English and British coins, campaign medals, orders and decorations, comemorative medals.*

• Jorvik Viking Centre (1984), Coppergate, **York.** Tel: 01904 615 505. *Coins and artefacts pertaining to the Viking occupation of York.*

• The Yorkshire Museum (1823), Museum Gardens, **York** YO1 7FR. Tel: 01904 687 687. *Roman imperial, medieval English and later coins, about 12,000 in all.*

Club
directory

Details given here are the names of Numismatic Clubs and Societies, their date of foundation, and their usual venues, days and times of meetings. Meetings are monthly unless otherwise stated. Finally, the telephone number of the club secretary is given; the names and addresses of club secretaries are withheld for security reasons, but full details may be obtained by writing to the Secretary of the British Association of Numismatic Societies, Chris Comber, numis@hotmail.co.uk or visiting the website at www.coinclubs.org.uk.

Ayeshire Coin Club 1st Thurs, Oct to April, 19.30. Call for Venue, Tel: 07527 240 016

Banknote Society of Scotland (1994) Meetings are held four times a year in Edinburgh. Email, bnss2006@ntlworld.com

Bath & Bristol Numismatic Society (1950). Fry's Club, Keynsham, Bristol. 2nd Thu, 19.30. Email: jagmartin553@gmail.

Bedfordshire Numismatic Society (1966). 2nd Thu. call for venue details: nigel.lutt2@virginmedia.com

Bexley Coin Club (1968). St Martin's Church Hall, Erith Road, Barnehurst, Bexleyheath, Kent. 1st Mon ,(exc Jan, Aug & Sept), 19.30. Tel: 020 8303 0510.

Birmingham Numismatic Society (1964). Friend's Meeting House, Bull Street. Email: bhamns@hotmail.co.uk.

Matthew Boulton Lunar Society (1994). The Old School House, Chapel Lane, Birmingham, B47 6JX Tel: 01564 821 582.

British Banking History Society. 22 Delamere Road, Gatley, Cheadle, SK8 4PH.

British Numismatic Society (1903). Warburg Institute, Woburn Square, London WC1H 0AB. Email: secretary@britnumsoc.org

Cambridgeshire Numismatic Society (1946). Friends' Meeting House, 12 Jesus Lane Cambridge, CB5 8BA. 4th Mon, (Sept–June), 19.30. Tel: 01223 332 918

Chester & North Wales Coin & Banknote Society (1996). Nags Head, Bunbury, Cheshire, CW6 9PB 4th Tue, 20.00. Tel: 01829 260 897

Crewe & District Coin and Medal Society. Memorial Hall, Church Lane, Wistaston, Crewe, CW2 8ER. 2nd Tue, (exc Jan & July), 19.30 Tel: 07828 602 611

Derbyshire Numismatic Society The Friends Meeting House, St Helen's Street, Derby. Tel: 01283 211623.

Devon & Exeter Numismatic Society, Courtenay Room, The St James Centre, Stadium Way, Exeter. 3rd Wed. Tel: 07745 985510.

Essex Numismatic Society (1966). Chelmsford Museum, Moulsham Street, Chelmsford, Essex. 4th Fri (exc Dec), 20.00. Tel: 01277 656 627.

Glasgow & West of Scotland Numismatic Society (1947). Ibrox Parish Church Halls, Clifford Street, Glasgow, G51 1QH. 2nd Thu, Oct-April, 19.30. Tel: 0141 641 2382, Email: glasgowcoinclub@aol.com.

Harrow Coin Club (1968). The Scout Building, off Walton Road, Wealdstone, Harrow, HA1 4UX. 2nd Mon, 19.30. Tel: 0208 368 3087.

Havering Numismatic Society (1967). Fairkytes Arts Centre, Billet Lane, Hornchurch, Essex, RM11 1AX 1st Tue, 19.30. Tel: 0208 5545 486. Email: mail@havering-ns.org.uk

Huddersfield Numismatic Society (1947). The County Hotel, 4 Princess Street, Huddersfield, HD1 2TT. 1st Mon (Sept to June) unless Bank Holiday then following Monday. Tel: 01484 866 814.

International Bank Note Society (London Branch) (1961). Spink, 69 Southampton Row, Bloomsbury, London, WC1B 4ET. Last Thu (exc Sept & Dec), 18.30.

International Bank Note Society (East Midlands Branch), Highfields Community Fire Station, Hassocks Lane, Beeston, Nottingham, NG9 2 GQ. Last Saturday of every odd month. Tel: 0115 928 9720.

Ireland, Numismatic Society of (Northern Branch). For dates and venues visit: www.numsocirelandnb.com

Ireland, Numismatic Society of, Ely House, 8 Ely Place, Dublin 2. For dates and venues visit: www.numismaticsocietyofireland.com

Ipswich Coin Club, Archdeacons House, 11 Northgate Street, Ipswich, IP1 3BX. 2nd Weds. www.ipnumsoc.org.uk.

Lancashire & Cheshire Numismatic Society (1933). Call for venue details. 3rd Sat, 14.00. Tel: 01204 849 469

London Numismatic Club (1947). Room 11 Mary Ward Center, 42 Queens Street, London, WC1N 3AQ. 1st Tues (except Jan, Aug and Sept). Email: g.buddle@btopenworld.com.

Loughborough Coin & Search Society (1964). Rosebery Medical Center, Rosebery Street, Loughborough, Leics, LE11 5DX 1st Thu, 19.30.

Northampton Numismatic Society (1969). Old Scouts RFC, Rushmere Road, Northampton, NN1 5RY. 1st Fri, 10.30.

Norwich Coin & Medal Society, The White Horse Inn, Trowse, Norwich, NR14 8ST. 3rd Mon. Tel: 01603 617 127.

Numismatic Society of Nottinghamshire (1948). Lecture Theatre, Lakeside Arts Center and Museu, University of Nottingham, University Park, Nottingham, NG7 2RD. 2nd Tue (Sep-Apr). Tel: 0115 928 0347.

Orders & Medals Research Society (1942). Spink, 69 Southampton Row, Bloomsbury, London, WC1B 4ET. Last Monday of the month (that is not a Bank Holiday) of the odd numbered months plus April and October. 18.00.

Ormskirk & West Lancashire Numismatic Society (1970). The Eagle & Child, Maltkiln Lane, Bispham Green L40 1SN. 1st Thu, 20.15. Tel: 01704 232 494

Peterborough & District Numismatic Society (1967). Belsize Community Centre, Celta Road Peterborough, Cambs. 4th Tue (exc June, July & Aug), 19.30. Tel: 01733 567 763.

Plymouth Numismatic Society. 3rd Tue. Call for venue details. Tel: 07399 276295.

Reading Coin Club (1964). Abbey Baptist Church, Abbey Square, Reading, RG1 3BE 1st Mon, 19.00. Tel: 01344 774 155.

Royal Numismatic Society (1836). Warburg Institute, Woburn Square, London, WC1H 0AB. (some meetings held at Spink, 69 Southampton Row, Bloomsbury Road, London WC1B 4ET). 3rd Tues 18.00. Email: info@numismatics.org.uk. Tel: 0207 323 8541.

St Albans & Hertfordshire Numismatic Society (1948). Call for venue and dates Tel: 01727 824 434.

Southampton and District Numismatic Society (1953). Central Baptist Church, Devonshire Road, Polygon, Southampton SO15 2GY. Email: sue717@btinternet.com.

South Manchester Numismatic Society. Nursery Inn, 258 Green Lane, Heaton Norris, Stockport, SK4 2NA. 1st and 3rd Tue (Mar–Oct), 1st Tue (Nov–Feb). Tel: 07818 422696.

South Wales & Monmouthshire Numismatic Society (1958). 1st Mon (except Bank Holidays when 2nd Mon), 19.30. For venue call Tel: 02920 561 564.

Thurrock Numismatic Society (1970). Stanley Lazell Hall, Dell Road, Grays, Essex, RM17 5JZ 3rd Wed, 19.30. Tel: 01375 413 964.

Tyneside Numismatic Society (1954). The Plough Inn, 369 Old Durham Road, Gateshead, NE9 5LA. 2nd Weds, 19.30. Tel: 07867 831 293

Wessex Numismatic Society (1948). Edward Wright Room, Beaufort Community Centre, Southbourne, Bournemouth, Dorset. 1st Tues (exc Aug), 20.00. Tel: 01425 501446.

Wiltshire Numismatic Society (1965). The Raven Inn, Poulshot, Nr. Devizes, Wiltshire. 3rd Weds, (March–Dec), 20.00. Tel: 01380 850145. Email: mark.woodlands@btinternet.com.

Worthing & District Numismatic Society (1967). The Chatsworth Hotel, Worthing, BN11 3DU. 2nd Thu, 20.00. Tel: 01903 239867

Yorkshire Numismatic Society (1909). Email for venues and dates. Email: t.abramson@ntlworld.com.

Important Notice to Club Secretaries:

If your details as listed are incorrect please let us know in time for the next edition of the **COIN YEARBOOK.** Amendments can be sent via post to: 40, Southernhay East, Exeter, Devon EX1 1PE or via email to: jayne@tokenpublishing.com

IMPORTANT ORGANISATIONS

ADA
The Antiquities
Dealers Association

Secretary: Susan Hadida, Duke's Court, 32 Duke Street, London SW1Y 6DU

IBNS
International
Bank Note Society

Membership Secretary: John Vanden Bossche
Email: uksecretary@ibns.biz

ANA
The American
Numismatic Association

818 North Cascade Avenue, Colorado Springs, CO 80903, USA

RNS
Royal Numismatic Society

Dept of Coins & Medals, British Museum, London WC1B 3DG.

BNTA
The British Numismatic
Trade Association

Secretary: Christel Swan 3 Unwin Mansions, Queens Club Gardens, London, W14 9TH

BAMS
British Art Medal Society

Philip Attwood, Dept of Coins & Medals, British Museum, London WC1B 3DG.

IAPN
International Association of
Professional Numismatists

Secretary: Jean-Luc Van der Schueren, 14 Rue de la Bourse, B–1000, Brussels.

BNS
British Numismatic Society

Secretary: Peter Preston-Morley.

Email: secretary@britnumsoc.0rg

Society activities are featured every month in the "Diary Section" of COIN NEWS magazine—available from all good newsagents or on subscription.
Telephone 01404 46972 for more details or log onto
www.tokenpublishing.com

As well as regular monthly meetings, Society members also have the opportunity to visit places of numismatic interest. The Numismatic Society of Ireland (pictured above) held its annual summer outing in July 2019, by visiting the new Central Bank of Ireland HQ Visitor Centre in the Dublin Docklands. Some 22 members attended and they were hosted by Linda O'Connor, Communications Associate, who guided the group around the various exhibits including enlarged plaster prototypes of the 1928 designs for the new Free State Coinage.

Directory
of auctioneers

Listed here are the major auction houses which handle coins, medals, banknotes and other items of numismatic interest. Many of them hold regular public auctions, whilst others handle numismatic material infrequently. A number of coin companies also hold regular Postal Auctions—these are marked with a 🅟

Abacus Auctions
19a Hampshire Road, Glen Waverley, Victoria 3150 Australia. www.prestigephilately.com

Auction World Company Ltd
1-15-5 Hamamatsucho,Minato-ku, Tokyo, 105-0013 Japan. www.auction-world.co

Baldwin's of St James
10 Charles II Street, London, SW1Y 4AA. Tel: 020 7930 7888, fax 0207 930 8214, Email: info@bsjauctions.com, www.bsjauctions. com.

Biddle & Webb
Icknield Square, Birmingham, B16 0PP. Tel: 0121 455 8042, www.biddleandwebb.com

Blyth & Co
Arkenstall Center, Haddenham, Cambs, CB6 3XD. Tel: 01353 930 094, www.blyths.com

Bonhams (incorporating Glendinings)
Montpelier Street, Knightsbridge, London, SW7 1HH. Tel: 020 7393 3914, www.bonhams.com.

BSA Auctions
Units 1/2, Cantilupe Court, Cantilupe Road, Ross on Wye, Herefordshire, HR9 7AN . Tel: 01989 769 529, www.the-saleroom.com

cgb.fr
36, Rue Vivienne, 75002, Paris, France. Email: contact@cgb.fr, www.cgb.fr.

Chilcotts Auctioneers
Silver Street, Honiton, EX14 1QN. Tel: 01404 47783, email: info@chilcottsauctioneers.co.uk

Christies
8 King Street, St James's, London SW1Y 6QT. Tel: 020 7839 9060.

Classical Numismatic Group Inc (Seaby Coins)
20 Bloomsbury Street, London, WC1B 3QA. Tel: 020 7495 1888 ,fax 020 7499 5916, Email: cng@cngcoins.com, www.historicalcoins.com. 🅟

The Coin Cabinet
Tel 0800 088 5350, www.thecoincabinet.co.uk.

Corbitts
5 Moseley Sreet, Newcastle upon Tyne NE1 1YE. Tel: 0191 232 7268, fax 0191 261 4130. www.corbitts.com

Croydon Coin Auctions
See entry under Goulborn in Dealers Lists.

Davissons Ltd.
PO Box 323, Cold Spring, MN 56320 USA. Tel: 001 320 685 3835, info@davcoin.com, www.davcoin.com.

Dix Noonan Webb (IAPN)
16 Bolton Street, Piccadilly, London, W1J 8BQ Tel: 020 7016 1700, auctions@dnw.co.uk, www.dnw.co.uk.

Duke's
Brewery Square, Dorchester, Dorset DT1 1GA. Tel: 01305 265 080, enquiries@dukesauctions. com www.dukes-auctions.com

David Duggleby Auctioneer
The Vine Street Salerooms, Scarborough, North Yorkshire YO11 1XN. Tel: 01723 507111

English Coin Auctions
3 Elders Street, Scarborough, YO11 1DZ Tel: 01723 364 760, www.englishcoinauctionscom

Jean Elsen & ses Fils s.a.
Avenue de Tervueren 65, B–1040, Brussels. Tel: 0032 2 734 6356, Email: numismatique@e lsen.euwww.elsen.eu.

Fellows & Sons
Augusta House, 19 Augusta Street, Hockley, Birmingham, B18 6JA. Tel: 0121 212 2131, www.fellows.co.uk.

B. Frank & Son
3 South Avenue, Ryton, Tyne & Wear NE40 3LD. Tel: 0191 413 8749, Email: bfrankandson@aol.com, www.bfrankandson.com.

Gadoury
57, rue Grimaldi, 98000 MONACO. Tel: 0 377 93 25 12 96, Email: contact@gadoury.com, www.gadoury.com.

Goldberg Coins & Collectibles
11400 W. Olympic Blvd, Suite 800, Los Angeles, Hills CA 90064. Tel: 001 310.551 2646, info@ goldbergcoins.com, www.goldbergcoins.com.

Gorny & Mosch GmbH
Giessener Münzhandlung, Maximiliansplatz 20, 80333 Munich. Phone: +49-89/24 22 643-0, info@gmcoinart.de

Heritage World Coin Auctions
6 Shepherd Street, Mayfair, London, W1J 7JE. Tel: 001 214 528 3500, Bid@HA.com www.ha.com).

International Coin Exchange
Charter House, 5 Pembroke Row, Dublin 2. Tel: 00353 8684 93355, email: iceauctiongalleries@ gmail.com, www.ice-auction.com.

Kleeford Coin Auctions
Tel: 01773 528 743, email: kleeford@btinternet. com ℗

Fritz Rudolf Künker
Nobbenburger, Strasse 4A, 49076, Osnabrüeck, Germany. Tel: 0049 5419 62020, fax: 0049 541 96 20 222, email: service@kuenker.de, www.kuenker.de

Lawrence Fine Art Auctioneers
The Linen Yard, South Street, Crewkerne, Somerset TA18 8AB. Tel: 01460 73041, email: enquiries@ lawrences.co.uk, www.lawrences.co.uk.

Lockdale Coins
52 Barrack Square, Martlesham Heath, Ipswich, Suffolk, IP5 3RF. Tel: 01473 627 110, sales@ lockdale.com, www.lockdales.com.

London Coins
Tel: 01474 871464, email: info@londoncoins. co.uk, www.londoncoins.co.uk.

Mavin International
20 Kramat Lane, #01-04/05 United House, Singapore 228773. Tel: +65 6238 7177,

Mitchells
47 Station Road, Cockermouth, Cumbria, CA13 9PZ. www.mitchellsantiques.co.uk

Morton & Eden Ltd
Nash House, St Georges Street, London W1S 2FQ. Tel: 020 7493 5344, info@mortonandeden.com, www.mortonandeden.com.

Mowbray Collectables
Email: paul@mowbrays.co.nz, www.mowbraycol lectables.co.nz

Myntauktioner i Sverige AB
Banergatan 17, 115 22 Stockholm.

Nesbits Auctioneer & Valuers
7 Clarendon Road, Soouthsea, Hants, PO5 2ED. Tel: 02392 295568, email: auctions@nesbits.co.uk

Noble Numismatics
169 Macquire Street, Sydney, NSW 2000 Australia. Tel: 0061 2922 34578, fax: 0061 29233 6009, email: info@noble.com.au, www.noble.com.au.

Numismatica Ars Classica NAC AG
Suite 1, Claridge House, 32 Davies Street, London W1K 4ND. Tel: 020 7839 7270, email: info@arsclassicacoins.com.

Numis-Or
4, Rue des Barques 1207, Geneva Switzerland Tel: 0041 2273 59255, email: info@numisor.ch, www.numisor.ch.

Pacific Rim Online Auction
P O Box 847, North Sydney, NSW 2060, Australia. Tel 0061 29588 7111, www.pacificrimonlineauctions.com Online coin auction.

Penrith, Farmers' & Kidds PLC
Skirsgill Saleroom, Penrith, Cumbria, CA11 0DN. Tel: 01768 890 781, email: info@pfkauctions. co.uk,www.pfkauctions.co.uk

Roma Numismatics Ltd
20 Fitzroy Square, London, W1T 6EJ. Tel: 020 7121 6518. www.romanumismatics.com

Chris Rudd (IAPN, BNTA)
PO Box 222, Aylsham, Norfolk, NR11 6TY. Tel: 01263 735 007, email: liz@celticcoins.com, www.celticcoins.com

Simmons Gallery
PO Box 104, Leytonstone, London. Tel: 020 8989 8097. www.simmonsgallery.co.uk. ℗

Smiths of Newent
The Old Chapel, Culver Street, Newent, GL18 1DB. Tel: 01531 821 776, email: enquiries@smithsauction-room.co.uk, www.smithsnewentauctions.co.uk.

Spink & Son Ltd
69 Southampton Row, Bloomsbury, London WC1B 4ET. Tel: 020 7563 4000, fax 020 7563 4066, email: concierge@spink.com, www.spink.com.

Stacks, Bowers and Ponterio
1231 East Dyer Road, Suite 100, Santa Ana, California, 92705, USA. Tel: 001 800 458 4646, email: info@StacksBowers.com, www.stacksbowers.com

Tennants Auctioneers
The Auction Centre, Leyburn, North Yorkshire, DL8 5SG. Tel: 01969 623 780, email: enquiry@ tennants-ltd.co.uk, www.tennants.co.uk.

The-saleroom.com
The Harlequin Building, 65 Southwark Street, London, SE1 0HR. Tel: 0203 725 555, email: sup port@auctiontechnologygroup.com, www.the-saleroom.com.

Thomson Roddick Auctioneers
The Auction Centre, Marconi Road, Carlisle, CA2 7NA. Tel: 01228 528 939, email: carlisle@ thomsonroddick.com. Also at The Auction Centre, 118 Carnethie Street, Rosewell, Edinburgh, EH24 www.thomsonroddick.com.

Timeline Auctions
The Court House, 363 Main Road, Harwich, Essex CO12 4DN Tel: 01277 815 121, email: enquiries@timelineauctions.com www.timelineauctions.com.

Trevanion and Dean
The Joyce Building, Station Road, Whitchurch, SY13 1RD. Tel: 01948 800 202, email: info@trevanionand dean.co.uk

Warwick & Warwick
Chalon House, Scarbank, Millers Road, Warwick CV34 5DB. Tel: 01926 499 031 fax 01926 491 906, email: richard.beale@warwickandwarwick.com, www.warwickandwarwick.com.

Whyte's Auctions
38 Molesworth Street, Dublin 2, Ireland. Tel: +00 3531 676 2888, www.whytes.com.

Peter Wilson Fine Art Auctioneers LLP
Victoria Gallery, Market Street, Nantwich, Cheshire, CW5 5DG. Tel: 01270 623878, email: auctions@peterwilson.co.uk, www.peterwilson. co.uk

Woolley & Wallis
51-61 Castle Street, Salisbury, Wiltshire SP1 3SU. Tel: 01722 424500, www.woolleyandwallis.co.uk

Directory
of fairs

Listed below are the names of the fair organisers, their venue details where known along with contact telephone numbers. Please call the organisers direct for information on dates etc.

Aberdeen
Doubletree by Hilton Hotel Aberdeen TreeTops, Springfield Road, Aderdeen, AB15 7AQ. *Alba Fairs Tel: 07767 020343.*

Berlin. World Money Fair 2020
Estrel Convention Center, Sonnenalle, 12057 Berlin, Germany. *Tel: +41(0)61 3825504.*

Berlin 2019
Messegelände am Funkturm, Hall 11/2, Messedamm 22, 14055 Berlin. Numismata International Tel: +49 (0) 89 268 359.

Birmingham
National Motor Cycle Museum, Bickenhill, Birmingham. *Midland Stamp & Coin Fair Tel: 01694 731 781, www.coinfairs.co.uk.*

Britannia Medal Fair
Carisbrooke Hall, The Victory Services Club, 63/79 Seymour Street, London, W2 2HF. *DNW Tel: 020 7016 1700.*

Cardiff
City Hall, Cathays Park, Cardiff, CF10 3ND. *M. J. Promotions. Tel: 01792 415293.*

Cheltenham
The Regency Hotel, Gloucester Road, GL51 0SS. St Andrews United Reform Church, Montpellier, GL50 1SP. *Mark Grimsley Tel: 0117 962 3203.*

Crewe
Memorial Hall, Church Lane, Wistaston, Crewe. CW2 8ER. Crewe & District Coin & Medal Society. Tel: 01270 661181.

Dublin International Coin Fair
Del Parker
Email: irishcoins2000@hotmail.com.

Dublin Coin Fair
Serpentine Hall, RDS, Ballsbridge, Dublin 4. *Mike Kelly Tel: 00353 86 8714 880.*

East Grinstead
Chequer Mead Arts Center, De La Warr Road, East Grinstead, RH19 3BS. *Malcolm Green Tel: 01342 327 554*

Exeter
The America Hall, De La Rue Way, Pinhoe, EX4 8PX. *Michael Hale Collectors Fairs Tel: 01749 677669.*

Frankfurt 2019
Ludwig-Erhard-Anlage1, 60327 Frankfurt, Hesse. *Numismata International Tel: +49 (0) 89 268 359.*

Harrogate
Old Swan Hotel, Swan Road, HG1 2SR. *Bloomsbury Fairs Tel: 01242 898 107.*

Inverness
Kingsmills Hotel, Culcabock Road, Inverness, IV2 3LP. *Alba Fairs Tel: 07767 020343.*

London
Holiday Inn, Coram Street, Bloomsbury, WC1 1HT. London Coin Fair, *Lu Vessid Tel: 01694 731 781*

London
Bloomsbury Hotel, 16-22 Great Russell Street, WC1 3NN. *Bloomsbury Fairs Tel: 01242 898 107.*

London IBNS
Venue as above. *IBNS Web: www.theibns.org*

Maastricht
Maastricht Exhibiton and Convention Center, Forum 100, 6229 GV Maastricht, The Netherlands. *mif events Tel: +32 (0) 89 46 09 33.*

Munich 2020
Lilienthalallee 40, 80939 Munich. *Numismata International Tel: +49 (0) 89 268 359.*

New York International Numismatic Convention 2020
Grand Hyatt Hotel, 109 East 42nd Street, New York 10022, USA. *www.nyinc.info/*

Pittsburgh World's Fair of Money 2020
David L. Lawrence Convention Center; Pittsburgh, PA. *American Numismatic Association. Tel: 001 800 514 2646.*

Plymouth
The Guildhall, Armada Way, PL1 2ER *Peter Jones Tel: 01489 582673.*

Salisbury
City Hall, Salisbury, SP2 7TU. Dauwalders of Salisbury. Tel: 01722 412100

Wakefield
Cedar Court Hotel, Denby Dale Road, Calder Grove, Wakefield, WF4 3QZ. *Eddie Smith Tel: 01522 684 681.*

Westcountry Collectors Fair
The Guildhall, Royal Parade, Plymouth, PL1 2EJ. *www.facebook.com/PlymACF*

Weston-super-Mare
Victoria Methodist Church Hall, Station Road, BS23 1XU. *Michael Hale Tel: 01749 677 669*

Worthing
Chatsworth Hotel, The Steyne, Worthing, BN11 3DU. Worthing & District Numismatic Society. Tel: 01903 239867

York
The Grandstand, York Race Course, YO23 1EX *York Coin Fair, Tel: 01793 513 431 (Chris Rainey), 020 8946 4489 (Kate Puleston).*

Dealers
directory

The dealers listed below have comprehensive stocks of coins and medals, unless otherwise stated. Specialities, where known, are noted. Many of those listed are postal dealers only, so to avoid disappointment always make contact by telephone or mail in the first instance, particularly before travelling any distance.

Abbreviations:
ADA— — Antiquities Dealers Association
ANA — American Numismatic Association
BADA — British Antique Dealers Association
BNTA — British Numismatic Trade Association
IAPN — International Association of Professional Numismatists
IBNS — International Bank Note Society
P — — Postal only
L — — Publishes regular lists

ABC Coins & Tokens
PO Box 52, Alnwick, Northumberland, NE66 1YE. Tel: 01665 603 851, email: d-stuart@d-stuart. demon.co.uk, www.abccoinsandtokens.com.

A. Ackroyd (IBNS)
62 Albert Road, Parkstone, Poole, Dorset BH12 2DB. Tel/fax: 01202 739 039, www.AAnotes.com.
P L Banknotes and Cheques

Joan Allen Electronics Ltd
5 & 6 The Courtyard, Market Square, Westerham, Kent TN16 1AZ. Tel: 01959 571 255. Metal Detectors.

Allgold Coins
P.O Box 260, Wallington, SM5 4H. Tel: 0844 544 7952, email: sales@allgoldcoins.co.uk, wwwallgoldcoins.co.uk. Quality Sovereigns.

A. J. W. Coins
Tel: 08456 807 087, email: andrewwide@ajw-coins. co.uk, www.ajw-coins.com. **P** Sovereigns and CGS-UK specialist.

Dave Allen Collectables
St Neots Antiques Emporium, 13 Fishers Yard, St Neots, PE19 2AG. Tel: 07541 461 021. Email: coinsandmedals@outlook.com, www.daveallencollectables.co.uk.
Coins, Medals, Banknotes, Bullion and Jewellery.

AMR COINS
PO Box 352, Leeds, LS19 9GG. Tel: 07527 569 308, www.amrcoins.com. Quality English Coins specialising in rare hammered and milled coins of exceptional quality.

Ancient & Gothic
PO Box 5390, Bournemouth, BH7 6XR. Tel: 01202 431 721 **P L** Greek, Roman, Celtic and Biblical coins. English Hammered Coins & Antiquities.

Argentum Coins
PO Box 130, Peterlee, Co Durham SR8 9BE
Tel: 07720 769 005, email: john.stephenson815@sky. com, www.argentumandcoins.co.uk.
British milled coins from 1662 to date.

Arghans
Unit 9, Callington Business Park, Tinners Way Moss side, Callington, PL17 7SH. Tel: 01579 382 405, email: keithp44@waitrose.com. British Banknotes.

ARL Collectables
P O Box 380, Reigate, Surrey, RH2 2BU. Tel: 01737 242 975, www.litherlandcollectables.com.
Coins, Banknotes, Medallions and Paper Emphemera.

SP Asimi
The Emporium, 112 High Street, Hungerford, RG17 0 NB. Tel: 01488 686959. British Milled Coins

Athens Numismatic Gallery
Akadimias 39, Athens 10672, Greece. Tel: 0030 210 364 8386, www.athensnumismaticgallery.com.
Rare & Common Sovereigns. British & World Coins.

Atlas Numismatics
Tel: 001 718643 4383, email: info@atlasnumismatics. com, www.atlasnumismatics.com
Ancient, World and US Coinage

ATS Bullion (BNTA)
2, Savoy Court, Strand. London, WC2R 0EZ.
Tel: 020 7240 4040, email: sales@atsbullion.com, www.atsbullion.com. Bullion and Modern Coins.

A. H. Baldwin & Sons Ltd (ANA, BADA, BNTA, IAPN)
399 The Strand, London WC2R 0LX.
Tel: 020 7930 6879, fax 020 7930 9450, email: coins@baldwin.co.uk Coins, Tokens, Numismatic Books.

B & G Coins
PO Box 1219, Spalding, PE11 9FY. Email: info@ bandgcoins.co.uk. Coins, Banknotes and Medals

Baird & Co
20 - 21 Gemini Business Park, Hornet Way, London, E6 7FF. Tel: 020 7474 1000, www.goldline.co.uk. Bullion Merchants

Bath Stamp and Coin Shop
12 -13 Pulteney Bridge, Bath, Avon BA2 4AY.
Tel: 01225 431 918, Vintage Coins and Banknotes.

Michael Beaumont
PO Box 8, Carlton, Notts NG4 4QZ. Tel: 0115 9878361. **P** Gold & Silver English/Foreign Coins.

Beaver Coin Room (BNTA)
57 Philbeach Gardens, London SW5 9ED.
Tel: 020 7373 4553. **P** *European coins and medals.*
R. P. & P. J. Beckett
Maes y Derw, Capel Dewi, Llandyssul, Dyfed
SA44 4PJ. Tel: 01559 395 276, email:
beckett@xin.co.uk. **P** *Coin Sets and Banknotes.*
Lloyd Bennett (BNTA)
PO Box 2, Monmouth, Gwent NP25 3YR. Tel:
07714 284 939, email: Lloydbennett@Coinofbritain.
biz, www.coinsofbritain.com *English Hammered and
Milled Coins.*
Berkshire Coin Centre
35 Castle Street, Reading, RG1 7SB. Tel: 0118 957
5593. *British and World Coins. Militaria.*
Stephen J. Betts
49-63 Spencer Street, Hockley, Birmingham B18
6DE. Tel: 0121 233 2413 **P L**,
*Medieval and Modern Coins, Counters, Jetons,
Tokens and Countermarks.*
Bigbury Mint
Unit 1 River Park, Ermington, Devon, PL21 9NT. Tel:
01548 830717. *Specialists in reproduction
Hammered Coins*
Jon Blyth
Office 63, 2 Lansdowne Row, Mayfair, London
W1J 6HL. Tel:07919 307 645, jonblyth@hotmail.com,
www.jonblyth.com. *Specialists in quality British Coins*
Bonhams (incorporating Glendinings)
Montpelier Street, Knightsbridge, London,
SW7 1HH. Tel: 0207 393 3914, www.bonhams.com.
Barry Boswell and Kate Bouvier
24 Townsend Lane, Upper Boddington, Daventry,
Northants, NN11 6DR. Tel: 01327 261 877, email:
kate@thebanknotestore.com. *British and World
Banknotes.*
James & Chester Brett
jc.brett@btinternet.com **P L** *British and World
Coins.*
J. Bridgeman Coins
129a Blackburn Road, Accrington, Lancs
Tel: 01254 384757. *British & World Coins.*
Britaly Coins Ltd
Victoria Court, 91 Huddersfield Road, Holmfirth,HD9
3JA. Tel: 07479 862 432, email: info@britalycoins.
co.uk, www.britalycoins.co.uk. *British and World
Coins.*
Arthur Bryant Coins
PO Box 67499, London, NW3 3SN, Tel: 07768 645
686, email: abcoins@live.co.uk,
www.bryantcoins.com. *British Coins and Medals.*
BRM Coins
3 Minshull Street, Knutsford,Cheshire, WA16 6HG.
Tel: 01565 651 480. *British Coins.*
Bucks Coins
St Mary's House, Duke Street, Norwich NR3 1QA
Callers by appointment only. Tel: 01603 927 020.
English Milled Coins, Celtic and Roman.
Iain Burn
2 Compton Gardens, 53 Park Road, Camberley,
Surrey GU15 2SP. Tel: 01276 23304.
Bank of England & Treasury Notes.
Cambridgeshire Coins
12 Signet Court, Swanns Road Cambridge,
CB5 8LA. Tel: 01223 503 073, email, info
cambridgeshirecoins.com,
www.cambridgeshirecoins.com. *Coins, Banknotes
and Accessories.*
Cambridge Stamp Centre Ltd
9 Sussex Street, Cambridge, CB4 4HU. Tel: 01223
63980. *British Coins.*

Castle Galleries
81 Castle Street, Salisbury, Wiltshire SP1 3SP.
Tel: 01722 333 734. *British Coins, Medals and Tokens.*
Cathedral Coins
23 Kirkgate, Rippon, North Yorkshire, HG4 1PB.
Tel: 01765 701 400
Cathedral Court Medals
First Floor Office, 30A Market Place, West Ripon,
North Yorks HG4 1BN. Tel: 01765 601 400. *Coin and
Medal Sales. Medal Mounting and Framing.*
Central Bank of Ireland
PO Box 559, Dublin 1. Tel: +353 (0) 1248 3605,
Ireland. *Issuer of new Coin and Banknote issues of
Ireland. Commemorative Coins and Coin Sets*
Lance Chaplin
17 Wanstead Lane, Ilford, Essex IG1 3SB.
Tel: 020 8554 7154. www.shaftesburycoins.com.
P L*Roman, Greek, Celtic, Hammered Coins and
Antiquities.*
Chard (BNTA)
32-36 Harrowside, Blackpool, FY4 1RJ. Tel: 01253
343081, www.chards.co.uk, *British and World Coins.*
Jeremy Cheek Coins Ltd
Tel: 01923 450385/07773 872686, email:
jeremycoins@aol.com. *Advice, valuation and
representation at auctions.*
Simon Chester Coins
196, High Road, London, Farnham, N22 8HH
Tel: 07774 886688, email:
simosimonchestercoins.com
British Milled Coins
Nigel A. Clark
28 Ulundi Road, Blackheath, London SE3 7UG.
Tel: 020 8858 4020, email: nigel.a.clark@btinternet.
com. **P L** *17th & 19th century Tokens. Farthings.*
Classical Numismatic Group (IAPN)
20 Bloomsbury Street, London, WC1B 3QA.
Tel: 020 7495 1888, email cng@cngcoins.com,
www.cngcoins.com. **P** *Ancient and world coins.
Publishers of the Classical Numismatic Review.
Regular High Quality Auctions of Ancient Coins.*
Paul Clayton (BNTA)
PO Box 21, Wetherby, West Yorkshire LS22 5JY.
Tel: 01937 582 693. *Modern Gold Coins.*
André de Clermont (BNTA)
10 Charles II Street, London, SW1Y 4AA. Tel: 020
7584 7200. *World Coins, especially Islamic.*
M. Coeshaw
PO Box 115, Leicester LE3 8JJ. Tel: 0116 287 3808.
P *Coins, Banknotes, Coin Albums and Cases.*
Philip Cohen Numismatics (ANA, BNTA)
20 Cecil Court, Charing Cross Road, London,
WC2N 4HE. Tel: 020 7379 0615, www.coinheritage.
co.uk
Coin & Collectors Centre
PO Box 22, Pontefract, West Yorkshire WF8
1YT. Tel: 01977 704 112, email sales@coincentre.
co.uk, www.coincentre.co.uk. **P***British Coins.*
Coinage of England
P.O. Box 442, Deal, Kent, CT14 4DE
Tel: 01304 2712 37, Email: info@coinageofengland.
co.uk. *Fine and Rare English Coins.*
Coincraft (ANA, IBNS)
45 Great Russell Street, London, WC1B 3JL.
Tel: 020 7636 1188 or 020 7637 8785, fax 020
7323 2860, email: info@coincraft.com. **L**
(newspaper format). *Coins and Banknotes.*
Coinote
74 Elwick Road, Hartlepool TS26 9AP. Tel: 01429 890
894. www.coinnote.co.uk. *Coins, Medals, Banknotes
and Accessories.*

Coinswap.co.uk
Swap, Sell or Trade Coins.
Coins of Canterbury
PO Box 47, Faversham, Kent,, ME13 7HX. Tel: 01795 531 980. **P** *English Coins.*
Colonial Collectables
P.O.Box 35625, Browns Bay, Auckland 0753, New Zealand. Email: richard@colonialcollectables.com British & World Coins.
Collectors' World (Mark Ray)
188 Wollaton Road, Wollaton, Nottingham NG8 1HJ. Tel: 01159 280 347. *Coins, Banknotes, Accessories.*
Constania CB
15 Church Road, Northwood, Middlesex, HA6 1AR. **P** *Roman and Medieval Hammered Coins.*
Colin Cooke
P.O. Box 602, Altrincham, WA14 5UN. Tel: 0161 927 9524, fax 0161 927 9540, email coins@colin cooke.com, www.colincooke.com. **L**British Coins.
Colonial Coins & Medals
218 Adelaide Street, Brisbane, QLD 4001. Email:coinshop@bigpond.net.au. *Auctions of World Coins*
Coopers Coins
PO Box 12703, Brentwood, Essex, CM14 9RB. Tel: 01277 560348, email: jack@cooperscoins.com. wwwcooperscoins.com British Coins
Copperbark Ltd
Suite 35, 37, St Andrew's Street, Norwich, NR2 4TP. Tel: 07834 434 780, email: copperbark.ltd@gmail. com, www.copperbark.com. *English, Russian and 17th Century Tokens.*
Corbitts (BNTA)
5 Mosley Street, Newcastle Upon Tyne NE1 1YE. Tel: 0191 232 7268, fax: 0191 261 4130. *Dealers and Auctioneers of all Coins and Medals.*
David Craddock
PO Box 3785, Camp Hill, Birmingham, B11 2NF. Tel: 0121 733 2259 **L**Crown to Farthings. Copper and Bronze Specialist. Some foreign.
Roy Cudworth
8 Park Avenue, Clayton West, Huddersfield HD8 9PT. *British and World Coins.*
Paul Dawson
47 The Shambles, York, YO1 7XL. Tel: 01904 654 769, email: pauldawsonyork@hotmail.com, www. pauldawsonyork.co.uk. *Ancient and British coins.*
Mark Davidson
PO Box 197, South Croydon, Surrey, CR3 0ZD. Tel: 020 8651 3890. *Ancient, Hammered & milled Coinage.*
Paul Davis
PO Box 418, Birmingham, B17 0RZ. Tel: 0121 427 7179. *British and World Coins.*
R. Davis
Tel: 01332 862 755 days / 740828 evenings, email: robdaviscc@gmail.com. *Maker of Traditional Coin Cabinets.*
Paul Davies Ltd (ANA, BNTA, IAPN)
PO Box 17, Ilkley, West Yorkshire LS29 8TZ. Tel: 01943 603 116, fax 01943 816 326, paul@ pauldaviesltd.co.uk. **P** *World Coins.*
Ian Davison
PO Box 256, Durham DH1 2GW. Tel 0191 3750 808. **L** *English Hammered and Milled Coins 1066–1910.*
Patrick Deane
Buckfastleigh, Devon. Tel: 01364 643969. *Tudors to Victoria. Hammered and milled gold and silver. 17th, 18th and 19th century tokens. Commemorative Medallions.*

Dei Gratia
PO Box 3568, Buckingham MK18 4ZS Tel: 01280 848 000.**P L** *Pre–Roman to Modern Coins. Antiquities, Banknotes.*
Den of Antiquity
PO Box 1114, Cambridge, CB25 9WJ. Tel: 01223 863 002, www.denofantiquity.co.uk.)
Ancient and Medieval Coins.
Clive Dennett (BNTA)
66 St Benedicts Street, Norwich, Norfolk, NR2 4AR. Tel: 01603 624 315, **L** *Specialising in paper money.*
C. J. Denton (ANA, BNTA, FRNS)
PO Box 25, Orpington, Kent BR6 8PU. Tel: 01689 873 690.**P** *Irish Coins.*
Detecniks
3 Orchard Crescent, Arundel Road, Fontwell. West Sussex BN18 0SA. Tel: 01243 545 060. *Retail shop. Wide range of Detectors.*
Michael Dickinson (ANA, BNTA)
Ramsay House, 825 High Road Finchley, London N12 8UB. Tel: 0181 441 7175.**P**
British and World Coins.
Douglassaville.com
Tel: 0118 918 7628, www.douglassaville.com. *Out of Print, Second-Hand and Rare Coin and Medal Books.*
Eagle Coins
Winterhaven, Mourneabbey, Mallow, Co. Cork, Ireland. Tel: 010 35322 29385.**P L** *Irish Coins.*
East of England Coins
Leprosy Mission Orton Goldhay, Peterborough, Cambridgeshire, PE2 5GZ. Tel: 01733235277 *Coins, Tokens and Banknotes*
Educational Coin Company
Box 892, Highland, New York 12528, USA. Tel:001 845 691 6100. *World Banknotes.*
Christopher Eimer (ANA, BNTA, IAPN)
PO Box 352 London NW11 7RF. Tel: 020 8458 9933, email: art@christophereimer.co.uk **P**
Commemorative Medals.
Malcolm Ellis Coins
Petworth Road, Witley, Surrey, GU8 5LX. Tel: 01428 685 566, www.malcolmelliscoins.co.uk). *Collectors and Dealers of British and Foreign Coins*
Elm Hill Collectables
41-43 Elm Hill, Norwich, Norfolk NR3 1HG. Tel: 01603 627 413. *Coins & Banknotes .*
Europa Numismatics (ANA, BNTA)
PO Box 119, High Wycombe, Bucks HP11 1QL. Tel: 01494 437 307 **P** *European Coins.*
Evesham Stamp & Coin Centre
Magpie Antiques, Manchester House,1 High Street, Evesham, Worcs WR11 4DA. Tel: 01386 41631. *British Coins.*
Michael E. Ewins
Meyrick Heights, 20 Meyrick Park Crescent, Bournemouth, Dorset BH3 7AQ. Tel: 01202 290 674. **P** *World Coins.*
Robin Finnegan Stamp Shop
83 Skinnergate, Darlington, Co Durham DL3 7LX. Tel: 01325 489 820/357 674. *World coins. World New Issues.*
Format of Birmingham Ltd (ANA, BNTA, IBNS)
PO Box 1276, Cheltenham, Gloucestershire, GL50 9ZW. Tel: 01242 518 495. **L** *Coins, Tokens and Medals.*
B. Frank & Son
3 South Avenue, Ryton, Tyne & Wear NE40 3LD. Tel: 0191 413 8749, Email: bfrankandson@aol. com, www.bfrankandson.com. *Coins, Banknotes and Cheques*

Galata Coins Ltd (ANA)
The Old White Lion, Market Street, Llanfylin, Powys SY22 5BX. Tel: 01691 648 765.🅿*British and World Coins.*

G. Gant
Glazenwood, 37 Augustus Way, Witham, Essex CM8 1HH. 🅿*British and Commonwealth Coins.*

A. & S. Gillis
59 Roy Kilner Way, Wombwell, Barnsley, South Yorkshire S73 8DY. Tel: 01226 750 371, www.gilliscoins.com. *Ancient Coins and Antiquities.*

Richard Gladdle—Northamptonshire
Suite 80, 29/30 Horse Fair, Banbury, Oxfordshire, OX16 0BW. Tel: 01327 858 511, email: gladdle@ plumpudding.org. *Tokens.* 🅿🅛

Glance Back Books
17 Upper Street, Chepstow, Gwent, NP6 5EX. Tel: 001291 626562. *Coins and Banknotes*

GM Coins
Tel: 01242 627 344, email: info@gmcoinsco. uk, www.gmcoins.co.uk. *Hammered and Milled Coins.*

Adrian Gorka Bond
Tel: 07500 772 080, email: sales@1stsovereign. co.uk, www.1stsovereign.co.uk. *Coins bought and sold.*

Goulborn
4 Sussex Street, Rhyl LL18 1SG. Tel: 01745 338 112. *English Coins and Medallions.*

Ian Gradon
PO Box 359, Durham DH7 6WZ. Tel 0191 3719 700, email: rarebanknote@gmail.com, www.worldnotes. co.uk. 🅛 *World Banknotes.*

Eric Green—Agent in UK for Ronald J. Gillio Inc
1013 State Street, Santa Barbara, California, USA 93101. Tel: 020 8907 0015, Mobile 0468 454948. *Gold Coins, Medals and Paper Money of the World.*

Philip Green
Suite 207, 792 Wilmslow Road, Didsbury, Manchester M20 6UG. Tel: 0161 440 0685. G*old Coins.*

Gurnhills of Leicester
8 Nothampton Street, Leicester, LE1 1PA.Tel: 07434 010 925. *British and World Coins and Banknotes.*

Hallmark Coins Ltd
PO Box 69991, I Canada Square, Canary Warf, London. Tel: 0800 612 7327 email: info@ hallmarkcoins.co.uk, www.hallmarkcoins.co.uk. *British Coins.*

Anthony Halse
PO Box 1856, Newport, Gwent NP18 2WA. Tel: 01633 413 238.🅿🅛*English and Foreign Coins and Tokens.*

A. D. Hamilton & Co (ANA)
7 St Vincent Place, Glasgow, G1 2DW. Tel: 0141 221 5423, email: jefffineman@hotmail.com, www. adhamilton.co.uk.*British and World Coins.*

Hammered British Coins
PO Box 2330, Salisbury, SP2 2LN. Tel: 07825 226 435, www.hammeredbritishcoins.com. *British Coins.*

Peter Hancock
40–41 West Street, Chichester, West Sussex, PO19 1RP. Tel: 01243 786 173. *World Coins, Medals and Banknotes.*

Hanocks
52–53 Burlington Arcade, London W1V 9AE. Tel: 020 7493 8904. *World Gold Coins.*

Hattons of London
PO Box 3719, Newcastle, ST55 9HH. Tel: 0333 234 3103. Email: enquiries@hattonsoflondon.co.uk 🅛 *Rare and Exclusive Coins*

Tom Hart Coins
Based in Devon. Tel: 07745 985 510. Email: woosworlduk@aol.com. *Coins, Medals and Antiques.*

Munthandel G. Henzen
PO Box 42, NL – 3958ZT, Amerogngen, Netherlands. Tel: 0031 343 430564 fax 0031 343 430542, email: info@henzen.org, www.henzen.org. 🅛*Ancients, Dutch and Foreign Coins.*

History In Coins
Tel: 07944 374600, email:andrewhowitt@hotmail.com, www.historyincoins.com. *World Coins.*

Craig Holmes
6 Marlborough Drive, Bangor, Co Down BT19 1HB. 🅿🅛*Low cost Banknotes of the World.*

R. G. Holmes
11 Cross Park, Ilfracombe, Devon EX34 8BJ. Tel: 01271 864 474. 🅿🅛 *Coins, World Crowns and Banknotes.*

HTSM Coins
26 Dosk Avenue, Glasgow G13 4LQ. Tel: 0141 562 9530, email: htsm@ntlworld.com🅿🅛 *British and foreign coins and Banknotes.*

M. J. Hughes Coins
27 Market Street, Alton, Hampshire, GU34 1HA. Tel: 01420 768 161, email: info@mjhughes.co.uk *World Coins and Bullion.*

T. A. Hull
15 Tangmere Crescent, Hornchurch, Essex RM12 5PL.🅿🅛 *British Coins, Farthings, Tokens.*

J. Hume
107 Halsbury Road East, Northolt, Middlesex UB5 4PY. Tel: 020 8864 1731.🅿🅛 *Chinese Coins.*

D. A. Hunter
Email: coins@dahunter.co.uk, www.dahunter.co.uk/ coins. 🅿🅛 *Uk and World Coins*

D. D. & A. Ingle
380 Carlton Hill, Nottingham, NG4 1JA. Tel: 0115 987 3325. *World Coins.*

R. Ingram Coins
206 Honeysuckle Road, Bassett, Southampton, SO16 3BU. Tel: 023 8032 4258, email: info@ ringramcoins.com, www.ringramcoins.com.🅿🅛 *Dealers in UK Coins.*

F. J. Jeffery & Son Ltd
Haines Croft, Corsham Road, Whitley, Melksham, Wilts, SN12 8QF. Tel: 01225 703 143.🅿 🅛, *British, Commonwealth and Foreign Coins.*

Richard W. Jeffery
Tel: 01736 871 263. 🅿 *British and World Coins, Banknotes.*

JN Coins
PO Box 1030, Ipswich, OP1 9XL. Tel: 07916 145 038, email@jncoins.co.ukwww.jncoins.co.uk). *British Coins from Celtic to Modern.*

KB Coins (BNTA)
PO BOX 499, Stevenage, Herts, SG1 9JT. Tel: 01438 312 661, fax 01438 311 990. www.kbcoins. com 🅛 *Mainly British Coins.*

Kleeford Coins
Tel: 07484 272 837, kleeford@btinternet.com www.kleefordcoins.webs.com, . 🅿 *Monthly Auctions of Coins, Banknotes, Tokens & Medals.*

K&M Coins
PO Box 3662, Wolverhampton WV10 6ZW. Tel: 0771 238 1880, email: M_Bagguley@hotmail. com. *English Milled Coins.*

Knightsbridge Coins (ANA, BNTA, IAPN, PNG)
43 Duke Street, St James's, London, SW1Y 6DD. Tel: 020 7930 8215/7597, info@knightsbridgecoins. com. *Quality Coins of the World.*

Lancashire Coin and Medal Co
31 Adelaide Street, Fleetwood, Lancs, FY7 6AD. Tel:
01253 779308. **P** *British Coins and Medals.*
Liberty Coins and Bullion
17g Vyse Street, Birmingham, B18 6LE: Tel: 0121
554 4432, www.libertycoinsbullion.co.uk. *Coins and
Precious Metals*
Lindner Publications Ltd
3a Hayle Industrial Park, Hayle, Cornwall TR27 5JR.
Tel: 01736 751 910, email: prinzpublications@gmail.
com. **L** *Manufacturers of Coin Albums, Cabinets
and Accessories.*
Jan Lis (BNTA)
Beaver Coin Room, 57 Philbeach Gardens, London
SW5 9ED. Tel: 020 7373 4553 fax 020 7373 4555.
By appointment only. *European Coins.*
Keith Lloyd
1 Dashwood Close, Pinewood, Ipswich, Suffolk
IP8 3SR. Tel: 01473 403 506. **P L** *Ancient Coins.*
Lockdale Coins (BNTA)
52 Barrack Square, Martlesham Heath, Ipswich,
Suffolk, IP5 3RF. Tel: 01473 627 110, www.lockdales.
com. **L** *World Coins, Medals and Banknotes*
Stephen Lockett (BNTA)
4–6 Upper Street, New Ash Green, Kent, DA3 8JJ.
Tel: 01474 871464. *British and World Coins.*
The London Coin Company
PO Box 495, Stanmore, Greater London, HA7 9HS
Tel: 0800 085 2933, 020 8343 2231,
www.thelondoncoincomany.com).
Modern Gold and Silver Coins.
Mike Longfield Detectors
83 Station Road, Balsall Common, nr Coventry,
Warwickshire CV7 7FN. Tel: 01676 533 274.
. *Metal Detectors.*
MA Shops
www.mashops.com. On-line coin mall. *Coins,
Medals, Banknotes and Accessories.*
Mannin Collections Ltd
5 Castle Street, Peel, Isle of Man, IM5 1AN. Tel:
01624 843 897, email: manncoll@advsys.co.uk, *IOM
Coins, Tokens, etc.*
Manston Coins of Bath
8 Bartletts St. Antique Centre, Bath. Tel: 01225
487 888. *Coins, Tokens and Medals.*
I. Markovits
1–3 Cobbold Mews, London W12 9LB.
Tel: 020 8749 3000. *Enamelled Coins.*
C. J. Martin Coins (BNTA)
The Gallery, Trent Park Equestrian Centre, Bramley
Road, London, N14 4UW. Tel: 020 8364 4565,
www.ancientart.co.uk. **P L** Bi– monthly catalogue.
Greek, Roman & English Hammered Coins.
Maverick Numismatics
07403 111843, www.mavericknumismatics.com).
Coin and Currency Design.
M. G. Coins & Antiquities
12 Mansfield, High Wych, Herts CM21 0JT. Tel 01279
721 719. **L** *Ancient and Hammered Coins,
Antiquities.*
M&H Coins
PO Box 10985, Brentwood, CM14 9JB. Tel: 07504
804 019, www.mhcoins.co.uk. **L** *British Hammered
and Milled Coins.*
Michael Coins
PO Box 3100 Reading RG1 9ZL. *World Coins and
Banknotes.*
Middlesex Coins
www.middlesexcoins.co.uk. Tel: 07753618613,
Email: marksaxby25@hotmail.com.
Quality rare coins specialists since 1999

David Miller Coins & Antiquities (ANA, BNTA)
PO Box 711, Hemel Hempstead, HP2 4UH. Tel/fax
01442 251 492. *Ancient Hammered English Coins.*
Timothy Millett
PO Box 20851, London SE22 0YN. Tel: 0208 693
1111, www.historicmedals.com. **L** *Historical
Medals.*
Nigelmills.net
PO Box 53126, London, E18 1YR. Email: nigelmills@
onetel.com,
www.nigelmills.net *Coins and Antiquities.*
Monetary Research Institute
PO Box 3174, Houston, TX 77253-3174, Tel: 001
713 827 1796, email: info@mriguide.com. *Bankers
Guide to Foreign Currency*
Moore Antiquities
Unit 12, Ford Lane Industrial Estate, Ford, nr.
Arundel, West Sussex BN18 0AA. Tel: 01243 824
232, email moore.antiquities@virgin.net.
Coins and Artefacts up to the 18th Century.
Mike Morey
19 Elmtrees, Long Crendon, Bucks HP18 9DG. **P L**
British Coins, Halfcrowns to Farthings.
Peter Morris (BNTA, IBNS)
1 Station Concourse, Bromley North Station,
Bromley, BR1 1NN or PO Box 223, Bromley,
BR1 4EQ. Tel: 020 8313 3410, email: info@
petermorris.co.uk, www.petermorris.co.uk
co.uk). **L** *British and World Coins, Proof
Sets and Numismatic Books.*
N3 Coins—London
Email: mail@n3coins.com,
www.n3coins.com. *Roman and Ancient Coins.*
Colin Narbeth & Son Ltd (ANA, IBNS)
20 Cecil Court, Leicester Square, London,WC2N.
4HE .Tel: 020 7379 6975, www.colin–narbeth.com
World Banknotes.
Newcastle Coin Dealers
7 Nile Street, North Shields, NE29 0BD. Tel: 07939
999 286, email: newcastlecoin@outlook.com, www.
newcastlecoindealers.co.uk. *Modern British and
World Coins/Banknotes*
John Newman Coins
P O Box 4890, Worthing, BN119WS. Tel: 01903
239 867, email: john@newmancoins.co.uk,
www.johnnewmancoins.co.uk. *English hammered
coins, British Milled Coins and British Tokens.*
Peter Nichols Cabinet Makers
The Workshop, 383a High Road,
Chilwell,Nottingham, NG9 5EA. Tel: 0115 922 4149,
email: orders@coincabinets.com,
www.coincabinets.com. *Manufacturers of Bespoke
Mahogany Coin and Medal Cabinets.*
Wayne Nicholls
PO Box 44, Bilston, West Midlands. Tel: 01543
45476. **L** *Choice English Coins.*
North Wales Coins Ltd (BNTA)
1b Penrhyn Road, Colwyn Bay, Clwyd. Tel: 01492
533 023. *British Coins.*
NP Collectables
9 Main Street, Gedney Dyke, Spalding, Lincs PE12
0AJ. Tel: 01406 365 211 **P L**. *English Hammered
and Milled Coins.*
Notability Notes (IBNS)
PO Box 3530, Swindon, SN2 9FZ. Tel: 07545
572 721, email: info@notability-banknotes.com,
www.notability-banknotes.com). British/World Notes.*
Numitrading.com
Online market place/trading platform.
Tel: 01702 667420, email: info@numitrading.com,
www.numitrading.com .

Odyssey Antiquities
PO Box 61, Southport PR9 0PZ.Tel: 01704 232 494. *Classical Antiquities, Ancient and Hammered Coins.*

Glenn S. Ogden
Tel: 01626 859 350 or 07971 709 427, email: glennogdencoins@hotmail.com,
www. glennogdencoins.com, 🅿🅛 *English Milled Coinage.*

John Ogden Coins
Hodge Clough Cottage, Moorside, Oldham OL1 4JW. Tel: 0161 678 0709🅿🅛*Ancient and Hammered.*

Don Oliver Gold Coins
Stanford House, 23 Market Street, Stourbridge, West Midlands DY8 1AB. Tel: 01384 877 901. *British Gold Coins.*

Roger Outing
36 Church Lane, Huddersfield, HD8 9LY. Tel: 01484 860 415, email: rogerandlizbanknotes4u.co.uk, www.chequemate4collectors.co.uk). *World Banknotes.*

P&D Medallions
PO Box 269, Berkhampstead, Herts HP4 3FT. Tel: 01442 865 127, www.pdmedallions.co.uk. 🅿 *Historical and Commemorative Medals.*

Del Parker
PO Box 310 Richmond Hill, GA 31324. Tel: + 1 2143521475, Email: irishcoins2000@hotmail. com.www.irishcoins.com. *Irish, American Coins. Irish Art Medals and Banknotes.* 🅛

Pavlos S. Pavlou
58 Davies Streer, Mayfair, London W1K 5JF. Tel: 020 7629 9449, email: pspavlou@hotmail.com. *Ancient to Modern*

PCGS
Tel:+33 (0) 949 833 0600, email:info@pcgs.com, www.pcgs.com. *Coin Grading and Authentication Service.*

www.pennycrowncoins.co.uk
PO Box 831, Amersham, HP6 9GF. Tel: 01494 776141. *Specialising in British Milled Coins 1662–1970.*

Penrith Coin & Stamp Centre
37 King Street, Penrith, Cumbria CA11 7AY. Tel: 01768 864 185.*World Coins.*

Pentland Coins (IBNS)
Pentland House, 92 High Street, Wick, Caithness KW14 L5. 🅟 *British and World Coins and Banknotes.*

Philatelic Heritage
35a High Street, Hungerford, RG17 0NF. Email philatelicheritage@gmx.com. Tel: 01488 684008 Coins & Stamps

B. C. Pickard
1 Treeside, Christchurch, Dorset BH23 4PF. Tel: 01425 275763, email: bcpickard@fsmail.net). 🅿 *Stone Age, Greek, Roman Items (inc. coins) for sale.*

Pobjoy Mint Ltd (ANA)
Millennium House, Kingswood Park, Bonsor Drive, Kingswood, Surrey KT20 6AY. Tel: 01737 818 182 fax 01737 818199. *Europe's largest private mint. New issues.*

George Rankin Coin Co Ltd (ANA)
325 Bethnal Green Road, London E2 6AH. Tel: 020 7739 1840 *World Coins.*

Mark Rasmussen (BNTA, IAPN)
PO Box 42, Betchworth, Surrey, RH3 7YR. Tel: 01306 884 880, email: mark.rasmussen@rascoins.com, www.rascoins.com. 🅛 *Quality Hammered, Milled Coins.*

Mark T. Ray (see Collectors World)

Rhyl Coin Shop
12 Sussex Street, Rhyl, Clwyd. Tel: 01745 338 112. *World Coins and Banknotes.*

Chris Rigby
PO Box 181, Worcester WR1 1YE. Tel: 01905 28028. 🅿🅛*Modern British Coins.*

Roderick Richardson (BNTA)
The Old Granary Antiques Centre, King's Staithe Lane, King's Lynn, PE30 1LZ. Tel: 01553 670 833, www.roderickrichardson.com. 🅛 *English, Hammered and Early Milled Coins. High quality lists issued.*

Charles Riley (BNTA)
PO Box 733, Aylesbury HP22 9AX. Tel: 01296 747 598, charlesrileycoins@gmail.com, www.charlesriley.co.uk. *Coins and Medallions.*

Robin–on–Acle Coins
193 Main Road Essex CO12 3PH. Tel: 01255 554 440, email: enquiries@robin–on–acle–coins. co.uk. *Ancient to Modern Coins and Paper Money.*

Roma Numismatics
20 Fitzroy Square, London, W1T 6EJ Tel: 020 7121 6518, www.romanumismatics.com. *Dealers and Auctioneers of Fine Ancient Coins.*

Royal Australian Mint
www.ramint.gov.au). *New Coin Issues.*

Royal Gold
PO Box 123, Saxonwold, 2132, South Africa, Tel: +27 11 483 0161, email: royalg@iafrica.com, www.royalgold.co.za. *Gold Coins.*

Colin de Rouffignac (BNTA)
57, Wigan Lane, Wigan, Lancs WN1 2LF. Tel: 01942 237 927. *P. English and Scottish Hammered.*

R. P. Coins
PO Box 367, Prestwich, Manchester, M25 9ZH. Tel: 07802 713 444, www.rpcoins.co.uk. *Coins, Books, Catalogues and Accessories.*

Chris A. Rudd (IAPN, BNTA)
PO Box 222, Aylsham, Norfolk, NR11 6TY. Tel: 01263 735 007 fax 01263 731 777, www.celticcoins.com.🅿🅛 *Celtic Coins.*

Colin Rumney (BNTA)
PO Box 34, Denbighshire, North Wales, LL16 4YQ. Tel: 01745 890 621. *All world including ancients.*

R & J Coins
21b Alexandra Street, Southend-on-Sea, Essex, SS1 1DA. Tel: 01702 345 995. *World Coins.*

Safe Albums (UK) Ltd
16 Falcon Business Park, 38 Ivanhoe Road, Finchampstead, Berkshire RG40 4QQ. Tel: 0118 932 8976 fax 0118 932 8612. *Accessories.*

Saltford Coins
Harcourt, Bath Road, Saltford, Bristol, Avon BS31 3DQ. Tel: 01225 873 512, email: info@saltfordcoins.com, www.saltfordcoins.com 🅿 *British, Commonwealth, World Coins and medallions.*

Satin Coins
PO Box 63, Stockport, Cheshire SK4 5BU. Tel: 07940 393 583 answer machine.

Scotmint Ltd
68 Sandgate, Ayr, Scotland KA7 1BX Tel: 01292 268 244, email: rob@scotmint.com, www.scotmint.com. *Coins, Medals and Banknotes. Retail shop.*

David Seaman
PO Box 449, Waltham Cross, EN9 3WZ. Tel: 01992 719 723, email: davidseamancoins@outlook.com. 🅿🅛 *Hammered, Milled, Maundy.*

Patrick Semmens
3 Hospital Road, Half Key, Malvern, Worcs WR14 1UZ. Tel: 0886 33123. **P** *European and British coins.*

Mark Senior
553 Falmer Road, Woodingdean, Brighton, Sussex Tel: 01273 309 359. By appointment only.
P L *Saxon, Norman and English hammered.*

S. E. Sewell
Cronin, Westhorpe Road, Finningham, Stowmarket, Suffolk, IP14 4TN. Tel: 01449 782 185 or 07739 071 822,
email: sewellmedals@hotmail.com, www.sewellmedals.co.uk). *Mainly British Milled.*

Sharps Pixley
54, St James's Street, London SW1A 1JT Tel: 020 7871 0532, www.sharpspixley.com. *Safe deposit boxes in St James's, buying and selling Gold Bullion.*

Silbury Coins
PO Box 281, Cirencester, Gloucs GL7 9ET. Tel: 01242 898 107, email: info@silburycoins.com, www.silburycoins.com. *Iron Age, Roman, Saxon, Viking, Medieval Coins and later.*

Simmons Gallery (ANA, BNTA, IBNS)
PO Box 104, Leytonstone, London E11 1ND Tel: 020 898 98097, www.simmonsgallery.co.uk. **L** *Coins, Tokens and Medals.*

E. Smith (ANA, IBNS)
PO Box 348, Lincoln LN6 0TX Tel: 01522 684 681 fax 01522 689 528. Organiser of the Wakefield (formally known as Leeds) monthly coin fair. **P** *World Coins and Paper Money.*

Neil Smith
PO Box 774, Lincoln LN4 2WX. Tel: 01522 522 772 fax 01522 689 528. *GB and World Gold Coins 1816 to date, including Modern Proof Issues.*

Jim Smythe
PO Box 6970, Birmingham B23 7WD. Email: Jimdens@aol.com.**P L** *19th/20th Century British and World Coins.*

Sovereign Rarities Ltd (BNTA)
32, St George Street, London W1S 2EA Tel: 0203 019 1185, www.sovereignrrrities.com. *Quality British and World Coins.*

Spink & Son Ltd (ANA, BNTA, IAPN, IBNS)
69 Southampton Row, Bloomsbury, London. WC1B 4ET. Tel: 020 7563 4000, fax 020 7563 4066, email: info@spinkandson.com, www.spink.com. *Ancient to Modern World Coins. Medals, Banknotes.*

Stamford Coins
65–67 Stamford Street, Bradford, West Yorkshire, BD4 8SD. Tel: 07791 873 595, email: stamfordcoins@hotmail.co.uk.

Stamp & Collectors Centre
404 York Town Road, College Town, Camberley, Surrey GU15 4PR. Tel:01276 32587 fax 01276 32505. *World Coins and Medals.*

St Edmunds Coins & Banknotes
PO Box 118, Bury St Edmunds IP33 2NE. Tel: 01284 761 894.

Sterling Coins & Medals
2 Somerset Road, Boscombe, Bournemouth, Dorset BH7 6JH. Tel: 01202 423 881. *World Coins & Medals.*

Drake Sterling Numismatics Pty Ltd
GPO Box 2913, Sydney 2001, Australia. UK callers Tel: 020 7097 1781, www.drakesterling.co.uk. *British and British Colonial Gold Coins*

Studio Coins (ANA, BNTA)
Studio 111, 80 High Street, Winchester, Hants SO23 9AT. Tel: 01962 853 156 email: stephenmitchell13@ bttconnect.com. **P** *English Coins.*

The Coin House
Tel: 01935 824 878, email: thecoinhouse@ btinternet.com. *Quality Investment Coins and Silver Bars.*

The East India Company
Tel: 0203 205 3394, email, service@ theeastindiacompany.com. *Gold and Silver Coins, retail premises.Gifts and collectables of historic interest.*

The Royal Mint
Llantrisant, Pontyclun, CF72 8YT. Tel: 01443 222111. *New coin minter/issuer. Also historic numismatics.*

Time Line Originals
PO Box 193, Upminster, RM14 3WH. Tel: 01708 222 384/07775 651 218, email: sales@time–lines. co.uk.

Stuart J. Timmins
Smallwood Lodge Bookshop, Newport, Salop. Tel: 01952 813 232. *Numismatic Literature.*

R. Tims
39 Villiers Road, Watford, Herts WD1 4AL.**P L** *Uncirculated World Banknotes.*

Token Publishing Ltd
40, Southernhay East, Exeter, Devon EX1 1PE, Tel: 01404 46972, email info@tokenpublishing.com, www.tokenpublishing.com
Publishers of COIN NEWS, COIN YEARBOOK, MEDAL YEARBOOK, BANKOTE YEARBOOK and suppliers of Numismatic Titles, Krause catalogues and Coin Accessories.

Michael Trenerry
PO Box 55, Truro, TR1 2YQ. Tel: 01872 277 977, email: veryfinecoins@aol.com. By appointment only. **L** *Roman, Celtic and English Hammered Coins and Tokens.*

Vera Trinder Ltd
Unit 3a, Hayle Ind Park, Hayle, Cornwall TR27 5JR. Tel:01736 751 910, email: richardvtrinder@aol.com www.veratrinder.co.uk. **L** *Coin Accessories.*

Robert Tye
7–9 Clifford Street, York, YO1 9RA. Tel: 0845 4 900 724, email: orders@earlyworlscoins.com. **P** *European and Oriental Hammered Coins. UK Coins www.uk–coins.com Rare British and Historical Medals*

Vale
Tel: 01322 405 911, email: valecoins@ntlworld.com *British Coins and Medals.*

Van der Schueren, John-Luc (IAPN)
14 Rue de la Borse, 1,000 Bussels, Belgium. Email: iapnsecret@compuserve.com, www.coins.be. . *Coins and Tokens of the World and of the Low Countries.*

Tony Vaughan Collectables
PO Box 364, Wolverhampton, WV3 9PW. Tel: 01902 27351. **P L** *World Coins and Medals.*

Victory Coins (BNTA)
PO Box 948, Southsea, Hampshire, PO1 9LZ. Tel: 023 92 751908. *British and World Coins.*

Mark J. Vincenzi (BNTA)
Rylands, Earls Colne, Essex CO6 2LE. Tel: 01787 222 555. **P** *Greek, Roman, Hammered.*

Mike Vosper
PO Box 32, Hockwold, Brandon IP26 4HX. Tel: 01842 828 292, email: mikevosper@vosper4coins. co.uk, www.vosper4coins.co.uk). *Roman, Hammered.*

Weighton Coin Wonders
50 Market Place, Market Weighton, York, Y043 3AL, Tel: 01430 879 740, www.weightoncoin.co.uk. *Modern Gold, Silver Proofs and Sets.*

Wessex Coins
PO Box 482, Southampton, SO30 9FB. Tel: 02380 972 059, email: info@wessexcoins.co.uk, www.wessexcoins.co.uk. *Ancient Greek, Roman, English Hammered Coins and Antiquities, also Shipwreck Treasure.*

Pam West (IBNS, BNTA)
PO Box 257, Sutton, Surrey, SM3 9WW. Tel: 020 8641 3224, email: pam@britishnotes.co.uk, www.britishnotes.co.uk. **P L** *English Banknotes and related publications.*

West Essex Coin Investments (BNTA, IBNS)
Croft Cottage, Station Road, Alderholt, Fordingbridge, Hants SP6 3AZ. Tel: 01425 656 459. *British and World Coins and Paper Money.*

West Wicklow Coins
Blessington, Co Wicklow, Ireland. Tel: 00353 45 858 767, email: westwicklowcoins@hotmail.com. Irish and *World Coins.*

Trevor Wilkin
PO Box 182 Cammeray, NSW 2602, Australia. Tel: 0061 9438 5040, email trevorsnotes@bigpond.com. *World Banknotes*

Simon Willis Coins
43a St Marys Road, Market Harborough, LE16 7DS. Tel:07908 240 978, swcoins@simonwilliscoins.com, www.simonwilliscoins.com. *Quality Hammered and Early Milled British Coins.*

Worldwide Coins (IBNS)
PO Box 11, Wavertree, Liverpool L15 0FG. Tel: 0845 634 1809, email: sales@worldwidecoins.co.uk, www.worldwidecoins.co.uk. *World Coins and Paper Money.*

World Treasure Books
PO Box 5, Newport, Isle of Wight PO30 5QE. Tel: 01983 740 712. **L** *Coins, Books, Metal Detectors.*

Barry Wright
54 Dooley Drive, Bootle, Merseyside. L3O 8RT. **P L** *World Banknotes.*

I. S. Wright (Australia Numismatic Co)
64 Parramatta Road, Forest Lodge NSW, 2037, Australia. Tel:0061 3 9264 7555, email: ausnumis@netconnect.comau. **P** *Coins, Banknotes, Medallions, Tokens.*

D. Yapp
PO Box 4718, Shrewsbury Mail Centre SY1 9EA. Tel: 01743 232 557, www.david-yapp.com. **L** *World and British Banknotes.*

York Coins
PO Box 160, Red Hook, New York 12571. Tel: 001 718 544 0120 email: antony@yorkcoins.com. *Ancient Coins.*

York Coin and Stamp Centre
Cavendish Antique & Collectors Centre, 44 Stone gate, York, YO1 8AS. *Retail Shop. Coins and Medals.*

Treasure
and the Law

Until the introduction of the new Treasure Act, the legal position regarding articles of gold, silver or bullion, found long after they were hidden or abandoned, was not as simple and straightforward as it might be supposed. Furthermore, this was a case where the law in England and Wales differed fundamentally from that in Scotland.

Treasure Trove was one of the most ancient rights of the Crown, deriving from the age-old right of the monarch to gold, silver or bullion treasure whose owner was not known. In England and Wales, the law applied only to objects made of, or containing, gold or silver, whether in the form of coin, jewellery, plate or bullion. Moreover, the object had to be shown to have been deliberately hidden with intent to retrieve and the owner could not be readily found. The English law therefore excluded precious stones and jewels set in base metals or alloys such as bronze or pewter. It also took no account of artifacts in pottery, stone, bone, wood or glass which might be of immense antiquarian value.

Found by a metal detectorist near Dover, Kent in 2019, a gold aureus of Allectus soared over its pre-sale estimate of £70,000–100,000 at DNW to secure a total of £552,000 — a new UK auction record.

In recent years, as a result of the rise in metal-detecting as a hobby, the archaeological lobby brought pressure to bear on Parliament to change the law and bring it into line with Scotland where the rules on Treasure Trove were far more rigorously interpreted. In Scotland the Crown is entitled to *all* abandoned property, even if it has not been hidden and is of little value. This applies even to objects dumped in skips on the pavement. Strictly speaking you would be committing a criminal offence if you removed an old chair from a skip without the owner's permission, although in practice such helping oneself rarely proceeds to a prosecution. In 1958 an archaeological expedition from Aberdeen University found several valuable artifacts on St Ninian's Isle, Shetland. These included silver vessels and ornaments, as well as a porpoise bone which had incised decoration on it. The archaeologists challenged the rights of the Crown to this treasure, arguing that the Crown would have to prove that the articles had been deliberately hidden, and that a porpoise bone was in any case not valuable enough to count as treasure. The High Court, however, decided that as long as the property had been abandoned, it belonged automatically to the Crown. Its value, intrinsic or otherwise, or whether or not it was hidden, did not make any difference. Since then, as a result of this decision in case law, the criteria for Treasure Trove have been very strictly applied in Scotland. It would have only required a similar test case in England or Wales to result in a similar tightening of the rules. This has been resisted, mainly by the detectorist lobby, but inevitably the government considered legislation to control the use of metal detectors, if not to ban them altogether.

Such is the sheer quantity of the Rauceby Hoard found buried in a pottery vessel in July 2017 in Lincolnshire that the full extent of this incredible find is finally being revealed (for the full story see COIN NEWS, July 2019).

In England and Wales a find of gold or silver coins, artifacts or ornaments, or objects which contain some of these metals, which appears to have been concealed by the original owner, was deemed to be Treasure Trove. It was not even necessary for the articles to be buried in the ground; objects concealed in thatched roofs or under the floorboards of buildings have been judged to be Treasure Trove. Such finds had to be notified immediately to the police who then informed the district coroner. He then convened an inquest which decided whether all or part of the find was Treasure Trove. Establishing the gold or silver content was straightforward, but the coroner's inquest had to decide whether the material was hidden deliberately and not just lost or abandoned, and that the owner could not be located. A gold coin found on or near a country footpath might reasonably have been dropped by the original possessor through a hole in pocket or purse and in such cases it was very unlikely that it would be deemed Treasure Trove, even if the coin turned out to be very rare. In this instance the coroner would then have had to determine who was the lawful owner of the find: the actual finder, the owner of the land where it was found or even the tenant of the land. As a rule, however, it was left to the finder and landowner to decide between them who the owner of the coin should be, and in some cases the matter could only be resolved by referring to a civil court.

For this reason it was vital that metal detectorists should secure permission *in writing* from landowners before going on to their land, defining rights and obligations on both sides, in order to determine the disposal or share-out of any finds or proceeds from the sale of finds, *beforehand*.

If the coroner decided that the articles were deliberately concealed, and declared them to be Treasure Trove, the find automatically reverted to the Crown. In practice the find was considered by the Treasure Trove Reviewing Committee of the Treasury. They might decide that although the articles, *invariably coins,* were gold or silver, they were so common that they were not required by the British Museum or one of the other great national collections, and would return them to the finder to dispose of at their discretion. If some or all of the coins were deemed vital for inclusion in a national collection the finder was recompensed with the full market value of the material. On the other hand, if someone found gold or silver which might be Treasure Trove and failed to declare it at the time, that person was liable to prosecution under the Theft Act 1968 should the find subsequently come to light. Not only could they face a heavy fine but the articles would be forfeit to the Crown, and of course no reward or recompense was then payable either.

The anomalies and inconsistencies of existing law on Treasure Trove were eliminated and the position considerably tightened up by the passage, on July 5, 1996, of the Treasure Act.

This rare gold stater, struck circa AD 25–40 by Epaticcus, a prince of the Catuvellauni tribe, was found in Surrey, not far from Runnymede, in a meadow on the south bank of the river Thames (image courtesy of Chris Rudd).

Announcing that the Treasure Act had received the Royal Assent, Lord Inglewood, National Heritage Minister, said, "This represents the first legislation on Treasure Trove to be passed in England and Wales and will replace Common Law precedents and practices dating back to the Middle Ages. The Act, which offers a clearer definition of treasure and simplified procedures for dealing with finds, will come into force after a code of practice has been drawn up and agreed by both Houses of Parliament". The Act came into force in England, Wales and Northern Ireland on September 24, 1997, replacing the Common Law of Treasure Trove.

The act was introduced as a Private Member's Bill by Sir Anthony Grant, after the failure of an earlier attempt by Lord Perth. For the first time, it would be a criminal offence to fail to report within 14 days the discovery of an item which could be declared Treasure Trove. Finders will continue to be rewarded for reporting their discoveries promptly, while landowners and occupiers will also be eligible for rewards for the first time.

The Treasure Act covers man-made objects and defines treasure as objects other than coins which are at least 300 years old and contain at least 10 per cent by weight of gold or silver; coins more than 300 years old which are found in hoards (a minimum of two coins if the precious metal content is more than 10 per cent, and a minimum of 10 coins if the precious metal content is below 10 per cent). The act also embraces all objects found in clear archaeological association with items which are treasure under the above definitions. It also covers any object which would have been Treasure Trove under the previous definitions (e.g. hoards of 19th century gold or silver coins).

An extension to The Act from January 2003 provides that groups of prehistoric bronze implements are also deemed to be Treasure.

The maximum penalty for failing to report the discovery of treasure within 14 days will be a fine of £5,000 or three months imprisonment, or both.

In Scotland the police pass the goods on to the procurator fiscal who acts as the local representative of the Queen's and Lord Treasurer's Remembrancer. If the articles are of little value, historically or intrinsically, the finder will usually be allowed to keep them. If they are retained for the appropriate national collection then a reward equal to the market value is payable.

A favourite haunt of metal-detectorists these days is the beach, and many hobbyists make quite a lucrative living by sweeping the beaches especially just after a Bank Holiday. It's surprising how much loose change gets lost from pockets and handbags over a holiday weekend. Technically the coins recovered from the beach are lost property, in which case they ought to be surrendered to the police, otherwise the finder may be guilty of theft. In practice, however, the law turns a blind eye to coins, on the sensible grounds that it would be impossible to prove ownership. On the other hand, banknotes are treated as lost property since someone could in theory at least identify a note as his by citing the serial number.

The potentially unique 2,000-year-old denarius of Carausius found by a policeman 30 years ago and only recently identified as a Roman rarity by his friend.

In the case of other objects, such as watches and jewellery, of course the law governing lost property is enforced, and the old adage of "finders keepers" does not apply. Any object of value, identifiable as belonging to someone, that is washed up on the foreshore or found in territorial waters is known technically as "wreck". This includes not just a wrecked ship, but any cargo that was being carried by a ship.

If wreck is not claimed by its owner, it falls to the Crown. In this case it is not necessary to prove deliberate concealment, as in the case of Treasure Trove. This law has a specific numismatic application in the case of the gold and silver coins washed up after storms around our shores, from Shetland to the Scillies. Such coins, emanating from wrecks of Spanish treasure ships and Dutch East Indiamen in particular, are well documented, and any such finds ought to be reported immediately to the police.

Stray finds of coins, as well as other objects of value, on public places, such as the street, a public park or a sports ground, are also subject to law. In this case the finder must take all reasonable steps to locate the owner. Anyone who keeps a coin without making reasonable effort to find the owner could be prosecuted for theft. As with the beach, however, such "reasonable effort" would clearly be impractical. Finding coins on private premises is another matter. In this case large bodies, such as the Post Office, British Rail, the British Airports Authority, bus companies, municipal authorities, hospitals, the owners of department stores, theatre and cinema proprietors and the like, may have bye-laws, rules and regulations for dealing with lost property found within their precincts, or in their vehicles. If you found a purse or wallet on a bus or train, or in a telephone kiosk or a shop, common sense (and your conscience) would tell you to hand it over to the driver, conductor, shopkeeper or official in charge.

As a rule, unclaimed lost property reverts eventually to the finder, but not always; British Rail and some other organisations have a rule that in such cases the property reverts to the organisation. In any event, failure to disclose the find immediately might render you liable to prosecution for stealing by finding.

Over the past 20 years, 13,000 finds have gone through the treasure process. Over 30 per cent of the objects found are now in museums to be enjoyed by millions of members of the public. This is an amazing achievement. However, some antiquities are escaping the net because of the definition of Treasure. For example, in 2010 a detectorist found a magnificent Roman helmet near Crosby Garrett in Cumbria. It was not caught by the definition of Treasure as it was a single find made of copper. It was subsequently bought by a private collector for £2.3 million. Government

Experts examine and catalogue coins from a find.

ministers want such rarities to be Treasure so that they can be acquired by a UK museum. The Act will be changed so that it catches anything worth £10,000 or more.

In 2017, the latest year for which figures are available, there were 1,267 archaeological finds in the UK. Many of these were made by amateur hobbyists with metal detectors. It is believed that some finds are being sold on-line without being declared to the PAS. It is likely that powers will be made available to challenge both sellers and buyers of such material.

John Andrew, Editorial Consultant, COIN NEWS.

SUBSCRIBE AND SAVE

Save over £10 on newsagent prices when you take out a subscription

Subscriber Benefits

- **FREE** delivery before the magazine goes on sale in the newsagents
- **FREE** classified advertising (for non-trade subscribers) worth £96
- **FREE** EXCLUSIVE online access to 12 years back issues of the magazine at your fingertips completely FREE to subscribers

The UK's biggest selling, award winning Coin Magazine

EVERY MONTH There is a great range of content, including **numismatic news**; a **"what's on"** section that lets collectors know about fairs, societies, auctions etc.; "**Auction Highlights**" reporting what has been happening in the sale rooms; articles on all aspects of numismatics; **book reviews**; a **dedicated banknote section** and a directory that allows readers to see what lists the main dealers are offering that month, as well as a host of other features of interest to both the serious and not-so-serious collector.

Read COIN NEWS every month from just £10 per quarter

(UK only by Direct Debit)

 01404 46972 | www.tokenpublishing.com | Token Publishing Ltd., 40 Southernhay East, Exeter, Devon, EX1 1PE

SUBSCRIBERS ORDER FORM
Your subscription will start from the next available issue

BEST DEAL

Pay By UK Direct Debit:
- ☐ One off payment £40 (12 issues)
- ☐ Quarterly payment of £10 (12 issues)—SPREAD THE COST
- ☐ One off payment £22 (6 issues)

By Credit or Debit card or *Cheque:
- ☐ £44 for 12 issues UK ☐ £22 for 6 issues UK
- ☐ £55 for 12 issues Europe/World Surface
- ☐ £65 for 12 issues Worldwide Airmail
- ☐ £12 for 12 issues Digital Magazine only Worldwide

*Please make cheques payable to Token Publishing Ltd

YOUR DETAILS
Title _____ Initial _____
Surname _____
Address _____
Postcode _____ Telephone _____
E-mail (for digital mag.) _____

CREDIT OR DEBIT CARD PAYMENT ☐ Visa ☐ Mastercard
Card Number

Issue no. | Authorisation code*
_____ * The last 3 digits from the back of the card
Valid from | Expiry date

Signature _____

INSTRUCTION TO BANK OR BUILDING SOCIETY TO PAY BY DIRECT DEBIT

 DIRECT Debit

Please fill in and send to: **Token Publishing Ltd,** 40 Southernhay East, Exeter, Devon, EX1 1PE

Originators reference
6 8 4 6 0 7

Reference no. to be completed by Token Publishing Ltd. | *For office use only*

Account Holder | Name of Bank

Sort Code | Bank Address

Account Number | Bank Postcode

Instructions to your Bank or Building Society. Please pay Token Publishing Ltd. Direct Debit from the account detailed in this instruction subject to the safeguards assured by The Direct Debit Guarantee. I understand that this instruction may remain with Token Publishing Ltd. and, if so, details may be passed electronically to my Bank/Building Society.

Signature | Date

Banks and Building Societies may not accept Direct Debit Instructions for some type of accounts.

This guarantee should be detached and retained by the payer

THE DIRECT DEBIT GUARANTEE

DIRECT Debit

- This Guarantee is offered by all banks and building societies that accept instructions to pay Direct Debits
- If there are any changes to the amount, date or frequency of your Direct Debit Token Publishing Ltd. will notify you 10 working days in advance of your account being debited or as otherwise agreed. If you request Token Publishing Ltd. to collect a payment, confirmation of the amount and date will be given to you at the time of the request.
- If an error is made in the payment of your Direct Debit, by Token Publishing Ltd. or your bank or building society you are entitled to a full and immediate refund of the amount paid from your bank or building society
  – If you receive a refund you are not entitled to, you must pay it back when Token Publishing Ltd. asks you to
- You can cancel a Direct Debit at any time by simply contacting your bank or building society. Written confirmation may be required. Please also notify us.

We will NEVER pass your details on to any other organisation, however we may send you information we feel is of interest to you. If you WANT to receive this information please tick this box ☐ (08/19)

Advertisers
directory

See our website at tokenpublishing.com for up-to-date dealer entries, with hyperlinks taking you directly to their websites.